VOLUME 1

# Recovery from Severe Mental Illnesses:
## Research Evidence and Implications for Practice

VOLUME 1

# Recovery from Severe Mental Illnesses:
## Research Evidence and Implications for Practice

Edited by Larry Davidson, Courtenay Harding, and LeRoy Spaniol

Center for Psychiatric Rehabilitation
Sargent College of Health and Rehabilitation Sciences
Boston University

Published by:

Center for Psychiatric Rehabilitation
Sargent College of Health and Rehabilitation Sciences
Boston University
940 Commonwealth Avenue West
Boston, MA 02215
http://www.bu.edu/cpr/


The Center for Psychiatric Rehabilitation is partially funded by the National Institute on Disability and Rehabilitation Research and the Center for Mental Health Services, Substance Abuse and Mental Health Services Administration.

Printed in the United States of America

Cover photo illustration, cover design, and text design by Linda Getgen

Library of Congress Control Number: 2005928298
ISBN–13: 978-1-878512-16-1
ISBN–10: 1-878512-16-1

*The publication of this book was supported by The Elizabeth Whitney Post Fund, Sargent College of Health and Rehabilitation Sciences, Boston University.*

*All proceeds from the sale of this book are used to further the work of the Center for Psychiatric Rehabilitation. No royalties are paid to the editors.*

VOLUME 1

## Chapter 2    Then What Happens to People Over Time?

## Foreword

Until the 1980s, and officially until the appearance of *DSM-III-R,* the understanding in our field was that a severe mental illness, particularly schizophrenia, almost universally followed a deteriorative course. With this understanding mental health researchers, not surprisingly, have tended to focus on psychopathology and symptoms, rather than on processes and interventions that promote role functioning and coping with mental illnesses. This lack of understanding of recovery no doubt inhibited the study of the positive outcomes of schizophrenia and other severe mental illnesses by focusing on maintenance and stabilization, rather than on growth-promoting interventions. More recently, however, research has begun to focus on recovering instrumental roles and quality of life in the community.

In the last several decades, several sources of data have converged to demonstrate that people with severe mental illnesses are achieving higher levels of role functioning, subjective well being, and adjustment than had previously been considered, and that severe mental illnesses are not universally deteriorative. One source of information has been the writing of people with severe mental illnesses. Another source of knowledge is the synthesis and dissemination of long-term outcome studies, which suggested that a significant percentage of people with severe mental illnesses were dramatically improving over time. Currently, according to Harding, there are 10 national and international longitudinal studies of 20 to 30 years duration investigating the recovery and community integration of people with schizophrenia and other severe mental illnesses. A final source of data is the research evidence suggesting that substantial improvements for individuals with severe mental illnesses can be effected through mental health interventions. All of these different types of evidence are covered in this groundbreaking text.

A review of systems-level literature and mental health policy is also included in this text. Even though there is as of yet no explicit consensus about the meaning of the term *recovery,* our current understanding of recovery is now guiding policies and practice in many state mental health systems as well as in entire countries like New Zealand.

Despite increasing and widespread use in mental health systems' practice, planning, and funding, the concept of recovery until recently has been poorly understood, poorly operationalized, and frequently used in policy/ political statements rather than as an empirically-based, operationally defined term. More recently, however, as shown by the readings in this text, there has been a convergence of thinking about the meaning of the term recovery and its definition. Taken together, these sources of information suggest that the recovery process: is a long-term, multidimensional process with both objective and subjective dimensions that should be viewed along a continuum (rather than dichotomous as recovered vs. not recovered). Also, recovery outcomes involve interdependent domains of functioning (including social, vocational, emotional, cognitive, and spiritual). Additionally, the literature indicates that recovery involves psychosocial adjustment to the disability itself; achievement of subjective well being; some degree of remission of the signs and symptoms of the illness; and improvement in instrumental role functioning and community integration.

One definition of recovery outcomes (as opposed to recovery processes) focuses on the psychological dimensions of recovery by suggesting that it involves the development of new meaning and purpose in life as a person grows beyond the effects of mental illness. Other authors have developed criterion-based definitions that emphasize instrumental role functioning across domains such as work, social functioning, and living independence as well as reduced symptomatology. There remains disagreement about the extent to which being symptom free is a requisite for recovery or whether the need for treatment, medications, or hospitalizations should factor into the definition. For example, in the Vermont follow-up study reported by Harding and Zahniser, the authors used the following definition of recovery from schizophrenia: "no signs or symptoms of mental illness, no current medications, work, relating well to family and friends, integrated into the community..." A further complication of the use of the term recovery is that some researchers and authors refer to recovery as an outcome while others refer to recovery as a process.

In essence, the term recovery is increasingly being used to denote a severely mentally ill person's potential for growth, healing, and community integration. The literature focused on in this text encompasses this broader understanding of recovery. This conception was largely absent from the last century's diagnostic schemes, maintenance-type interventions, and mental health research. Furthermore, for most of the previous century, throughout North America and Europe, people with severe mental illnesses were not expected to recover, and were also dehumanized and devalued by both society and sometimes inadvertently by treatment professionals. The view that people with mental illnesses lacked potential for growth and change, and responded only to interventions designed to prevent deterioration has gradually dissipated. This change in practice and attitudes essentially views people with psychiatric disabilities as "people first." This text represents the first attempt at presenting the research that has led to this paradigm shift.

The advent of the awareness of recovery has started to change the field of mental health significantly; we are now just beginning that transformation process (President's New Freedom Commission on Mental Health, 2003).

This book is a beginning effort at overviewing the key literature that empirically supports this new understanding of recovery. Also addressed are the key roles that the person, peers, family members, practitioners, and researchers can play in recovery policy and practice.

WILLIAM A. ANTHONY, PHD

President's New Freedom Commission on Mental Health. (2003). *Achieving the promise: Transforming mental health care in America, final report* (No. Pub. No. SMA-03-3832.). Rockville, MD: U.S. Department of Health and Human Services.

The first research to document the fact that not all people with schizophrenia manifest the progressive deteriorating course proposed by Kraepelin to distinguish this condition from other psychiatric conditions with less virulent courses was published by Strauss and Carpenter in 1972. That was 33 years ago. Even given the 25-year span it typically takes for scientific breakthroughs to make their way into routine clinical practice (IOM, 2002), it is surprising, and troubling, how much of the mental health field remains ignorant of these findings, thereby perpetuating, albeit unwittingly, the Kraepelinian legacy of hopelessness, helplessness, and despair. Even as these volumes are going to press, the American Psychiatric Association is considering adoption of a new diagnostic category for the next version of the *DSM*, which they have labeled "schizophrenia in remission." Even this step, which is limited to relief of symptoms and still is not without its own controversy, falls well short of recognizing the broad heterogeneity consistently found in the outcome of schizophrenia in many studies conducted in multiple countries over the last 35 years. While others may speculate about the reasons why it has taken psychiatry so long to acknowledge and incorporate this body of knowledge, or what function perpetuating Kraepelin's legacy may serve for the field, we offer these volumes as corrective measures to counteract the prevailing ignorance.

In our opinion, our timing could not be better. The last 5 years in the history of mental health policy in the United States in particular have led to broad adoption of the term *recovery* in relation to serious mental illnesses. Beginning with the landmark 1999 Report on Mental Health of the Surgeon General (DHHS, 1999), and culminating (thus far) in the 2003 Final Report of the President's New Freedom Commission on Mental Health, entitled *Achieving the Promise: Transforming Mental Health Care in America* (DHHS, 2003), a notion of recovery that had resided largely on the margins of psychiatry has been unceremoniously dumped into the mainstream of clinical practice. This is not to say that "recovery" did not already have its advocates within the field. The Community Support Movement as a whole, and the discipline of Psychiatric Rehabilitation more specifically, embraced early notions of recovery as well as the eloquent spokespersons of recovery who were themselves ex-patients, survivors, or consumers. What began to change with the Surgeon General's Report was that this notion which had been held dear by an energetic and idealistic minority was now being proposed as the overarching aim and principle for the field as a whole. As the vision statement of the New Freedom Commission Report explicitly and adamantly announces: "We envision a future when everyone with a mental illness will recover" (DHHS, 2003).

Reactions to this forceful statement have been mixed. Mental health advocates and psychiatric rehabilitation practitioners have rejoiced, of course, but with the nagging suspicion that all of their hard work is about to be co-opted by the very field they have been fighting against for the last 30 years. Many providers, family members, and people with psychiatric disabilities welcome the introduction of a positive and hope-filled message, feeling that it is long overdue. Among those professionals who are more skeptical, some dismiss what they view as recovery "rhetoric" as simply the latest fad in a field that has been slow to embrace the importance of evidence. Others view the introduction of recovery as a short-sighted political gesture that is at least ill-advised, if not altogether irresponsible, claiming that notions such as self-care, self-determination, and client choice are code words used by an uncaring populace to disguise the real agenda of cutting services, and thereby costs. The various forms of skepticism that have surfaced share a common perception that there is no evidence justifying use of the term recovery in relation to serious mental illnesses, dismissing arguments to the contrary as, in the words of one reviewer, "unsubstantiated rubbish."

It is to these skeptics, as well as to the hundreds of thousands of people with psychiatric disabilities, their loved ones, and the compassionate professionals who devote their careers to caring for and supporting them, that these volumes are addressed. We have identified and collected representative publications from the last 30 years of research and clinical and rehabilitative practice that present the evidence supporting use of the term recovery in relation to serious mental illnesses. This literature addresses both the natural history of the illness as well as the effectiveness of various interventions addressing different domains of functioning, such as vocational, emotional, social, physical, cognitive, and spiritual. Overall, it offers a highly variegated picture of a complex, dynamic, and ever evolving condition that, on the one hand, may become lethal when left untreated, but which, on the other hand, also can be contained, managed, and/or overcome over time by the majority of people who experience it. In addition, despite the long-standing belief that psychiatry is a "soft" science in which pretty much anything can masquerade as treatment (from psychoanalysis to lobotomy), the evidence suggests that psychiatric interventions are at least as effective, and in many cases more effective, than their established medical counterparts (DHHS, 1999). Indeed, to the degree that we can emerge out from under the long shadow cast by stigma, discrimination, and societal insensitivity to the needs and dignity of people with serious mental illnesses, we all have much to be hopeful about.

We close this preface with one cautionary note, however. In spite of its broad adoption by policy makers, politicians, and professionals across the globe, the term "recovery" has many different meanings when used in relation to serious mental illnesses. We explore several of these meanings in our first chapter. Throughout the entirety of these volumes, it will be important for the reader to keep in mind that there are dramatically different uses of the same term by different investigators for different purposes. When evaluating or applying the findings of any of the publications reprinted here, it would be wise for the reader to ask him or herself: What definition or sense of the term recovery is being used here, in relation to what population of persons, from which perspective, and to what ends? We offer only two of the possible uses of the term to illustrate this point.

The research alluded to above, which began with the seminal work of Strauss, Carpenter, and others in the 1970s, utilized a conventional medical sense of the term recovery, restricted to the narrow perspective of clinical investigation. In this case, recovery meant the absence of any symptoms, signs, or other sequaelae of the illness. Many people were found to recover from serious mental illnesses in this sense in a way similar to how people recover from other medical conditions such as the flu, an infection, or (in the case of a longer-term course of illness) asthma. Some within the field, including some advocates, insist that this is the only viable or accurate use of the term recovery and suggest that any other use serves solely to obfuscate the issue.

Increasingly common, however, is a use of the term recovery which resembles more a disability paradigm than a purely medical one. In this sense of the term, recovery refers to a person's right and ability to live a safe, dignified, and meaningful life in the community of his or her choice despite continuing disability associated with the illness. Borrowed initially from the addiction self-help community, this sense of recovery refers instead to learning how to live fully in the presence of a disabling condition. As a result, this sense of recovery makes no sense for people who recover fully from their illness in the biomedical sense of the term used above. In other words, this sense of recovery is most relevant for those people whose illness does not simply "go away." Why, then, use the term recovery to refer to this process of learning how to manage and minimize the destructive impact of one's illness on one's life? Doesn't this just confuse things unnecessarily? From our perspective, it is important to include this sense of recovery in the following text because this is the term, and the sense of recovery, that has been chosen and promoted by people living with mental illnesses. For many of them, the term recovery represents first and foremost a crucial civil rights issue that they face as a consequence of several thousand years of discrimination. In the words of Patricia Deegan, one of the most eloquent spokespersons for this sense of the term: "The concept of recovery is rooted in the simple yet profound realization that people who have been diagnosed with a mental illness are human beings" (1992, p. 12).

We understand the ambiguity and confusion that is introduced into a field when one term is used by so many different people to mean such very different things. We agree that this is not an ideal situation, nor does it represent an optimal strategy for promoting the health and well-being of people with psychiatric disabilities. It is, nonetheless, the situation in which we find ourselves. We offer one other recommendation in this regard in addition to encouraging the reader to be as clear as possible about which sense of recovery is being used when and by whom. This recommendation is that we all agree to accept the basic civil rights claims made by people with psychiatric disabilities as our point of departure. This means that we accept the premise that people with psychiatric disabilities are, and remain, people just like everyone else—i.e., just like people who do not have psychiatric disabilities—until we discover otherwise, and then only in the specific ways for which we have accumulated persuasive evidence. Why is this important?

The longitudinal research described above not only discovered a broad heterogeneity in outcome for schizophrenia across people, but also found heterogeneity in functioning across various domains, such as vocational, emotional, social, physical, cognitive, and spiritual, within any given individual over time. Some people may experience florid positive symptoms of hallucinations and delusions while having no cognitive deficits, while others may suffer from profound negative symptoms and cognitive impairments while having few observable positive symptoms. And these profiles can change, even within the same individual, over time. Psychosis does not take over the entirety of the person, as Kraepelin had suggested, but exerts various degrees of impact on various domains of functioning. It leaves some domains of functioning intact, so that people retain areas of health and competence that co-exist alongside of symptoms and dysfunction. As a result, the person is very much still there and should be accorded all of the rights and responsibilities that accrue to this status unless and until he or she offers persuasive evidence to the contrary.

Until we fully accept this premise, we will continue in our research and our practice to stumble across findings that reflect the fact that people with mental illnesses are in fact just like people in general. Several of the contributions to these volumes, including some of our own, conclude with such insights. While still useful to the field, for example, the findings of our early supported socialization studies have been considered somewhat anti-climactic in their suggestion that friendship is important for people with psychiatric disabilities (i.e., just like it is for everyone else). Until we can get beyond proving such obvious, if nonetheless overlooked, points, we will make little progress in determining what it is that is unique in the challenges presented by mental illness and what it is that is specific to the illness that people need to learn to manage and recover from. In reviewing the existing research base for where we are as a field currently, we hope not only to silence the skeptics amongst us, but, even more importantly, to provide the foundation for this next generation of even more promising research.

LARRY DAVIDSON, PhD
COURTENAY HARDING, PhD
LEROY SPANIOL, PhD

Deegan, P.E. (1992). The independent living movement and people with psychiatric disabilities: Taking back control over our own lives. *Psychosocial Rehabilitation Journal, 15*(3), 3–19.

Institute of Medicine. (2001). *Crossing the quality chasm: A new health system for the 21st century.* Washington, DC: National Academy Press.

President's New Freedom Commission on Mental Health. (2003). *Achieving the promise: Transforming mental health care in America, final report* (No. Pub. No. SMA-03-3832.). Rockville, MD: U.S. Department of Health and Human Services.

U.S. Department of Health and Human Services. (1999). *Mental health: A report of the Surgeon General.* Rockville, MD: U.S. Department of Health and Human Services, Substance Abuse and Mental Health Services Administration, Center for Mental Health Services, National Institutes of Health, National Institute of Mental Health.

## Introduction to Chapter 1

*Larry Davidson*

In this first chapter, we begin with a recent paper that attempts to summarize the various meanings of the term *recovery* both inside and outside of mental health, in the hope that this will provide a useful framework for the remainder of the two volumes. We then examine the ten long-term follow-up studies of serious mental illnesses that lay the groundwork for the possibility of recovery, and demonstrate consistently that 50 to 60% of each sample were able to experience significant improvements in the illnesses and in their lives. These studies contain many important findings, including a broad heterogeneity in outcome; early course fluctuations followed by later decreases in severity; the failure of traditional indicators to predict course or outcome over the longer term; the existence of multiple pathways to recovery, including the restoration of social and occupational functioning; and the fact that many people do not continue to take psychiatric medications for the entirety of their lives as we have come to expect (and as we continue to teach to patients and their families). John Strauss reflects upon his many years of research involving face-to-face interviews with people with psychiatric disability. He restates his key finding of the possibilities for recovery and describes his frustration with the lack of acceptance by mental health professions of this now well documented fact.

The next several contributions to this chapter represent the perspectives and experiences of people who have recovered, to various degrees, from serious mental illnesses, providing by virtue of their own lives a different kind of "evidence" of the possibility of recovery. As a result of their own struggles and accomplishments, Patricia Deegan, Shery Mead, and Mary Ellen Copeland have become extremely effective, as well as eloquent, spokespersons within the Recovery Movement. Their contributions suggest a number of factors and processes that promote, facilitate, and/or sustain recovery, highlighting also the central role that the person plays in learning about, managing, compensating for, and minimizing the destructive impact of his or her illness. As Harding's summary of long-term follow-up studies offers a review of what we know about the more narrow, biomedical sense of recovery (i.e., referring to the absence of symptoms, signs, and corrections of the deficits associated with the illness), these two contributions offer a review of that sense of recovery promoted most vigorously by the Consumer/Survivor/User Movement.

Following these consumer accounts, Spaniol and colleagues present qualitative findings pertaining to processes of recovery culled from narrative accounts of people with serious mental illnesses who have experienced significant improvements in their condition. They suggest, in particular, that people go through phases of recovery, beginning with being overwhelmed by and struggling with the disability prior to learning how to live with and then finally live beyond the limitations of the disability. Reflecting one of the major unanticipated adverse consequences of deinstitutionalization, Drake and colleagues then review the impact of substance use disorders on the lives of people with serious mental illnesses. Since people with serious mental illnesses have been able to live the majority of their adult lives outside of institutional settings, substance use and abuse has become the single most detrimental factor negatively impacting on outcome. In addition to reviewing these data, this paper also describes the failures of fragmented systems to address co-occurring disorders and offers hope for the development and dissemination of more effective practices based on an integrated model of treatment and rehabilitation. Harding's article identifies some major myths about serious mental illnesses that serve as attitudinal and belief barriers to the treatment and recovery process. We then end this chapter, as we do each of the following chapters, with a first-person account that describes in rich, narrative detail the ways in which these various factors interweave within the life context of any given individual and/or family affected by serious mental illnesses.

By the end of this chapter, we hope that our readers will grasp the possibility of at least two different senses of recovery in serious mental illnesses, be able to identify a variety of factors that facilitate or impede recovery, and begin to have a better understanding of what processes of recovery look like and involve for people living with these conditions.

# Recovery in Serious Mental Illness: Paradigm Shift or Shibboleth?

*Larry Davidson, Maria J. O'Connell, Janis Tondora, Martha Staeheli, and Arthur C. Evans*

Larry Davidson, PhD, Maria J. O'Connell, PhD, Janis Tondora, PsyD, Martha Staeheli, and Arthur C. Evans, PhD; Program for Recovery and Community Health of Yale University and the Connecticut Department of Mental Health and Addiction Services.

**Abstract:** The notion of recovery in serious mental illness has become a dominant force in federal and state mental health policy arenas, as is evident in the Surgeon General's Report on Mental Illness and in the more recent President's New Freedom Commission Final Report. In both of these potentially influential documents, recovery is stipulated as the overarching goal of mental health care and also as the foundation for policy and programmatic reforms at the state and local levels. Theses advances have occurred despite the fact that there is much confusion, and little consensus, in the field about the nature of recovery in serious mental illness, the various components of processes that comprise recovery, or the most effective ways in which recovery can be facilitated or promoted. This paper offers a conceptual framework for distinguishing between the various uses of the term recovery in primary medical care, trauma, addiction, and serious mental illness, and then reviews the existing literature on mental health recovery. In recognition of the danger of this notion becoming the latest in a series of shibboleths within mental health, we conclude with a discussion of the implications of mental health recovery for meaningful reforms of policy and practice.

> *"The important thing…is not to be cured, but to live with one's ailments"*—
> *Albert Camus (1955, p. 29).*

After slowly ripening on the margins of the mental health community for over two decades, the notion of "recovery" has emerged recently as a dominant force among individuals with serious mental illnesses, their loved ones, and the professionals and public officials who serve them. Most recently, it has taken center stage through its prominent role in both the Surgeon General's Report on Mental Health (DHHS, 1999) and the President's New Freedom Commission on Mental Health's Final Report (2003). In this potentially important report, the Commission recommended "fundamentally reforming how mental health care is delivered in America" in order to be reoriented to the goal of recovery (2003, p. 4). Yet despite, and also perhaps because of, the recent widespread proliferation of the concept, it has been difficult to reach consensus on any one definition, or even on any one list of essential aspects, of the concept (Bullock, Ensing, Alloy & Weddle, 2000; Drake, 2000; Hatfield, 1994; Jacobson, 2001; Jacobson & Greenley, 2001; Sullivan, 1994; Young & Ensing, 1999). In fact, the only thing about which most involved parties seem to be able to agree is that the notion of recovery has become the focus of a considerable amount of confusion, dialogue, and debate between and among various constituencies within the mental health community. For any significant progress to be made in achieving the recovery goals of either the Surgeon General or the New Freedom Commission's Reports, clarity and consensus must be achieved in relation to this important concept. The following article is one contribution to this process.

### BACKGROUND

There are many possible sources of this confusion. In the first place, two different clinical and political forces have come together around similar, but not identical, approaches to the possibility, nature, and extent of improvement in serious mental illness. Beginning with the World Health Organization's International Pilot Study of Schizophrenia launched in 1967, there have been a series of long-term, longitudinal outcome studies conducted around the world, all of which have produced a consistent picture of a broad heterogeneity in outcome for schizophrenia and other severe psychiatric disorders (Carpenter & Kirkpatrick, 1988). With respect specifically to schizophrenia, this line of research has documented partial to full recovery in between 25 to 65% of each sample. Recovery in this context has been defined as amelioration of symptoms and other deficits associated with the disorder to a sufficient degree so that they no longer interfere significantly with daily functioning, allowing the person to resume personal, interpersonal, and vocational activities within what is considered a normal range by the person's culture. What these studies suggest is that at least one quarter, and up to two thirds, of people diagnosed with schizophrenia will achieve this form of recovery from the disorder and its associated effects (e.g., Davidson & McGlashan, 1997; McGlashan, 1988).

A somewhat different use of the term recovery has been introduced by the Mental Health Consumer/Survivor Movement. This sense of recovery does not require remission of symptoms or other deficits, nor does it constitute a return to normal daily functioning, but involves instead viewing psychiatric disorder as only one aspect of a whole person. Unlike in most physical illnesses, people may consider themselves to be "in recovery" according to this view while continuing to have, and be affected by, mental illness. What recovery seems to involve is that people overcome the effects of being a mental patient—including rejection from society, poverty, substandard housing, social isolation, unemployment, loss of valued social roles and identity, and loss of sense of self and purpose in life—in order to retain, or resume, some degree of control over their own lives. As being a mental patient is considered traumatic, advocates in this Movement argue that a return to a pre-illness state is not only impossible, but also would diminish the gains the person has had to make to overcome the disorder (Chamberlain, 1978; Jacobson & Greenley, 2001.)

The convergence of these distinct perspectives, along with a variety of other clinical, political, and social factors, has contributed to a situation in which the term recovery is now in danger of becoming merely the latest in a line of shibboleths within mental health (Fink, 1988); that is, words that are used frequently and connote a kind of insider status (being in sync with the latest fad or fashion) without having any meaningful or substantive content. As Jacobson and Greenley noted in their recent review of the recovery movement in state mental health systems, seldom does one word surface so frequently across the separate domains of social policy, outcomes research, services design and provision, system reform and advocacy, and personal narratives in the absence of a uniform or consistent meaning. As they describe:

> Recovery is variously described as something that individuals experience, that services promote, and that systems facilitate, yet the specifics of exactly what is to be experienced, promoted, or facilitated—and how—are often not well understood either by the consumers who are expected to recover or by the professionals and policy makers who are expected to help them (2001, p. 482).

The increasingly ubiquitous yet elusive nature of the concept has contributed to a remarkable inconsistency in the degree to which recovery principles are translated into actual clinical practices that can be assessed and that professionals can then be held accountable for delivering. In the face of such ambiguity, it becomes relatively easy for providers to make claims to be offering "recovery-oriented" care; in many cases, however, simply repackaging old wine in the new bottle of recovery language (Jacobson & Greenley, 2001). As is often the case with ideas that move rapidly from the fringe to the mainstream of service systems, one is then left with the question: "If everybody is doing it, how come nothing is getting done?" (Marrone, 1994).

We believe that this dilemma arises partly due to confusion about what exactly "it" is—in this case, the "it" being recovery. In this paper, we identify some of the sources of the current confusion related to the notion of recovery, offer a conceptual framework to distinguish recovery in mental illness from recovery in other disorders, and delineate several components of the sense of recovery being used at present within the consumer/survivor and psychiatric rehabilitation communities. In closing, we propose a broad understanding of recovery from mental illness that may still be useful in moving the field a step or two beyond current practice and research.

## A CONCEPTUAL FRAMEWORK FOR RECOVERY

In order to begin to address the ambiguity and uncertainty surrounding notions of recovery in mental health, we turned first to the dictionary. A cursory review of the entry for recovery suggests one potential source of the confusions concerning the term, given that Webster offers the following four different definitions (which we paraphrase for ease of comprehension):

> 1) A return to a normal condition; 2) An act, instance, process, or period of recovering; 3) Something gained or restored in recovering; and 4) The act of obtaining usable substances from unusable sources, as with waste material.

Without forcing square pegs into round holes, we suggest that these four definitions are useful in clarifying the different senses of recovery currently being used within the behavioral health field at large in relation to a range of psychiatric and substance use disorders and across the domains described above. In the following, we examine these definitions of the term and argue that each term is most appropriate to one category as opposed to others from among the four categories of: 1) acute physical conditions; 2) trauma and its sequelae; 3) substance use disorders; and 4) severe psychiatric disorders. Once differentiated in this way, it becomes obvious that all four variants of recovery may co-exist and/or interact within the context of any given individual's life, encouraging an appreciation of the different ways in which individuals manage to live with, and despite, various combinations of behavioral health conditions.

### 1) Physical Recovery: Return to a Normal Condition

This definition of recovery represents by far the most common use of the term, and a use that is perfectly appropriate when referring to the resolution of acute physical conditions such as a cold, the flu, or a broken bone. In all of these cases, recovery is taken to mean that the person has been restored, through whatever means, to the same presumably normal condition she or he had prior to the onset of the illness or the precipitating event that led to the condition (e.g., skiing accident). In all of these cases, there also is an assumption that a healthy state existed prior to the onset of disease and/or dysfunction; i.e., that people are naturally healthy until something happens to deprive them of their health, recovery then being restoration of the person to this prior state (Davidson & Strauss, 1995). Although these assumptions might be questioned, this definition represents a relatively well-accepted use of the term recovery and one that is not a source of contention within physical medicine when applied to acute conditions that leave people in relatively the same state they were in prior to first experiencing the condition.

Recovery takes on a different meaning within physical medicine, however, when applied to chronic conditions such as asthma, diabetes, or cancer. In these cases, the person is not expected to be restored to a previous, premorbid, condition of health. To the degree that the term recovery is used at all in relation to these more prolonged conditions (e.g., partial recovery from a stroke, being in recovery from cancer), it ordinarily is taken to mean a partial return to normal functioning or to incorporate one of the different meanings described below, no longer referring to restoration to a previous condition of health. We suggest that a considerable amount of the controversy within behavioral health in relation to the term recovery stems from a misuse of this meaning of the term to apply to other non-acute conditions such as severe psychiatric and substance use disorders. Were this first definition of restoration to a normal state following an acute illness or episode the only legitimate meaning of recovery, then the term could justifiably be dismissed as inappropriate for many cases of severe psychiatric and substance use disorders; a majority of which are prolonged conditions.

### 2) Trauma Recovery: An Act or Process of Recovering

Aside from its common uses in physical medicine in relation to definition #1 above (e.g., as in a "recovery room" being a place where you recover from the immediate effects of surgery), this second definition of recovery primarily has been commandeered for political and clinical purposes by victims of interpersonal trauma and the people who work with, support, or advocate for, them. As one of several important sources of the distinction between this definition and #1 above, proponents of current trauma models argue that there can be *no* return to a previous or normal condition following trauma. In fact, one of the defining characteristics of trauma is that it leaves the person forever changed as a result, having neither the same sense of personal identity nor of the world at large that existed prior to the event (Herman, 1992; van der Kolk, McFarlane & Weisaeth, 1996). Even if only by accentuating a person's sense of vulnerability and/or the unpredictability of the world, trauma brings about significant alterations in the person's life from which there can be no return. Referred to variously as being "robbed of one's innocence," having one's "world turned upside down," or having the "sky come crashing down," trauma theory suggests that the person cannot return to a pre-trauma naïveté (Janoff-Bulman, 1992). In what sense, then, can a person who has experienced significant trauma be said to be "in recovery"?

In this case, recovery has come to signify an active *process* of confronting and working through, or integrating, the traumatic events so that their destructive impact on one's life is minimized as one moves forward into a future, post-trauma, in which oneself and one's world have changed (Briere, 1996; Herman, 1992; McCann & Pearlman, 1992). Using the term in this sense is not to imply that everyone who has experienced a traumatic event has to confront or integrate the event and its effects. In fact, many people who experience trauma do neither of these things without incurring life-long repercussions. For such individuals, the notion of being "in recovery" would make no sense, however, as they would be unlikely to view themselves as having to recover. The notion of being "in recovery" from trauma appears to apply more narrowly to those individuals who suffer negative consequences and prolonged effects from trauma, whether or not this is formally diagnosed as post-traumatic stress disorder. In these cases, recovery is viewed as a more constructive alternative to continued victimization by the trauma. Continuing to be victimized by the traumatic events perpetuates post-traumatic stress symptoms such as flashbacks, hypervigilance, and dissociation that continue to cause distress and to disrupt the person's life, and restricts one's life to within the confines imposed by the trauma, blocking the person from moving forward. Overcoming this sense of victimization is not to be confused, however, with any form of accepting the trauma per se. In cases of sexual abuse and rape—the paradigmatic examples of interpersonal traumatization—it is, according to trauma theory, neither necessary nor recommended for the person to become resigned to such heinous acts in order to be considered "in recovery" (Briere, 1996; Gilfus, 1999).

Being in recovery instead involves being engaged in an active process of making sense of the trauma and incorporating it into one's life in such a way that its destructive impact decreases over time. Admittedly a gradual process that may not end until the person dies (i.e., being *in recovery* from trauma rather than recovered), recovery is a process of moving the trauma and its immediate effects from the forefront of the person's awareness (the "figure"), where it exerts considerable control over his or her day-to-day life, into less prominent domains on the periphery of the person's awareness (the "ground") where it is largely under the person's control or is at least no longer considered intrusive.

The dimension of control also is prominent in both of the remaining definitions of recovery, as the path from figure to ground traversed by traumatic events and their impact is similar to the path traversed by both addictions and psychiatric disorders as the person goes from being controlled *by* them to bringing them under some degree of personal control. What may be unique to trauma and to this sense of recovery is the transformation from victim to survivor; a transformation that has more in common with life-threatening illnesses like cancer than with psychiatric or substance use disorders.

### 3) Addiction Recovery: Something Gained or Restored

Borrowing from physical medicine, but predating use of the term recovery in referring to the aftermath of trauma, the first use of the term "recovery" in behavioral health can be traced to the self-help movement in the addiction community (White, 1998). Beginning with Alcoholics Anonymous and extending through its several abstinence-based 12-step derivatives (Cocaine Anonymous, Narcotics Anonymous, etc.), people who are achieving or maintaining abstinence from drug or alcohol use following a period of addiction have been describing themselves as being "in recovery" from their addiction for over half a century (White, 2000). In this tradition, "in recovery" is meant to signify that the person is no longer using substances but, due to the long-term nature of addiction, continues to be vulnerable to "slips" or relapses and therefore has to remain vigilant in protecting his or her sobriety.

Based on this definition, it is possible that many people who have used substances to an extent that would have met criteria for a DSM-IV diagnosis of substance use disorder at one point earlier in their lives, but who are no longer actively using or finding it necessary to protect their sobriety, would not consider themselves to be "in recovery." Similarly, people who have experienced a traumatic event but who no longer feel that their lives are impacted by the event or its aftereffects might no longer consider themselves to be "in recovery" from the trauma. Although for some people it may apply to the remainder of their lives, being in recovery from addiction appears to pertain more specifically to the period following the addiction in which the person is aware of the efforts involved in remaining abstinent and in which there continues to be a sense of vulnerability to relapse. In this sense, recovery in addiction is not only hard-won, but it also must be protected and reinforced through persistent vigilance and adherence to the self-help principles which made recovery possible in the first place (e.g., attending 12-step meetings).

In addition to being in recovery from the addiction, this process involves addressing the effects and side effects of the addiction as well. The self-help tradition within the addiction community recognizes that living the life of addiction generates many negative effects on one's life beyond the addiction per se, including detrimental effects on one's relationships, on one's ability to learn or work, and on one's self-esteem, identity, and confidence. Having lost control not only of one's substance use but also of one's life as a whole, this sense of being in recovery involves the person's assuming increasing control over his or her substance use while resuming responsibility for his or her life. In this sense, addiction recovery involves both of the terms used by Webster in the third sense of recovery: gained *and* restored. What is gained is a person's sobriety, but in the achievement of sobriety and in creating an environment that will protect and reinforce sobriety, the person also has had to restore his or her life as a whole. Being in recovery thus often involves returning to school or work, making amends to others who have been hurt, repairing damaged relationships, and, in general, learning how to live a clean and sober life (Beattie & Longabaugh, 1997; Longabaugh & Wirtz, 1998).

For many people in the self-help community, achieving recovery may be the first time they have felt like they have known how to live without their addiction, tracing its origins back to their earlier lives even prior to actual substance use. For these people, a clean and sober life is not so much restored by abstinence as it is created for the first time; a gain which they credit to their recovery above and beyond sobriety. It is not unusual in such cases for people in recovery from an addiction to believe they are now a better person for having gone through the addiction and recovery process than if they had never become addicted in the first place. Although it is possible that people suffering from some acute physical conditions, or having experienced a trauma, may believe that they are better off now for having gone through such ordeals, it is a less common occurrence here than in the case of addiction. It is unusual for someone recovering from the flu or rape, for example, to say that she or he has gained something of value in the process. It is not unusual, however, for people in addiction recovery to have done, and to say, so.

### 4) Mental Health Recovery: Obtaining Usable Substances from Unusable Sources

As noted in our introduction, long-term longitudinal studies published over the last 30 years have consistently and convincingly documented a heterogeneity in course and outcome for severe psychiatric disorders. Given this heterogeneity, "recovery" has come to mean different things to people experiencing different courses of illness. For those fortunate individuals who experience one episode of major depression or psychosis from which they then return to a healthy state, our first definition of recovery from physical health conditions is the most appropriate. We can say of these people that they have recovered fully from their psychiatric disorder, having been restored to their previous level of functioning. Although representing a significant proportion of the people experiencing psychiatric disorders at any given time (approximately 30%), such individuals seldom disclose their psychiatric history or define themselves in terms of this isolated episode of dysfunction, preferring to return (quietly) to the normal lives they led previously. In such cases, the person is unlikely to require long-term mental health care and is unlikely to describe him- or herself as being "in recovery."

The relatively recent notion of being "in recovery" from a serious mental illness appears to apply instead to those individuals who have a prolonged course and for whom the outcome of their disorder is less certain. This meaning of the term recovery was introduced by the Mental Health Consumer/ Survivor Movement that emerged in its contemporary form approximately 50 years ago, as former patients of state hospitals began to congregate in urban areas around the country in the early days of deinstitutionalization (Chamberlin, 1978; Gartner & Reissman, 1984). Groups of ex-patients came together both to protest the treatment—from their view, incarceration—they had received in state hospitals and also to develop their own network of support. As the movement began to gather momentum in the 1970s, ex-patients and other advocates strove for new language to express their emerging, alternative vision of mental illness.

The meaning recovery came to take on within the context of this vision parallels to some degree its use in the addiction field, involving the person's assuming increasing control over his or her psychiatric condition while reclaiming responsibility for his or her own life; a life that previously had been either subsumed by the disorder and/or taken over by others. In addition to borrowing this meaning of recovery from the addiction community, and being fueled by the fires of the outcome research described above (i.e., demonstrating that many people can and do recover from serious mental illness), another influence on the Consumer/Survivor Movement's use of the term recovery was the Independent Living Movement established by people with physical disabilities (DeJong, 1979). At the interface of these several diverse streams a somewhat unique use of the term recovery—a use that we suggest corresponds to Webster's fourth definition, i.e., the process of obtaining usable substances from unusable sources—has emerged in community mental health.

Despite the overlap described above, there are several ways in which this definition differs from use of the term in the addiction field. Being in recovery from an addiction invariably involves some degree of abstinence; it requires, that is, a change in the person's condition from being controlled by the addiction to the addiction being under at least some degree of control. While a vulnerability to relapse remains a core element of addiction recovery, a person who continues to use actively cannot be considered to be in recovery; i.e., active substance use in the context of a lack of awareness of one's addiction precludes recovery. The same cannot be said, however, for psychosis. In this respect, the mental health community borrows more from the Independent Living Movement in arguing that recovery remains possible even while a person's condition may not change. It is not reasonable to insist that a person with paraplegia, after all, regain his or her mobility in order to be considered in recovery. In the case of mental health, in whatever way recovery is defined it must allow room for the person's continuing to have the disorder in question. If it does not require a change in the person's psychiatric condition per se, then what does recovery from serious mental illness represent or entail?

In order to flesh out what such a notion of recovery involves, we conducted a concept analysis of recovery as described in consumer/survivor and psychiatric rehabilitation literatures; those bodies of literature in which this sense of recovery has figured most prominently. The first thing we discover when we turn to this focused domain is that there is little consensus even in this literature about the definition of recovery (Bullock, et al., 2000; Drake, 2000; Hatfield, 1994; Jacobson, 2001; Jacobson & Greenley, 2001; Sullivan, 1994; Young & Ensing, 1999). What recovery involves appears to depend upon whom you ask. Despite the lack of a uniform conceptualization, most definitions of recovery involve some component of acceptance of illness, having a sense of hope about the future, and finding a renewed sense of self. For example, three of the more often cited definitions of recovery offered in this literature are:

> Recovery involves the development of new meaning and purpose in one's life as one grows beyond the catastrophic effects of psychiatric disability (Anthony, 1993).

> Recovery refers to the...real life experience of persons as they accept and overcome the challenge of the disability (Deegan, 1988, p. 150).

> Recovery is a process by which people with psychiatric disabilities rebuild and further develop important personal, social, environmental, and spiritual connections, and confront the devastating effects of discrimination through...empowerment (Spaniol & Koehler, 1994, p. 1).

Such definitions obviously differ from those employed in clinical research, in which recovery involves alleviation of the symptoms that cause a person distress or ill health and/or a return to his or her premorbid level of functioning (Young & Ensing, 1999). Recovery, from this perspective, is an absence of something undesired, such as illness or symptoms, or the removal of something that was not part of a person's life prior to the illness, such as medications or hospitalization (White, 2000; Whitwell, 2001). While this model also may include more positive, objective indicators of improvement such as employment, housing, and relationships, the focus remains nonetheless on removing obstacles to an otherwise normal or healthy state (Davidson & Strauss, 1995; Jacobson & Curtis, 2000). From the perspective of consumer/survivors and psychiatric rehabilitation practitioners, however, recovery is not understood as a static "end product or result" (Deegan, 1996a). It is neither "synonymous with cure" nor does it simply involve a return to a premorbid state (Deegan, 1993; Jacobson & Greenley, 2001; Walsh, 1996).

Rather, it is a life-long process that involves an indefinite number of incremental steps in various life domains (Deegan, 1988; Frese & Davis, 1997; Hatfield, 1994; Jacobson & Curtis, 2000). As a result, many people view the process of recovery as something that almost defies definition. It is often described as more of an attitude, a way of life, a feeling, a vision, or an experience (Deegan, 1988, 1996a) than a return to health or any kind of clinical outcome per se.

One reason that recovery in this sense is not typically viewed as a return to a previous state is that advocates often view the experiences of disability, treatment, hospitalization, stigma, and discrimination associated with their psychiatric disorder as having changed their lives irrevocably. Like trauma survivors who can never simply return to their lives prior to the traumatic event, mental illness in its more severe forms may be experienced as a life-threatening and life-altering condition. For example, Walsh (1996) describes how mental illness had such a profound effect on him that it was impossible for him to return to his life as it was before the illness: "I agree that we can never go back to our 'premorbid' selves. The experience of disability and stigma attached to it, changes us forever." Some people, in addition, would not want to go back to their lives prior to their experiences of illness because that would in effect deny an important part of their existence (Corrigan & Penn, 1998) and/or negate gains they have made in the process of recovery (Davidson & Strauss, 1992).

This last element speaks to the fact that recovery—in contrast to an absence of symptoms, relief from effects of illness, or remediation of difficulties (either due to a reduction in symptoms or improved methods of coping with symptoms and secondary consequences of illness)—often involves growth and an expansion of capacities. It is in this sense that we find Webster's fourth definition of recovery as "obtaining usable substances from unusable sources" to be most relevant. In this case, the unusable sources are psychiatric disorder, stigma, and their associated effects and side effects, while the usable substances derived from these experiences are the ways in which the person finds her or himself able to rise to the challenge and reclaim a meaningful and gratifying life despite, or beyond the limitations of, the disorder. This form of recovery requires the person to discover and draw upon intrinsic, but often untapped, strengths aside from the disorder, often in the face of what may be unremitting symptoms and other sequelae of the illness. As a result, many people indicate that one of the more essential aspects of their recovery was incorporating the illness as only a minor part of a newly expanded sense of self. This new sense of identity requires expansion of the person's pre-morbid sense of self in order to include all of the skills and strengths the person has had to discover and/or acquire in learning how to live with, and minimize the intrusion of, his or her disorder while still striving to achieve his or her life goals.

Because, from this perspective, the process of recovery may be different for different people, it is difficult to come up with one set of essential ingredients that will be true for all. Our concept analysis of the consumer/survivor and psychiatric rehabilitation literatures did reveal several common aspects of the journey of recovery, however. These are described briefly in Table 1. Each of these areas both assumes and illustrates the basic principle of this form of recovery: a redefinition of one's illness as only one aspect of a multi-dimensional sense of self capable of identifying, choosing, and pursuing personally meaningful goals and aspirations despite continuing to suffer the effects and side effects of mental illness (Davidson & Strauss, 1992; Hatfield, 1994; Pettie & Triolo, 1999; Rigdway, 2001; Young & Ensing, 1999).

## DISCUSSION

We have reviewed the various meanings of recovery across different clinical conditions and healthcare contexts—e.g., from physical illness, traumatic experiences, and substance use—in order to establish a foundation upon which to conceptualize an alternative vision of recovery from serious mental illness. What have we learned from this review and what implications do these lessons hold for psychological practice and research?

From the consumer/survivor and psychiatric rehabilitation literatures we have learned that recovery from serious mental illness does not require remission of symptoms or of other deficits brought about by the disorder. Rather, recovery appears to involve incorporation of one's illness within the context of a sense of hopefulness about one's future, particularly about one's ability to rebuild a positive sense of self and social identity despite remaining mentally ill. This process also appears to involve overcoming the effects of being a mental patient including rejection from family, peers, and society as a whole; poverty, unemployment, and substandard housing; loss of valued social roles and identity; loss of sense of self as an effective social agent and of the sense of purpose and direction associated with it; and loss of control over, and responsibility for, one's major life decisions.

Rather than leading the person back to a pre-existing state of health, the processes by which people with serious mental illness are to achieve these components of recovery are considered to be ongoing or lifelong in nature. Finally, given the traumatic nature of being a mental patient, people should not expect to return to the lives they led prior to onset of their illness. Like other trauma, these experiences change the person's life forever. The best that can be hoped for is a multi-dimensional sense of self and a personally meaningful and rewarding life of which the illness becomes a smaller and smaller part over time. Whether such a view of recovery can be reconciled with the approach of conventional clinical psychology and embraced by the mental health community as a whole remains to be determined.

As useful and important as this notion of recovery may be both personally and politically, its relevance to processes of improvement may be limited to the extent that it differs substantially from the definition of recovery utilized in outcome research. The consumer/survivor and rehabilitation literatures identified components that people who have had a serious mental illness have found important in reclaiming their lives *despite* continuing to have a disorder. The research that demonstrated a heterogeneity in outcome for people with schizophrenia used a much more narrow definition of recovery that explicitly *included* remission of symptoms and remediation of deficits; both of which are *excluded* from the literature reviewed above. Insofar as we are interested in understanding processes that lead to remission in symptoms and remediation of deficits, this literature will therefore be limited in its applicability. Such issues as stigma and acceptance of illness, for example, would not necessarily be of concern to someone who was no longer ill. Similarly, milder forms of the illness, from which people might recover more rapidly, would most likely not require wholesale redefinitions of self and of one's relation to the world.

If the consumer/survivor and rehabilitation literatures are addressing a phenomenon fundamentally different from that studied by clinical research, is there still reason for clinicians, clinical investigators, and policy makers to be concerned with the various definitions of recovery promoted in these literatures? In closing, we suggest that there are at least two important reasons that these literatures need to be addressed, if not integrated, within professional psychology. Both of these reasons are based on the fact that the consumer/survivor and rehabilitation vision of recovery has been introduced into, and since permeated, the principles, practices, and daily life of federal and state mental health authorities and many of the people and families they serve, as the New Freedom Commission's Report amply demonstrates. Given this reality, recovery could be taken either to represent an important, and previously unappreciated, dimension of treatment and rehabilitation that moves the field ahead (reason one) or to represent the latest in a series of shibboleths which, if misused or misunderstood, could actually be detrimental to the field and to the people we serve (reason two).

Is there a way in which adopting the language of "being in recovery" from serious mental illness might move the field as a whole ahead? Based on the lack of consensus even within the consumer/survivor and rehabilitation literatures, arriving at a shared meaning of recovery will require an inclusive approach that necessarily defines the term in an open-ended way that allows

**Table 1. Common Elements of Recovery**

| Element | Description | Sources |
|---|---|---|
| Renewing Hope and Commitment | Having a sense of hope and believing in the possibility of a renewed sense of self and purpose, accompanied by desire and motivation, is essential in recovery. This sense of hope may be derived spiritually and/or from others who believe in the potential of a person, even when he/she cannot believe in him/herself. | Davidson, Chinman et al, 1997; Davidson, Stayner, Nickou, Styron, Rowe, Chinman, 2001; Deegan, 1996b; Fisher, 1994; Jacobson & Curtis, 2000; Jacobson & Greenley, 2001; Mead & Copeland, 2000; Smith, 2000; Young & Ensing, 1999 |
| Redefining Self | Perhaps the most overarching aspect of recovery, redefining self involves reconceptualizing mental illness as simply one aspect of a multi-dimensional identity rather than assuming a primary social role as "mental patient." | Ahern & Fisher, undated; Davidson & Strauss, 1992; Deegan, 1996; Hatfield, 1994; Pettie & Triolo, 1999; Ridgway, 2001; Spaniol & Zipple, 1994; Young & Ensing, 1999 |
| Incorporating Illness | Often described as a first step to recovery, acknowledging and accepting the limitations imposed by one's illness helps one discover talents, gifts, and possibilities that allow a person to pursue and achieve life goals despite the presence of disability. | Deegan, 1988, 1993; Hatfield, 1994; Munetz & Frese, 2001; Ridgway, 2001; Sayce & Perkins, 2000; Smith, 2000; Sullivan, 1994; Young & Ensing, 1999 |
| Being Involved in Meaningful Activities | Expanding and occupying normal, functional social roles (e.g., spouse, worker, student, taxpayer, friend, etc.) and making worthwhile contributions to a community of one's choice is a cornerstone of recovery. | Anthony, 1993; Davidson, et al., 2001; Jacobson & Greenley, 2001; Lunt, 2000; Ridgway, 2001; Young & Ensing, 1999 |
| Overcoming Stigma | People must recover from the social consequences and societal stigma as well as from the effects of the illness itself. Recovery involves developing resilience to stigma and/or actively fighting against it. | Deegan, 1996b; Houghton, 2004; Perlick, 2001; Ridgway, 2001 |

| Element | Description | Sources |
|---|---|---|
| Assuming Control | People must assume primary responsibility for their transformation from a disabled person to a person in recovery. Assuming control over one's life and treatment contributes to the redefined sense of self as an active, effective agent. Opportunities must be available for people to make choices and people must have options from which to choose. People must also be afforded opportunities to succeed and fail. | Anthony, 1993; Bassman, 1997; Baxter & Diehl, 1998; Deegan, 1996b, 1988; Fisher, 1994; Fisher, undated; Frese, Stanley, Kress, & Vogel-Scibilia, 2001; Hatfield, 1994; Jacobson & Curtis, 2000; Jacobson & Greenley, 2001; Leete, 1994; Lehman, 2000; Lovejoy, 1982; Lunt, 2000; Mead & Copeland, 2000; Munetz & Frese, 2001; Ridgway, 2001; Smith, 2000; Walsh, 1996; Young & Ensing, 1999 |
| Becoming Empowered and Exercising Citizenship | As a sense of empowerment and control over one's life emerges, people in recovery begin to demand the same rights (e.g., the right to decide where to live, whom to love, how to spend one's time) and take on the same responsibilities (e.g., paying taxes, voting, volunteering) as other citizens. | Fisher, undated a, 1994; Jacobson & Greenley, 2001; Munetz & Frese, 2001; Ridgway, 2001; Walsh, 1996; Young & Ensing, 1999 |
| Managing Symptoms | Although complete symptom remission is not necessary, being able to manage symptoms in some way is essential for recovery. Recovery involves periods of good and difficult times, setbacks and accomplishments, and times when symptoms may be more or less controlled. A shift occurs from simply receiving services to actively participating in and using treatments of one's choice to bring symptoms under some degree of control. | Deegan, 1996b; Fisher, 1994; Ridgway, 2001 |
| Being Supported by Others | Recovery is not done alone. Becoming interdependent in one's community and having supportive others and role models, whether they be family members or friends, professionals, community members, or peers provides encouragement through the difficult times and to help celebrate the good. | Baxter & Diehl, 1998; Fisher, 1994; Jacobson & Greenley, 2001; Mead & Copeland, 2000; Ridgway, 2001; Smith, 2000; Sullivan, 1994; Young & Ensing, 1999 |

room for various combinations of the dimensions reviewed in Table 1. An inclusive definition respects the principle that recovery is a unique process for each individual (Anthony, 1993). In order for this principle to impact practice, however, it will need to be operationalized in a way that goes beyond the simple, but difficult to achieve, notion of individualized treatment planning; a notion already accepted as a standard of care by the Joint Commission on the Accreditation of Healthcare Organizations and other regulatory bodies. What is new about recovery-oriented care cannot simply be its focus on the person as a unique individual, but must include a new vision of the goal and nature of care; i.e., what is to be considered possible for people with serious mental illness and what the person's role can be in pursuing what is possible, given his or her disorder.

As we noted above, the alternative vision of recovery that emerges is closer to the vision put forth by people involved in the Independent Living Movement. By adopting this vision—in contrast to the stigmatized view of mental illness they inherited unwittingly—people with psychiatric disorders identify themselves as "normal" people who have disabilities as articulated, for example, in the Americans with Disabilities Act of 1990 (Davidson et al., 2001; Deegan, 1993). Having a psychiatric disability should in this way be no different from having any other form of disability, whether a mobility, visual, or auditory impairment. Within this perspective, people with any of these disabilities are still able to strive for a whole, meaningful, and gratifying life given the assumption that their disability is going to be with them for an extended period, if not for the remainder of their lives.

Such a vision of recovery, which could be equally relevant to chronic physical conditions such as diabetes and paraplegia, represents a departure from current practice in at least two ways. First, it stands in contrast to the prevailing goals of treatment over the last half century that have been eradication of symptoms and illness and "maintenance" of the person in the community (Davidson et al., 2001). If one takes as an analogy for schizophrenia an illness like diabetes or a condition like paraplegia, it is easier to see how these goals fall well short of what the person with the illness or condition expects from life. As we noted above, it would not be reasonable to insist that a person with paraplegia regain his or her mobility in order to participate fully in community life. It is for this reason that we have cut curbs in our sidewalks and made public spaces and transportation accessible to wheelchairs. Similarly, we do not demand that adolescents be cured of their diabetes before they can learn to drive a car, or that adults with diabetes no longer need insulin in order to pursue their personal and professional aspirations. Extrapolated to mental illness, the principle becomes: people with psychiatric disabilities need not delay resuming a full life while waiting for their symptoms, deficits, or illness to disappear—while waiting, that is, to be cured. While remaining important, eradicating symptoms and remediating deficits become secondary to the person's desire to reclaim his or her life in the community, especially when the illness resists all efforts toward eradication.

Second, with acceptance of a disability model of mental illness comes acceptance of the importance of the person's environment. As disability is the product of person-environment interactions (NIDRR, 2003) strategies to promote recovery need to focus simultaneously on the individual and on his or her environment. Attending solely to the person's symptom or functional status in the absence of consideration of environmental influences (whether challenges or supports), for example, would be like teaching a person with a visual impairment to read Braille but then not posting Braille signs on elevators, doors, or other public spaces. While you might demonstrate in the first instance that the person can learn Braille, you would have done little to increase his or her participation in community life. Just as it is not reasonable for researchers to question if people with deafness need *either* to learn sign language or to have visual aids in their apartment to notify them when the phone or doorbell rings, it is not reasonable to ask if people with psychiatric disabilities need either treatment *or* environmental modifications. When the aim is not just to reduce or minimize dysfunction but to achieve community inclusion, it is no longer appropriate to continue such an "either or" approach. The most useful and appropriate question rather becomes "what *combination of treatment and supports* is required for this person to participate fully in community life?"

We have discovered in our own research that, within the context of persistent symptoms and dysfunction, this sense of recovery can be experienced at the concrete level of enjoying a glass of iced tea on a hot summer day or not having to eat one's hamburger alone (Davidson et al., 2001a, 2001b). What such experiences offer the person is the sense that life can still be good, worthwhile, enjoyable, and/or meaningful because such experiences prove that there is more to my life than my disability. We suggest that appreciating that this is the perspective of the person in treatment or rehabilitation—regardless of whether or not it is shared by the clinician—does in fact alter care in a significant way. First of all, it introduces the notion that there is more to the person than his or her disorder, and that the person has needs, desires, and aspirations apart from minimizing his or her disability. In fact, from the person's perspective the purpose of minimizing the disability is not only to decrease suffering but, equally important, it is to allow the person to pursue his or her goals with as little interference as possible. Thus, when informed by the person's perspective on what she or he would like to be doing despite remaining disabled, the focus of the clinician's efforts shift from the symptoms or disability per se to the ways in which these difficulties are getting in the person's way. With the assumption that every person, no matter how disabled, will still find some experiences more worthwhile, enjoyable, or meaningful than others, this vision of recovery becomes universally accessible, with everyone being considered capable, to some extent and in some ways, of having a fuller life.

While belief in the universal potential for this form of recovery is in many ways preferable to the field's traditional pessimistic prognosis of chronicity, it is not without its own limitations. This leads to our second reason for grappling with the recovery literature. For example, if we are to embrace an inclusive definition that implies that all people *can* recover, it is possible that there will be increased social pressure on people that they *must* recover. In moderation, such a position may stimulate individuals, as well as the professionals who support them, to pursue normalized roles and activities. However, when this position is taken to an extreme it lends itself to abuse. People may be prematurely pressured to take up new challenges that are unrealistic in consideration of the limitations imposed by their illness (e.g., maintain competitive employment) or that might be inconsistent with their personal process of recovery (e.g., not everyone wants to assume a more active role in their service planning). An inclusive notion of recovery should not be abused in support of a "get tough" approach to service planning or to the rationing of entitlements. Rather, the concept should be applied in such a way that encourages, but does not mandate, regaining a meaningful sense of belonging in one's community.

In the end, Deegan (1996b) reminds us that our job is not to "judge who will and who will not recover. Our job is to establish strong, supportive relationships with those we work with" in order to maximize their chances for recovery. At this point, we know that each person has a 50/50 chance of partial to full recovery even as narrowly defined by clinical research, but we cannot yet predict who will and who will not achieve this degree of recovery. Therefore—particularly given the field's history of overly bleak pronouncements and the detrimental effects these have had on generations of individuals and families—the risk is considered too great not to believe in the potential of every person for recovery. One of the major challenges that remains for psychologists, both in practice and in research, is then to identify ways to promote this form of recovery at the same time that we are promoting other, more conventional, forms of recovery such as symptom remission. Consistent with what our colleagues in developmental and community psychology have known for a while, a recovery framework suggests that our role need no longer be confined to treating illness and remediating deficit but can also include interventions aimed at enhancing social interactions and experiences of pleasure, success, and competence. Just as life cannot be lived solely by minimizing dysfunction, health cannot be promoted solely by reducing disease alone (Davidson, Staeheli, Stayner & Sells, 2004). In this way, allowing our practice and research to be informed by the best of what this new sense of recovery offers promises to open a new window onto a rich but relatively unexplored landscape.

### REFERENCES

Ahern, L. & Fisher, D. (undated). Personal Assistance in Community Existence: PACE. Recovery at your own pace. *National Empowerment Center Newsletter.*

Anthony, W. A. (1993). Recovery from mental illness: The guiding vision of the mental health service system in the 1990s. *Psychosocial Rehabilitation Journal, 16*(4), 11–23.

Bassman, R. (1997). The mental health system: Experiences from both sides of the locked doors. *Professional Psychology. Research and Practice, 28*(3), 238–242.

Baxter, E.A. & Diehl, S. (1998). Emotional stages: Consumers and family members recovering from the trauma of mental illness. *Psychiatric Rehabilitation Journal, 21*(4), 349–355.

Beattie, M., & Longabaugh, R. (1997). Interpersonal factors and post-treatment drinking and subjective well-being. *Addiction, 92*(11), 1507–1522.

Briere, J. (1996). *Therapy for adults molested as children: Beyond survival (2nd ed.).* New York: Springer.

Bullock, W. A. Ensing, D.S., Alloy, V. E., & Weddle, C. C. (2000). Leadership education: Evaluation of a program to promote recovery in persons with psychiatric disabilities. *Psychiatric Rehabilitation Journal, 24*(1), 3–13.

Camus, A. (1951). *The myth of Sisyphus and other essays* (J. O'Brien, Trans.). New York: Vintage Books.

Carpenter, W. T., & Kirkpatrick, B. (1988). The heterogeneity of the long-term course of schizophrenia. *Schizophrenia Bulletin, 14,* 645–652.

Chamberlin, J. (1978). *On our own: Patient-controlled alternatives to the mental health system.* New York: McGraw Hill.

Corrigan, P. W., & Penn, D. L. (1998). Disease and discrimination: Two paradigms that describe severe mental illness. *Journal of Mental Health (UK), 6,* 355–366.

Davidson, L. (1997). Vulnérabilité et destin dans la schizophrénie: Prêter l'oreille á la voix de la personne. (Vulnerability and destiny in schizophrenia: Hearkening to the voice of the person). *L'Evolution Psychiatrique, 62,* 263–284.

Davidson, L., Chinman, M., Kloos, B., Lambert, S., Stayner, D.A., & Tebes, J.K. (1997). Mental illness as a psychiatric disability: Shifting the paradigm toward mutual support. *The Community Psychologist, 30,* 19–21.

Davidson, L., & McGlashan, T. H. (1997). The varied outcomes of schizophrenia. *Canadian Journal of Psychiatry, 42,* 34–43.

Davidson, L., Stayner, D.A., Nickou, C., Styron, T. H., Rowe, M., & Chinman, M. J. (2001). "Simply to be let in": Inclusion as a basis for recovery. *Psychiatric Rehabilitation Journal, 24*(4), 375–388.

Davidson, L., & Strauss, J.S. (1992). Sense of self in recovery from severe mental illness. *British Journal of Medical Psychology, 65*(2), 131–145.

Davidson, L., & Strauss, J.S. (1995). Beyond the biopsychosocial model: Integrating disorder, health and recovery. *Psychiatry: Interpersonal and Biological Processes, 58,* 44–55.

Deegan, P. E. (1988). Recovery: The lived experience of rehabilitation. *Psychosocial Rehabilitation Journal, 11*(4), 11–19.

Deegan, P. E. (1993). Recovering our sense of value after being labeled. *Journal of Psychosocial Nursing, 31*(4), 7–11.

Deegan, P. E. (1996a). Recovery and the conspiracy of hope.

Deegan, P. E. (1996b). Recovery as a journey of the heart. *Psychiatric Rehabilitation Journal, 19,* 91–97.

Deegan, P. E. (2001). Recovery as a self-directed process of healing and transformation. In Brown, Catana (Ed). (2001). *Recovery and wellness: Models of hope and empowerment for people with mental illness.* (pp. 5–21). New York, NY, US: Haworth Press, Inc.

DeJong, G. (1979). Independent lining: From social movement to analytic paradigm. *Archives of Physical Medicine and Rehabilitation, 60,* 435–446.

Drake, R. E. (2000). Introduction to a special series on recovery. *Community Mental Health Journal, 36*(2), 207–208.

Fink, P.J. (1988). Is "biopsychosocial" the psychiatric shibboleth? *American Journal of Psychiatry, 145,* 1061–1067.

Fisher, D. (undated a). *Health care reform based on the empowerment model of recovery.* National Empowerment Center.

Fisher, D. (undated b). *Elements of managed care needed to promote recovery of mental health consumers.* Unpublished Manuscript. Lawrence, MA.

Fisher, D. (1994). Health care reform based on an empowerment model of recovery by people with psychiatric disabilities. *Hospital & Community Psychiatry, 45*(9), 913–915.

Frese, F. J. & Davis, W. W. (1997). The consumer-survivor movement, recovery, and consumer professionals. *Professional Psychology: Research and Practice, 28*(3), 243–245.

Frese, F. J., Stanley, J., Kress, K., & Vogel-Scibilia, S. (2001). Integrating evidence-based practices and the recovery model. *Psychiatric Services, 52*(11), 1462–1468.

Gartner, A., & Reissman, F. (1984). *The self-help revolution.* New York: Human Sciences Press.

Gilfus, M. (1999). The price of the ticket: A survivor-centered appraisal of trauma theory. *Violence Against Women, 5*(11), 1238–1258.

Hatfield, A. B. (1994). Recovery from mental illness. *The Journal of the California Alliance for the Mentally Ill, 5*(3), 6–7.

Herman, J. L. (1992). *Trauma and recovery.* New York: Basic Books.

Houghton, F. (2004). Flying solo: Single/unmarried mothers and stigma in Ireland. *Irish Journal of Psychological Medicine, 21*(1), 36–37.

Jacobson, N. (2001). Experiencing recovery: A dimensional analysis of recovery narratives. *Psychiatric Rehabilitation Journal, 24*(3), 248–256.

Jacobson, N., & Curtis, L. (2000). Recovery as policy in mental health services: Strategies emerging from the states. *Psychiatric Rehabilitation Journal, 23*(4), 333–341.

Jacobson, N., & Greenley, D. (2001). What is recovery? A conceptual model and explication. *Psychiatric Services, 52*(4), 482–485.

Janoff-Bulman, R. (1992). *Shattered assumptions: Towards a new psychology of trauma.* New York: Free Press.

Leete, E. (1994). Stressor, symptom, or sequelae? Remission, recovery, or cure? *The Journal of the California Alliance for the Mentally Ill, 5*(3), 16–17.

Lehman, A.F. (2000). Putting recovery into practice: A commentary on "What recovery means to us." *Community Mental Health Journal, 36*(3), 329–331.

Longabaugh, R., & Wirtz, W. (1998). Network support for drinking: Alcoholics Anonymous and long-term matching effects. *Addiction, 93*(9),1313–1334.

Lovejoy, M. (1982). Expectations and the recovery process. *Schizophrenia Bulletin, 8,* 605–609.

Lunt, A. (2000). Recovery: Moving from concept toward a theory. *Psychiatric Rehabilitation Journal, 23*(4), 401–405.

Marrone, J. (1994). If everybody is doing it, how come it doesn't get done. *Psychosocial Rehabilitation Journal, 18*(1), 131–135.

McCann, I. L., & Pearlman, L. A. (1990). *Psychological trauma and the adult survivor: Theory, therapy, and transformation.* New York: Brunner/Mazel.

McGlashan, T. H. (1988). A selective review of recent North American long-term follow-up studies of schizophrenia. *Schizophrenia Bulletin, 14,* 515–542.

Mead, S. & Copeland, M.E. (2000). What recovery means to us: Consumers' perspectives. *Community Mental Health Journal, 36*(3), 315–328.

Munetz, M. R. & Frese, F. J. (2001). Getting ready for recovery: Reconciling mandatory treatment with the recovery vision. *Psychiatric Rehabilitation Journal, 25*(1), 35–42.

National Institute of Disability Rehabilitation and Research. (2003). *NIDRR's Long Range Plan: Independent Living and Community Integration Research.* Department of Education: Author.

Perlick, D.A. (2001). Special section on stigma as a barrier to recovery: Introduction. *Psychiatric Services, 52*(12), 1613–1614.

Pettie, D., & Triolo, A.M. (1999). Illness as evolution: The search for identity and meaning in the recovery process. *Psychiatric Rehabilitation Journal, 22*(3), 255–263.

President's New Freedom Commission on Mental Health. (2003). *Achieving the Promise: Transforming mental health care in America, Final Report* (No. Pub. No. SMA-03-3832.). Rockville, MD: U.S. Department of Health and Human Services.

Ridgway, P. A. (2001). Re-storying psychiatric disability: Learning from first person narrative accounts of recovery. *Psychiatric Rehabilitation Journal, 24*(4), 335–343.

Sayce, L., & Perkins, R. (2000). Recovery: Beyond mere survival. *Psychiatric Bulletin, 24*(2).

Smith, M.K. (2000). Recovery from a severe psychiatric disability: Findings of a qualitative study. *Psychiatric Rehabilitation Journal, 24*(2), 149–159.

Spaniol, L., & Koehler, M. (1994). *The experience of recovery.* Boston: Boston University, Center for Psychiatric Rehabilitation.

Sullivan, W. P. (1994). A long and winding road: The process of recovery from severe mental illness. *Innovations and Research, 3,* 19–27.

U.S. Department of Health and Human Services. (1999). *Mental health: A report of the Surgeon General.* Rockville, MD: U.S. Department of Health and Human Services, Substance Abuse and Mental Health Services Administration, Center for Mental Health Services, National Institutes of Health, National Institute of Mental Health.

van der Kolk, B., McFarlane, A., & Weisaeth, L. (Eds.). (1996). *Traumatic stress: The effects of overwhelming experience on mind, body, and society.* New York: Guilford Press.

Walsh, D. (1996). A journey toward recovery: From the inside out. *Psychiatric Rehabilitation Journal, 20*(2), 85–90.

White, W. L. (1998). *Slaying the dragon: A history of addiction treatment and recovery in America.* Bloomington, IL: Chestnut Health Systems.

White, W. L. (2000). *Toward a new recovery movement: Historical reflections on recovery, treatment, and advocacy.* www.treatment.org [Retrieved 1-23-01].

Whitwell, D. (2001). Recovery as a medical myth. *Psychiatric Bulletin, 25*(2), 75.

Young, S. L., & Ensing, D.S. (1999). Exploring recovery from the perspective of people with psychiatric disabilities. *Psychiatric Rehabilitation Journal, 22,* 219–231.

# Changes in Schizophrenia Across Time: Paradoxes, Patterns, and Predictors

*Courtenay M. Harding*

Professor Courtenay M. Harding, PhD, is at the Institute for the Study of Human Resilience and the Center for Psychiatric Rehabilitation at Boston University.

This paper was previously published as a chapter in C. I. Cohen, *Schizophrenia into Later Life: Treatment, Research, and Policy,* American Psychiatric Association Press, 2003, and is reprinted with permission.

There exist two polar, yet accurate, views about the outcome of schizophrenia. Huber et al. (1979), after studying the outcome of schizophrenia in 502 patients for more than 2 decades, wrote: "Schizophrenia does not seem to be a disease of slow progressive deterioration. Even in the second and third decades of illness, there is still a potential for full or partial recovery" (p. 595). Nine other such studies agree. Yet today, we have dayrooms, shelters, and public mental health caseloads consistently overcrowded with persons chronically languishing with the diagnosis of schizophrenia. Furthermore, *DSM-IV* (American Psychiatric Association 1994) indicates that complete remission is likely uncommon, and they go on to describe a variable course of exacerbations and remissions for some patients and a chronic one for most persons. Although this is an improvement from earlier, more dire, predictions of a deteriorating course for all patients (e.g., American Psychiatric Association 1980, 1987; Kraepelin, 1902), a significant discrepancy remains between the prognostic expectations of official psychiatry and the findings of 10 long-term studies completed during the last 3 decades of the twentieth century. Arguments against this paradox have often centered around the use of other diagnostic systems in these studies, although most are similar to the *DSM-IV*. This article shows that regardless how wide or narrow such systems are, patients still persist in improving across time and thus have much to teach us.

Some of the 10 catamnestic (or longitudinal follow-up) studies of schizophrenia analyzed particular areas of functioning, whereas others did not. Some of these reports were published in the authors' native languages and were only translated roughly by the author and colleagues. The end of the article will target a few implications for treatment and research. Other key factors that also shape the long-term course of schizophrenia (and that are not yet mentioned in *DSM-IV*) include 1) the neural plasticity and recalibration of the aging brain, 2) gender differences and the effects of hormones, 3) cognitive decline in the face of a nonstimulating environments, 4) medical comorbidities, and 5) misdiagnosis and other iatrogenic effects of treatment. Such crucial ingredients, which help or hinder forward progress in persons with schizophrenia, contribute further pieces of the puzzle inherent in the paradox.

### BRIEF OVERVIEW OF TEN CONTEMPORARY FOLLOW-UP STUDIES OF 2 TO 3 DECADES IN LENGTH

The common practice in psychiatric research is to follow samples of convenience for only those subjects who remain in treatment. However, the following longitudinal studies investigating schizophrenia and other serious mental illnesses followed intact cohorts across a period of 2 to 3 decades, regardless of whether the subjects were still in treatment. By not following samples of convenience and by maintaining follow-up for such a long time, these studies provide a new view of schizophrenia. They also give evidence that challenges our preconceptions about chronicity and allows us to rethink models and treatment. Each of these projects was reported within the past 30 years or so, during an era of keen interest and funding of such studies. Each provides significant evidence confirming the wide heterogeneity of outcome, and each finds that approximately one half to two thirds of people with schizophrenia can achieve a state of significant improvement or even recovery (Bleuler, 1972/1978; Ciompi & Müller, 1976; DeSisto et al., 1995a, 1995b; Harding et al., 1987b, 1987c; Hinterhuber, 1973; Huber et al., 1979; Kreditor, 1977; Marinow, 1974; Ogawa et al., 1987; Tsuang et al., 1979). Table 1 summarizes data from these studies.

As can be seen in the table, the studies were conducted in seven countries. Studies outside the United States consisted of primarily urban samples, whereas the American studies examined rural samples. Altogether, a total of 2,429 patients (sample range 115–502) were followed for an average of approximately 28 years (range 20–37 years). The percentage of patients showing significant clinical improvement ranged from 46% to 84% (median value 53%), and the percentage of patients who were considered socially recovered ranged from 21% to 77% (median value 49%). Thus, a wider range among studies was found for social response than for clinical response. Together, these studies help to rebalance the picture of schizophrenia.

#### Switzerland #1—The Burghölzli Hospital Studies

The first of these studies was conducted in Zurich, Switzerland. Manfred Bleuler (1972/1978) began following a sample of patients admitted to the Burghölzli Hospital between April 1942 and December 1943 and maintained follow-up over the next 2 decades, regardless of whether the patients remained in treatment—something his father did not do. His sample consisted of 100 males and 108 females with diagnoses of schizophrenic psychoses.

**Table 1 Long-term Studies of Schizophrenia**

| Study | Sample Size (*n*) | Average Length (years) | Percent of Subjects Recovered and/ or Significantly Improved* | Percent of Subjects Socially Recovered |
|---|---|---|---|---|
| M. Bleuler 1972/ 1978, Switzerland | 208 | 23 | 53–68 | 46–59[a] |
| Hinterhuber 1973, Austria | 157 | 30 (approx.) | 75 | 77 |
| Huber et al. 1975, Germany | 502 | 22 | 57 | 56 |
| Ciompi and Müller 1976, Switzerland | 289 | 37 | 53 | 57 |
| Kreditor 1977, Lithuania | 115 | 20+ | 84 | NI |
| Tsuang et al. 1979, United States | 200 | 35 | 46 | 21[b] |
| Marinow 1986, Bulgaria | 280 | 20 | 75 | NI |
| Harding et al. 1987b, 1987c, United States | 269 | 32 | 62–68 | 68[c] |
| Ogawa et al. 1987, Japan | 140 | 22.5 | 56[d] | 47 |
| DeSisto et al. 1995a, 1995b, United States | 269 | 35 | 49 | _[e] |

Note. *Recovered = no further symptoms, no use of psychotropic drugs, living independently in the community, working, and relating well to others, with no behaviors that are considered to be odd or unusual; significantly improved = all of the above, but one domain of functioning. NI= not enough information to rate.

[a] Multiple admissions vs. first admissions.

[b] Marital status only recorded.

[c] Live interviewed DSM-III schizophrenia group—the hardest data.

[d] Derived by adding 33% recovered with a conservative 23% as improved (from 43% listed).

[e] When variables not chosen for matching criteria were covaried out of the Maine-Vermont comparison, differences in social functioning lost statistical significance.

Source. Adapted from Harding and Keller 1998.

The diagnostic criteria used were a combination of those from his father, Eugen Bleuler, and Emil Kraepelin and were considered to be narrower than those of the American *DSM-II* (American Psychiatric Association, 1968) and wider than the *DSM-III* (American Psychiatric Association, 1980). M. Bleuler excluded patients with brain disease, endocrine disorders, poisoning, latent schizophrenia, neurosis, mixed psychosis (schizoaffective), or a previous course. This strategy had been unavailable to Kraepelin. Sixty-eight of the 208 (33%) probands studied were considered first admissions. Their ages ranged from 16.0 to 67.5 years, with an average age of 40 years. After considerable research, M. Bleuler (1972/1978) concluded that these subjects came from "the same sectors of the population as do all schizophrenics hospitalized in the Canton of Zürich during the period in question" (p. 12). None of the probands in this study died of brain disease during the follow-up period.

The Burghölzli Hospital Study was conducted in a systematic and comprehensive manner using structured instruments as well as clinical interviews. M. Bleuler (1972/1978) found that 68% of the first-admission patients and 53% of the multiple-admission patients significantly improved or recovered. Among the many findings reported were that 1) life histories revealed that most patients had experienced "disturbances in their home life," but no one particular type stood out and no direct causal linkages could be established; 2) genetics appeared to play a role, but only a partial one (citing discordant monozygotic twins and other family data); 3) therapy may or may not have played a key role in the recovery process; 4) E. Bleuler's (1911/1950) "group of schizophrenias," which implied different etiologies, was still elusive; and 5) gender differences played a role. Bleuler focused on getting to know these patients and their relatives personally, and further social functioning was determined from criteria of work, independence from care, and living in a nonsheltered environment. No social impairment was observed for 46% of the overall cohort and for 59% of members of the first-admission subsample. With regard to sex differences, Bleuler found a 6:1 female-to-male ratio of improvement, and females showed a slight edge over the males in the recovered and mild impairment categories. He said, "I have found the prognosis of schizophrenia to be more hopeful than it has long been considered to be" (Bleuler, 1984).

### Austria—Hinterhuber's Study

Between 1930 and 1940, 157 people with schizophrenia were first admitted to the Innsbruck Psychiatric Clinic in Austria (Hinterhuber, 1973). At follow-up, 99 (63%) of these patients had died or were presumed dead, and 58 (37%) were still alive. Data were extracted from several sources, including structured questionnaires, interviews with relatives, and biographies. Hinterhuber (1973) used diagnostic criteria from Bleuler, Kraepelin, and

Schneider to study the sample, which was composed of 87 women and 70 men considered to have "obvious schizophrenia." Using data from all sources, the results, which were published primarily in German, revealed that 50% of these patients were "released from treatment," but 33% remained enrolled in continued full-time care. In measures of psychopathology, 29.2% of the sample was reportedly "cured" of their schizophrenia, with another 45.6% improved and 30.5% still ill. Work functioning had remarkably resumed, with 77% working full time, 20% working part time, and the remaining 8% in family care. Subjects who had incurred injuries prior to illness (34.6%) remained mostly in the "severe final stages" of illness, with only 21% falling into the "cured" category. Course modifiers leading to poorer outcomes included psychological trauma, genetic loadings, and interestingly, later onset (after age 40 years).

### Switzerland #2—The Lausanne Investigations

The "Lausanne Investigations" were conducted by Ciompi and Müller (1976), who undertook the longest follow-up study reported in the world literature. They conducted assessments of 92 men and 197 women across a median length of 36.9 years ($SD$ = 13.3 years), with a range of up to 64 years after first admission to the University Psychiatric Clinic. Of the sample, 20% had catamnestic histories of more than 50 years' duration. Thus, Ciompi and Müller's findings might be considered closer to E. Bleuler's concept of *Reichtung Prognose* ("final prognosis"). The average age of males at follow-up was 75.2 years; females averaged 75.8 years. This sample was considered to be representative of the 1,642 patients admitted to the clinic who were 64 years of age or younger at their first admission and who were 65 years of age or older at the beginning of the study in 1963 (Ciompi & Müller 1976). The initial large group ($N$ = 1,642) was targeted to study mortality and causes of death.

These investigators used a combination of Kraepelinian and Bleulerian criteria. Inclusion symptoms for schizophrenia included "disturbance of psychotic proportions...marked by manifold and alternating combinations of the so-called primary disorders of thought and emotion, autism, ambivalence, loss of contact, and experience of depersonalization or derealization" (Ciompi 1980, p. 607). Patients with questionable diagnoses of schizophrenia were excluded. The research team conducted 2-hour semistructured interviews in the probands' homes, and more data were collected through records, correspondence, and interviews of family, friends, and others in care systems (agencies and clinicians). Because of the complexities of human beings and schizophrenia, outcome domains were measured separately before being combined into a "recovered," "improved," or "deteriorated" status.

Results were quite varied. Highlights revealed that the average mortality rate for those in the sample was 173%, versus 100% for the Swiss population (Ciompi, 1980), with women suffering the most, at 185% (vs. males at 161%). Twenty percent of subjects had been hospitalized for more than 20 years. Ciompi pointed out that hospitalization rates were also influenced by many social and economic factors (e.g., system, family, social structures).

Symptoms among the patients changed considerably over time. For example, 62% of all individual symptom profiles had "vanished" in old age...and [an] additional 11% were clearly improved, with just 20% who remained unchanged in old age or had intensified" (Ciompi 1980, p. 611). However, only about a third of these patients were doing exceptionally well in social relationships. Classical predictors, including "good premorbid social, familial, and professional adaptation, few premorbid personality disorders; a marriage, completion of vocational training, and a higher premorbid occupational level," held into old age. Furthermore, it was found that "the disease tends to run a more favorable course, the more acute, the more lively, and the more mobile the onset of the illness." Finally, Ciompi (1980) noted that "treatment factors were much less important for the long-term course than the above-described personality and disease factors." (p. 615).

Sex similarities were found, with 66.3% of the women in the "recovered" or "mild" categories compared with 61% of the men; whereas 7.1% of the men became worse, only 3.3% of the women did so (Ciompi 1980). Five patients demonstrated very late improvement. Using composite ratings, the team found "59% recovered or mild end states" (p. 616). Ciompi (1980) later concluded that "the long-term evolution of schizophrenia is much better than hitherto admitted," which was in keeping with the conclusions of "Bleuler and Huber, [who] both concluded that schizophrenia is in no way 'basically' or even 'predominately' [an] unfavorable 'disease process' running an inexorably deteriorating course" (Ciompi 1980, p. 616).

### United States #1—The Iowa 500 Study

In the first American study, the Iowa 500 Study assessed 100 patients with mania, 225 patients with depression, and 200 patients with schizophrenia who had been part of the annual admissions to Iowa State Psychopathic Hospital during the 1930s and 1940s. An additional group of 160 nonpsychiatric surgical patients (appendectomy or herniorrhaphy) was selected for a control group (Tsuang et al., 1979). These investigators applied the narrow Feighner criteria and clinical judgment to the comprehensive records available of that era (Feighner et al., 1972). The study concluded that these diagnoses were validated by follow-up information (a la Kraepelin) as well as family studies. Of 3,800 admissions, 874 charts were initially reviewed, with 20% to 63% of records rejected depending on the chart diagnosis for schizophrenia (i.e., 63% of those diagnosed with schizophrenia were rejected) (Winokur & Tsuang, 1996).

In the schizophrenia sample, 48.5% were females; 20% were married; 50% had poor premorbid psychosocial adjustment; 28% were high school graduates; median age at onset was 25 years; age at admission was 27 years; and only 26% had been discharged to the community (this was an era of custodial care with essentially no treatment [Winokur & Tsuang 1996]). Follow-up data were extracted from letters sent by social workers to the families for several of the early years. No information was available on 4%, only 17% of patients were interviewed, and 25% had information supplied by family or friends, with 53% supplied by physicians or other hospital admissions (Winokur & Tsuang, 1996). The fieldwork of the very long-term follow-up period (average = 37 years) consisted of interviewing those patients still living who could be found ($n$ = 86 of 200, or 43%) and first-degree relatives and evaluating all available records. The Iowa Structured Psychiatric Interview (ISPI; Tsuang et al., 1980) was administered by non-medical interviewers. Current diagnosis was based on data from the ISPI and on medical records through a consensus of three clinicians. Patients or first-degree relatives who had died or who refused to participate were given an "approximate" diagnosis based on medical records. Twenty screening questions were used for both reliability and validity of all diagnoses with little data reported.

Only four major outcome domains were measured: marital, residential, and occupational status and psychiatric symptoms. The criteria for good outcome were married or widowed, living in one's own home or with a relative, employed, retired, homemaker or student, and no symptoms. A fair rating was defined as divorced or separated, living in a nursing or county home, incapacitated due to physical illness, and some symptoms. A poor rating was considered if the patient was single or never married, living in a mental hospital, not working due to mental illness, and experiencing incapacitating symptoms. At long-term follow-up 30 to 40 years after the index hospitalization, 39 of 186 (21%) had a good marital outcome and 22 of 186 (12%) were rated as fair. For occupational status, 65 of 186 (35%) had good outcome, with an additional 14 of 186 (8%) with fair levels. For residential status, outcomes for 64 of 186 (34%) were good and another 89 (48%) were fair. For psychiatric status, 38 of 186 (20%) were rated as good, with 48 of 186 (26%) at fair levels. Winokur and Tsuang (1996) noted that disorientation and memory deficit at admission seemed to predict poorer outcome. Sex differences (men = 102; women = 98) were not reported in the overall outcome variables. Although these investigators focused on the 54% of patients who were rated as doing poorly, they neglected to point out that 46% of the cohort was actually doing much better. Nonetheless, the findings showed that outcomes for schizophrenia were at the end of a sequence ranging from affective disorders having the best outcome to schizoaffective disorders to paranoid-type schizophrenia to disorganized type having the worst outcome.

### Lithuania—"Late Catamnesis of Recurrent Schizophrenia with Prolonged Remissions"

In an observational study, Kreditor (1977) studied patients with episodic schizophrenia ($N = 115$) over a period of 20 years in five regions of Riga at the National Dispensary. The sample consisted of 38 men and 77 women with an age range of 35 to 82 years. Approximately 54% were 50 years or older. Diagnostic criteria for schizophrenia were fairly broad. Ninety-seven (84%) of these patients had long-term remissions that extended 8 to 40 years. Kreditor identified two types of episodic courses, one with occasional episodes and the other with multiple episodes. Ninety-seven subjects had prolonged remissions (including 39% with 20–40 years remitted), and only 18 became worse. Predictors of long-term remission were "harmony of premorbid personality," lack of or low occurrence of character pathology, late onset (ages 30–40 years), and affective stability. The two course type groups differed in premorbid personality, age at onset, and illness course. "The data give ground to eliminate the prognostic criteria of the probability of long-term remissions" (Kreditor 1977, pp. 110–113).

### Germany—The Bonn Investigations

Huber et al. (1979) followed 502 of 758 admissions to the University Psychiatric Clinic of Bonn, Germany, between 1945 and 1959. Of these patients, 142 died before follow-up (including 7 [4.9%] who were suicides). Of those probands still living, 209 males and 293 females were assessed for 22.4 catamnestic years with personal interviews by the clinical team between 1967 and 1973. This part of the sample was believed to be representative of the usual admission profile for the clinic. Relatives reported on the status of an additional 26 probands (4%); 34 (7%) more were lost to follow-up, and 6 (1%) had brain diseases. Forty-eight (10%) refused interviews; however, the investigators found that this group consisted mainly of persons with good prognostic factors such as above-average intelligence and upper-class status. The investigators used the combination criteria of Schneider (based primarily on Kraepelin) and Eugen Bleuler, which had also been used by Manfred Bleuler (1972/1978). Like Bleuler, Ciompi, Harding, and others, they did not use outcome to define the diagnosis. Furthermore, "no symptoms or syndromes at the time of onset could be used to predict with any certainty whatever, the differentiation between malignant or benign, process or non-process,...schizophrenic...psychoses" (Huber et al. 1980, p. 593). Sixty-seven percent became cohort members at first admission.

The authors reported that 57% of their subjects were improved and/or recovered. Other instruments found that 22.1% had achieved complete remission, with an additional 40.2% demonstrating "noncharacteristic residual syndromes." Thirty-five percent were considered to have "characteristic residual syndromes." Fifty-six percent of the cohort was judged to be socially recovered (meaning that they had returned to their premorbid fully employed status)—"all the more remarkable when only 13% had participated in any outpatient rehabilitation program" (p. 595). Social functioning was highly correlated with outcome of psychopathology (Huber et al. 1980). Sex differences were found in better outcome for females in general and specifically in social outcome. Schizophrenia in first-degree relatives tended to differentiate men with poorer outcomes. Females were more likely to have better outcomes if they had multiple episodes with clear-cut precipitating factors. Females also tended to have more florid symptoms but a later illness onset. Complete remission, more favorable outcomes, and social recovery tended to occur in females. Cerebral atrophies occurred more often in males, who also had more psycho-organic disorders of the elderly. Course was described as "phasic" in 22%, "surges" in 48%, and "sluggish" in 21%. The authors identified 76 course types, which they reduced to 12 categories. They also noted that outcome shifted among some cohort members no matter how long a certain status was in effect. However, they found that "no reasonably reliable prognosis for the individual patient is possible" (p. 604).

### Bulgaria—Marinow's Long-Term Follow-Up Study

A 2-decade study (mean = 20.2 years) conducted in Bulgaria by Marinow (1986) followed 280 male schizophrenia patients who had been discharged from hospitalization between 1946 and 1950. The cross-sectional outcomes for members of this cohort were measured every 5 years. Subjects were assessed on variables such as psychopathology and social and work functioning. Each factor was then combined into a summed total outcome or "prognostic" score. Findings revealed that at least 50% of subjects had a "favorable" outcome, with approximately 25% improved and another 25% with a poor outcome. Marinow found the course picture to be one of mixed signals with conflicting indicators of long-term outcome and concluded that it was impossible to predict future status for individuals. In a later study of persons with schizophrenia ($N = 634$) whose illness duration ranged from 2 to 20 years, Marinow (1988) found that long-term outcome had greater correlation with the patient's marital status, ability to work, and with neuroleptic treatment than with illness history, number of readmissions, and length of hospitalizations, but he was unable to "predict prognosis." The diagnostic criteria used in this study appear to have been wider than those used in American, Swiss, and German studies.

### United States #2—The Vermont Longitudinal Research Study

A second American long-term catamnestic study was conducted in Vermont for which base reports were published in the 1980s (Harding et al. 1987b, 1987c). This study is the longest study of deinstitutionalized patients to be conducted in the United States (ranging up to 62 years after first admission) and one of the longest studies of schizophrenia. The sample of 269 patients (144 females and 125 males) with severe and persistent mental illness was selected from the back wards of Vermont State Hospital in the mid-1950s.

Probands were provided with a "rehabilitation unit" after 2 years of only modest responses to long trials of clinically therapeutic dosages of phenothiazine. The patients and their multidisciplinary clinicians jointly created a federally funded, comprehensive model demonstration, biopsychosocial rehabilitation program that targeted self-sufficiency and community integration (Chittick et al., 1961). Their combined effort in the hospital provided training in activities of daily living and social skills; continued medication; vocational assessment, training, placement, and continued supports; patient government; peer support groups; case management; and careful deinstitutionalization.

A substudy of the parametric characteristics of the entire hospital census ($N = 1,300$) revealed that the back-ward patients in the cohort had the most chronic course and were the most severely ill and disabled (especially the males) patients compared with the hospital population at large (Harding et al., 1987b). The study cohort had an average of 16 years of illness and 10 years of total disability. Furthermore, these patients were shown to be among 19% who remained in the hospital during the previous 5 years or longer while other patients were admitted and discharged (G.W Brooks, unpublished study [*Retained Patients with Schizophrenia from 1920s to 1970s*], October 1975). This group is considered to be the most chronic cohort ever studied in the world literature and therefore should have had the worst long-term outcome.

Members of the cohort were carefully deinstitutionalized in the late 1950s into a pioneering community mental health system and were provided rehabilitation for 10 years, until 1965, by the same team from the hospital (Chittick et al., 1961). In the community, all aspects of community care were established, including a range of residential and occupational placements and supports, outpatient clinics, inclusion in natural community organizations, and continuity of care long before community mental health centers were established (Chittick et al., 1961). They were followed for an average of 32 catamnestic years, with a range of 22 to 62 years after first admission. A major follow-up study funded by the National Institute of

Mental Health was initiated in the early 1980s, at which time 97% of the Vermont cohort was located (262 of 269). The average age of the surviving interviewed cohort at follow-up was 61 years. A comprehensive and structured instrument battery was implemented, with all the interrater and interitem concordance testing reported (Harding et al., 1987b, 1987c). The field interviewers were blinded to the patients' records, and the record abstractors were blinded to outcome. Both cross-sectional and longitudinal measures were assessed. Prospectively gathered records and retrospective data were used to fill in the longitudinal picture, along with vocational rehabilitation records and structured interviews of family, friends, and clinicians. Recalibration of the index-admission diagnosis from the 1950s to the then new *DSM-III* (American Psychiatric Association, 1980) was performed with interrater trials that achieved a kappa level of .78 ($p < .0007$) (Harding et al. 1987c).

The original cohort was recorded to have 213 of 269 (79%) members with schizophrenia. The rediagnostic effort, done without the previous diagnosis assigned and according to DSM-III criteria, reduced that number to 118 (55%). Although the investigators followed 97% of the total sample of 269 subjects, only the hardest data were reported for outcome of schizophrenia, unlike in other studies. Those probands, who were rediagnosed, primarily with schizoaffective disorders, psychosis not otherwise specified, and atypical psychosis, were excluded from the analysis of schizophrenia and outcome, as were those who were deceased.

In a review of North American follow-up studies, McGlashan (1988) mistakenly reported that these patients had very late average onsets, in their 30s. He later corrected that report to a mean onset of 24.2 years for males and of 27.1 years for females (Childers & Harding, 1990; McGlashan, 1991). McGlashan also originally thought that these patients were the workers of the hospital and were retained by the staff until the rehabilitation study, another misconception that he subsequently corrected (McGlashan, 1991).

With 24% of the cohort deceased, an important methodological balance was introduced. Instead of simply comparing the demographic and illness variables with the surviving cohort, a special protocol was introduced that systematically interviewed the family, friends, and clinicians connected to these patients in one room in order to piece together the life lived by the patients until their deaths. This strategy revealed that instead of the most seriously ill cohort members dying first, leaving the less ill members reporting better outcomes, the subjects mirrored the same proportions of recovered, improved, or unimproved persons found in the live cohort (Harding et al. 1987b). Other long-term studies have combined information for the living and deceased subjects.

The interview instrument battery used in the follow-up study consisted of 15 standard scales and schedules (Harding et al., 1987a, 1987b). Much to their surprise, the Vermont investigators found that nearly two thirds of the subjects from this chronic, severely ill cohort met stringent objective criteria for recovery and/or significant improvement. Of the whole, 62% to 68% achieved significant improvement or recovery across multiple domains of function, increased work (40%), reestablished social relationships (68%), and self-care (81%) (Harding et al., 1987c). Sixty-eight percent showed no further signs or symptoms of schizophrenia, with 45% of that group having no symptoms at all. All of these areas were predicted in the *DSM-III* to deteriorate or remain at marginal levels (American Psychiatric Association 1980). Instead, the domains not only reconstituted and improved but also developed further in two thirds of the cohort.

Recovery criteria included no psychiatric medications, no symptoms, no behaviors that could be construed as those of a "mental patient," being employed, relating well with others, and living outside the hospital. Significant improvement meant that the person had achieved recovery in all but one of these domains. Social functioning was measured by several widely used and standard structured assessments and was another area that showed reconstitution and further development in 62% to 68% of subjects (Harding et al., 1987c). Sex differences were also examined in the surviving DSM-III schizophrenia sample, which had 41 men and 41 women. Females, who had had the better premorbid functioning scores (Childers & Harding, 1990), were shown to have lost their competitive advantage and ended up at only a trend level better than their male counterparts, who had consistently performed more poorly on all subscales and overall score of the Premorbid Adjustment Scale (PAS). Harding and Hall (1997) suggested that the explanation for the performance decrement seen in women might be the loss of estrogen protection at midlife (see also Seeman, 1995). Furthermore, the men appeared to have slowly gained in strength across time (Harding, 1994; Harding & Hall, 1997; Harding et al., 1987c). Nevertheless, women's scores on the Community Adjustment Scale (Consalvo et al., 1984, cited in Harding, 1994) remained slightly higher than those of men, despite the fact that they had longer lengths of stay in the hospital. Women also demonstrated more productivity, had less evidence of psychotic symptomatology, and evidenced higher levels of functioning in social relationships (Harding & Hall, 1997).

During the initial data analyses, Strauss and Harding wrote, "we have gathered some evidence that the course of schizophrenia is a more complex, dynamic, and heterogeneous process than has been heretofore appreciated or predicted by diagnostic specificity" (Strauss & Harding 1984, p. 349).

### Japan—Gumma University Hospital Study

Ogawa et al. (1987) conducted a 21- to 27-year follow-up of 140 consecutive patients (67 males and 73 females) discharged from the Department of Neuropsychiatry at the Gumma University Hospital in Japan between 1958 and 1962. At entry to the cohort, 81% of these patients were younger than 30 years; 79% were first admissions and resided primarily in the provincial town of Maebashi, northwest of Tokyo. These patients were provided with a program of "neuroleptic drugs, the open-door system, and intensive aftercare" (Ogawa et al., 1987, p. 758). The hospital's rehabilitation model was called *Seikatasu-rinsko* and was described as "clinical work in a patient's everyday life" (p. 750), which was reported as a combination of case management and individual counseling techniques.

At follow-up, 93% of the 140 members of this cohort were assessed, with 105 still living an average of 23.6 years after index hospitalization (range = 21–27 years). One hundred subjects were alive and interviewed. In addition to the *International Statistical Classification of Diseases, 9th Revision, Clinical Modification* (ICD-9-CM; World Health Organization 1978) rediagnosis, subjects were also evaluated on social functioning indices with Egurna's Social Adjustment Scale (ESAS; Eguma, 1962; Ogawa et al., 1987). Information was acquired from multiple data sources. The data were not analyzed with regard to sex differences.

The results revealed that 57% of the subjects were considered to be "fully self-supportive" (i.e., fully productive, living in own home and often also married, psychologically recovered, with a return to premorbid levels of functioning and independent social life without clinical interventions as well as maintenance of a normal family life). "Semi-self-supportive" ratings were given to another 19% and 34% were considered to be "hospitalized and maladjusted cases." The Japanese team concluded that social recovery was greater than improvement in psychiatric status. They conducted monthly assessments of social adjustment and reported patterns of adjustment across time. These patterns showed multiple fluctuations early in the illness course, with later differentiation between the self-supporting and chronically institutionalized groups (Ogawa et al., 1987).

### United States #3—The Maine–Vermont Longitudinal Comparison Study

The most recent American study was conducted in Maine (DeSisto et al., 1995a, 1995b) and, to my knowledge, is the only matched comparison study of very long outcome ever reported in the world literature. In this study, patients from the Vermont Longitudinal Research Study (*N* = 269) were matched by age, sex, diagnosis, and length of hospitalization with patients in Augusta State Hospital who were treated during the same era and in similar catchment areas as defined by health and census data. The Maine study employed the same research protocols as the earlier Vermont study and incorporated the careful rediagnostic workups that the Vermont Longitudinal Project had used (DeSisto et al., 1995a, 1995b). The study also used the same treatment era and intraproject reliability testing. Of the Vermont patients, 97% were tracked for an average of 32 years after first admission; 94% of Maine patients were tracked across an average of 36 years. The major difference between the two study cohorts was that whereas subjects in the Vermont cohort had been part of a comprehensive model rehabilitation demonstration program, the Maine patients had experienced primarily traditional custodial care.

The Maine–Vermont study had an average of 36 catamnestic (time since first admission) years. Following the rediagnostic work, the sample comprised 102 subjects with DSM-III schizophrenia (57 males and 45 females). Comparisons of the two matched cohorts revealed significant differences. After covarying out several variables that could not be matched (e.g., urban vs. rural residence, level of education), three very strong findings held: Vermont patients 1) had much stronger community functioning ($p < .001$), 2) much stronger work functioning ($p < .009$), and 3) substantially reduced symptoms ($p < .002$). Overall, global functioning results found Vermont patients at 68% and Maine patients at 49% ($p < .0001$). Sex differences were found in the Maine cohort, with women rated better in premorbid social functioning.

## WHAT HAVE WE LEARNED FROM THESE STUDIES?

In the following sections I assess the combined findings described above to determine what we might learn about the domains of diagnosis and time, symptom course, social functioning, ability to work again, psychopharmacology and side effects, predictors of long-term outcome, and reconstitution of lives.

### Diagnosis and Time: Not as Strong a Predictor as Once Thought

In the field of psychiatry, diagnosis has long been reified and conceived of as a "lifetime" label (American Psychiatric Association 1980, 1994). In the United States, psychiatry tended to be ethnocentric, especially after an analysis showed that American clinicians overdiagnosed schizophrenia based on DSM-II criteria (American Psychiatric Association, 1968) in comparison with clinicians in the United Kingdom (Cooper et al., 1972). Thus, although the Swiss and German studies used criteria narrower than those of Eugen Bleuler but wider than the Kraepelinian-based *DSM-III* (American Psychiatric Association, 1980), American investigators discounted the European findings and proceeded to make criteria narrower and narrower.

However, the narrowness of the criteria used does not predict uniformly poor outcome, as was once thought (Harding et al., 1979, 1987c). The narrow Feighner criteria employed by the Iowa 500 study identified such a poor-outcome group with more efficiency (Tsuang et al., 1979, 1981). This approach was a trade-off, because it made the cohort findings less generalizable to the entire population with schizophrenia. However, much to everyone's surprise, even the sample identified in this manner has found heterogeneity in outcome. With one exception, these long-term studies revealed that diagnoses could be reconceived as "cross-sectional working hypotheses" (Harding, 1998, p. 321) that need to be reviewed and revised over time and in many cases eventually discarded. There is evidence that patients with schizophrenia have more difficulty in achieving good long-term outcome than do many patients coping with affective and schizoaffective disorders, as found by the Iowa 500 group and others. However, the Vermont sample and others have demonstrated that even this effect is reduced to a trend level across decades. In an opposite approach, Vaillant (1975) also found heterogeneity when he attempted to follow up the other end of the continuum, the so-called good-prognosis patients. Discovering heterogeneity after 10 years, he concluded that "prognosis and diagnosis are two different dimensions of psychosis," in direct contradiction to Kraepelin (1902).

### Symptom Course—Ever-Widening Heterogeneity with Early Fluctuations and Later Decrease of Virulence

Eugen Bleuler (1911/1950) called the disorder "a group of schizophrenias," and follow-up investigators are aware of the wide variation of individual histories, which supports Kendler's complex model of gene–person–environment interaction (Kendler & Eaves, 1986). Huber et al. (1975) suggested 76 course types, indicating the wide heterogeneity found, but eventually reduced these to 12. Ciompi (1980) also published a diagram of 8 course types. His chart, with accompanying percentages, has been perceived as the standard by which course and outcome regularly proceed. However, Childers and Harding (1990) found evidence in the Burghölzli Hospital reports and the Vermont findings that these percentages are not written in stone but rather depend on the composition of the cohort. This observation means that predicting a probable long-term course for individuals is difficult if not impossible.

### Predictors of Long-Term Outcome Weaken Over Time

Although some studies, such as the Lausanne Investigations, found that the classical predictors held across time, an unpublished manuscript by Harding and colleagues showed that the classical predictors of outcome in schizophrenia research can also fade in power to trend levels across decades. Such predictors include gender, type of onset, early versus late onset, symptom profile, and age at onset. The predictive power of sex, which has classically shown strong evidence in favor of females, weakens across time, perhaps as the protective effects of estrogen wear off with menopause (Seeman, 2003). Menopausal women in the Vermont cohort lost their edge to the trend level, whereas the men grew increasingly stronger (improved in functioning and had fewer symptoms) across time. The only predictors that showed resistance to weakening over time were certain types of negative symptoms.

### Restoration of Social Functioning

Harding et al. (1987a) and Harding and Keller (1998) analyzed the literature on social functioning and schizophrenia, which describes poor premorbid adjustment, deterioration during illness, feelings of isolation and estrangement, disordered emotional responsivity, bizarre behavior and speech that can drive friends and family away, and the symptom of blunted affect, which increases social isolation. The long-term studies revealed that social functioning most often is restored and even undergoes further development after a schizophrenic psychosis. Many of the studies found that this effect happened with greater frequency or was highly correlated with improvement in psychological functioning.

### Regaining the Ability To Work Again

The assumption that once-psychotic persons are unable to work has been challenged repeatedly by a number of investigators (e.g., Anthony et al., 1984; Drake et al., 1999). Strauss and Carpenter (1974) showed that the best predictor of working is past work experience. Furthermore, diagnosis and symptoms did not predict work or social functioning or outcome across 5 years of follow-up. Previous social functioning did cross over to help predict work functioning. In the Maine–Vermont comparison, the subjects were matched and also happened to have had similar work histories prior to being hospitalized. The Vermont patients, who had participated in an intensive vocational rehabilitation program, continued working throughout the follow-up period at a rate of 30% to 40%, with an additional 20% engaging in volunteer work within their communities. The Maine patients who did not receive vocational rehabilitation struggled to regain their employment status. The Vermont model focused on rehabilitation, self-sufficiency, and community integration; by contrast, the Maine model emphasized stabilization, maintenance, and entitlements (DeSisto et al., 1995a; 1995b).

### Psychopharmacology and the Assumption of Lifetime Use Not Supported

There is an assumption—albeit one not supported in the literature—that most persons with schizophrenia need to remain on antipsychotic medication all of their lives. However, the Vermont study revealed that 20% were no longer receiving prescriptions for medication; 30% had drawers full of medications never taken; 25% had invented targeted strategies before Herz et al. (1991) and Carpenter et al. (1988); and the remaining 25% were taking their medications religiously, having been so threatened with recurring psychosis by past clinicians that their current clinicians were unable to taper their dosage. Harding (1998) concluded that perhaps only a small group of patients really needed continuing medications across a lifetime and recommended that the findings be investigated further. The idea of lifetime use of antipsychotics has been assumed because of the myth "once a schizophrenic, always a schizophrenic" or nowadays reframed as "once a broken brain, always a broken brain."

### Many Pathways to Improvement and Recovery

M. Bleuler (1972/1978) observed that "the long-term experience gleaned from my probands revealed one fact most impressively, namely that successful results can be achieved through totally different methods" (p. 441). Furthermore, in the Vermont–Maine comparison, the investigators were startled to find that although significant outcome differences were found between the samples (which may have been attributable to the rehabilitation program in Vermont versus the custodial care in Maine), 49% of Maine patients continued forward toward improvement. At first, DeSisto et al. (1991) thought that the greater forward progress of the Vermont patients was due to decisions made at the top of the system—that is, Vermont appeared clear and consistent in its mission and comprehensive in its programs whereas Maine did not. Although some of this environmental impact may have been operative, Maine patients continued to improve despite the vagaries of their system of care.

After looking at all of the long-term studies across many treatment eras and finding that patients persisted toward recovery and/or improvement, new thoughts began to emerge about the power of human relationships, no matter what services are being delivered. The Vermont patients reported that they received the greatest benefit when they were told that someone believed in them: "Someone believed in me, someone told me I had a chance to get better." To Harding, this illustrated the importance of hope and showed that hope was connected to the natural self-healing capacities of people. She began to write about neural plasticity (e.g., Harding, 1998). Andreasen (2001, p. 31) stated recently, "brain plasticity...stresses that our brains are in constant dynamic change, which occurs as a consequence of the impact of experience on our mental functions and states." Strauss and Harding (1990) suggested that treatment providers and research investigations need to target developmental issues and course of disorder as "two interacting systems," especially in this era of biological psychiatry. They described both positive (amplifying) and negative (limiting) feedback loops within this interaction.

Given the arguments of schools fighting for certain models of treatment as more effective than other models, one wonders whether clinicians may need to rethink this stance. An alternative plan calls for clinicians to collaborate with one another and with their patients by employing a range of treatment options—depending on the ever-changing needs of patients—with warmth, encouragement, optimism, and persistence.

### Rebalancing the Picture for Schizophrenia

The long-term course of schizophrenia is vastly different than what has been extrapolated from short-term studies as well as from older cohorts of convenience formed by patients still in systems of care for a wide variety of reasons. Such reasons include lack of incentives to get better, self-fulfilling prophesies derived from pessimistic attitudes and continuing severity of symptoms, and the expectation of lifetime diagnostic specificity and need for psychopharmacology.

In regard to treatment, M. Bleuler (1972/1978) suggested that "The inner life of the schizophrenic is never 'burnt out.' It always continues on its way. When ceaseless attempts are made to establish contact with him as with a normal person, and he is not left to stand aside like an outsider, a communal relationship is established that means a great deal to both the patient and the doctor" (p. 442). In fact, Bleuler taught us to see "the person behind the disorder" with comments such as "seriously 'demented' schizophrenics have not lost touch with a healthy psychic life,...in their case, healthy perception, memory, recall, judgment, and feeling are merely concealed behind their pathological behavior" (M. Bleuler, 1972/1978, p. 191).

### SUMMARY OF FINDINGS

For the past century, the course of schizophrenia has been thought to be a downward course for most if not all patients. In this chapter I presented evidence from the long-term literature that revealed a very different outcome. These studies found wide heterogeneity of course and social and work functioning, significant weakening of traditional predictors, and an interaction of adult development with symptom course. The discussion detailed the possibilities for a more positive outcome emerging from such studies. Explanatory models were proposed of neural plasticity, the change from extreme anxiety and fear arising from the experience of schizophrenia itself, to "active coping" through rehabilitation, hope and optimism, recalibration of neurobiological mechanisms during the aging process, and human endurance and resilience.

The most remarkable finding of these long-term studies is the confluence of results showing that at least 50% to 60% of each intact cohort studied across 2 to 3 decades significantly reclaimed their lives, even in the face of persisting beliefs that this would be impossible. Reconstructed lives have begun to erode the old beliefs, and new strategies with a recovery vision are beginning to be employed.

Acknowledgments
The author thanks Dr. Zlatka Russinova of Boston University for quickly translating the Lithuanian article.

## REFERENCES

American Psychiatric Association. (1968). *Diagnostic and statistical manual (2nd ed.)*. Washington, DC: Author.

American Psychiatric Association. (1980). *Diagnostic and statistical manual (3rd ed.)*. Washington, DC: Author.

American Psychiatric Association. (1987). *Diagnostic and statistical manual (3rd ed., revised)*. Washington, DC: Author.

American Psychiatric Association. (1994). *Diagnostic and statistical manual (4th ed.)*. Washington, DC: Author.

Andreasen, N. C. (2001). *Brave new brain: Conquering mental illness in the era of the genome*. Oxford, England: Oxford University Press.

Anthony, W. A., Howell J, & Danley, K. S. (1984). Vocational rehabilitation of the psychiatrically disabled. In M. Mirabai (Ed.), *The chronically mentally ill: Research and services*. (pp 215–237). Jamaica, NY: Spectrum Publications.

Bleuler, E. (1950). *Dementia praecox, or the group of schizophrenias (1911)*. Translated by J. Zinkin. New York: International Universities Press.

Bleuler, M. (1978). *The schizophrenic disorders: Long-term patient and family studies* (1972). Translated by Clemens SM. New Haven, CT: Yale University Press.

Bleuler, M. (1984). The old and new picture of the schizophrenic patient. *Schweizer Archiv fur Neurologie, Neurochirurgie und Psychiatrie, 135,* 143–149.

Carpenter, W. T. Jr., Heinrichs, D. W., & Wagman, A. M. (1988). Deficit and nondeficit forms of schizophrenia: the concept. *American Journal of Psychiatry, 145,* 578–583.

Childers, S. E., & Harding, C. M. (1990). Gender, premorbid social functioning, and long-term outcome in DSM-III schizophrenia. *Schizophrenia Bulletin, 18,* 309–318.

Chittick, R. A., Brooks, G. W., Irons, F. S., et al. (1961). *The Vermont story*. Burlington, VT: Queen City Press.

Ciompi, L. (1980). Catamnestic long-term study on the course of life and aging of schizophrenics. *Schizophrenia Bulletin, 6,* 606–618.

Ciompi, L., & Müller C. (1976). *Lebensweg und Alter der Schizophrenen: Eine katamnestische Longzeitstudie bis ins senium*. Berlin: Springer-Verlag.

Cooper, J. E., Kendell, R. E., Gurland, B. J., et al. (1972). *Psychiatric diagnoses in New York and London*. Oxford, England: Oxford University Press.

DeSisto, M. J., Harding, C. M., Howard, M. A., et al. (1991). *Perspectives on rural mental health: A comparison of mental health system policy and program development in Maine and Vermont.* Augusta, ME: Kennebec Press.

DeSisto, M., Harding, C. M., Ashikaga, T., et al. (1995a). The Maine and Vermont three-decade studies of serious mental illness, I: Matched comparison of cross-sectional outcome. *British Journal of Psychiatry, 167,* 331–338.

DeSisto, M., Harding, C. M, Ashikaga, T., et al. (1995b). The Maine and Vermont three-decade studies of serious mental illness, II: Longitudinal course comparisons. *British Journal of Psychiatry, 167,* 338–342.

Drake, R. E., Becker, D. R., Clark, R. E., et al. (1999). Research on the individual placement and support model of supported employment. *Psychiatric Quarterly, 70,* 289–301.

Eguma, Y. (1962). The prevention of failure in the rehabilitation of discharged schizophrenic patients. *Folia Psychiatrica et Neurologica Japonica, 64,* 921–927.

Feighner, J. P., Robins, E., Guze, S. B., et al. (1972). Diagnostic criteria for use in psychiatric research. *Archives of General Psychiatry, 26,* 57–63.

Harding, C. M. (1994). Speculations on the measurement of recovery from severe psychiatric disorder and the human condition. In R. J. Ancill, S. Holliday, G. W. MacEwan, (Eds.), *Schizophrenia: Exploring the spectrum of psychosis* (pp 153–169). Chichester: Wiley & Sons.

Harding, C. M. (1998). Reassessing a person with schizophrenia and developing a new treatment plan. In J. Barron, (Ed.), *Making diagnosis meaningful: Enhancing evaluation and treatment of psychological disorders.* Washington, DC: American Psychological Association.

Harding, C. M., & Hall, G. M. (1997). Long-term outcome studies of schizophrenia: Do females continue to display better outcome as expected? *International Review of Psychiatry, 8,* 409–418.

Harding, C. M., & Keller, A. B. (1998). Long-term outcome of social functioning. In K.T. Mueser, N. Tarrier, (Eds.), *Handbook of social functioning in schizophrenia* (pp. 134–148). Boston, MA: Allyn & Bacon.

Harding, C. M., Brooks, G. W., Ashikaga, T., et al. (1987a). Aging and social functioning in once-chronic schizophrenic patients 22–62 years after first admission: The Vermont story. In N. Miller, G. Cohen, (Eds.), *Schizophrenia and aging.* New York: Guilford.

Harding, C. M., Brooks, G. W., Ashikaga, T., et al. (1987b). The Vermont longitudinal study of persons with severe mental illness, I: Methodology, study, sample, and overall status 32 years later. *American Journal of Psychiatry, 144,* 718–726.

Harding, C. M., Brooks, G. W., Ashikaga, T., et al. (1987c). The Vermont longitudinal study of persons with severe mental illness, II: Long-term outcome of subjects who retrospectively met DSM-III criteria for schizophrenia. *American Journal of Psychiatry, 144,* 727–735.

Herz, M. I., Glazer, W. M., Mostert, M. A., et al. (1991). Intermittent versus maintenance medication in schizophrenia: Two year study results. *Archives of General Psychiatry, 48,* 333–339.

Hinterhuber, H. (1973) Zur Katamnese der Schizophrenien. *Fortschritte der Neurologie Psychiatrie, 41,* 527–588.

Huber, G., Gross, G., & Schüttler, R. (1975). A long-term follow-up study of schizophrenia: Psychiatric course of illness and prognosis. *Acta Psychiatrica Scandinavica, 52,* 49–57.

Huber, G., Gross, G., & Schüttler, R. (1979). Schizophrenie: Verlaufs und sozialpsychiatrische Langzeit unter suchfigen an den 1945 bis 1959 in Bonn hospitalisierten schizophrenen Kranken. *Monographien aus dem Gesamtgebiete der Psychiatrie. Bd. 21.* Berlin: Springer-Verlag.

Huber, G., Gross, G., & Schüttler R. (1980). Longitudinal studies of schizophrenic patients. *Schizophrenia Bulletin, 6,* 592–605.

Kendler, K., & Eaves, Q. (1986). Models for joint effect of genotype and environment on liability to psychiatric illness. *American Journal of Psychiatry, 143,* 279–289.

Kraepelin, E. (1902). *Dementia praecox, in clinical psychiatry: A textbook for students and physicians, (6th ed.).* Translated by A.R. Diefendorf. New York: Macmillan.

Kreditor, D. Kh. (1977). Late catamnesis of recurrent schizophrenia with prolonged remissions (according to an unselected study). *Zh Nevropatol Psikiatr Im SS Korsakova, 77*(1), 110–113.

Marinow, A. (1974). Klinisch-statische und katamnestische Untersuchungen und chronisch Schizophrenen 1951–1960 und 1961–1970. *Archiv für Psychiatrie und Nervenkrankheiten, 218,* 115–124.

Marinow, A. (1986). Prognostication in schizophrenia. *Psychopathology, 19*(4), 192–195.

Marinow, A. (1988). Prognosis and outcome in schizophrenia. *International Journal of Mental Health, 17,* 63–80.

McGlashan, T. A. (1988). A selective review of recent North American long-term follow-up studies of schizophrenia. *Schizophrenia Bulletin, 14,* 515–542.

McGlashan, T. A. (1991). A selective review of recent North American long-term follow-up studies of schizophrenia. In S. Martin, J. Goset, S. Grob, (Eds.), *Psychiatric treatment: Advances in outcome research* (pp 61–105). Washington, DC: American Psychiatric Press.

Ogawa & Miya, M., Watarai, A., et al. (1987). A long-term follow-up study of schizophrenia in Japan—With special reference to the course of social adjustment. *British Journal of Psychiatry, 151,* 758–765.

Seeman, W. (1995). Sex and schizophrenia. *Canadian Journal of Schizophrenia, 30,* 313–315.

Seeman, W. (2003). In C. Cohen (Ed.), *Schizophrenia into later life* (chapter 8). Washington, DC: American Psychiatric Publishing, Inc.

Strauss, J. S., Carpenter, W. T. Jr. (1974). The prediction of outcome in schizophrenia, II: Relationship between predictor and outcome variables. *Archives of General Psychiatry 31,* 37–42.

Strauss, J. S., & Harding, C. M. (1984). How serious is schizophrenia? Comments about prognosis. *Advances in Biological Psychiatry 19,* 1597–1600.

Strauss, J. S., & Harding, C. M. (1990). Relationships between adult development and the course of mental disorder. In J. E. Rolf, A. Masten, (Eds.), *Risk and protective factors in the development of psychopathology* (pp 514–525). New York: Cambridge University Press.

Tsuang, M. T., Woolson, R. F., & Fleming, J. A. (1979). Long-term outcome of major psychoses, I: Schizophrenia and affective disorders compared with psychiatrically symptom-free surgical conditions. *Archives of General Psychiatry, 36,* 1295–1301.

Tsuang, M. T., Woolson, R. F., & Simpson, J. C. (1980). The Iowa Structured Psychiatric Interview: Rationale, reliability, and validity. *Acta Psychiatrica Scandinavica, 62* (suppl 283), 1–38.

Tsuang, M. T., Woolson, R. E., & Simpson, J. C. (1981). An evaluation of the Feighner criteria for schizophrenia and affective disorder using long-term outcome data. *Psychological Medicine, 11,* 281–287.

Vaillant, G. E. (1975). Paper presented at the 128th annual meeting of the American Psychiatric Association, Anaheim, CA.

Winokur, G., & Tsuang M. T. (1996). *The natural history of mania, depression, and schizophrenia.* Washington, DC, American Psychiatric Press.

World Health Organization. (1978) *International statistical classification of diseases, 9th revision, Clinical modification.* Geneva, Switzerland, World Health Organization.

## What Is the Reality about Severe Mental Disorder?

*John S. Strauss*

John S. Strauss, MD, is professor emeritus of psychiatry, Yale University School of Medicine, Department of Psychiatry.

Sometimes, both in my life and in my research career in psychiatry, I have felt like a sailboat blowing just a little off wind. I like to think that my direction in psychiatry, along with that of many others, is the search for what is really there—what is the nature of psychiatric disorder, and what really is treatment. But, it often seems to me that in the field of psychiatry, the wind of theory and belief is missing much of that reality, blowing off that course. It is not clear to me why more people don't see that. Perhaps all this may sound a bit grandiose, but let me explain.

Since medical school, I have been both a clinician and a researcher. My research has always involved interviews with patients, and I have always been one of the interviewers. As a researcher, I have dealt with scientific method and the nature of proof, of going beyond impressions and beliefs, often involving problems of measurement, sampling, and data analysis—problems that may be difficult for the clinician to see. But, as a clinician and interviewer, I have seen ways in which accepted theory, concepts, and methods can be insufficient for reflecting real people. The dual role of clinician and researcher is a wonderful combination because it provides a perspective on the real world that is unparalleled. It makes it possible to see how the concepts generated and followed by one may not be adequate from the perspective of the other. It also makes it possible to consider how those concepts might be improved.

For example, take the concept of outcome in schizophrenia. In the 1960s, Will Carpenter, John Bartko, and I participated in the International Pilot Study of Schizophrenia (World Health Organization, 1973). It was a nine center project with headquarters at the World Health Organization in Geneva. The goal of that project was to develop instruments (structured interviews and rating scales) to be able to evaluate patients and their outcomes in different cultures. In our Washington center we helped to develop the methods and then used them to study a cohort of patients in the Washington area. From our data and experiences we wrote a series of papers on diagnosis, diagnostic criteria, outcome, and its predictors. We noted many things, some of which ran counter to the dominant beliefs and concepts of the day. For example, in one paper (Strauss, 1969) I described that symptoms (such as hallucinations and delusions) did not seem to be discrete entities but that rather there seemed to be a continuum between symptom "types," so that some people described experiences that were "sort of like a voice" in that they could "sort of hear it" but that were also "like a thought." I described the implications of such a finding for concepts of psychiatric disorder and the processes that it involves, suggesting for example that it might be more accurate to consider dimensions of abnormality rather than discrete types, dimensions between different types of symptom processes as well as between "abnormal" and "normal" processes. This would imply that to understand mental illness and its origins and to create optimal treatments, we might need to think in terms of "more or less" rather than in terms of "does this person have this illness or this symptom or not."

Such an emphasis on using careful observations and data to define the "real processes" that reflect illness has its roots in centuries of medical thinking of course. The use of longitudinal observations has been particularly prominent. Hippocrates, in attempting to define such processes, used longitudinal observations, as did Sydenham in his studies of infectious diseases. And it was the work of Kraepelin at the end of the 19th century attempting to define such processes in what he called *dementia praecox* (essentially what we call schizophrenia) that many consider to be the basis of modern psychiatry. Essentially, Kraepelin said we know there is a disease *dementia praecox* because all the people who have it have an inevitable downhill course. Thus the course was viewed as identifying a single "disease process" even though the patients so identified had diverse types of symptoms.

This emphasis on disease identification by defining a process was a major step in bringing psychiatry beyond merely identifying syndromes, clusters of symptoms, without bothering to be certain that they reflected an underlying disease. In general medicine, for example, it had been long noted that the group of symptoms constituting the syndrome "dropsy" ( generalized body swelling), in fact, reflected many basically different disease processes.

In our follow-up studies of patients with schizophrenia, in contrast to the concepts of Kraepelin that had been largely accepted in psychiatry, we found that patients with schizophrenia had a wide range of outcomes over 2 years, some patients indeed getting worse, others staying more or less the same, and others improving significantly. In some former patients we found no current signs of disorder at 2-year follow-up (Strauss & Carpenter, 1974).

When we presented these findings at national meetings, reasonably enough, even importantly, there were many questions and criticisms. Were we using adequate diagnostic criteria? Was a 2-year follow-up period long enough? To pursue the former question we rediagnosed our patients using various diagnostic systems and found no differences from the orginal outcome findings. We carried out longer term outcome studies, the results of which were consistent with the earlier findings. Even more important, over

30 other follow-up studies have been carried out by many investigators since, some with follow-up intervals of 25 years and longer (e.g., Harding, Brooks, Ashikaga, Strauss & Breier, 1987). All of these have found essentially the same results that we did.

Such questions and further studies are exactly what science is about at its best. They are the beauty of our field. What is more difficult to explain is another group of responses. When we first presented our findings at conferences, frequently someone in the audience would get up during the discussion period and say simply, "Your results are not possible. We know they cannot be true." (Sometimes someone in the audience would get up and say, "Well that's not new. We knew all the time that people with schizophrenia could get better." It was always a temptation to suggest that the two should go outside and argue it out, but being more or less well brought up, I never did). Even more significantly, when we submitted our first paper with these findings to a major psychiatric journal, we received a letter of rejection with the comment of the major reviewer, "This cannot be true." Our sailboat clearly was not going in the direction that the wind was trying to blow us. We submitted that article to an even more prestigious journal and it was immediately accepted.

Even more disturbing, now, over 30 years later, and following many studies conducted in many different countries with essentially the same results and none supporting Kraepelin's conclusion, residents are often still being taught that people with schizophrenia never improve, and patients are often being taught by their doctors or in some psychoeducation programs, that "You have a disease like diabetes. You will have it all your life. You will have to take medications all your life and there are certain things you will never be able to do."

Why? At first, I was mostly just angry that mental health professionals continued to ascribe to a belief system involving teaching and practice that ran totally contrary to an entire mass of scientific data. What was being taught and learned was clearly wrong. But beyond being wrong, it was often harmful, stripping patients of hope and condemning them to treatment that was often primarily custodial or at best palliative. The message was, "You need to learn to live with your illness" or worse.

Since those early follow-up studies over 30 years ago, my research sailboat has gone through many waters and experienced many similar winds. We have suggested that there is not one outcome (and hence not one longitudinal process) in schizophrenia but many processes somewhat independent of each other, including duration of illness, negative symptoms, work, and social relations. We have suggested that those outcomes and their predictors imply that the processes involved constitute open linked systems, that is, each area tends to predict itself (to be continuous over time) while still having some correlations with the other systems. These findings led us to propose a multiaxial diagnostic system for *DSM-III*, a proposal that was accepted (Strauss, 1975). But these findings had implications that should go much further. They, along with subsequent work, suggested that there is a complex relationship between "disorder" and "functioning" (such as work and social relations functioning ), that is a relationship between the "abnormal" and the "normal" aspects of the life of a person with severe mental disorder. They imply furthermore a process in which not only the abnormal (i.e., "illness") affects the normal (i.e., "functioning"), but in which the normal influences the abnormal both in assisting improvement and in worsening a disorder.

In other analyses of our data we brought back Hughling-Jackson's concept of positive and negative symptoms from his work in the 19th century, because we found in our data that these two groups of symptoms had different longitudinal implications (and thus probably defined separate processes) (Strauss, Carpenter & Bartko, 1974). We suggested that different diagnostic categories were not discretely separate but that many patients actually fell in between diagnostic categories and between the diagnostic categories and "normal" (Strauss, Gabriel, Kokes, Ritzler, VanOrd & Tarana, 1979). We suggested further, following an initial suggestion by one of our research subjects, that patients, even those with schizophrenia, act on their own behalf to get better, and suggested the diverse and important ways in which they do that (Strauss, 1999). That patient had opened up the whole issue of subjectivity, suggesting in brief, that seeing patients essentially as billiard balls, more or less merely "compliant" (to use a term that fortunately is being increasingly criticized), is not only bad practice, but also is bad science. I continue to explore this immense area conceptually and methodologically, this area of the person with disorder as a person, a concept that can be summarized (but with the danger of encapsulating it too narrowly) as "subjectivity." Here, the main question in our trying to understand the processes of mental disorder is the possibility that what the patient does or doesn't do and his or her experiences other than symptoms, may be more basically related to the "disorder" itself than the symptoms that have caught our attention as mental health professionals. This is an old question in psychiatry, for Bleuler, for example (Bleuler, 1950), but one which I think can be approached in new and perhaps more fruitful ways.

Underneath the issue of taking subjectivity more seriously in constructing our science of mental health is one that I think is even more basic, how does mental disorder relate to processes of being human more generally, that is, what is the relationship between what we call mental disorder and ordinary human functioning. And finally but closely related is what seems to me the most fundamental issue of our field: how can we make the mental health field a human science? Specifically, how can we combine or adapt scientific principles to the fact that we are dealing with human beings, beings who are not billiard balls merely reacting, but who have desires and motivation, feelings and a sense of meaning, all of which also influence actions, experiences, disorders and responses, to say nothing of entire lives? A major approach to understanding the "human" side of this problem is learning how the arts and especially the theater, which focus so effectively on human experience, can teach us. Ultimately it may be possible in some way to combine artistic principles and scientific principles.

In trying to listen closely to patients, I have often felt like that sailboat, not wanting necessarily to follow the direction in which our conceptual and methodologic wind was blowing, and finding great pleasure in finding new ways to understand the reality of the patient and new ways conceptually, methodologically, and in teaching, for trying to see "what is really going on out there." It has also been important to me to try to understand why we as mental health professionals have often found it so difficult to notice that reality.

This work and orientation raises two questions that seem crucial in regard to the focus of the current volumes. The first is a conceptual question. How can we be so sure that it makes sense in theory, practice, and research to separate illness from functioning? It seems, for example, that presupposing a sharp break between "basic" research about the nature of disorder and rehabilitation, as we have done in the structure of our research funding institutions, in our training, in the words we use, in our practice, and in our concepts, is just another way (like saying "people with schizophrenia don't improve") of creating structures, concepts, and methods that prevent us from learning what is really there. It also may prevent us from hearing what patients are trying, often very hard, to tell us. For example, when a person says, "When I work I don't hear voices," how can we be sure that working does not contribute to the illness getting better? (There are many quicky explanations like "that's just distraction" or "but it doesn't last" (neither does a neuroleptic if you don't take more of it). But really, why do we dismiss such data so quickly? Only because they don't fit our current beliefs? Or what does it indicate that patients often say "The most important thing for my getting better was someone who cared?" Is a meaningful social linking really part of the healing (treatment?) process? And if so, what does that tell us about the nature of mental illness? And about treatment? There is so much to learn.

The second question I raise in the context of these volumes is equally basic. It is the question of why it has been so difficult for people to accept and deal with the many issues that to a clinician, and to a clinician-researcher, seem so important and so obvious. This failure to deal with certain issues and findings is most flagrant in the example of the diversity in the course of schizophrenia described above that has been so often replicated and never disproved. How is it that our field continues often to teach and to act as though patients with schizophrenia can't improve in spite of all (literally all) the data to the contrary? Previously, that is to say until about 4 weeks before I wrote this, it made me furious that our field could be so stupid (I'm sorry, but it is the only word that fits my sentiments accurately ). With the help of some friends, however, I was able to talk more about this and begin to look at it more coolly. (My friends were being a bit like the psychologist who suggests that it might be important not only to complain about very wealthy people not contributing more to the millions of their fellow humans suffering from one or another of the rampant serious misfortunes, we should also, so the argument goes, study these very wealthy people, without rancor, to learn how they can buy hundreds of pairs of shoes for example when they know that people are starving to death ). Anyway, several approaches for our common failure as mental health professionals to change our views and to pursue important leads struck me as possibilities. Here, I have no data, only suggestions:

First, as Phil May used to suggest, there is always a problem of getting research findings into practice and teaching. This is not necessarily specific to our field.

Second, it seems to me, that as a field, whether we are always aware of it or not, we lean heavily for our sense of legitimacy on the teachings and ways of thinking of Kraepelin as the "father" of modern psychiatry and on those who followed him. In a field that has often been derided from many sides, such legitimacy is particularly important and vulnerable. Kraepelin was a very smart person and a very good observer, although what he did not know, and probably could not know, about issues of sampling and other methodologic problems probably account at least partly for the conclusions he reached which were wrong.

Third, we work in an emotionally difficult field. Around the time when I started to become less furious about our lag in accepting the diverse outcome of schizophrenia, I was in Paris and several (non-mental health professional) friends happened to ask me within a space of a few days, "but how can you work with such sick people without it causing you major problems yourself?" I hadn't heard that question for years. They weren't asking it snidely or accusingly, just asking it. I think some of the sense of their question was correct. We work in an emotionally difficult field, often wonderfully rewarding, but nevertheless, difficult. We probably do a lot of things to protect ourselves. For those of us who are psychiatrists, these include things we learned in medical school when we first started to cut into a human body in anatomy class, such as how to get distance from our patients. We need to protect ourselves. That is totally understandable. Having a conceptual and institutional structure in which to do it can be helpful. If it doesn't also cause harm! Perhaps we need a new conceptual and institutional structure to help us deal with the new knowledge and with the ignored data about severe mental disorders.

And finally, perhaps part of that third suggestion above, dealing adequately with this information about diversity of course, complexity of outcome and treatment, and subjectivity, is a lot to ask of us. The sociologist Edgar Morin (1990) wrote a book on complex thinking. There, he discusses how very difficult it is to think in complex terms. I believe he is right. It is difficult to learn, to do treatment, to do research, to have responsability, if we live in a world of complexity. But I also believe that if we are to get closer to the real world of mental disorders, their causes and their treatments, we're just going to have to deal with that complexity more adequately.

**REFERENCES**

Bleuler, E. (1950). *Dementia praecox or the group of schizophrenias,* 1911. (Zinkin, J. trans) 1950. International Universities Press. New York.Morin, E. (1990). *Introduction à la pensée complexe.* ESF éditeur. Issy-les-Moulineaux.

Harding, C.M., Brooks, G.W., Ashikaga, T., Strauss, J.S., & Breier, A. (1987). The Vermont longitudinal study of persons with severe mental illness: I. Methodology, study sample, and overall status 32 years later. *American Journal of Psychiatry, 144* (6), 718–726.

Morin, E. (1990). *Introduction à la pensée complexe.* Paris: EST Éditeurs.

Strauss, J.S. (1969). Hallucinations and delusions as points on continua function: Rating scale evidence. *Archives of General Psychiatry, 31,* 581–586.

Strauss, J.S. (1975). A comprehensive approach to psychiatric diagnosis. American Journal of Psychiatry, 132 (11): 1193–1197.

Strauss, J.S. (1996). Subjectivity. Journal of Nervous and Mental Disease, 184(4): 205–212. Reprinted as Subjektivitet, in Dialog, 1999, 9(3): 37–50. Translated into Norwegian by Rimestad, Soren.

Strauss, J.S., & Carpenter, W.T., Jr. (1974) Characteristic symptoms and outcome in schizophrenia. *Archives of General Psychiatry, 30*(1): 429-434.

Strauss, J.S., Carpenter, W.T., Jr., & Bartko, J.J. (1974). Speculations on the processes that underlie schizophrenic symptoms. Schizophrenia Bulletin, 11, 61–70.

Strauss, J.S., Gabriel, K.R., Kokes, R.F., Ritzler, B.A., VanOrd, A., & Tarana, E. (1979). Do psychiatric patients fit their diagnoses? Patterns of symptomatology as described with the biplot. *Journal of Nervous and Mental Disease, 167,* 105–113.

World Health Organization (1973). *The International Pilot Study of Schizophrenia.* Author.

# Recovery as a Journey of the Heart

*Patricia Deegan*

At the time of original publication Patricia Deegan, PhD, was program director, Northeast Independent Living Program, Lawrence, Massachusetts, and consultant, National Empowerment Center, Lawrence.

This article appeared in the *Psychiatric Rehabilitation Journal*, 1996, 19(3), and is reprinted with permission.

This article was originally presented at the Alliance for the Mentally Ill of Massachusetts/Department of Mental Health of Massachusetts Curriculum and Training Committee Conference at the Massachusetts State House on May 10, 1995.

I would like to thank you for this opportunity to speak with you today. I am especially pleased to be speaking to so many faculty and field supervisors. Your task is very important. You are teaching students who will become tomorrow's mental health professionals. The message I would like to bring to you today is that it is not enough to merely teach them facts and figures and knowledge. We must also help students to seek wisdom.

There is a difference between knowledge and wisdom. The etymological root of the word *knowledge* comes from the Middle English, *to recognize*. And indeed students in the various mental health related disciplines are required to recognize and to master a specific field of knowledge. They are required to know how to conduct empirical inquiry, to formulate findings, to contribute to theoretical models, to learn clinical skills, etc. However students are not required to seek wisdom. Wisdom comes from the Greek *eidos* and *idein* which means to see the form or essence of that which is. Thus most students emerge from their studies full of knowledge or the ability to recognize things, but they lack wisdom or the ability to see the form or essence of that which is.

For example, when we teach our students about the heart, we teach them that the heart is a pump; a type of organic machine with valves and chambers. And indeed, in time they learn to recognize the anatomical heart in all its detail. After successfully passing their final anatomy exam we say, "This student knows about the heart." But in wisdom we would have to doubt this statement.

Wisdom would seek the form or essence of the heart. In wisdom we would see that the anatomical heart, which we have given our students to study, is *nobody's* heart. It is a heart that could belong to any*body* and therefore it belongs to no-*body*. Wisdom would have us understand that there is another heart. There is a heart that we know about long before we are taught that the heart is a pump. I am speaking here of the heart that can break; the heart that grows weary; the hardened heart; the heartless one; the cold heart; the heart that aches; the heart that stands still; the heart that leaps with joy; and the one who has lost heart. Wisdom demands that we teach students of the human sciences about the essence of this heart. The human heart. Not the pump that beats in *any body* but the one that lives in *my body* and in *your body*.

In a similar fashion we pass on knowledge about mental illness. Students emerge from school with knowledge about neurotransmitters and schizophrenics and bipolars and borderlines and multiples and OCDs. They become experts in recognizing illness and disease. But this is where we so often fail them. We fail them because we have not taught them to seek wisdom to move beyond mere recognition in order to seek the essence of what is. We have failed to teach them to reverence the human being who exists prior to and in spite of the diagnosis we have placed upon them. Just as the generic, anatomical heart does not *exist,* neither does the "schizophrenic" or "the multiple" or the "bipolar" exist outside of a generic textbook. What exists, in the truly existential sense, is not an illness or disease. What exists is a human being and wisdom demands that we see and reverence this human being before all else. Wisdom demands that we whole heartedly enter into a relationship with human beings in order to understand them and their experience. Only then are we able to help in a way that is experienced as helpful.

Those of us who have been labeled with mental illness are first and foremost human beings. We are more than the sum of the electrochemical activity of our brain. Our hearts are not merely pumps. Our hearts are as real and as vulnerable as valuable as yours are. We are people. We are people who have experienced great distress and who face the challenge of recovery.

The concept of recovery is rooted in the simple yet profound realization that people who have been diagnosed with mental illness are human beings. Like a pebble tossed into the center of a still pool, this simple fact radiates in ever larger ripples until every corner of academic and applied mental health science and clinical practice are affected. Those of us who have been diagnosed are not objects to be acted upon. We are fully human subjects who can act and in acting, change our situation. We are human beings and we can speak for ourselves. We have a voice and can learn to use it. We have the right to be heard and listened to. We can become self determining. We can take a stand toward what is distressing to us and need not be passive victims of an illness. We can become experts in our own journey of recovery.

The goal of recovery is not to get mainstreamed. We don't want to be mainstreamed. We say let the mainstream become a *wide* stream that has room for all of us and leaves no one stranded on the fringes.

The goal of the recovery process is not to become normal. The goal is to embrace our human vocation of becoming more deeply, more fully human. The goal is not normalization. The goal is to become the unique, awesome, never to be repeated human being that we are called to be. The philosopher Martin Heidegger said that to be human means to be a question in search of an answer. Those of us who have been labeled with mental illness are not de facto excused from this most fundamental task of becoming human. In fact, because many of us have experienced our lives and dreams shattering in the wake of mental illness, one of the most essential challenges that faces us is to ask, "who can I become and why should I say 'yes' to life?"

To be human means to be a question in search of an answer. However, many of us who have been psychiatrically labeled have received powerful messages from professionals who in effect tell us that by virtue of our diagnosis the question of our being has already been answered and our futures are already sealed. For instance, I can remember such a time during my third hospitalization. I was 18 years old. I asked the psychiatrist I was working with, "What's wrong with me?" He said, "You have a disease called chronic schizophrenia. It is a disease that is like diabetes. If you take medications for the rest of your life and avoid stress, then maybe you can cope." And as he spoke these words I could feel the weight of them crushing my already fragile hopes and dreams and aspirations for my life. Even some 22 years later, those words still echo like a haunting memory that does not fade.

Today I understand why this experience was so damaging to me. In essence the psychiatrist was telling me that my life, by virtue of being labeled with schizophrenia, was already a closed book. He was saying that my future had already been written. The goals and dreams that I aspired to were mere fantasies according to his prognosis of doom. When the future has been closed off in this way, then the present loses its orientation and becomes nothing but a succession of unrelated moments. Today I know that this psychiatrist had little wisdom at that time. He merely had some knowledge and recognized me as "the schizophrenic" who had been handed down through the generations by Kraeplin and Bleuler. He did not see *me*. He saw an illness. We must urge our students to seek wisdom, to move beyond mere recognition of illness, and to wholeheartedly encounter the human being who comes for help. It is imperative that we teach students that relationship is the most powerful tool they have in working with people.

Beyond the goals of recovery, there is the question of the process of recovery. How does one enter into the journey of recovery? Today I would like to begin a conceptualization of recovery as a journey of the heart. We will begin in that place where many people find themselves; in that place of being hard of heart and not caring anymore.

Prior to becoming active participants in our own recovery process, many of us find ourselves in a time of great apathy and indifference. It is a time of having a hardened heart. Of not caring anymore. It is a time when we feel ourselves to be among the living dead: alone, abandoned, and adrift on a dead and silent sea without course or bearing. If I turn my gaze back I can see myself at 17 years old, diagnosed with chronic schizophrenia, drugged on Haldol and sitting in a chair. As I conjure the image the first thing I can see are that girl's yellow, nicotine stained fingers. I can see her shuffled, stiff, drugged walk. Her eyes do not dance. The dancer has collapsed and her eyes are dark and they stare endlessly into nowhere.

People come and people go. People urge her to do things to help herself but her heart is hard and she cares about nothing except sleeping, sitting, and smoking cigarettes. Her day consists of this: At eight in the morning she forces herself out of bed. In a drugged haze she sits in a chair, the same chair every day. She begins smoking cigarettes. Cigarette after cigarette. Cigarettes mark the passing of time. Cigarettes are proof that time is passing and that fact, at least, is a relief. From 9 A.M. to noon she sits and smokes and stares. Then she has lunch. At 1 P.M. she goes back to bed to sleep until 3 P.M. At that time she returns to the chair and sits and smokes and stares. Then she has dinner. Then she returns to the chair at 6 P.M. Finally it is 8 o'clock in the evening, the long awaited hour, the time to go back to bed and to collapse into a drugged and dreamless sleep.

This scenario unfolds the next day and the next and then the next, until the months pass by in numbing succession, marked only by the next cigarette and the next…

During this time people would try to motivate me. I remember people trying to make me participate in food shopping on Wednesday or to help bake bread or to go on a boat ride. But nothing anyone did touched me or moved me or mattered to me. I had given up. Giving up was a solution for me. The fact that I was "unmotivated" was seen as a problem by the people who worked with me. But for me, giving up was not a problem, it was a solution. It was a solution because it protected me from wanting anything. If I didn't want anything, then it couldn't be taken away. If I didn't try, then I wouldn't have to undergo another failure. If I didn't care, then nothing could hurt me again. My heart became hardened. The spring came and went and I didn't care. Holidays came and went and I didn't care. My friends went off to college and started new lives and I didn't care. A friend whom I had once loved very much came over to visit me and I didn't care. I remember sitting and smoking and saying almost nothing. And as soon as the clock struck 8, I remember interrupting my friend in mid sentence and telling her to go home because I was going to bed. Without even saying goodbye I headed for my bed. My heart was hard. I didn't care about anything.

I trust that the picture I am painting here is familiar to many of us. We recognize this picture of apathy, withdrawal, isolation, and lack of motivation. But if we go beyond mere recognition in search of wisdom we must dig deeper. What is this apathy, indifference, hardness of heart that keeps so many people in a mode of survival and prevents them from actively entering into their own journey of recovery? Is it merely the negative symptoms of schizophrenia? I think not. I believe that becoming hard of heart and not caring anymore is a strategy that desperate people who are at the brink of losing hope, adopt in order to remain alive.

Hope is not just a nice sounding euphemism. Hope and biological life are inextricably intertwined. Martin Seligman's (1975) work in the field of learned helplessness offers us great insight into the chiasmic intertwining of hope and biological life. He sights two examples. The first is a published report by Dr. H. M. Lefcourt (1973):

> This writer witnessed one such case of death due to a loss of will within a psychiatric hospital. A female patient who had remained in a mute state for nearly 10 years was shifted to a different floor of her building along with her floor mates, while her unit was being redecorated. The third floor of this psychiatric unit where the patient in question had been living was known among the patients as the chronic, hopeless floor. In contrast, the first floor was most commonly occupied by patients who held privileges, including the freedom to come and go on the hospital grounds and to the surrounding streets. In short, the first floor was an exit ward from which patients could anticipate discharge fairly rapidly. All patients who were temporarily moved from the third floor were given medical examinations prior to the move, and the patient in question was judged to be in excellent medical health though still mute and withdrawn. Shortly after moving to the first floor, this chronic psychiatric patient surprised the ward staff by becoming socially responsive such that within a two week period she ceased being mute and was actually becoming gregarious. As fate would have it, the redecoration of the third floor unit was soon completed and all previous residents were returned to it. Within a week after she had been returned to the hopeless unit, this patient...collapsed and died. The subsequent autopsy revealed no pathology of note and it was whimsically suggested at the time that the patient had died of despair. (p. 182–183)

The second example is that of an army medical officer named Major F. Harold Kushner. Major Kushner was shot down over North Vietnam and he was interned in a prisoner of war camp from 1968 to 1973. Here is how Dr. Seligman relates the story:

When Major Kushner arrived at First Camp in January 1968, Robert has already been captive for two years. He was a rugged and intelligent corporal from a crack marine unit, austere, stoic, and oblivious to pain and suffering. He was 24 years old...Like the rest of the men, he was down to a weight of ninety pounds and was forced to make long, shoeless treks daily with ninety pounds of manioc root on his back. He never griped...Despite malnutrition and terrible skin disease, he remained in very good physical and mental health. The cause of his relatively fine shape was clear to (Major) Kushner. Robert was convinced that he would soon be released. The Viet Cong had made it a practice to release, as examples, a few men who had co operated with them... Robert had done so, and the camp commander had indicated that he was next in line for release, to come in six months...

The [designated] month came and went, and [Robert] began to sense a change in the guards' attitude toward him. Finally it dawned on him that he had been deceived, that he wasn't going to be released. He stopped working and showed signs of severe depression: he refused food and lay on his bed in a fetal position, sucking his thumb. His fellow prisoners tried to bring him around. They hugged him, babied him and, when this didn't work, tried to bring him out of his stupor with their fists. He defecated and urinated in bed. After a few weeks, it was apparent to Kushner that Robert was moribund: although otherwise his gross physical shape was still better than most of the others, he was dusky and cyanotic. In the early hours of a November morning he lay dying in Kushner's arms. For the first time in days his eyes focused and he spoke: "Doc, Post Office Box 161, Texarkana, Texas. Mom, Dad, I love you very much..." Within seconds, he was dead. (p. 168)

Seligman (1975, p. 168) goes on to comment:

Hope of release sustained Robert. When he gave up hope, when he believed that all his efforts had failed and would continue to fail, he died. Can a psychological state be lethal? I believe it can. When animals and men learn that their actions are futile and that there is no hope, they become more susceptible to death. Conversely, the belief in control over the environment can prolong life.

To paraphrase I would say that when those of us with psychiatric disabilities come to believe that all of our efforts are futile; when we experience that we have no control over our environment; when nothing we do seems to matter or to make the situation better; when we follow the treatment teams' instructions and achieve their treatment goals for us and still no placement opens up in the community for us; when we try one medication after another after another and none of them seem to be of any help; when we find that staff do not listen to us and that they make all of the major decisions for us; when staff decide where we will live, with whom we will live; under what rules we will live, how we will spend our money, if we will be allowed to spend our money, when we will have to leave the group home, and at what time we will be allowed back into it, etc. etc. etc., then a deep sense of hopelessness, of despair begins to settle over the human heart. And in an effort to avoid the biologically disastrous effects of profound hopelessness, people with psychiatric disabilities do what other people do. We grow hard of heart and attempt to stop caring. It is safer to become helpless then to become hopeless.

Of course, the great danger is that staff will fail to recognize the intensity of the existential struggle that the person who is hard of heart is struggling with. The danger is that the staff will simply say, "Oh, this person just has a lot of negative signs and symptoms and that's a poor prognosis and we mustn't expect much from this person." Or staff may become judgmental and dismiss us as simply being lazy and unmotivated. Or the staff may succumb to their own despair and simply write us off as being "low functioning."

It is imperative that the instructors and field trainers of the next generation of mental health professionals help today's students to avoid these pitfalls. It is imperative that students be helped to understand that being hard hearted and not caring are highly motivated, adaptive strategies used by desperate people who are at great risk of losing hope. We must help students understand and empathize with the deep existential struggle that is at the heart of this dark night of despair.

There are a number of things I tell students about how to work with people who appear to be hard of heart, apathetic, and unmotivated. First I help the student understand the behavior in terms of its existential significance. I want the student to grasp the magnitude of what it is they are asking a person to risk when they ask them to start to care about something again. I want them to understand that under the hardened heart lies the breaking heart. How much suffering, how much loss can a human heart hold before it breaks? It is not a crazy thing to try to protect such a vulnerable heart. Students must be helped to honor the strategy of giving up and to understand that perhaps that person shall never risk again. In any case, it is only the person whom we are trying to help who has the power to take the risk, to care about something—something as simple perhaps as caring enough to put a poster on their bedroom wall, or caring enough to wear some new clothes or to try a job placement. These may seem like small things but if we understand their full existential significance, such acts are small steps toward caring, toward admitting that I just might want to participate in the human community again.

Secondly, I ask students to suspend their perception of people as chronic mental patients and to try to see the individual as a hero. I ask them, could you have survived what this individual has survived? Perhaps this individual has done what you could not do. Perhaps they are not weak and fragile sick people. Perhaps those of us with psychiatric disabilities are incredibly strong and have fiercely tenacious spirits. Could you live on $530 a month and cope with a disability at the same time? If a student can momentarily drop out of his or her distanced professional posture and, in true humility, come to see a person with a psychiatric disability as a hero who has survived, then I say there is a good prognosis for that student. That student has a chance of being human hearted while working in the human services and this is no small accomplishment.

Finally, I try to help students understand that although they do not have the power to change or motivate the person with a psychiatric disability who is hard of heart, they do have the power to change the environment, including the human interactive environment, in which that person is surviving. When working with a person with a psychiatric disability who is hard of heart, who has given up and who is motivated not to care anymore, we must understand that this is a person who feels they have no power. They experience all the power to be in the hands of others. They experience what psychologists call an external locus of control. For such people it is imperative to create an environment in which there are choices to be made. I am speaking here, not of forced choice such as either you take your medications or you go back to the hospital (this is little more than coercion), but of real choices. I am speaking here of all types of choices, from small concerns such as what flavor ice cream you want, to what coffee shop you want to go to, to what kind of vocational goals you might want to pursue, etc.

The person with a hardened heart will reject, reject, and reject again these invitations to choose. However the staff must not fall into despair, feel like their efforts are futile, grow hard of heart, and stop caring themselves. If they do this, then they are doing exactly what the person with a psychiatric disability is doing. Staff must avoid this trap. They must do what the person cannot yet do. Staff must role model hope and continue to offer options and choices even if they are rejected over and over again.

Additionally, environments must include opportunities for people to have accurate information. Information is power and information sharing is power sharing. People who feel powerless can increase their sense of self-efficacy by having access to information. People who feel powerless also feel that what they say does not matter. Taking the time to listen to people and to help them find their own unique voice is important. Having a voice in developing rules, as well as having a say in the hiring and evaluation of staff, are important ways of exercising a voice that for too long has been silenced. Finally, it is important to have other people with psychiatric disabilities working as paid staff. Role models provide hope that maybe I, too, can break out of this hardened heart and begin to care again. People who are defending themselves against the possibly lethal effects of profound hopelessness must see that there is a way out and that actions they take can inch them ever closer to their desired goal. They need to see that the quality of life can get better for people who have been similarly diagnosed. They need to see that there are opportunities for improving their situation. That is why hiring people with psychiatric disabilities as mental health professionals and staff is so important. It is also why exposure to peer support, self help, and mutual support are so important.

Choice, options, information, role models, being heard, developing and exercising a voice, opportunities for bettering one's life: these are the features of a human interactive environment that support the transition from not caring to caring, from surviving to becoming an active participant in one's own recovery process. Creating such environments are the skills that tomorrow's mental health professionals must master.

As for myself, I cannot remember a specific moment when I turned that corner from surviving to becoming an active participant in my own recovery process. My efforts to protect my breaking heart by becoming hard of heart and not caring about anything lasted for a long time. One thing I can recall is that the people around me did not give up on me. They kept inviting me to do things. I remember one day, for no particular reason, saying yes to helping with food shopping. All I would do was push the cart. But it was a beginning. And truly, it was through small steps like these that I slowly began to discover that I could take a stand toward what was distressing to me.

I know that anger, especially angry indignation, played a big role in that transition. When that psychiatrist told me the best I could hope for was to take my medications, avoid stress and cope, I became enraged. (However, I was smart enough to keep my angry indignation to myself because rule #1 is never get enraged in a psychiatrist's office if you're labeled with chronic schizophrenia!) I also remember that just after that visit I made up my mind to become a doctor. I was so outraged at the things that had been done to me against my will in the hospital as well as the things I saw happen to other people, that I decided that I wanted to get a powerful degree and have enough credentials to run a healing place myself. In effect, I had a survivor mission that I felt passionately about.

I was also careful not to share my newfound aspiration with anyone. Imagine what my psychiatrist would have said to me if I had announced at age 18, having virtually flunked out of high school, with a combined GRE score of under 800, with a diagnosis of chronic schizophrenia, that I was planning on getting my Ph.D. in clinical psychology. "Delusions of grandeur!" But in essence that is precisely what I did. Starting with one course in English Composition at the local community college I slowly made my way. Dragging my textbooks into the mental hospital with me or trying to read with double vision due to Prolixin, I inched my way forward. I had a strong spirituality that really helped. I had a strong therapeutic alliance with a psychotherapist. I lived with really weird hippies who had tolerance for lots of weird behavior including my psychotic episodes. After some experimenting in my early teens, I somehow intuited that drugs and alcohol were bad news for me and I did not use them even though the people around me did. In retrospect, I know this was a wise decision. I read tons of books about healing and psychopathology and personality theory in an effort to understand myself and my situation. I was always trying new ways of coping with symptoms including my relentless auditory hallucinations. And perhaps most importantly of all, when I got out of bed in the morning, I always knew the reason why I had a purpose in life, I had been called, I had a vocation, and I kept saying yes to it. Even in the present I must make a daily affirmation of my vocation in order to keep going. The temptation to give up is still strong sometimes.

My journey of recovery is still ongoing. I still struggle with symptoms, grieve the losses that I have sustained, and have had to get involved in treatment for the sequela child abuse. I am also involved in self help and mutual support and I still use professional services including medications, psychotherapy, and hospitals. However, now I do not just take medication or go to the hospital. I have learned to use medications and to use the hospital. This is the active stance that is the hallmark of the recovery process.

There is more to the recovery process than simply recovering from mental illness. We must also recover from the effects of poverty and second class citizenship. We must learn to raise our consciousness and find our collective pride in order to overcome internalized stigma. Finally, many of us emerge from mental health treatment settings with traumatic stress disorders related to having sustained or witnessed physical, sexual, and/or emotional abuse at the hands of staff. As one long-term veteran of mental health services wrote:

> The stuff I've been through was like a nightmare. Sometimes I go back into the nightmare. I cry every night about it. Remembering it is like

being in the nightmare again...Sometimes I scream at night because I dream about the hospital I was raped in or some other hospital I've been in. (LaLime, 1990)

Sometimes recovering from mental illness is the easy part. Recovering from these deep wounds to the human heart takes much longer.

Recovery does not mean cure. Rather recovery is an attitude, a stance, and a way of approaching the day's challenges. It is not a perfectly linear journey. There are times of rapid gains and disappointing relapses. There are times of just living, just staying quiet, resting and regrouping. Each person's journey of recovery is unique. Each person must find what works for him- or herself. This means that we must have the opportunity to try and to fail and to try again. In order to support the recovery process mental health professionals must not rob us of the opportunity to fail. Professionals must embrace the concept of the dignity of risk and the right to failure if they are to be supportive of us.

In closing, I would like to add that all around the world, people who have been psychiatrically labeled are organizing. We are organizing on the local, state, national, and international level. We are developing a collective voice and are fighting to overcome oppression, poverty, discrimination, and stigma. We are saying no to second class health care, poor or non existent housing, and to the indignities that so often come with psychiatric hospitalizations including the barbaric use of restraint and seclusion. We are sitting at the table in dialogue with service providers and policy makers to find alternatives to involuntary treatment. We are joining with other disability groups to form a broad coalition of 40 million Americans with disabilities to achieve equity in health care, support services, and entitlements.

We are also beginning to define our experiences in our own terms and to educate mental health professionals about our experience and what helps. We are fortunate to have the National Empowerment Center in Lawrence, Massachusetts. The National Empowerment Center is a completely consumer run and controlled national technical assistance center supported through funding from the Center for Mental Health Services. We have developed many innovative trainings and resources. For instance, we have a new training available that is entitled "Hearing Voices That Are Distressing: A Simulated Training Experience and Self-help Strategies." In this workshop designed for mental health practitioners and students, participants listen to an audiotape that was designed by people who hear voices to simulate the experience of hearing voices that are distressing. Participants listen to the tape while having to undergo a series of tasks including a mental status exam, a community outing, a day treatment activity group, and psychological testing. After the simulated training participants have the opportunity to learn many self-help strategies that help to control or eliminate distressing voices.

A new age is upon us. We must help the students of today to understand that people with psychiatric disabilities are human beings with human hearts. Our hearts are as real and as vulnerable and as valuable as yours are. Understanding that people with psychiatric disabilities are first and foremost people who are in process, growing and changing is the cornerstone of understanding the concept of recovery. We must not let our hearts grow hard and calloused toward people with psychiatric disabilities. Our role is not to judge who will and will not recover. Our job is to create environments in which opportunities for recovery and empowerment exist. Our job is to establish strong, supportive relationships with those we work with. And perhaps most of all, our greatest challenge is to find a way to refuse to be dehumanized in the age of managed profit, and to be bold and brave and daring enough to remain human hearted while working in the human services.

### REFERENCES

Deegan, P. (1990). Spirit breaking: When the helping professions hurt. *The Humanistic Psychologist, 18*(3), 301–313.

LaLime, W. (1990). Untitled speech used as part of Lowell MPOWER's anti-stigma workshop. Lowell, Massachusetts.

Lefcourt, H. M. (1973). The function of the illusions of control and freedom. *American Psychologist, 28,* 417–425.

Seligman, M. E. P. (1975). *Helplessness: On depression, development and death.* San Francisco: Freeman.

# What Recovery Means to Us: Consumers' Perspectives

*Shery Mead and Mary Ellen Copeland*

At the time of original publication, Shery Mead, MSW, was executive director of the Stepping Stone Peer Counselor Center in Claremont, NH, and Next Step in Lebanon, NH; and Mary Ellen Copeland, MS, MA, was a private mental health consultant and trainer.

This article originally appeared in the *Community Health Journal,* 2000, 36(3), 315–328, and is reprinted with permission.

**Abstract:** In this article two consumer leaders use their own experiences to explain the meaning and significance of recovery. They emphasize the importance of hope, personal responsibility, education, advocacy, and peer support. They also address controversial issues, such as the nature of the therapeutic relationship, the place of medications in symptom control, and the need for attitudinal changes in mental health professionals.

### INTRODUCTION

Recovery has only recently become a word used in relation to the experience of psychiatric symptoms. Those of us who experience psychiatric symptoms are commonly told that these symptoms are incurable, that we will have to live with them for the rest of our lives, that the medications, if they (health care professionals) can find the right ones or the right combination, may help, and that we will always have to take the medications. Many of us have even been told that these symptoms will worsen as we get older. Nothing about recovery was ever mentioned. Nothing about hope. Nothing about anything we can do to help ourselves. Nothing about empowerment. Nothing about wellness.

Mary Ellen Copeland says:

When I was first diagnosed with manic depression at the age of 37, I was told that if I just kept taking these pills—pills that I would need to take for the rest of my life—I would be OK. So I did just that. And I was "OK" for about 10 years until a stomach virus caused severe lithium toxicity, after that I could no longer take the medication. During the time I was taking the medication I could have been learning how to manage my moods. I could have been learning that relaxation and stress reduction techniques and fun activities can help reduce the symptoms. I could have been learning that I would probably feel a lot better if my life wasn't so hectic and chaotic, if I wasn't living with an abusive husband, if I spent more time with people who affirmed and validated me, and that support from other people who have experienced these symptoms helps a lot. I was never told that I could learn how to relieve, reduce, and even get rid of troubling feelings and perceptions. Perhaps if I had learned these things and had been exposed to others who were working their way through these kinds of symptoms, I would not have spent weeks, months, and years experiencing extreme psychotic mood swings while doctors searched diligently to find effective medications.

Now the times have changed. Those of us who have experienced psychiatric symptoms are sharing information and learning from each other that these symptoms do not have to mean that we must give up our dreams and our goals, and that they don't have to go on forever. We have learned that we are in charge of our own lives and can go forward and do whatever it is we want to do. People who have experienced even the most severe psychiatric symptoms are doctors, lawyers, teachers, accountants, advocates, and social workers. We are successfully establishing and maintaining intimate relationships. We are good parents. We have warm relationships with our partners, parents, siblings, friends, and colleagues. We are climbing mountains, planting gardens, painting pictures, writing books, making quilts, and creating positive change in the world. And it is only with this vision and belief for all people that we can bring hope to everyone.

### SUPPORT FROM HEALTH CARE PROFESSIONALS
Sometimes our health care professionals are reluctant to assist us in this journey—afraid that we are setting ourselves up for failure. But more and more of them are providing us with valuable assistance and support as we make our way out of the system and back to the life we want. Recently I (Mary Ellen) spent a full day visiting with health care professionals of all kinds at a major regional mental health center. It was exciting to hear over and over the word recovery. They were talking about educating the people they work with about providing temporary assistance and support for as long as necessary during the hard times, about working with people to take responsibility for their own wellness, to explore with them the many options available to address their symptoms and issues, and to send them on their way, back to their loved ones and into the community.

A word that these dedicated health care professionals used over and over again was "normalize." They are trying to see for themselves, and help the people they work with to see, these symptoms on a continuum of the norm rather than an aberration—that these are symptoms that everyone experiences in some form or other. That when, either from physical causes or stress in our lives, they become so severe that they are intolerable, we can work together to find ways to reduce and relieve them. They are talking about less traumatic ways to deal with crises when symptoms become frightening and dangerous. They are talking about respite centers, guest homes, and supportive assistance so a person can get through the hard times at home and in the community rather than in the frightening scenario of a psychiatric hospital.

### KEY FACETS OF RECOVERY

*1. There is hope.* A vision of hope that includes no limits. Even when someone says to us, "You can't do that because you've had or have those symptoms, dear!", we know it's not true. It is only when we feel and believe that we are fragile and out of control that we find it hard to move ahead. Those of us who experience psychiatric symptoms can and do get well. I (Mary Ellen) learned about hope from my mother. She was told she was incurably insane. She had wild, psychotic mood swings unremittingly for 8 years. And then they went away. After that she worked very successfully as a dietitian in a large school lunch program and spent her retirement helping my brother raise seven children as a single parent and as volunteer for a variety of church and community organizations.

We don't need dire predictions about the course of our symptoms something that no one else, regardless of their credentials, can ever know. We need assistance, encouragement, and support as we work to relieve the symptoms and get on with our lives. We need a caring environment without feeling the need to be taken care of.

Too many people have internalized the messages that there is no hope, that they are simply victims of their illness, and that the only relationships they can hope for are one sided and infantilizing. As people are introduced to communities and services that focus on recovery, relationships change to being more equal and supportive in both directions. As we feel valued for the help we can offer as well as receive, our self-definitions are expanded. We try out new behaviors with each other, find ways in which we can take positive risks, and find that we have more self-knowledge and more to offer than we were led to believe.

*2. It's up to each individual to take responsibility for his or her own wellness.* There is no one else who can do this for us. When our perspective changes from reaching out to be saved to working to heal ourselves and our relationships, the pace of our recovery increases dramatically.

Taking personal responsibility can be very difficult when symptoms are severe and persistent. In these cases, it is most helpful when our health care professionals and supporters work with us to find and take even the smallest steps to work our way out of this frightening situation.

*3. Education is a process that must accompany us on this journey.* We search for sources of information that will help us to figure out what will work for us and the steps we need to take in our own behalf. Many of us would like health care professionals to play a key role in this educational process—directing us to helpful resources, setting up educational workshops and seminars, working with us to understand information, and helping us to find a course that resonates with our wishes and beliefs.

*4. We must advocate for ourselves.* Often people who have experienced psychiatric symptoms have the mistaken belief that we have lost our rights as individuals. As a result, our rights are often violated, and these violations are consistently overlooked. Self-advocacy becomes much easier as we repair self-esteem damaged by years of chronic instability—and come to understand that we are often as intelligent as anyone else, and always as worthwhile and unique with special gifts to offer the world—and that we deserve all the very best that life has to offer. It is also much easier if we are supported by health care professionals, family members, and supporters as we reach out to get our personal needs met.

All people grow through taking positive risks. We need to advocate for people's rights:

- making life and treatment choices for themselves,

- building their own crisis and treatment plans,

- having the right to obtain all their records,

- accessing information around medication side effects,

- refusing any treatment (particularly those that are potentially hazardous),

- choosing their own relationships and spiritual practices,

- being treated with dignity, respect, and compassion, and

- creating the life of their choice.

*5. Peer support is a key component of recovery.* The nationwide focus on peer support is a result of the recognition of the importance of support in working toward recovery. Throughout New Hampshire, peer support centers are providing communities where people can go, even when their symptoms are the most severe, and feel safe and secure.

Peer support holds minimal assumptions about people's capabilities and limits. It avoids categories and hierarchical roles (doctor/patient) and emphasizes that people move from focusing on themselves to trying out new behaviors with one another and ultimately committing to a larger process of building a community. The crisis respite center at Stepping Stones Peer Support

Center in Claremont, New Hampshire, carries this concept a step further by providing around-the-clock peer support and education in a safe, supportive atmosphere. Peers support one another in moving through and beyond difficult situations, and help each other learn how a crisis can be an opportunity for growth and change. An example of this was when a member who was having lots of difficult thoughts came into the center to avoid hospitalization. His goal was to be able to talk through his thoughts without feeling judged, categorized, or told to increase his medication. After several days he went home feeling more comfortable and connected to others with whom he could continue to interact. He committed to staying in and expanding on the relationships that he built while in the respite program.

Through the use of support groups and building a community that defines itself as it grows, many people find that their sense of who they are expands. As people grow, they move ahead in other parts of their lives.

Support, in a recovery-based environment, is never a crutch or a situation in which one person defines or dictates the outcome. Mutual support is a process in which the people in the relationship strive to use the relationship to become fuller, richer human beings. Although we all come to relationships with some assumptions, support works best when both people are willing to grow and change.

### THE NEED FOR MUTUAL SUPPORT IN PROFESSIONALS SETTINGS

We believe that the need for mutual support extends into clinical settings. Though clinical relationships may never truly be mutual or without some assumptions, we can all work to change our roles with each other in order to discard the kinds of paternalistic relationships some of us have experienced in the past. Some of the questions that health care professionals can ask themselves in this regard are:

- How much of our own discomfort are we willing to sit with while someone is trying out new choices?

- How are our boundaries continuously being redefined as we struggle to deepen each individual relationship?

- What are the assumptions we have about this person, by virtue of his/her diagnosis, history, and lifestyle? How can we put aside our assumptions and predictions in order to be fully present to the situation and open to the possibility for the other person to do the same?

- What are the barriers that might prevent both of us from stretching and growing?

A truly supportive therapeutic relationship begins with honesty and a willingness to take a critical look at assumptions learned during training. Clinical support, in a recovery environment, means at the same time that clinicians attempt to take care of a person, they also hold the person accountable for his or her behavior and believe in the ability to change.

Moving beyond assessment or prognosis, we see that no one is beyond hope. Everyone has the ability to make choices. Even though health care professionals have traditionally been asked to define treatment and prognosis, they have to look through the layers of learned helplessness, years of institutionalization, and difficult behaviors, so that they can creatively help a person reconstruct a life narrative that is defined by hope, challenge, accountability, mutual relationship, and an evolving self-concept.

As part of our support health system, care professionals need to continue to examine their own roadblocks to change, understand where they get "stuck" and dependent, and look at their own less-than-healthy ways of coping. Health care professionals need to relate to us that they have their own struggles and own that change is hard for all. They need to look at our willingness to "recover" and not perpetuate the myth that there is a big difference between themselves and people they work with. Support then becomes truly a mutual phenomenon where the relationship itself becomes a framework in which both people feel supported in challenging themselves. The desire to change is nurtured through the relationship, not dictated by one person's plan for another. The outcome is that people don't continue to feel separate, different, and alone.

### HOW PROFESSIONALS CAN ADDRESS LEARNED HELPLESSNESS

Clinicians often ask us, "What about people who aren't interested in recovery and have no interest in peer support and other recovery concepts?" What we often forget is that most people resist change. It's hard work! People have gotten used to their identities and roles as ill, victims, fragile, dependent, and even as unhappy. Long ago we learned to "accept" our illnesses, give over control to others and tolerate the way of life. Think how many people live like this who don't have diagnosed illnesses. It's easier to live in the safety of what we know, even if it hurts, than it is to work hard to change or develop hope that conceivably could be crushed.

A clinical mistake, we believe, has been assuming that people know what they need and want, and that they are ready to change their way of being. People who have been in the mental health system for many years have developed a way of being in the world, and particularly being in relationship with professionals, in which their self-definition as patient has become their most important role.

Our only hope for accessing internal resources that have been buried by layers of imposed limitations is to be supported in making leaps of faith, redefining who we'd like to become, and taking risks that aren't calculated by someone else. We need to be asked if our idea of who we'd like to become is based on what we know about our "illnesses." We need to be asked what supports we would need to take new risks and change our assumptions about our fragility and our limitations. When we see our closest friends and supporters willing to change, we begin to try out our own incremental changes. Even if this means buying ingredients for supper instead of a TV dinner, we need to be fully supported in taking the steps toward recreating our own sense of self and be challenged to continue to grow.

Recovery is a personal choice. It is often difficult for health care providers who are trying to promote a person's recovery when they find resistance and apathy. Severity of symptoms, motivation, personality type, accessibility of information, perceived benefits of maintaining the status quo rather than creating life change (sometimes to maintain disability benefits), along with the quantity and quality of personal and professional support, can all affect a person's ability to work toward recovery. Some people choose to work at it very intensively, especially when they first become aware of these new options and perspectives. Others approach it much more slowly. It is not up to the provider to determine when a person is ready to make progress—it is up to the person.

### SKILLS AND STRATEGIES FOR RELIEVING SYMPTOMS
Through ongoing research, Mary Ellen Copeland has learned that people who experience psychiatric symptoms commonly use the following skills and strategies to relieve and eliminate them:

- Reaching out for support—connecting with a non-judgmental, non-critical person who is willing to avoid giving advice, who will listen while the person figures out for himself or herself what to do.

- Being in a supportive environment surrounded by people who are positive and affirming, but at the same time are direct and challenging—avoiding people who are critical, judgmental, or abusive.

- Peer counseling—sharing with another person who has experienced similar symptoms.

- Stress reduction and relaxation techniques—deep breathing, progressive relaxation, and visualization exercises.

- Exercise—anything from walking and climbing stairs to running, biking, or swimming.

- Creative and fun activities—doing things that are personally enjoyable like reading, creative arts, crafts, listening to or making music, gardening, and woodworking.

- Journalizing—writing in a journal anything you want, for as long as you want.

- Dietary changes—limiting or avoiding the use of foods like caffeine, sugar, sodium and fat that may worsen symptoms.

- Exposure to light—getting outdoor light for at least a half hour per day, enhancing that with a light box when necessary.

- Learning and using systems for changing negative thoughts to positive ones—working on a structured system for making changes in thought processes.

- Increasing or decreasing environmental stimulation—responding to symptoms as they occur by either becoming more or less active.

- Daily planning—developing a generic plan for a day to use when symptoms are more difficult to manage and decision-making is difficult.

- Developing and using a symptom identification and response system that includes:

  – a list of things to do every day to maintain wellness.

  – identifying triggers that might cause or increase symptoms and a preventive action plan.

  – identifying early warning signs of an increase in symptoms and a preventive action plan.

  – identifying symptoms that indicate the situation has worsened and formulating an action plan to reverse this trend.

  – crisis planning to maintain control even when the situation is out of control.

In self-help recovery groups, people who experience symptoms are working together to redefine the meaning of these symptoms, and to discover skills, strategies, and techniques that have worked for them in the past and that could be helpful in the future.

## THE ROLE OF MEDICATIONS IN RECOVERY

Many people feel that medications are helpful in reducing the most difficult symptoms. In the past, medications have often been seen as the only rational option for reducing psychiatric symptoms. In the recovery scenario, medications are one of many options and choices for reducing symptoms. Others include the recovery skills, strategies, and techniques listed previously, along with treatments that address health-related issues. Though medications are certainly a choice, we believe that medication compliance as the only strategy to control symptoms is not appropriate.

People who experience psychiatric symptoms have a hard time dealing with the medication side effects such as obesity, diminished sexual function, dry mouth, constipation, extreme lethargy and fatigue. In addition, they fear the long-term side effects of the medications. Those of us who experience these symptoms know that many of the medications we are taking have been on the market for a short time—so short that no one really knows the long-term side effects. We know that tardive dyskinesia was not recognized as a side effect of neuroleptic medication for many years. We fear that we are at risk of similar irreversible and destructive side effects. We want to be respected by health care professionals for having these fears and for sometimes choosing not to use medications that are compromising the quality of our lives.

When people who have shared similar experiences get together, they begin to talk about their concerns about medications and alternatives that could be helpful. They build up a kind of group empowerment that begins to challenge the notion of medications as the only way to address their symptoms. Many physicians, on the other hand, worry that stopping the medication will worsen symptoms. These can become polarized views and amplify the hierarchical relationship. People feel that if they question their doctors about decreasing or getting off medications, they will be threatened with involuntary hospitalization or treatment. Doctors fear that people are jumping on an unreliable bandwagon that may lead to severe symptoms and jeopardize the person's safety. Consequently, talk about medication often goes on without counsel with doctors.

In a recovery-based environment, more effort needs to be spent focusing on choice and self-responsibility around behavior. If the complaint is that medications control behavior and thoughts while extinguishing pleasurable, motivational kinds of feelings, there is a need to develop a dialogue about symptoms so that each person has choices and options. Shery Mead has developed a visual image of a car wash that has been useful to her and many others. She says:

If I think about early stages of symptoms as driving towards the car wash, there are still many choices I can make before my wheels engage in the automatic treads. I can veer off to the side, stop the car, or back up. I am also aware that once my wheels are engaged in the car wash that, though it feels out of my control, the situation, based on self-observation, is that it is time-limited and I can ride it out and will eventually come out on the other side. My behavior, even when I am "white knuckling it" through the car wash, is still my choice and in my control. This process has helped others define triggers, watch their automatic response, develop self-critical skills about their own defense mechanisms, and ultimately even ride out the car wash better. Although medications can be helpful in making it through the car wash without ending up in a dangerous situation, there are many more proactive skills that help each of us develop our own techniques, making personal responsibility a more desirable outcome.

### RISKS AND BENEFITS OF USING A "RECOVERY" VISION

Because feelings and symptoms are often unpredictable, our health care professionals may fear that we will "decompensate" (a nasty word to many of us) and may put ourselves or others at risk. Health care professionals become fearful that, if they do not continue to take care of and protect people as they have in the past, people will become discouraged, disappointed, and may even harm themselves. It must be recognized that risk is inherent in the experience of life. It is up to us to make choices about how we will live our lives; it is not up to health care professionals to protect us from the real world. We need our health care professionals to believe that we are capable of taking risks and to support us as we take them.

Clinicians working in a recovery-based environment will enjoy the positive reinforcement of successful experiences in working with people who are growing, changing, and moving on with their lives. The recovery focus and the increased wellness of more of us will give health care professionals more time to spend with those who experience the most severe and persistent symptoms, giving them the intense support they need to achieve the highest levels of wellness possible.

In addition, health care professionals will find that instead of providing direct care for people who experience psychiatric symptoms, they will be educating, assisting, and learning from them as they make decisions and take positive action in their own behalf. These care givers will find themselves in the rewarding position of accompanying those of us who experience psychiatric symptoms as we grow, learn, and change.

The implications of a recovery vision for services to adults with "severe mental illness" will be that providers of services will learn from us as we work together to define what wellness is for each of us on an individual basis and explore how to address and relieve the symptoms that prevent us from leading full and rich lives.

The hierarchical health care system may gradually become less rigid as people understand that health care professionals should not only provide care, but also work with a person to make decisions about treatment and about life. Those of us who experience symptoms are demanding treatment as adult partners. This progression will be enhanced, as more people who have experienced symptoms become providers themselves.

While the benefits of a recovery vision for mental health services need study, we believe that they include:

- Cost effectiveness. As we learn safe, simple, inexpensive, non-invasive ways to reduce and eliminate symptoms, there will be less need for costly, invasive interventions and therapies. We will live and work interdependently in the community, supporting our family members and ourselves.

- Reduced need for hospitalization, time away from home and personal supports, and the use of harsh, traumatic and dangerous treatment that often exacerbate rather than relieve symptoms, as we learn to manage our symptoms using normal activities and supports.

- Increased possibility of positive outcomes. As we recover from debilitating symptoms, we can do more and more of the things we want to do with our lives, and work toward and meet our life goals and dreams.

- As we normalize people's feelings and symptoms, we build a more accepting, diverse culture.

### PERSONAL SAFETY AND DANGEROUSNESS

With the increased focus on recovery and the use of self-help skills to alleviate symptoms, it is hoped that fewer and fewer people will find themselves in a situation where they are a danger to themselves or someone else. If the symptoms should become that severe, people may have developed their own personal crisis plan—a comprehensive plan that would tell close supporters when they need to step in and take over responsibility for their care, and exactly what these supporters need to do to keep the situation from becoming a disaster. These plans are working, protecting people, and saving lives. It allows those of us who experience symptoms to be in control, even when it seems as if things are out of control.

While more and more people are working on recovery and developing active recovery plans for themselves, there are many people who do not choose to do this work, who may not have developed a crisis plan or even be interested in having such a plan, or whose symptoms are so severe or accelerate so rapidly that they become a danger to themselves or others. While disagreement on this important topic is widespread, the authors, both of whom have been at risk of self-harm, agree that those of us who experience self-destructive symptoms need to be accountable for our behavior—just like anyone else. If we let our symptoms escalate to the point where they are a danger to us or someone else, or we have not developed crisis plans to protect ourselves and others, then we have to accept the consequences of our behavior. That may mean that we have to be detained in a psychiatric or other facility until our symptoms have subsided or until we have served criminal sentences. However, in the criminal justice system, alternative forms of restraint should be used rather than methods that further exacerbate symptoms or traumatize us, as with any other person. There is no place for harsh restraining devices, seclusion rooms and body searches.

### GUIDELINES FOR RECOVERY-ORIENTED SERVICES

The following guidelines for health care professionals should guide and enhance all recovery work while decreasing resistance and lack of motivation:

- Treat the person as a fully competent equal with the capacity to learn, change, make life decisions, and take action to create life change, no matter how severe the symptoms.

- Never scold, threaten, punish, patronize, judge, or condescend to the person, while being honest about how you feel when that person threatens or condescends to you.

- Focus on how the person feels, what the person is experiencing, and what the person wants rather than on diagnosis, labeling, and predictions about the course of the person's life.

- Share simple, safe, practical, non-invasive, and inexpensive or free self-help skills and strategies that people can use on their own or with the help of their supporters.

- When necessary, break tasks down into the smallest steps to insure success.

- Limit the sharing of ideas and advice. One piece of advice a day or visit is plenty. Avoid nagging and overwhelming the person with feedback.

- Pay close attention to individual needs and preferences, accepting individual differences.

- Assure that planning and treatment is a truly collaborative process with personal choice as the bottom line.

- Recognize strengths and even the smallest bit of progress without being paternalistic.

- Accept that a person's life path is up to them.

- As the first step toward recovery, listen to the person, let them talk, hear what they say and what they want, making sure their goals are truly theirs and not yours—understanding that what you might see as being good for them may not be what they really want.

- Ask yourself, "Is there something going on in the individual's life which is getting in the way of change or moving toward wellness, e.g. learned helplessness?"

- Encourage and support connection with others who experience psychiatric symptoms.

- Ask yourself, "Would this person benefit from being in a group led by others who have experienced psychiatric symptoms?"

The person who experiences psychiatric symptoms should determine the course of his or her own life. No one else, even the most highly skilled health care professional, can do the work for us. We need to do it for ourselves with your guidance, assistance, and support.

# The Process of Recovery from Schizophrenia

*Leroy Spaniol, Nancy J.Wewiorski, Cheryl Gagne, and William A. Anthony*

At the time of original publication, the authors were at the Center for Psychiatric Rehabilitation, Sargent College of Health and Rehabilitation Sciences, Boston University, Boston, MA.

The article originally appeared in the *International Review of Psychiatry*, 2002, 14, 327–336 and is reprinted with permission. The *International Review of Psychiatry* is published by Taylor & Francis Ltd (http://www.tandf.co.uk/journals).

**Abstract:** To facilitate future research on recovery from schizophrenia a qualitative, longitudinal analysis was conducted with individuals participating in rehabilitation to identify themes associated with improvement in functioning and subjective experience. Twelve individuals with a diagnosis of schizophrenia or schizoaffective disorder were randomly selected from a just concluded 2-year study of psychiatric rehabilitation. Each individual was followed for an additional 4 years. Every 4 to 8 months each person participated in a semi-structured, audiotaped interview about his or her current life experiences. The tapes were evaluated independently by three assessors for themes and phases that emerged from these life experiences. The qualitative analysis characterized the process of recovery as having phases, dimensions, indicators, and barriers to recovery. This empirically derived description of the process of recovery, from the perspective of people who are experiencing it, can be used to generate research hypotheses for future studies to further our understanding and to promote recovery from schizophrenia.

## INTRODUCTION

Over the last decade the vision of recovery from psychiatric disability has been a focus at the Boston University Center for Psychiatric Rehabilitation. The significance of recovery for research, education, services, and policy was emphasized by the Center's staff during the decade of the 1990s by means of journal articles (Anthony, 1991; 1993a; Spaniol et al., 1997), books (Spaniol & Koehler, 1994; Spaniol et al., 1994), video and audiotapes (Anthony, 1993b; 1994), and dozens of lectures and workshops.

Derived from first person narratives (Deegan, 1988; Leete, 1989), recovery from mental illness was defined as the development of new meaning and purpose in one's life, beyond the symptoms, disability, and stigma of mental illness. Recovery was further delineated as a process of healing physically and emotionally, of adjusting one's attitudes, feelings, perceptions, beliefs, roles, and goals in life (Anthony, 1991; 1993a; Spaniol et al., 1997).

Despite the development of working definitions by several groups (Warner, 1985; Lieberman et al., 1993; 1994), recovery has remained an illusory concept. The present study is based on the notion that our working definitions are only hypotheses, and that much empirical work is needed to further our understanding of recovery (Liberman et al., 2002). We do not feel ready to make specific, operational definitions based on our limited sample and exploratory work. It seems premature to develop anything more than conceptual ideas, especially since recovery does not appear to be a linear process. The present study obtained, over a 4-year period, first hand accounts from individuals diagnosed with schizophrenia or schizoaffective disorder who were trying to better their lives. These individuals had previously participated in a 2-year study of psychiatric rehabilitation designed to improve their vocational functioning. The purpose of this follow-up study is to lay the groundwork for future research about recovery from schizophrenia by using qualitative data to describe the recovery process, its major dimensions, and factors that appear to be associated with the process.

## METHODS

### Sample

This qualitative study of recovery processes builds on recently completed research on vocational rehabilitation involving 242 subjects with various mental disorders. Because these individuals had previously chosen to receive an intervention designed to improve vocational functioning, it was assumed that they were motivated to improve their lives and thus would be more likely to show functional and personal improvement over the 4-year study period. We identified several thematic patterns related to recovery processes that emerged from intensive interviews and observations with 12 individuals over a 4-year period that met Structured Clinical Interview for DSM-III-R (SCID) criteria for schizophrenia or schizoaffective disorder. These 12 individuals came from a random selection of 20 individuals from among 135 subjects in the 4-year follow-up study. Two of these 20 individuals dropped out after one or two interviews and were lost to the study. Eighteen individuals remained as participants in the qualitative study, of whom 12 had received a SCID diagnosis of schizophrenia or schizoaffective disorder. Table 1 presents descriptive characteristics of the 12 study participants. These individuals were all unmarried at the time of the study and ranged in age from 30 to 53 years. They were a diverse group whose education ranged from less than high school to graduate level. They included three African-American males, one Southeast Asian male, two Caucasian males, four African-American females, and two Caucasian females. Three were born outside the USA.

**Table 1. Characteristics of Study Participants**

| Case Number | Recovery Level at Base | Recovery Level at Endpoint | Gender | Age at Base | Age of MI Onset | Race | Random Group | Marital Status | Education Level | MH Diagnosis | SA Diagnosis | Childhood/Family SES |
|---|---|---|---|---|---|---|---|---|---|---|---|---|
| 1 | 1 | 1 | M | 37 | – | Bl | C | Single | <HS | 295.9 | Yes | Poverty |
| 2 | 1 | 1 | M | 41 | 18 | Bl | C | Divorced | <BA | 295.7 | Yes | Poverty |
| 3 | 2 | 2 | F | 46 | 21 | Bl | C | Single | MA | 295.7 | Yes | Middle class |
| 4 | 2 | 2 | M | 38 | 20 | As | E | Single | HS | 295.7 | Yes | Middle class |
| 5 | 2 | 2 | M | 35 | 16 | Wh | C | Single | <HS | 295.9 | Yes | Poverty |
| 6 | 2 | 2 | M | 45 | 20 | Bl | C | Single | BA | 295.7 | Yes | Middle class |
| 7 | 2 | 2 | F | 39 | 20 | Bl | E | Single | <HS | 295.7 | No | Middle class |
| 8 | 2 | 2 | F | 44 | 22 | Bl | E | Widow | BA | 295.3 | Yes | Middle class |
| 9 | 2 | 3 | F | 53 | 40 | Bl | C | Divorced | <BA | 295.9 | No | Middle class |
| 10 | 2 | 3 | M | 30 | 19 | Wh | E | Single | HS | 295.3 | No | Poverty |
| 11 | 2 | 3 | F | 41 | 37 | Wh | E | Single | BA | 295.9 | No | Middle class |
| 12 | 2 | 3 | F | 40 | 32 | Wh | E | Single | <BA | 295.9 | No | Middle class |
| Mean | | | | 40.75 | 24.09 | | | | | | | |
| (SD) | | | | (5.88) | (8.22) | | | | | | | |

Key: Gender: M—male, F—female; Race: Bl—Black/African-American, AS—Asian, Wh—White/causasian; Random Group: C—control, E—experimental; Education level: < HS—less than High School, HS-High School Graduate; < BA—some college, BA—Baccalaureate degree, MA—Masters degree.

### Data Collection

Open-ended, taped interviews conducted every 4 to 8 months over a period of 8 years focused on participants' experiences with, and understandings of, their illnesses. Interviewers recorded their observations in detailed notes. Participants were paid stipends for an average of seven interviews over 4 years. Interview guidelines developed by three project staff, two of whom had experienced a psychiatric disability themselves, were reviewed and revised with a project advisory group comprised of five people with psychiatric disability. Two experienced project staff, a clinical psychologist, and a rehabilitation counselor, conducted the interviews. Interviews were informal and conversational, averaging about 1 hour and focusing on the participant's experiences and life events over the past few months. Interviewers attempted to obtain information on their hopes, goals, coping, risks, critical events, stability, friendships, family relationships, intimacy, service providers, work, education, living situations, recreation, environmental issues, medication, recovery attitudes, religion, financial issues, mental health issues, substance abuse issues, supports, barriers, and explanatory frameworks. The triangulation of data using multiple data sources, multiple methods, and multiple interviewers was intended to increase the validity of the study.

### Data Analysis

In the initial qualitative study involving the full cohort of 18 individuals with a severe psychiatric disability, three project staff listened repeatedly to the interview tapes, extracted key information, and produced typed overviews of the interviews. The overviews, as well as interviewer observations and notes, provided the data sources for the initial qualitative analysis involving all 18 participants. Data were analyzed for coherent themes and patterns related to recovery and tentative constructs were developed inductively (Miles & Huberman, 1994). These constructs, along with others found in the recent recovery literature, suggested some important general elements of recovery, including phases, facilitators, and barriers.

Subsequently, the first and third authors, who were two of the three investigators in the initial qualitative study, and the second author, who was not involved in the initial analysis, conducted a thematic analysis focused solely on the 12 participants with schizophrenia or schizoaffective disorder. We reviewed, coded, and summarized all interview documents across time for each participant with a particular focus on identifying phases in the recovery process and factors related to that process. We included demographic and diagnostic information in our evolving formulations and made cross-case comparisons where appropriate. We ultimately ordered cases according to where participants appeared to be on a recovery continuum. The dimensions used for this analysis emerged from the interviews. We mapped out individual changes in the various domains and tracked personal, social, and environmental changes for each individual. Then we organized these data into meta-matrices, time-ordered charts, and concept maps and compared individuals and groups of individuals across various dimensions.

## RESULTS

### Phases of Recovery

The 18 participants in the initial qualitative study described experiences over 4 years that tended to cluster into three broad general phases of recovery. However, the boundaries between phases were not precise and there was movement within and between phases. The experiences of the 12 participants with schizophrenia also fell into these three broad phases: being overwhelmed by the disability, struggling with the disability and living with the disability. From the self-help literature, we conceptualized a fourth phase: living beyond the disability.

*Overwhelmed by the disability.* This phase begins around the time of onset of major mental illness and can last for months or for many years. Daily life can be a struggle mentally and even physically. The person tries to understand and control what is happening, but often feels confused, disconnected from the self and others, out of control, and powerless to control his or her life in general. The person lacks self-confidence and may fear becoming overwhelmed by internal or external experiences. There is a longing for connection with others, but established relationships with family and others are often fragile or non-existent. New relationships can be very difficult to establish and are often transient. The person is unable to articulate clear goals or has goals that are not well anchored in reality.

Of the 12 participants with a schizophrenia-spectrum diagnosis, 2 remained at this phase throughout the study. Both were African-American males from impoverished backgrounds, now in their early 40s, who had struggled with mental illness and co-occurring substance use since their early 20s. The following vignette describes one of these participants.

Mr. F. is a 41-year-old divorced African-American man diagnosed with schizophrenia and substance abuse (alcohol and cocaine) disorder. He was raised in poverty in the inner city neighborhood where he has lived all his life. He has difficulty creating a time-line of his experiences, describing his life as "like a revolving door. One minute it's one way, another minute it's another way." He has had many periods of homelessness, unemployment, detoxification, and hospitalization in psychiatric and forensic settings. His first psychotic break occurred around age 18. He wanted to become an engineer and attended college and worked in a scientific laboratory in his early 20s, but recently has worked only sporadically in menial jobs.

Over the 5 years of the study, he had several periods of sobriety during which he was relatively stable and received support from the mental health system. He lived in a residence for people with dual diagnosis that was "like a real home"! He participated in a work program with the goal of getting an education in culinary arts. He appreciated the supportive social environment of the local psychosocial clubhouse. "I'm a pretty lonely guy...I'm getting to know more people now. Before, the only people I knew were street people." While in sobriety, he was more stable, he felt hopeful that "there's love out there," he acknowledged some of his social problems, and he paid more attention to worrisome physical health problems. He spoke with much emotion about the needs of his family and his concerns about them, expressing particular concern about a brother with mental illness who had been missing for several years. He helped his family by babysitting for his grandchildren and sending money weekly to his incarcerated son because "prison is a terrible place to be if you don't have money."

But his dual disability frequently overwhelmed him. Relapses on alcohol and cocaine typically led to involuntary hospitalization or incarceration. He said he actually felt better being in prison than being in the mental health system. At the end of the study, Mr. F. felt overwhelmed by defeat in his attempts to achieve some stability. He was angry at the mental health system because he did not feel respected. He considered medication a means to keep him shackled to the mental health system. Although he was experiencing psychotic symptoms and abusing alcohol, he was managing to stay out of the hospital. He explained, "I stay away from anyone who has anything to do with the mental health system."

*Struggling with the disability.* Moving beyond the acute phase, the person begins to develop an explanation for what is happening to him or her, often couched in medical and/or psychosocial terms, and faces the likelihood that it will continue for some time. The person recognizes the need to develop ways of coping with the disability in order to have a satisfying life. However, the disability remains a very present and persistent reality and the fear of failure can be very deep. The person may be very cautious about starting new activities for fear of losing the tenuous stability that often follows the receipt of resources and supports from the mental health system. If the person has not yet developed confidence about being able to manage symptoms, he or she may delay taking steps that probably could be handled successfully.

Medication can be helpful, but is often not sufficient for progressing beyond this phase. Some people continually struggle with distressing medication side effects or experience acute symptoms that are not relieved by psychotropic medication. Coping strategies such as sleeping, talking to a friend, cutting back on activities, using medication, or avoiding stress may be used to manage symptoms such as disordered thinking, auditory hallucinations, depressed feelings, or anxiety. A person in this phase also may be struggling to control substance use or to manage serious health conditions. This phase is characterized by building strength and confidence in the ability to act in one's own interest.

Six subjects were "struggling" with mental illness throughout the course of the study. They included a Caucasian male in his mid-30s, a Southeast Asian male in his late 30s, an African-American male in his mid-40s, and three African-American females, all in their 40s. Except for the Caucasian male who had his first psychotic break at age 16, these individuals first experienced schizophrenia in their early 20s. All had a co-occurring substance abuse disorder except for one of the African-American females. The following vignette describes her situation.

Ms. W. is a 41-year-old single African-American woman who was raised by her mother and grandmother in a working class, church-centered family with a strong work ethic. She spends about 12 to 16 hours per week in vocational activities at a local psychosocial clubhouse but is concerned about how work may affect her disability benefits. She feels pressured by her case manager to go to the clubhouse. "It's that [the clubhouse] or day treatment." She lives in her own apartment, but would prefer not to live alone because she is terrified living in a dangerous, "drug-infested" inner city neighborhood.

Prior to her involvement with the mental health system, Ms. W. was an ambitious and successful high school student. The deaths of her mother and grandmother were devastating losses that left her without any adult support by age 18. She never completed high school, became involved in a physically abusive relationship, and had her first psychiatric hospitalization at age 20 following the death of her infant daughter. Throughout her 20s, Ms. W. had many psychiatric hospitalizations, always involuntary. Over the past 10 years, she has held a variety of part-time entry-level jobs in the food services industry that she has left because of boredom, difficulties with co-workers, or fears of losing her social security benefits. She often speaks of her losses and the violence she has experienced and witnessed in the mental health system and in her neighborhood. "I need to get my spirit going again. My spirit is broke from all the things I have been through."

Although she finds her current psychotropic medication somewhat helpful, she has strong negative feelings about mental health providers. She lacks confidence in her case manager, saying, "she doesn't always make the best decisions for me...one minute she is helping me and the next minute she is playing games with me." She goes on, "I'm not crazy about the doctor, either, because I asked him how long I have to be in the mental health system and he says, 'forever,' and I don't believe I have to be in it forever." About mental health personnel she says, "the power of having power over another person goes to their heads."

Despite frequent psychiatric symptoms and daily fears about her personal safety, Ms. W. perseveres in working toward her goals and is hopeful about continuing to progress in her recovery. Her religious beliefs have sustained her over the years. She says, "I made up my mind when I lost my mother and grandmother that I wouldn't worry because the angels are watching over me." She frequently takes classes offered in the community and at her church and has a desire to return to college so that she can get a job helping other women who have been victimized. She would very much like to meet and marry a man who goes to church, has a job, and will be kind to her.

*Living with the disability.* In this phase of recovery the person has come to terms with the disability and feels confident about managing it. The person has a stronger sense of self and a feeling of confidence about having some control over his or her life. The person has learned that a satisfying life is possible despite having a disability. The person now utilizes effective coping strategies to deal with the disability and assumes a number of meaningful roles. There is consistency and security in the people, roles, and environments in his or her life. While the person still feels limited by the disability, he or she has found a niche in the world.

Four individuals progressed from "struggling with" to "living with" their schizophrenia over the course of the project. They included an African-American woman with illness onset in her early 40s, two Caucasian women in their 40s, one with illness onset in her early 30s, the other with illness onset in her late 30s, and a Caucasian male in his early 30s whose illness onset was at age 19. None of these individuals had a substance abuse disorder. The vignette below describes one participant in this phase of recovery.

Ms. P. is 42-year-old single Caucasian woman who works as an office assistant for a political action organization and lives in her own apartment. She loves her work and finds her co-workers supportive and kind. She has many friends and a best friend with whom she spends most evenings and weekends. She was diagnosed with schizophrenia in her early 30s. For the first 7 years following her diagnosis she spent most of her time in a day treatment program and lived in a group home. Frequent suicidality resulted in many psychiatric hospitalizations.

During the 5 years of the study, Ms. P. used psychotropic medication and worked with a therapist and community treatment team that she says, "really care for me." She credits her therapist for her emotional growth and improvement. In addition to working and spending time with her best friend, Ms. P. is active in a local social club for adults with psychiatric disabilities and very active in her Catholic church. Although she occasionally feels hopeless and suicidal, she generally feels capable of handling her emotions. She no longer blames her illness for all the bad things in her life. "I don't scapegoat my own illness." Ms. P. sees her illness as "partly chemical and partly emotional."

Over the years she has struggled to find a comfortable role within her family. "It's hard to feel good about myself in my family. They all have accomplished so much." When Ms. P. completed an intensive year-long training program in computer and office skills for people with psychiatric disabilities, she proudly said, "I never succeeded before...the course gave me a sense of self-worth, self-esteem, and self-confidence." She believes that this is what enabled her to get a job that she likes.

Ms. P. has a clear sense of her needs and her limitations. She knows that "daily structure keeps me out of the hospital" so she plans to continue working, but only very part time so that she can keep her disability check. Near the end of the study, she was diagnosed with type II diabetes and was learning to manage that condition. She remained optimistic about her future and hopes to marry a man who does not have a mental illness.

*Living beyond the disability.* Although none of our 12 subjects were in this final phase, we have conceptualized it from descriptions in the self-help literature (Blanch et al., 1993; Weingarten, 1994; Stocks, 1995). In this phase of recovery the disability is a much smaller part of the person's world and does not significantly interfere with having a satisfying and contributing life. The person feels well connected to self, to others, to various living, learning, and working environments, and experiences a sense of meaning and purpose in life. This phase overlaps with the definition of recovery offered by Liberman and colleagues in this issue (Liberman et al., 2002).

### Tasks of Recovery

The experiences of our participants pointed to certain basic general tasks associated with the process of recovery. One is developing an explanatory framework for understanding the experience of schizophrenia. While those at the beginning phase of recovery tended to have no clear explanation for their symptoms and experiences, those who were "struggling with" or "living with" their psychiatric condition explained their experience in a variety of ways—as an emotional breakdown brought on by environmental stress, as a personal test or trial presented by God, as a drug-induced reaction, as "a chemical imbalance," or as a medically treatable condition. One woman who was "living with" schizophrenia described it as "partly chemical and partly emotional."

A second task of recovery is to get some control over the illness itself. Often, this was achieved at least partly through regular use of psychotropic medications that had minimal distressing side effects. Getting control over the illness also required having effective coping skills and strategies for dealing with symptoms and stressors as well as the presence of various supports such as family connections, financial resources, stable housing, collaborative relationships with treatment providers, and access to needed mental health services. To get control over the schizophrenia when there was also a co-occurring substance abuse disorder, it was necessary to control substance use as well.

A third task of recovery is to move into roles that are meaningful, productive, and valued in the larger society. Except when they were actively abusing substances, all participants were working on this task throughout the study period. However, only those individuals who were at the stage of "living with" their disability had settled into a comfortable existence that included success and stability in several roles. The most commonly sought role was as a "worker." However, participants were also trying to establish themselves as parents, friends, caretakers, and spouses.

### Challenges to Recovery

Among participants in the study, no one stood out as having a notably different level of severity of schizophrenia. It was clear, however, that some individuals were struggling more and facing far greater challenges than others in their efforts to progress in recovery. Our analysis pointed to three factors which seemed to be associated with the degree of challenge faced by individuals working on mental health recovery: 1) the presence of comorbid substance abuse, 2) the environmental context for recovery, particularly the interrelated factors of race and social disadvantage, and 3) the age of onset of schizophrenia. Participants who had a co-existing substance abuse disorder, who were African-American, and who were from severely disadvantaged backgrounds encountered the greatest challenges to recovery. In contrast, participants with late onset schizophrenia and advantaged backgrounds seemed to progress more smoothly and more quickly in their recovery, although their challenges were by no means small.

*Substance abuse.* Seven of the 12 subjects were struggling with a substance abuse disorder in addition to schizophrenia. During periods of active substance use, even when psychiatric symptoms were present, the substance abuse disorder became the predominant disabling condition and seemed to preclude making any progress in mental health recovery. During periods of sobriety, these individuals were working on two fronts, mental illness and substance abuse. However, progress quickly eroded whenever there was a return to drugs or alcohol. Active abuse affected more areas than just the mental health recovery process. It typically led to the loss of important resources and supports for coping with the psychiatric disability such as stable housing and supportive relationships with family, friends, and providers.

Managing substance use required a great deal of personal strength and drew on the individual's often-limited reserves and resources. Compared to managing mental illness alone, effective management of the dual disability required more resources from the formal service sector, a stronger informal support network, and greater resilience and stamina within the self. Among our participants, those with a co-occurring substance abuse disorder tended to be persons of color who were "overwhelmed by" or "struggling with" schizophrenia, while those without a substance abuse disorder tended to be Caucasians who had progressed to the phase of "living with" their disability.

*Poverty and disadvantage.* While 7 of the 12 participants came from middle class backgrounds, 11 were living on extremely limited incomes during the course of the study and seemed to be locked into a condition of poverty with no way out. A 42-year-old African-American man put it this way: "You just resign yourself to the fact that there's never enough money." Participants' quality of life was almost entirely dependent on the meager resources available through entitlement and benefit programs. Those who did not have subsidized housing tended to live in extreme poverty. However, even with subsidized housing, individuals often had ongoing concerns about their daily survival and personal safety. Participants who were poor, but not living in the most extreme poverty, tended to be those who had an employment history that qualified them for more than the minimal level of disability income, those who supplemented their disability income with "under the table" employment, those who had subsidized housing, and those with access to additional resources from family or others.

Nine participants had a history of homelessness and five had a period of homelessness during the course of this study. One woman who was not homeless utilized free meal programs regularly. One 45-year-old woman said she was willing to comply with the rules of her group home only because she feared becoming homeless again. In general, participants demonstrated considerable skill and resourcefulness in obtaining the resources needed for their daily survival. At times, dealing with poverty was a greater challenge than dealing with mental illness. When their most basic needs were not met, participants devoted their energies to daily survival and had insufficient strength to work on mental health recovery. One 41-year-old African-American woman who lives in a high-crime area put it bluntly: "It's very stressful being poor." Stability and security were so important to these individuals that they were often extremely reluctant to give up concrete resources such as Social Security Disability Income. Overall, the efforts of these individuals to obtain or retain basic resources and to establish some measure of personal security consumed a great deal of time and energy.

*Race.* African-American participants experienced the double stigma of race and mental illness. Many talked about the obstacles that African-Americans had to overcome in this society and described the insensitivity of the mental health system to their circumstances. One 42-year-old woman believed that "racism in America" was the primary cause of her problems and pain. Another college-educated woman, also in her 40s, believed that racism was an insurmountable obstacle. "They say that a better education prepares you for a better life and that's a lie." Substance abuse and poverty were common in the lives of participants of color and in the lives of those around them. The combined effects of being an African-American male and a heavy user of drugs or alcohol presented enormous obstacles to recovery. All 3 African-American males, the 1 Southeast Asian male, and 2 of the 4 African-American females had a substance abuse disorder.

*Age of onset.* The participants most prepared for the tasks of recovery tended to be those who did not have to deal with mental illness until after they already had some experience and success in adult roles. These were individuals with late onset schizophrenia. Their illness interrupted an already established adult life and consequently was experienced as traumatic and debilitating. However, their life experience provided a reserve of resources from which to draw. Prior to the onset of mental illness, many had completed their educations and had satisfying adult relationships, well-developed work habits, and career paths. Although mental illness brought a loss of meaningful roles, there remained some sense of personal competence, based on past experience. One woman with late onset schizophrenia reflected, "I feel lucky because I can look back on my adult life and I have something to rebuild on." After meeting others who had an earlier onset of mental illness, she concluded that recovery was much easier for her. "I saw a lot of people around me who were a lot sicker. Some young people never had a formed personality...I was 37 years old and had something to rebuild."

### Supports for Recovery

Those who progressed in recovery had supports to help manage the painful experiences and challenging process of recovery. The presence of one or more supportive people in their lives seemed to be essential. Participants consistently identified specific family members, peers, friends, and professionals who facilitated their recovery process by offering hope, encouragement, and opportunities. Every participant who was "living with" schizophrenia had some meaningful connection to family members. One 42-year-old Caucasian woman who had had the same therapist for 8 years praised their work together and emphasized the importance of the long-term relationship. She explained that in the past she would have a therapist for 9 months, not feel connected to them, and then feel abandoned when they left.

Effective medication that alleviated the acute symptoms of schizophrenia was another critical support. Participants often noted that they began to feel hopeful and to gain more control over their lives after changing to a medication that was more effective or that had fewer side effects. On the most basic level, people needed concrete resources such as food, clothing, shelter, and access to supportive therapeutic environments as well as medical, substance abuse, and psychiatric treatment. As discussed above, managing the stresses of poverty was at least as difficult as managing the mental illness.

Many participants felt they had divine support and relied on their religious faith for strength and sustenance. Even those with no formal church affiliation often referred to God as a source of support. This was especially true of African-Americans. In addition, organized religion seemed to serve a protective function for 3 of the 4 African-American females and 1 of the 2 Caucasian females. These participants regularly attended church services and 2 of the African-American women found that the church offered them a valued role in their community. As one woman stated, "If I'm feeling a bit poorly, I know that just going to the church is going to make me feel better."

### Developmental Process of Recovery

Recovery appeared to be experienced as a developmental process. As 2 participants put it, "I have grown up a lot" and "I know a lot more [than at the beginning of my illness]." Some saw recovery as a process of gaining more control over their lives. People seemed to know when they were ready to take another step. When options and opportunities were available and they made a move, such as out of day treatment, into a clubhouse, back to work, or into a more desirable living situation, participants seemed to experience a period of increased energy and activity. However, growth also brought periods of instability and increased vulnerability. For example, taking a progressive step could result in the loss of existing supports from the mental health system and, consequently, lead to increased difficulty in managing one's life.

Many participants gradually began to acknowledge their clinical improvement and better quality of life. One 32-year-old man who had progressed from "struggling with" to "living with," after reflecting on the fact that he had been out of hospital for 8 years, was working part time, and living in his own apartment after living in a group home for 12 years, commented, "Even I have to admit that I am doing better. I've been afraid to say that in case I get sick again." Over time, individuals gradually increased their sense of self, gained a sense of personal power, built connections with others, developed new meaning and purpose in their lives, and established themselves as contributing members of their communities.

One woman with late onset schizophrenia progressed rapidly compared to the others. In a period of 4 years, she moved from being "overwhelmed" through "struggling with" to "living with" her illness. However, the experiences of the other participants demonstrate how slow the recovery process can be. Seven participants made slow, steady progress, 3 fluctuated, and 1 declined. Although many of those who continued "struggling" did make some progress in recovery, it tended to be extremely slow with ups and downs as well as plateau periods used for integration and consolidation of gains, healing, confidence building, and re-energizing of the self.

Participants often made some progress and then took a great deal of time to integrate it. The work of recovery was exhausting and painful, and required a great deal of persistence. The 4 individuals who were able to progress from "struggling with" to "living with" their schizophrenia over the course of study tended to be quite hopeful about continuing their progress. In contrast, those who had remained for decades at the phase of "overwhelmed" or "struggling with" seemed to have little hope for recovery. As one 42-year-old African-American man who had been "overwhelmed" for many years expressed, "I've been this way for so many years that this is the only way I know how to be."

### DISCUSSION

Our qualitative longitudinal data allow a glimpse into the very personal experiences of individuals who are dealing with the effects of schizophrenia in the face of substantial physical, psychological, and social barriers. Their stories personalize the experience of having schizophrenia and reveal the heroic efforts of individuals who persist, against great odds, in the quest for respect and personal satisfaction in their lives.

These findings offer some beginning insights into the process of recovery experienced by people with schizophrenia. Based on our repeated intensive interviewing of 12 individuals over a 4-year period, we were able to identify some themes and patterns in this process. The recovery experiences of these participants followed a progression through three broad phases that we characterize as "overwhelmed by," "struggling with," and "living with" the disability. As participants moved through these phases, they worked on three basic tasks: 1) they sought an explanation for their experience; 2) they tried to control the disability; and 3) they attempted to establish themselves in meaningful and productive roles. Because this study considered the person within his or her environmental context, we were able to consider some of the environmental factors that constrain or facilitate the developmental process of recovery. The impact of the social and physical context for recovery, particularly those conditions associated with poverty and disadvantage, was striking among our participants. The degree of challenge participants encountered in their recovery varied and appeared to be related to a) the co-occurrence of a substance abuse disorder; b) the extent of environmental stressors and constraints associated with poverty, disadvantaged background, and race; and c) the age of onset of schizophrenia. Progress was facilitated by the availability of both concrete resources and social supports. Those who were Caucasian, who had substantial resources and supports, and who were in their 30s at the onset of schizophrenia progressed most rapidly and experienced the greatest gains in their recovery. In contrast, those participants who were African-American males with a co-existing substance abuse disorder experienced minimal sustained progress in their mental health recovery.

This study contributes to the evolving recovery literature. We found phases, tasks, challenges, supports, and processes that are remarkably similar to aspects of recovery described by other authors (Deegan, 1988; Strauss et al., 1985; Davidson & Strauss, 1992; Baxter & Diehl, 1998; Young & Ensing, 1999; Mead & Copeland, 2000; Townsend et al., 2000). In addition, our participants at the phase of "living with" schizophrenia consistently met the recovery criteria proposed by Liberman and colleagues (Liberman et al., 2002). All 4 individuals in this phase of recovery at the end of our study had sustained symptom remission, were employed, lived independently of supervision, and had an age-appropriate social network.

Although more evidence is needed, our findings do suggest that some frequently proposed elements of a comprehensive mental health care system may also be essential for promoting recovery among individuals with schizophrenia. These elements include: 1) integrated mental health and substance abuse services (Drake et al., 1998; Mueser et al., 1998); 2) provision of a level of resources that allow for a lifestyle above the poverty level (Saraceno & Barbui, 1997; Alverson et al., 1998); 3) access to effective medications; and 4) ongoing flexible services offered within a structure and timeframe that recognizes the variety of patterns that the individual course of recovery may take (Anthony, 2000). Important individual-level services might include supportive psychotherapy, skill development interventions, and supported employment, education, and housing. We expect that our findings will stimulate a number of research questions and hypotheses among other researchers.

Of course, a full understanding of the recovery process is not possible from the limited evidence available from these 12 cases. How recovery occurs, its dimensions, and the courses it may take must be fully explored in future research. There is a need to examine the extremes of the recovery continuum; both individuals who make little or no discernable progress in recovery and individuals who progress to "living beyond" mental illness. It also is necessary to conduct more prospective studies that follow many individuals over long periods of time. With our current state of knowledge, it is premature to propose a comprehensive model of recovery. Far more research is needed to identify all the elements in the complex process of recovery and to adequately investigate the relationships among relevant variables in this process. This study raises important questions for future researchers to investigate.

## CONCLUSIONS

From this study, it is clear that there is much more to learn from people who are themselves involved in the process of recovery. Although we have offered some broad-brush findings about recovery among people with schizophrenia, the incredible variety of individual experience has not been adequately examined. The themes and phases that we have identified are based on limited data and we do not want to highlight or suggest certainty about a phenomenon that is still being explored. Our qualitative results are consistent with that segment of the literature (Davidson & Strauss, 1992; Mead & Copeland, 2000) that describes recovery as a process of self-discovery, self-renewal, and transformation that involves adjusting one's attitudes, feelings, perceptions, beliefs, roles, and goals in life. The inclusion of the concept of recovery in the recent Surgeon General's Report on Mental Illness (US Department of Health and Human Services, 1999) provides hope that a recovery orientation will continue to grow within the mental health field. As we move to promote recovery among individuals with schizophrenia, a group traditionally viewed as having a poor prognosis, a broad research agenda focused specifically on recovery must be established and pursued.

Acknowledgments

This study was supported by the National Institute on Disability and Rehabilitation Research within the Department of Education, and the Center for Mental Health Services (CMHS), a division of the Substance Abuse and Mental Health Services Administration (Grant # H133B40024). The findings and interpretation of the data expressed in this article do not necessarily represent the views of NIDRR or the CMHS, but are the sole responsibility of the authors.

## REFERENCES

Alverson, H., Alverson, M., Drake, R.E. & Becker, D.R. (1998). Social correlates of competitive employment among people with severe mental illness. *Psychiatric Rehabilitation Journal, 22,* 34–40.

Anthony, W.A. (1991). Recovery from mental illness: the new vision of services researchers. *Innovations and Research, 1,* 13–14.

Anthony, W.A. (1993a). Recovery from mental illness: The guiding vision of the mental health service system in the 1990s. *Psychosocial Rehabilitation Journal, 16*, 11–23.

Anthony, W.A. (1993b). *The decade of recovery (audiotape)*. Boston: Boston University Center for Psychiatric Rehabilitation.

Anthony, W.A. (1994). *Toward a vision of recovery for mental health and psychiatric rehabilitation services* (videotape). Boston: Boston University Center for Psychiatric Rehabilitation.

Anthony, W.A. (2000). A recovery-oriented service system: setting service system level standards. *Psychiatric Rehabilitation Journal, 24*, 159–168.

Baxter, E.A. & Diehl, S. (1998). Emotional stages: consumers and family members recovering from the trauma of mental illness. *Psychiatric Rehabilitation Journal, 21*, 349–355.

Blanch, A., Fisher, D., Tucker, W., Walsh, D. & Chassman, J. (1993). Consumer-practitioners and psychiatrists share insights about recovery and coping. *Disability Studies Quarterly, 13*, 17–20.

Davidson, L. & Strauss, J.S. (1992). Sense of self in recovery from severe mental illness. *British Journal of Medical Psychology, 65*, 131–145.

Deegan, P. (1988). Recovery: The lived experience of rehabilitation. *Psychosocial Rehabilitation Journal, 11*, 11–19.

Drake, R.E., Mercer-Mcfadden, C., Mueser, K.T., Mchuoo, G.J. & Bond, G.R. (1998). Review of integrated mental health and substance abuse treatment for patients with dual disorders. *Schizophrenia Bulletin, 24*, 589–608.

Leete, E. (1989). How I perceive and manage my illness. *Schizophrenia Bulletin, 15*, 197–200.

Liberman, R.P., Kopelowicz, A., Ventura, J. & Gutktnd, D. (2002). Operational definition and factors related to recovery from schizophrenia. *International Review of Psychiatry, 14*, 255–272.

Liberman, R.P., Kopelowicz, A. & Young, A. (1994). Biobehavioral treatment and rehabilitation of schizophrenia. *Behavior Therapy, 25*, 89–107.

Lieberman, J., Jody, D., Geisler, S., Alvir, J., Loebel, A., Szymanski, S., Woerner, M., & Borenstetn, M. (1993). Time course and biological correlates of treatment response in first-episode schizophrenia. *Archives of General Psychiatry, 50*, 369–376.

Mead, S. & Copeland, M.E. (2000). What recovery means to us: Consumers' perspective. *Community Mental Health Journal, 36*, 315–328.

Miles, M.B. & Huberman, A.M. (Eds.) (1994). *Qualitative data analysis (2nd Edition)*. Thousand Oaks: Sage Publications.

Mueser, K.T., Drake, R.E. & Noordsy, D.L. (1998). Integrated mental health and substance abuse treatment for severe psychiatric disorders. *Journal of Practical Psychiatry and Behavioral Health, 4*, 129–139.

Saraceno, B. & Barbui, C. (1997). Poverty and mental illness. *Canadian Journal of Psychiatry, 42*, 285–290.

Spaniol, L., Gagne, C. & Koehler, M. (1997). Recovery from serious mental illness: what it is and how to assist people in their recovery. *Continuum, 4,* 3–15.

Spaniol, L. & Koehler, M. (Eds.) (1994). *The experience of recovery.* Boston: Boston University Center for Psychiatric Rehabilitation.

Spaniol, L., Koehler, M. & Hutchinson, D. (1994). *Recovery workbook: Practical coping and empowerment strategies for people with psychiatric disability.* Boston: Boston University Center for Psychiatric Rehabilitation.

Stocks, M.L. (1995). In the eye of the beholder. *Psychiatric Rehabilitation Journal, 19,* 89–91.

Strauss, J.S., Hafez, H., Lieberman, P. & Harding, C.M. (1985). The course of psychiatric disorder. III: longitudinal principles. *American Journal of Psychiatry, 142,* 289–296.

Townsend, W., Boyd, S. & Griffin, G. (2000). *Emerging best practices in mental health recovery.* Ohio: The Ohio Department of Mental Health.

U.S. Department of Health and Human Services (1999). *Mental health: A report of the Surgeon General.* Rockville: U.S. Department of Health and Human Services, Substance Abuse and Mental Health Services Administration, Center for Mental Health Services, National Institutes of Health, National Institute of Mental Health.

Warner, R. (1985). *Recovery from schizophrenia: Psychiatry and political economy.* London: Routledge & Kegan Paul.

Weingarten, R. (1994). The ongoing process of recovery. *Psychiatry, 57,* 369–375.

Young, S.L. & Ensing, D.S. (1999). Exploring recovery from the perspective of people with psychiatric disabilities. *Psychiatric Rehabilitation Journal, 22,* 219–231.

# The Course, Treatment, and Outcome of Substance Disorder in Persons with Severe Mental Illness

*Robert E. Drake, Kim T. Mueser, Robin E. Clark, and Michael A. Wallach*

At the time of original publication, the author affiliations were as follows: Robert Drake, MD, PhD, Kim Mueser, PhD, and Robin Clark, PhD, were at the New Hampshire-Dartmouth Psychiatric Research Center, Hanover, NH; Michael A. Wallach, PhD, was at Duke University, Durham, NC.

This article originally appeared in the *American Journal of Orthopsychiatry,* 1966, 66(1), 42–51 and is reprinted with permission.

**Abstract:** Individuals with co-occurring substance abuse and severe mental illness are particularly vulnerable to negative outcomes. This paper reviews findings on the longitudinal course of dual disorders in traditional treatment systems that provide separate mental health and substance abuse programs; describes the movement toward programs that integrate both types of treatment at the clinical level; reviews evidence related to outcomes in integrated treatment programs; and discusses health care policy changes that would encourage effective treatments.

Despite intensified concern over the problem of dual diagnosis, as described by Osher and Drake (1996), little is known about the longitudinal course of substance use disorders in persons with severe mental illness. This paper will examine the evidence regarding longitudinal course, outcomes in the traditional treatment system, the movement toward establishing integrated treatment programs, and emerging research on the effects of integrated treatment. The mental health policy implications of research on the longitudinal course of dual disorders will also be considered.

## THE TRADITIONAL TREATMENT SYSTEM

Longitudinal course is difficult to understand in the traditional treatment system, which provides separate, uncoordinated mental health and substance abuse programs. Most dually diagnosed persons are in and out of each kind of treatment, with little cross-monitoring. This type of parallel treatment in separate programs for people with dual disorders was the standard prior to recent efforts to integrate mental health and substance abuse treatments in dual diagnosis programs. Another difficulty in understanding longitudinal course with traditional treatment is that most of the studies undertaken have followed clients for no more than 12 to 18 months. Unfortunately, lengthier follow-up studies of individuals with severe mental illness have rarely assessed substance abuse.

Prospective follow-up studies tend to show that those with severe mental illness and co-occurring substance disorder have poorer psychosocial adjustment, at least over the short term, than do individuals with severe mental illness only. Homelessness and institutionalization are the most frequently measured indicators of pschosocial adjustment. Drake and Wallach (1989) found that severely mentally ill patients followed in the community for 1 year had higher rates of rehospitalization if they were dually diagnosed. Among those with schizophrenia, even moderate drinking led to higher rates of rehospitalization (Drake, Osher, & Wallach, 1989). Osher et al. (1994) and Cuffel and Chase (1994) also found higher rates of hospitalization over a 1-year follow-up. Caton, Wyatt, Felix, Grunberg, and Dominguez (1993) found that, over 18 months, men who moved out of a homeless shelter into stable housing arrangements were more likely to be rehospitalized and to return to homelessness if they had co-morbid substance disorder. Belcher (1989) followed mentally ill patients discharged from a state hospital for 6 months and found that use of alcohol and drugs strongly predicted homelessness. Similarly, the five McKinney demonstrations for homeless people with severe mental illness indicated that substance abuse was a key factor in housing crises and returns to homelessness (Center for Mental Health Services, 1994). In a related outcome, Linszen, Dingemans, and Lenior (1994) found that those patients with schizophrenia who abused cannabis had more psychotic relapses during 1-year follow-up. Studies that have examined rates of hospitalization or homelessness retrospectively are not considered here. These latter studies often show more mixed results, in part because they can be biased by assessment at hospital admission, which selects for recidivists.

Short-term follow-up studies under traditional treatment also show that substance disorder tends to persist among those with severe mental illness. Bond, McDonel, Miller, and Pensec (1991) found no change in substance abuse among dually diagnosed patients followed in assertive community treatment or among those followed in a "usual treatment" control group for 18 months. Lehman, Herron, Schwartz, and Myers (1993) similarly found no changes in alcohol or drug use over 1 year for patients in day treatment. Morse, Calsyn, Allen, Tempelhoff, and Smith (1992) found no change in quantity of alcohol consumption over 1 year among homeless persons with dual disorders who participated in a research study that did not provide a specific intervention for substance abuse. The recently completed McKinney demonstration projects similarly found no change in substance abuse over 1 year (Lehman, personal communication, June 1995). Cuffel and Chase (1994) found that the prevalence of substance disorder in a sample of persons with schizophrenia in the Epidemiological Catchment Area study showed no change over 1 year, despite fluctuations in active abuse status, because remission and relapse rates were balanced.

Few data are available on course of substance abuse in the traditional treatment system over longer periods of time. Okin, Borus, Baer, and Jones (1995) followed up former long-term state hospital patients who had been released an average of 7.5 years earlier into structured community residences. Clinicians' ratings of need for substance abuse treatment showed no change. Findings of this study were limited by a low rate of substance abuse in this deinstitutionalized group. In a study of vocational rehabilitation, we (Drake & Becker, 1995) examined 61 clients with severe mental disorder and a lifetime diagnosis of alcohol or drug use disorder. Only eight of these clients were participating in integrated dual diagnosis treatment. According to self-report, there were no reductions over 2½ years in the number of active users or in the days of alcohol and drug use. This vocational study was limited by assessing days of use rather than abuse.

Thus, the few available follow-up studies indicate that substance abusing patients with severe mental disorders tend to have worse outcomes than do abstainers and to continue to abuse alcohol and drugs, at least over the short run. However, we really do not know if use and abuse over time follow epidemiologic trends in the larger society (Chen & Kandel, 1995) or if, on the other hand, persons with psychiatric disorder are either more or less likely to moderate or stop their use over time. Negrete and Knapp (1986) reported a marked decline in the use of cannabis among patients with schizophrenia over the age of 30. Similarly, Drake and Wallach (1993) found that a higher than expected proportion of those with severe mental illness became abstainers over time. In many patient samples, estimates of the proportion with recent or current abuse are lower than lifetime prevalence rates (Mueser, Bellack, & Blanchard, 1992), suggesting that some of the patients may have attained at least temporary remission. On the other hand, the follow-up studies reviewed above indicate that substance use disorder in this population tends to persist over time.

One optimistic note comes from cross-sectional evidence in two small-sample studies. Currently non-abusing schizophrenic patients with a history of substance disorder were found to have service utilization patterns similar to those of patients who had never abused (Bartels et al., 1993; Zisook et al., 1992). Former substance abusers in one study also had fewer schizophrenic symptoms than did lifetime abstainers, suggesting that they may be less ill when not abusing drugs (Zisook et al., 1992). In other words, risk status for the negative outcomes associated with substance disorder may be reduced when patients attain abstinence.

These general findings regarding the chronicity and slow rate of recovery from substance disorder among individuals with severe mental illness are broadly comparable to longitudinal findings on substance disorder in the general population (Vaillant, 1983; 1988). Substance disorder tends to be a chronic relapsing problem that persists over many years for most people, and a small but cumulative proportion of most samples achieve stable remission each year. That long-term course for those with mental illness is worse than this, however, remains a possibility.

One caveat regarding the above study is that most of the assessments of substance abuse were based on self-report alone. Studies consistently show that there are many positive urine tests among psychiatric patients who deny abuse (Crowley, Chesluk, Dilts, & Hart, 1974; Galletly, Field & Prior, 1993; Shaner et al., 1993; Stone, Greenstein, Gamble, & McLellan, 1993). Valid assessment in this population clearly requires multiple instruments or modes of assessment (Drake, Alterman, & Rosenberg, 1993). Therefore, current estimates of substance use disorders may be lower than the actual rates.

### THE MOVEMENT TOWARD INTEGRATED TREATMENT

In the early 1980s, clinicians and researchers began to identify a group of young persons with severe mental illness—labeled "young chronic" patients in the literature—who were characterized by their disruptive behavior, lack of institutional experience, and management difficulties in the community (Bachrach, 1982; Pepper, Kirshner, & Ryglewicz, 1981). These patients did not seem to fit into existing community mental health programs that had been established largely to facilitate the deinstitutionalization of dependent, long-term hospital patients. Their substance use was often described in these reports as one of several attributes of their difficult behavior. By the mid 1980s, clinicians and researchers realized that these patients' use of substances was more than a manifestation of their psychiatric disorders; it was a further disorder promoted by the cultural reality of substance availability in the community. According to customary criteria, they in fact had substance disorders as well as severe mental illnesses. Thus, the concept of co-occurring disorders, or dual diagnosis, was established (Ridgely, Osher, Goldman, & Talbot, 1987).

With conceptualization of the dual diagnosis problem came a clearer picture of the poor fit between dually diagnosed patients and the existing treatment system. Mental health and substance abuse services were provided in separate, parallel treatment streams that demonstrated little capacity to modify their programs and to cooperate with one another to individualize services for those with dual disorders. As far as each stream was concerned, the dually diagnosed patient had one disorder too many. Myriad problems in the traditional, parallel treatment system were related to training differences, administrative conflicts, clinical and ideological disagreements, interagency miscommunications, disorder-specific categorical boundaries, and funding mechanisms. In the parallel model, the burden of integrating different philosophies, recovery models, and interventions fell on the patient; in other words, it rarely occurred. The net result was that patients were typically extruded from one type of program (and often from both) and were rarely engaged in concurrent mental health and substance abuse treatments.

Evidence continues to accumulate on the difficulties of parallel treatment. Wolfe and Sorensen (1989) noted that dually diagnosed patients continue to be the most difficult to manage clinically and administratively in the emergency setting. Hellerstein, Rosenthal, and Miner (1995) recently documented the enormous and rapid attrition rate in the parallel service system. Noordsy, Schwab, Fox, and Drake (1996) found that, across several studies, a large majority of dually diagnosed patients were unable to use Alcoholics Anonymous and the traditional self-help system, especially in the early phases of recovery, even with facilitation. The McKinney demonstration programs did not plan for integrated substance abuse treatment, but all five projects discovered in the field that clients did not connect with the existing substance abuse service system and began to advocate for integrated substance abuse treatments (Center for Mental Health Services, 1994). Poor outcomes continue to be attributed to barriers within the traditional service system (Ridgely, Goldman & Willenbring, 1990).

To overcome the poor fit between dually diagnosed patients and the parallel treatment system, (Ridgely et al., 1987) recommended comprehensive treatment programs that integrated mental health and substance abuse treatment at the level of clinical delivery. Numerous others since that time have provided integrated treatment philosophies, offered clinical models, and discussed principles of integrated treatment. Minkoff (1989), for example, clarified the analogous process of recovery for the two types of disorders. Kline, Harris, Bebout, and Drake (1991) pointed out that integration offers several critical advantages: it avoids a substance abuse system that is typically unresponsive to dually diagnosed persons with severe mental illness; it avoids breakdowns between separate agencies and systems; it takes advantage of ready access to patients already within the mental health system; and it requires clinicians and programs, rather than clients, to make treatments compatible.

Over the past 10 years, psychiatric programs that serve people with severe mental disorders have moved toward integrating substance abuse/dual diagnosis treatment into comprehensive mental health programs (Carey, 1996); Drake, Bartels, Teague, Noordsy & Clark, 1993; Drake & Noordsy,

1994; Lehman & Dixon, 1995; Miller, 1994; Minkoff & Drake, 1991; Rosenthal, Hellerstein & Miner, 1992; Ziedonis & Fisher, 1994). A variety of clinical models have been described in the literature, including one statewide program (Drake, Teague & Warren, 1990). In addition to integration of mental health and substance abuse treatments, many of these programs share common elements such as assertive outreach, comprehensive services, and flexibility. Several incorporate intensive case management approaches (Drake & Noordsy, 1994; Durell, Lechtenberg, Corse & Frances,1993; Fariello & Scheidt, 1989; Teague, Schwab & Drake, 1990). Another common recommendation is for stage-wise treatment, based on the finding that clients often require motivational interventions before they are ready to participate in abstinence-oriented interventions (Carey, 1996; Drake, Bartels, et al., 1993; Fariello & Scheidt, 1989; McHugo, Drake, Burton, & Ackerson, 1995; Mueser et al., 1992; Osher & Kofoed 1989; Ziedonis & Fisher, 1994). Many programs also recommend group substance abuse interventions, particularly for clients lacking in motivation (Greenfield, Weiss & Tohen, 1995; Noordsy & Fox, 1991; Osher & Kofoed, 1989). Several clinicians have also pointed out the need to modify prescribing practices to avoid medications with addictive potential (Osher & Kofoed, 1989; Zweben & Smith, 1989).

### INITIAL FINDINGS REGARDING INTEGRATED TREATMENT

At this point, more than 30 studies of integrated treatment have been completed (Drake, Mercer-McFadden, Mueser, McHugo & Bond, 1995). Most of these are limited by methodological weaknesses: small samples, relatively brief follow-ups, inadequate measurement of substance use, lack of experimental designs, and treatment drift over time. Samples are often insufficient because of the difficulty of recruiting and retaining dually diagnosed persons in studies. Moreover, since many of these patients who begin treatment are not motivated to reduce substance use, the usual 1-year follow-up period is often too short to demonstrate improvement.

Experimental designs are difficult to implement in field settings, and studies of dual diagnosis treatment have rarely been attempted in academic settings. A further complication is due to the aforementioned shift in clinical beliefs about the most effective treatment for dually disordered clients. Prior to 1990, the standard approach involved parallel mental health and substance abuse treatments. Since then, the movement toward integrated treatment has resulted in control groups that at least drift in that direction and sometimes receive a form of integrated treatment from the outset. Thus, a control group consisting traditional, parallel services (i.e., complete reliance on the separate substance abuse treatment system), is almost impossible to achieve in practice. Clinicians in the ostensible control condition may rapidly discover that the existing substance abuse system is ineffective in treating patients with severe mental illness and begin to offer integrated substance abuse treatment themselves. Therefore, even randomized studies tend to compare two different approaches to integrated treatment, rather than integrated versus parallel treatments (Drake, Bebout et al., 1993).

Some of the clearest findings from the existing studies of integrated treatment will be summarized in the paragraphs that follow. Early, uncontrolled studies with small samples showed decreased hospital use among those who stayed in integrated dual diagnosis groups (Hellerstein & Meehan, 1987; Kofoed, Kania, Walsh & Atkinson, 1986). Subsequently, the National Institute of Mental Health funded 13 demonstrations between 1987 and 1990. These programs targeted a variety of high-risk groups with dual disorders, such as inner-city residents, minorities, women with children, and migrant farm workers. Most of these studies were limited by short follow-ups (generally 1 year) and lack of control or comparison groups. Nevertheless, outcomes of the 13 projects provide some consistent information about the treatment of dually disordered clients (Mercer-McFadden & Drake, 1995): 1) All of these programs were successful in engaging clients in outpatient dual diagnosis services, with retention rates of approximately 75 to 85%. 2) Engagement in outpatient dual diagnosis services generally led to decreased utilization of inpatient and institutional services. 3) The studies found minimal or no reduction in substance abuse over 1 year. 4) Treatment of substance abuse was complicated not only by measurement difficulties and short follow-ups but also by the consistent finding that the dually diagnosed patients in these programs were not motivated to participate in the abstinence-oriented treatments that were offered. Thus, a consistent and critical finding for the field was that motivational interventions were needed to help prepare dually diagnosed clients for traditional, abstinence-oriented interventions. A recent experimental study confirmed that an integrated treatment approach was superior to parallel services at engaging clients as outpatients (Hellerstein et al., 1995).

In another recent study, Jerrell and Ridgely (1995a) used a quasi-experimental design and followed 147 dually diagnosed patients in one of three forms of integrated treatment (case management, cognitive-behavioral, or 12-Step) for 12 months and 98 of them for 18 months. Pre-post data (not specified by treatment group) showed improvements in several areas: interviewer ratings of work, independent living and social functioning; self-reported satisfaction with work and family relationships; and observed psychiatric symptoms. There were no overall changes in the rate of alcohol-related symptoms, alcohol use, drug use, or hospitalization. A second paper from the same study (Jerrell & Ridgely, 1995b) indicated that clients in the cognitive-behavioral condition showed greater improvement on alcohol use, although the other two conditions experienced greater implementation difficulties (Ridgely & Jerrell, 1996).

Recently, three long-term, uncontrolled studies of integrated treatment have indicated positive outcomes on substance abuse. Durell et al. (1993) followed 84 patients with severe mental illness in intensive case management for 18 months or longer. Among the 51% ($N = 43$) who were also substance abusers, two thirds showed reduced substance abuse at follow-up. Drake, McHugo, and Noordsy (1993) followed 18 schizophrenic patients with alcoholism for 4 years in an integrated outpatient dual diagnosis program in which assertive case management assured linking the patients with substance abuse treatments. After 4 years, 11 (61%) were stably nonabusing according to self-report, clinical records, and clinician ratings. In a 7-year follow-up study of 148 patients with severe mental disorders in Boston, Bartels, Drake, and Wallach (1995), using case-manager ratings, found that approximately 25% of those with alcohol use disorder and 35% of those with drug use disorder achieved abstinence over 7 years, while slightly higher percentages achieved remission (defined as at least 6 months of abstinence or nonproblematic use). The patients were in a system that, although not truly integrated, did have an integrated inpatient treatment unit and outpatient case managers who provided 12-step counseling and actively linked clients with traditional substance abuse treatment programs and self-help programs.

In another recently completed, long-term study in New Hampshire, 215 patients with major mental illness (schizophrenia, schizoaffective disorder, or bipolar disorder) plus substance use disorder were assigned to two forms of integrated treatment: intensive case-management teams with clinician-client ratios of 1:10, or regular case-management teams with ratios of 1:30. Both programs provided integrated mental health and substance abuse treatments. Clients were followed for 3 years. Results have not been analyzed by treatment condition, but initial results indicate several findings for the overall study group (Mueser, Drake & Miles, 1997). Hospitalization was reduced dramatically during the first 6 months of the study; global improvements in functional status were continuous throughout the 3 years; most of the clients moved steadily through the motivational stages of substance abuse treatment (engagement, persuasion, active treatment, and relapse prevention); and nearly half of the dually diagnosed clients attained some degree of abstinence by the end of 3 years. Moreover, these optimistic findings regarding outcomes were based on multimodal assessments of substance use.

Despite the lack of controlled studies, the weight of the evidence from the studies in hand is quite positive. The research to date indicates that dually diagnosed patients, despite their adjustment difficulties in the community, can be engaged in regular outpatient services and stabilized with minimal reliance on hospitalization. Furthermore, these patients can be induced to participate in substance abuse treatment programs that are tailored for co-occurring disorders and appropriate for their motivational stage. Finally, the long-term follow-up data indicate that recovery from substance abuse is possible and that such changes are associated with improvements in other outcome domains. Integrated treatment seems to be a promising means of reducing substance abuse and its associated negative outcomes in dually diagnosed patients.

### POLICY IMPLICATIONS

Although further research is needed, longitudinal data on dual disorders suggest that integrated treatment can lower hospitalization costs, reduce or eliminate substance use, and lead to other improvements in quality of life. Unfortunately, financing and administrative policies do not always support long-term, integrated treatment. Separate administration of substance abuse and mental health programs contributes to treatment fragmentation and may decrease the likelihood that substance use disorders will be detected, thus delaying recovery and increasing costs. Current financing and payment mechanisms often lead providers to focus on short-term horizons or offer subtle incentives for them to exclude people with dual disorders from treatment (Ridgely et al., 1990; Mercer-McFadden, 1998).

For the majority or people with dual disorders, substance abuse problems improve only very slowly without focused long-term treatment. Recognition of substance-use problems is the first step toward appropriate intervention. Because dual disorders are associated with higher treatment costs, early detection may reduce expenditures significantly over time. Separate organizational structures and funding streams for treating substance abuse and mental illness, deficiencies in clinical training, and unreliable assessment methods all contribute to low rates of detection. Administrative leadership at federal, state, and local levels is needed to ensure that mental health providers do not dismiss substance abuse as someone else's problem and that substance abuse providers do not do the same with people who have severe mental disorders. Many clinicians need additional training in the special problems of dual disorders and in the most up-to-date methods for assessing substance use or abuse disorders. Finally, the assessment methods that are used currently need to be made more reliable and easier to apply (Drake, Mueser & McHugo, 1995).

Methods of paying for treatment of mental illness and substance use disorders are often designed for acute problems and do not support long-term treatment. Limits on outpatient visits or yearly expenditures tend to discourage the type of motivational interventions that are necessary for many people, and capitated payment systems may cause providers to restrict access to more expensive treatment. Effective treatment may require new payment models, such as multi-year capitated contracts, that encourage providers to take a longitudinal view of treatment. Strengthening the long-term commitment to clients also requires that primary responsibility for engaging, motivating, and maintaining clients in treatment be assigned clearly to a particular provider or agency.

With increased efforts to control costs has also come a heightened concern for the outcomes of treatment. Greater emphasis on the results rather than the amount of treatment holds promise for eliminating ineffective treatments and for encouraging better ones. However, if payers emphasize only short-term outcomes, providers may be discouraged from investing the time needed to engage and motivate clients who are not prepared to begin immediately a course of abstinence-oriented treatment.

Because people with dual disorders tend to be associated with higher treatment and societal costs, it is particularly important that policy makers consider how financing and organizational reform will affect their treatment outcomes in a realistically long-term time frame. Unfortunately, a lack of relevant research on the longitudinal course of illness reduces most policy discussions about dual disorders to speculation. Current attempts to control public spending for health care could prove detrimental to people with co-occurring severe mental illness and substance use disorders, particularly if emerging data on the long-term benefits of integrated treatment are not considered, However, if policy makers take a longer view, reform efforts offer hope for significantly improving a treatment system that has not served people with dual disorders well in the past.

### CONCLUSIONS

Ten years ago, the only treatment options available for people with co-occurring substance abuse and severe mental illness were parallel treatments in separate programs. These efforts were often uncoordinated and ineffective, leading to pessimism regarding outcomes for patients with dual disorders. Over the past 10 years, programs that integrate substance abuse and mental health treatments have been rapidly emerging. Initial evidence indicates that integrated treatments, if consistently applied over several years, are quite effective. Clients in integrated treatment programs achieve remission or recovery substance abuse at a more rapid rate than would be otherwise expected and experience improvements in other outcome domains correlated with substance abuse, such as residential stability. Public policy changes must encourage providers to assume longitudinal responsibility for these highly vulnerable clients.

## REFERENCES

Bachrach, L. L. (1982). Young adult chronic patients: An analytical review of the literature. *Hospital and Community Psychiatry, 33,* 189–197.

Bartels, S. J., Drake, R. E., & Wallach, M. A. (1995). Long-term course of substance use disorders among patients with severe mental illness, *Psychiatric Services, 46,* 248–251.

Bartels, S. J., Teague, G. B., Drake, R. E., Clark, R. E., Bush, P., & Noordsy, D. L. (1993). Substance abuse in schizophrenia: Service utilization and costs. *Journal of Nervous and Mental Disease, 181,* 227–232.

Belcher, J. R. (1989). On becoming homeless: A study of chronically mentally ill persons. *Journal of Community Psychology, 17,* 173–185.

Bond, G. R., McDonel, E. C., Miller, L. D. & Pensec, M. (1991). Assertive community treatment and reference groups: An evaluation of their effectiveness for young adults with serious mental illness and substance abuse problems. *Psychosocial Rehabilitation Journal, 15*(2), 31–43.

Carey, K. (1996). Substance use reduction in the context of outpatient psychiatric treatment: A collaborative, motivational, harm reduction approach. *Community Mental Health Journal, 32*(3), 291-306.

Caton, C. L. M., Wyatt, R. J., Felix, A., Grunberg, J., & Dominguez, B. (1993). Follow-up of chronically homeless mentally ill men. *American Journal of Psychiatry, 150,* 1639–1642.

Center for Mental Health Services (1994). *Making a difference: Interim status report of the McKinney Research Demonstration Program for Homeless Mentally Ill Adults.* Rockville, MD: Substance Abuse and Mental Health Services Administration, U.S. Department of Health and Human Services.

Chen, K., & Kandel, D. B. (1995). The natural history of drug use from adolescence to the mid-thirties in a general population sample. *American Journal of Public Health, 85,* 41–47.

Crowley, T. J., Chesiuk, D., Dilts, S., & Hart, R. (1974). Drug and alcohol abuse among psychiatric admissions. *Archives of General Psychiatry, 30,* 13–20.

Cuffel, B. J., & Chase, P. (1994). Remission and relapse of substance use disorders in schizophrenia: Results from a one year prospective study. *Journal of Nervous and Mental Disease, 182,* 342–348.

Drake, R. F., Alterman, A. I., & Rosenberg, S. R. (1993). Detection of substance use disorders in severely mentally ill patients. *Community Mental Health Journal, 29,* 175–192.

Drake, R. E., Bartels, S. J., Teague, G. B., Noordsy, D. L., & Clark, R. E. (1993). Treatment of substance abuse in severely mentally ill patients. *Journal of Nervous and Mental Disease, 181,* 606–611.

Drake, R. E., Bebout, R. R., Quimby, E., Teague, G. B., Harris, M., & Roach, J. P. (1993). Process evaluation in the Washington, D.C., dual diagnosis study. *Alcoholism Treatment Quarterly, 10,* 113–124.

Drake, R. E., & Becker, D. R. (1995). *The course of substance use among dually diagnosed patients participating in supported employment program.* Unpublished paper.

Drake, R. E., McHugo, G. J., & Noordsy, D. L. (1993). Treatment of alcoholism among schizophrenic outpatients: 4-year outcomes. *American Journal of Psychiatry, 150,* 328–329.

Drake, R. E., Mercer-McFadden, C., Mueser, K. T., McHugo, G. J., & Bond, G. R. (1995). *A review of outcome studies on integrated dual diagnosis treatment.* Paper presented at the NIMH conference on Improving Collaboration Between Mental Health and Criminal Justice Systems in Community Care for Persons with Severe Mental Illness. Albuquerque, New Mexico.

Drake, R. E., Mueser, K. T., & McHugo, G. J. (1995). Using clinician rating scales to assess substance use among persons with severe mental illness. In L. I. Sederer & B. Dickey (Eds.), *Outcomes assessment in clinical practice* (pp. 113-116). Baltimore: Williams & Wilkins.

Drake, R. E., & Noordsy, D. L. (1994). Case management for people with coexisting severe mental disorder and substance use disorder. *Psychiatric Annals, 24,* 427–431.

Drake, R. E., Osher, F. C., & Wallach, M. A. (1989). Alcohol use and abuse in schizophrenia: A prospective community study. *Journal of Nervous and Mental Disease, 177,* 408–414.

Drake, R, E., Teague, G. B., & Warren, R. S. (1990). New Hampshire's dual diagnosis program for people with severe mental illness and substance abuse. *Addiction Recovery, 10,* 35–39.

Drake, R. E., & Wallach, M. A. (1989). Substance abuse among the chronic mentally ill. *Hospital and Community Psychiatry, 40,*1041—1046.

Drake, R. E., & Wallach, M. A. (1993). Moderate drinking among people with severe mental illness. *Hospital and Community Psychiatry, 44,* 780–782.

Durell, J., Lechtenberg, B., Corse, S., & Frances, R. J. (1993). Intensive case management of persons with chronic mental illness who abuse substances. *Hospital and Community Psychiatry, 44,* 415–416, 428.

Fariello, D., & Scheidt, S. (1989). Clinical case management of the dually diagnosed patient. *Hospital and Community Psychiatry, 40,* 1065–1067.

Galletly, C. A., Field, C. D., & Prior, M. (1993). Urine drug screening of patients admitted to a state psychiatric hospital. *Hospital and Community Psychiatry, 44,* 587–589.

Greenfield, S. F., Weiss, R. D., & Tohen, M. (1995). Substance abuse and the chronically mentally ill: A description of dual diagnosis treatment services in a psychiatric hospital. *Community Mental Health Journal, 31,* 265–277.

Hellerstein, D. J., & Meehan, B, (1987). Outpatient group therapy for schizophrenic substance abusers. *American Journal of Psychiatry, 144,* 1337–1339.

Hellerstein, D. J., Rosenthal, R. N., & Miner, C. R. (1995). A prospective study of integrated Outpatient treatment for substance-abusing schizophrenic patients. *American Journal of Addictions, 4,* 33–42.

Jerrell, J. M., & Ridgely, M. S. (1995a). Evaluating changes in symptoms and functioning of dually diagnosed clients in specialized treatment. *Psychiatric Services, 46,* 233–238.

Jerrell, J. M., & Ridgely, M. S. (1995b). Comparative effectiveness of three approaches to serving people with severe mental illness and substance abuse disorders. *Journal of Nervous and Mental Disease, 183,* 566–576.

Kline, I., Harris, M., Bebout, R. R., & Drake, R. E. (1991). Contrasting integrated and linkage models of treatment for homeless, dually diagnosed adults. In K. Minkoff & R.E. Drake (Eds.), *Dual diagnosis of major mental illness and substance disorder* (pp. 95–106). San Francisco: Jossey-Bass.

Kofoed, L., Kania, J., Walsh, T., & Atkinson, R. M. (1986). Outpatient treatment of patients with substance abuse and coexisting psychiatric disorders. *American Journal of Psychiatry, 143,* 867–872.

Lehman, A. F., & Dixon, L. (Eds.). (1995). *Double jeopardy: Chronic mental illness and substance abuse.* New York: Harwood Academic Publishers.

Lehman, A. F., Herron, J. D., Schwartz, R. P., & Myers, C. P. (1993). Rehabilitation for adults with severe mental illness and substance use disorders: A clinical trial. *Journal of Nervous and Mental Disease, 181,* 86–90.

Linszen, D. H., Dingemans, P. M., & Lenior, M. E. (1994). Cannabis abuse and the course of recent-onset schizophrenic disorders. *Archives of General Psychiatry, 51,* 273–279.

McHugo, G. J., Drake, R. E., Burton, H. L., & Ackerson, T. M. (1995). A scale for assessing the stage of substance abuse treatment in persons with severe mental illness. *Journal of Nervous and Mental Disease, 183,* 762–767.

Mercer-McFadden, C., & Drake, R. E. (1995). *A review of 13 NIMH demonstration projects for young adults with severe mental illness and substance abuse problems.* Rockville, MD: Community Support Program, Center for Mental Health Services, US Department of Health and Human Services.

Mercer-McFadden, C., Drake, R.E., Clark, R.E., Verven, N., Noordsy, D.L., & Fox, T.S. (1998). *Substance abuse treatment for people with severe mental disorders: A program manager's guide.* Concord, NH: New Hampshire-Dartmouth Psychiatric Research Center.

Miller, N. S. (Ed.). (1994). *Treating coexisting psychiatric and addictive disorders.* Center City, MN: Hazelden.

Minkoff, K. (1989). An integrated treatment model for dual diagnosis of psychosis and addiction. *Hospital and Community Psychiatry, 40,* 1031–1036.

Minkoff, K., & Drake, R. E. (Eds.). (1991). *Dual diagnosis of major mental illness and substance use disorder.* San Francisco: Jossey-Bass.

Morse, G. A., Calsyn, R. J., Allen, G., Tempelhoff, B., & Smith, R. (1992). Experimental comparison of the effects of three treatment programs for homeless mentally ill people. *Hospital and Community Psychiatry, 43,* 1005–1010.

Mueser, K. T., Bellack, A. S., & Blanchard, J. J. (1992). Comorbidity of schizophrenia and substance abuse: Implications for treatment. *Journal of Consulting and Clinical Psychology, 60,* 845–856.

Mueser, K. T., Drake, R. E., & Miles, K. M. (1997). The course and treatment of substance use disorder in persons with severe mental illnesses. National Institute of Drug Abuse (NIDA). *Research Monographs, 171,* 86–109. Rockville, MD: U.S. Department of Health and Human Services.

Negrete, J. C., & Knapp, W. P. (1986). The effects of cannabis use on the clinical conditions of schizophrenics. In L.S. Harris (Ed.), *Problems of drug dependence.* Rockville, MD: National Institute on Drug Abuse.

Noordsy, D. L., & Fox, L. (1991). Group intervention techniques for people with dual disorders. *Psychosocial Rehabilitation Journal, 15,* 67–78.

Noordsy, D. L., Schwab, B., Fox, L., & Drake, R. E. (1996). The role of self-help programs in the rehabilitation of persons with severe mental disorders and substance use disorders. *Community Mental Health Journal, 32,* 71–86.

Okin, R. L., Borus, J. F., Baer, L., & Jones, A. L. (1995). Long-term outcome of state hospital patients discharged into structured community residential settings. *Psychiatric Services, 46,* 73–78.

Osher, F. C., & Drake, R. E. (1996). Reversing a history of unmet needs: Approaches to care for persons with co-occurring addictive and mental disorders. *American Journal of Orthopsychiatry, 66,* 4–11.

Osher, F. C., Drake, R. E., Noordsy, D. L., Teague, G. B., Hurlbut, S. C., Biesanz, J. C., & Beaudett, M. S. (1994). Correlates and outcomes of alcohol use disorder among rural outpatients with schizophrenia. *Journal of Clinical Psychiatry, 55,* 109–113.

Osher, F. C., & Kofoed, L. L. (1989). Treatment of patients with psychiatric and psychoactive substance abuse disorders. *Hospital and Community Psychiatry, 40,* 1025–1030.

Pepper, B., Kirshner, M. C., & Ryglewicz, H. (1981). The young adult chronic patient: Overview of a population. *Hospital and Community Psychiatry, 32,* 463–467.

Ridgely, M. S., Goldman, H. H., & Willenbring, M. (1990). Barriers to the care of persons with dual diagnoses: Organizational and financing issues. *Schizophrenia Bulletin, 16,* 123–132.

Ridgely, M. S., & Jerrell, J. M. (1996). Analysis of three interventions for substance abuse treatment of severely mentally ill people. *Community Mental Health Journal, 32*(6), 561–572.

Ridgely, M. S., Osher, F. C., Goldman, H. H., & Talbott, J. A. (1987). *Executive summary—Chronic mentally ill young adults with substance abuse problems: A review of research, treatment, and training issues.* Baltimore, MD: Mental Health Services Research Center, University of Maryland School of Medicine.

Rosenthal, R. N., Hellerstein, D. J., & Miner, C. R. (1992). A model of integrated services for outpatient treatment of patients with comorbid schizophrenia and addictive disorders. *American Journal of Addictions, 1,* 1–10.

Shaner, A., Khalsa, E., Roberts, L., Wilkins, J., Anglin, D., & Hsieh, S. (1993). Unrecognized cocaine use among schizophrenic patients. *American Journal of Psychiatry, 150,* 758–762.

Stone, A. M., Greenstein, R. A., Gamble, G., & McLellan, A. T. (1993). Cocaine use by schizophrenic outpatients who receive depot neuroleptic medication. *Hospital and Community Psychiatry, 44,* 176–177.

Teague, G. B., Schwab, B., & Drake, R. E. (1990). *Evaluating programs for young adults with severe mental illness and substance abuse.* Arlington, VA: National Association for State Mental Health Program Directors.

Vaillant, G. E. (1983). *Natural history of alcoholism.* Cambridge, MA: Harvard University Press.

Vaillant, G. E. (1988). What can long-term follow-up teach us about relapse and prevention of relapse in addiction? *British Journal of Addiction, 83,* 1147–1157.

Wolfe, H. L., & Sorensen, J. L. (1989). Dual diagnosis patients in the urban psychiatric emergency room. *Journal of Psychoactive Drugs, 21,* 169–175.

Ziedonis, D. M., & Fisher, W. (1994). Assessment and treatment of comorbid substance abuse in individuals with schizophrenia. *Psychiatric Annals, 24,* 477–483.

Zisook, S., Heaton, R., Mornaville, J., Kuck, J., Jernigan, T., & Braff, D. (1992). Past substance abuse and clinical course of schizophrenia. *American Journal of Psychiatry, 149,* 552–553.

Zweben, J. A., & Smith, D. E. (1989). Considerations in using psychotropic medication with dual diagnosis patients in recovery. *Journal of Psychoactive Drugs, 21,* 221–228.

# Empirical Correction of Seven Myths about Schizophrenia with Implications for Treatment

*Courtenay M. Harding and James H. Zahniser*

At the time of original publication, Courtenay M. Harding, PhD, was with the Western Interstate Commission for Higher Education, Mental Health program and the School of Medicine, University of Colorado; and James H. Zahniser, PhD, was with the Mental Health Corporation of Denver.

This article originally appeared in *Acta Psychiatrica Scandanavica*, 1994, 90 (suppl 384), 140–146 and is reprinted with permission.

**Abstract:** This paper presents empirical evidence accumulated across the last 2 decades to challenge seven long-held myths in psychiatry about schizophrenia which impinge upon the perception and thus the treatment of patients. Such myths have been perpetuated across generations of trainees in each of the mental health disciplines. These myths limit the scope and effectiveness of treatments offered. These myths maintain the pessimism about outcome for these patients thus significantly reducing their opportunities for improvement and/or recovery. Counter evidence is provided with implications for new treatment strategies.

There are at least seven prevalent myths about schizophrenia that often discourage clinicians and significantly impact the perception, and thus the treatment, of patients. All of these myths have been challenged by research data, yet they persist in training and practice across mental health disciplines. This paper endeavors to contribute a more balanced and contemporary view of the person with schizophrenia in order to reenergize clinicians and revitalize treatment approaches.

### Myth: Once a schizophrenic always a schizophrenic.

### Reality: There is ever widening heterogeneity of outcome across time.

Kraepelin (1902) initiated the myth by categorically splitting mental illness into either good outcome (manic depression) or poor outcome (*dementia praecox*). Diagnosis was verified or invalidated by the outcome. Even Eugen Bleuler (1908), who was originally more optimistic about the outcome of schizophrenia, later decided that there was never "full *restitutio ad integrum*." Harding and associates (1987, 1992) explained that these two pivotal investigators suffered from "the clinician's illusion" (Cohen & Cohen, 1984). The "illusion" occurs when clinicians repeatedly see the few most severely ill in their caseloads as "typical" when, in fact, such patients represent a small proportion of the actual possible spectrum. The Scandinavians have generally held a broader view as evidenced by their use of the category "reactive psychosis" (Angst, 1986). However, even in Scandinavia, pessimism has remained about patients who were unable to fit these criteria or patients who fit these criteria, but failed to improve quickly.

*Evidence.* Recent worldwide studies have investigated the assumption of downward course and all have found wide heterogeneity in the very long-term outcome (over 2 decades) for schizophrenia, despite differences in diagnostic criteria used (Ciompi & Muller, 1976; Huber, Gross & Schuttler, 1979; Tsuang, Woolson & Fleming, 1979; Bleuler, 1978; Harding et al., 1987a; Harding et al., 1987b; DeSisto et al., 1995a; Desisto et al., 1995b). The European studies have often been dismissed in the U.S. because of the perception that their criteria were not equivalent and because of sheer ethnocentricity. However, notwithstanding the criticisms of diagnostic differences (valid or not), all of these studies have come to the same conclusions. The longer investigators followed an identified intact cohort (whether probands were in or out of treatment), the more pronounced the picture of increasing heterogeneity and improvement in function. These studies have consistently found that one half to two thirds of patients significantly improved or recovered, including some cohorts of very chronic cases. The universal criteria for recovery have been defined as no current signs and symptoms of any mental illness, no current medications, working, relating well to family and friends, integrated into the community, and behaving in such a way as to not being able to detect having ever been hospitalized for any kind of psychiatric problems. All of these investigators of long-term studies were trained in the older, more pessimistic conceptual models and were surprised by their own findings. Because the myths had been repeated so often, they had become reified. The strong belief systems and resistance, encountered by these investigators, were caused by many factors and were not easily altered by one study (Harding, Zubin & Strauss, 1987; Harding, Zubin & Strauss, 1992). However, there is now a confluence of results.

*Suggested treatment strategies.* Slowly, these investigators have all persisted. The beliefs about course and outcome are changing. Clinical practices and programs are being restructured (Test & Stein, 1978; Rotelli & Dell'Aqua, 1991; Liberman, Mueser & Wallace, 1986; Ciompi, 1980; Mosher & Burti, 1989). The mental health disciplines are getting the message. Given the evidence, it is suggested that treatment programs be constructed "as if" everyone will turn the corner toward significant improvement and/or recovery. This suggestion is made because the state of the art does not permit clinicians to triage patients on the basis of prognostic factors. In schizophrenia, particularly the multiple episodic types, the display of early symptom severity and dysfunction in illness trajectories may persist for many years. Then, as the illness lifts, the patient's energy returns, thinking clears, coping strategies for stressors improves, and he or she inches the way toward improvement in both function and symptom reduction. This is the opposite picture of a relentless downhill course for most patients as described by Kraepelin. This long process of recovery implies a revision of what the clinician tells patients and their families about prognosis ("You have a very serious illness which takes some time to work itself through. However, worldwide data shows that more than 50% of patients significantly improve or even recover. We will be there to walk with you on this journey toward recovery"). This new message keeps a small spark of hope alive. Hope promotes the self-healing capacity inherent in any recovery process for any illness (Cousins, 1979; Siegel, 1986; Herth, 1990). Treatment also means a cohesive, comprehensive biopsychosocial approach to the whole person (Moyers, 1993; Engel, 1980), and a collaborative effort between the patient, the family, the clinical team, other community agencies, and natural networks. Treatment means celebrating the small moves forward, and learning from the steps backward, in a manner which does not blame the patient, the team, or the family. Treatment means environmental engineering to reduce the stressors. Important to remember is the need to re-evaluate repeatedly because the same structured environment that enables a patient to organize a disorganized brain can become psychotegenic later when a now organized brain faces a much too organized environment (Strauss et al., 1985).

**Myth: A schizophrenic is a schizophrenic is a schizophrenic.**

**Reality: There is wide individual heterogeneity within the diagnostic category.**

Paraphrasing "Rose is a rose is a rose" (Stein, 1934), there is a tendency in the field to lump everyone with the same diagnosis together for treatment and research.

*Evidence.* In reality, every group of patients has substantial heterogeneity. In addition to the major impact of gender (Seeman & Lang, 1990), there are considerable differences in age, developmental tasks, education levels, job histories, symptom presentation, coping skills and other personality strengths and weaknesses, meaning systems, and response to stress in general and to stress of particular situations (Harding et al., 1987). Further, it should be noted that the field has forgotten the heterogeneity of schizophrenia, itself. When E. Bleuler renamed *dementia praecox,* he called it "the group of schizophrenia" (Bleuler, 1911). Recently, Kendler (1986) has developed several models of genetic-environmental interaction and weighting in the etiology of schizophrenia. His models make a great deal of sense given the wide heterogeneity of our patients.

*Suggested treatment strategies.* The heterogeneity, described previously, requires a comprehensive, biopsychosocial assessment of each patient's unique status, the place in his or her own course trajectory, and ecological niche. Individual differences require individualized treatment planning, an appreciation of developmental achievements or strivings, and a recognition of the "person behind the disorder" (Bleuler, 1978). In order for clinicians to achieve this level of understanding, they must consider the task as a genuinely collaborative enterprise with both the patient and others who know him or her well. Continued assessment of changing, ongoing status is especially important after years of severe psychopathology and dysfunction, given the longitudinal nature of these disorders. The use of "timeliness"or "life charts" is recommended in this endeavor by collecting data in a chronological comprehensive life history, as well for setting a collaborative tone for treatment (Vaillant, 1980; Meyer, 1951). Attention to individual differences, life histories, and developmental steps, will encourage patients to perceive themselves, not as "schizophrenics," but rather as people, who happen to have schizophrenia. Consumers repeatedly note that this recognition of their "personhood" plays a critical role in their recovery and re-acquisition of their sense of well being (Campbell & Schraiber, 1989; Lovejoy, 1982).

### Myth: Rehabilitation can be provided only after stabilization.

### Reality: Rehabilitation should begin on day one.

This myth has been deeply embedded within a narrow but popular version of the medical model. "Real treatment" in today's managed care climate consists of assessment, diagnosis, and medication. Anything else, such as rehabilitation, must wait until stabilization and is often considered to be an ancillary service. But stabilization usually leads just to "maintenance" and not to rehabilitation.

*Evidence.* "Real treatment" has been only modestly successful in reducing symptoms, and in helping the patient by increasing the levels of functioning in self care, work, interpersonal relationships, and integration back to the community. However, there is a burgeoning field of psychiatric rehabilitation that combines with medical treatments to significantly improve the patient's level of functioning (Adler, 1981; Anthony, Cohen & Cohen, 1983). The problem has been a paucity of integrated models proposed to incorporate all of these facets of care. The notable exceptions have been Engel's "biopsychosocial model" (Engel, 1980) and Adler and associates' paper (Adler, 1981) which set forth an expanded medical model as a task for psychiatry. Adler's model delineates the tasks for psychiatry to be legal, societal-rehabilitative, educative-developmental, as well as medical. Anthony (Anthony, Cohen & Cohen, 1983) has proposed a rehabilitation model but left out most of the illness factors.

*Suggested treatment strategies.* Rehabilitation is accruing an honored place in the treatment of patients as a key modality in partnership with psychopharmacology. Skill building (e.g., how to manage one's symptoms, managing one's medication, learning how to manage a budget, acquiring a job skill, conducting social conversation), all raise a patient's self-esteem and lower symptoms. Anything that lowers symptoms and improves function deserves to be called and reimbursed as "treatment" (Liberman, Mueser & Wallace, 1986; Anthony, Cohen & Cohen, 1983; Breier & Strauss, 1983; Diamond, 1984).

**Myth: Why bother with psychotherapy for schizophrenia?**

**Reality: Supportive psychotherapy is crucial for integrating the experience and enhancing continued adult development.**

Research findings, regarding the ineffectiveness of psychotherapy in curing schizophrenia, have led to widespread discouragement in this area and to a relative lack of innovation and research. Heinrichs (1986) concluded from his review that "the kindest interpretation of controlled studies to date is that the benefit of psychotherapy with schizophrenia has not yet been demonstrated." However, instead of abandoning psychotherapy altogether, the challenge is for clinicians to use psychotherapy appropriately for maximum benefit.

*Evidence.* Two main lines of evidence support the judicious use of psychotherapy. First, surveys and personal accounts of consumers have indicated that they value psychotherapy and find it to be beneficial in various ways (Coursey, Keller & Farrell, 1995; Legatt, 1986; Ruocchio, 1989; Coursey, Farrell & Zahniser, 1991). Second, several different types of psychosocial interventions have demonstrated positive impact on the lives of persons with schizophrenia including family interventions (see below), group therapies tailored to the needs of persons with schizophrenia (Kanas, 1986; Kanas, 1991), and very specific, targeted cognitive remediation (Chadwick & Lowe, 1990; Green, 1993).

*Suggested treatment strategies.* To accept that psychotherapy cannot help persons with schizophrenia reinforces the dangerous and erroneous message that such persons are separate, distinct, and deficient relative to others. On the other hand, a realistic and appropriate approach to the use of psychotherapy in the overall treatment plan can facilitate patients' recovery by integrating their experiences of a life interrupted by severe illness and by helping them learn coping strategies. Coursey (1989) clarified the basis of a sound psychotherapy for persons suffering from schizophrenia: 1) psychotherapy should not be seen as competing with medication but, rather, as complementary to it; 2) psychotherapy can and should address the personal, human issues raised by having a serious mental illness; 3) psychotherapy must be practical, thus making use of educational as well as experiential approaches to help individuals learn to manage the disorder; and 4) psychotherapy should address the "normal problems of living that people with schizophrenia have to deal with just as anyone else does" (p. 351).

Neligh and Kinzie (1983) have identified ten practical approaches to accomplish the goals mentioned above. These authors suggest the following: 1) accepting the current level of functioning without pressure to change, 2) determining the appropriate frequency of contact for each patient, 3) selecting a comfortable style of relating, 4) modeling desirable social attitudes, 5) facilitating problem-solving skills, 6) providing a safe place for patients to express emotions, 7) managing dependence, 8) effecting changes in the patient's environment, 9) setting limits and discussing consequences of actions, as well as, 10) establishing rules for confidentiality and the need to share information across systems of care. These authors propose a respectful, humane approach that emphasizes positive social behaviors, upbeat emotional tone, the provision of advice, information sharing, compliments, jokes, and companionship, as well as sharing in the triumphs and tragedies of life. Such supportive psychotherapy may increase self-esteem, facilitate awareness of limitations, avoid deterioration and/or hospitalization, prevent undue dependence, and improve levels of function.

### Myth: Patients must be on medication all their lives.

### Reality: It may be a small percentage who need medication indefinitely.

This myth has been generated by physicians for a wide variety of reasons. First, it is an attempt to underscore the importance of taking medication in a power struggle with the patient. Secondly, if a physician believes in Myth #1 "once a schizophrenic always a schizophrenic" or its corollary "once a broken brain always a broken brain," then the physician believes that medication is the key to maintenance of lifelong stabilization.

*Evidence.* There are no data existing which support this myth. When analyzing the results from the long term studies, it was clear that a surprising number (at least 25–50%), were completely off their medications, suffered no further signs and symptoms of schizophrenia, and were functioning well. Over time, most patients altered their dosages and schedules. These behaviors often resulted in relapses early on in their illness trajectories when the illness was raging. The physicians in charge often felt justified and the patients felt defeated. Part of the trouble lay in human nature since there is usually only a 40 to 50%, compliance rate for any kind of prescription taking in the U.S. by any kind of patient (Diamond, 1984). Other problems involved: 1) the patient's lack of understanding about having an illness, 2) becoming disoriented enough not to manage taking medication, 3) the lack of clear knowledge about the reasons for and the skills needed in taking medication, 4) the frequent increase of covert and overt side effects that are unpleasant or undesirable (e.g., dyskinesia, dystonia akinesia, akathisia, obesity, impotence, dry mouth, weight gain), and 5) the lack of engineering to reduce environmental stressors. Such high stressors have been shown to increase relapse rates in some patients even if medicated intramuscularly. However, even though patients experimented with their medications and learned to use them more regularly, the long-term studies found that more subjects than not eventually discovered through trial, error, and time, that they were able to function without medication later on in their illness trajectories.

*Suggested treatment strategies.* Most successful approaches involve the following: a strong patient-physician collaboration (Neligh & Kinzie, 1983), targeted psychoeducational and skill-building strategies aimed at prodromal and chronic symptom recognition and medication management (Liberman, Mueser & Wallace, 1986), as well as built-in re-assessment strategies and standardized side effects monitoring techniques (Neligh & Kinzie, 1983).

**Myth:  People with schizophrenia cannot do anything except low-level jobs.**

**Reality:  People with schizophrenia can and do perform at every level of work.**

The idea that persons with schizophrenia are unable to work or can only achieve a low level of function because of their illness has had long standing credence especially in the United States. Anthony and associates (1984) reported in their review of the literature that only 10 to 30% of patients worked full time throughout a year or at follow-up. This finding has reinforced this perception.

*Evidence.* The early vocational approach consisted primarily of sheltered workshops designed originally for the developmentally disabled (Ciardello, 1981). Until recently, little thought was given about whether or not these workshops were appropriate settings for these patients or for those with serious mental illnesses. In addition, there has been minimal appreciation about the power of stigma, the low priority in the vocational rehabilitation ladder, distinct systems problems at the interface (such as rigidity, isolation, compensatory ad hoc operations, and narrow frames of reference [Harding et al., 1987; Anthony et al., 1984]). However, in their 1974 follow-up study, Strauss and Carpenter (1974) found that symptoms and levels of functioning, such as work, were only loosely related to one another in an "open-linked" fashion. The Vermont Longitudinal Research Project (Harding et al., 1987) also found that, in their "improved but not recovered group," wide heterogeneity existed within the same person with some cohort members working well despite ongoing and persistent hallucinations and/or delusions. These patients had learned not to tell anyone because it "upset"others. For other patients work became the primary treatment strategy to reduce symptomatology (Strauss et al., 1985; Breier & Strauss, 1983; McCrory, 1988).

Across time, clinicians have appreciated the interactive therapeutic effects of work on illness (e.g. Galen [172 AD] "Employment is nature's best physician and is essential to human happiness"[see Strauss, 1968, p. 663 ]). Harding, Strauss, Hafez, and Lieberman (1987) discovered that "despite this basic understanding of human functioning, the integration of work into systems that treat severe mental illness is limited, sporadic, and inadequately addressed" (p. 317). When a rehabilitation program has a strong emphasis and a cohesive approach for clients, the long-term trajectory is significantly enhanced and the work histories greatly altered (Harding et al., 1987; Desisto et al., 1995b).

*Suggested treatment strategies.* At the current time, vocational and other forms of rehabilitation are accomplished by "persistent, energetic personnel inventing ingenious solutions to the roadblocks set up at the system interfaces" (Harding et al., 1987). To treat the patient first means to "treat" the system of care in order to encourage flexibility, collaboration, databased training, and a unified theoretical framework. Other approaches have been laid out such as the vocational strategies of "choose-get-keep" job model from the Boston group headed by Anthony and associates (1984). They formulate a rehabilitation diagnosis, develop a rehabilitation plan (which incorporates resources available and needed), and devise individually constructed interventions. This collaboration involves career counseling, skills training, placement, and work training to keep the job once the person has one (such as getting to work on time and dressing neatly and maintaining appropriate social interaction [Anthony et al., 1984]).

### Myth: Families are the etiological agents.

### Reality: Families as collaborators can provide critical information and provide environments to lower a relative's vulnerability to episodes.

The myth, that families cause schizophrenia, flourished prior to the most recent biological revolution in psychiatry. Proponents of this myth targeted the family's severe dysfunctions, especially in the area of communication, as the cause of schizophrenia. For example, after observing communication difficulties in persons with schizophrenia, many theorists (Bateson et al., 1956; Lidz, 1973; Wynne & Zinger, 1977) reasoned that the dysfunctions were learned through interaction with disturbed family members. Although many investigators have since discarded this myth, it has survived even in the current biological era, such that numbers of clinicians and academics, who train students in the different mental health disciplines, still believe it (Lefley, 1992).

*Evidence.* Although family researchers have demonstrated that the emotional and interactional climate of families can help precipitate relapses in their relatives (Brown, Birley & Wing, 1972) as well as the efficacy of enhanced family communication in lowering vulnerability to relapse (Goldstein & Doane, 1982), they have failed to show that family factors are necessary and sufficient causes of schizophrenia (Falloon, 1988; Zubin & Spring, 1977). No evidence exists that a family's psychosocial climate, communication patterns, or parenting practices are primary causes of schizophrenia. In fact, despite the finding that vulnerable individuals from families high in expressed emotion (EE) are more likely to relapse, the majority of families are not rated high on this factor (Lefley, 1992). Many families, who are low in EE, may very well represent a biologic protective factor (Falloon, 1988). Family researchers now recognize that it is the co-occurrence of an ill individual's behaviors and the various emotional/interactional characteristics of a family's response that often precipitates symptoms. The available evidence suggests that schizophrenia is an episodic disorder which, not unlike many other episodic disorders (e.g., asthma, Crohn's Disease, arthritis), is often vulnerable to environmental stresses and triggers. Stressors, such as family environment, are now not considered to be sufficient in and of themselves to be considered etiological agents of the underlying disorder.

*Suggested treatment strategies.* The optimal roles of families in treatment, and the appropriate relationships between clinicians and families are now well established, if not widely realized. Families need, and want, education, information, coping and communication skills, emotional support, and to be treated as collaborators (Bernheim, 1982). As many authors have noted (Beels & McFarlane, 1982), scientific theories of family causation contributed to the alienation between professionals and families, as well as to the guilt and burden that families feel. For this reason, clinicians need to make a special effort to solicit the collaboration and involvement of family members. In some cases it may even be necessary to entice families into collaboration by acknowledging the difficulties they have experienced and apologizing for the way they have been treated by the mental health system. Once a relationship is established, clinician, patient, and family can work together to identify needs and appropriate interventions. Many families benefit from communication training, psychoeducation about the illness, and coping strategies. Fortunately, several effective models exist (Leff et al., 1982; Kanter, Lamb & Loeper, 1987; Huber, et al., 1980). In addition to assisting families in the acquisition of skills and knowledge, it is important for the clinician to encourage families to develop realistic, yet optimistic expectations about their relatives' chances for improvement (see previous discussion of Myth

#1), and about their own ability to contribute to the recovery process, thus helping to relieve family burden.

## CONCLUSION

This paper has reviewed seven prevailing myths about the group of schizophrenias. The authors have proposed counter evidence to each myth. Some treatment strategies were suggested to enhance the possibility of improvement and recovery through reduction of symptoms and the increase of levels of functioning for patients. It is hoped that this paper will encourage clinicians, program designers, policy makers, patients and their families to deal more effectively with these difficult and often prolonged disorders. A longitudinal perspective about schizophrenia should imbue everyone with a renewed sense of hope and optimism. After studying 508 patients across 22 years, Huber and colleagues (1980) stated that "schizophrenia does not seem to be a disease of slow, progressive deterioration. Even in the second and third decades of illness, there is still potential for full or partial recovery." All of the recent long-term follow-up investigators have recorded the same findings (Ciompi & Muller, 1976; Huber, Gross & Schuttler, 1979; Tsuang, Woolson & Fleming, 1979; Bleuler, 1978; Harding et al., 1987a; Harding et al., 1987b; DeSisto et al., 1995a; Desisto et. al., 1995b).

## REFERENCES

Adler, D. (1981). The medical model and psychiatry's tasks. *Hospital and Community Psychiatry, 32,* 387–392.

Angst, J. (1986). European long-term followup studies of schizophrenia. *Schizophrenia Bulletin, 14*(4), 501–513.

Anthony, W.A., Howell, J. & Danley, K.S. (1984). Chapter 13. Vocational rehabilitation of the psychiatrically disabled. In M. Mirabi (Ed.), *The chronically mentally ill. Research and services,* 215–237.

Anthony, W.A., Cohen, M.R. & Cohen, B.F. (1983). The philosophy, treatment process, and principles of the psychiatric rehabilitation approach. *New Directions in Mental Health,* 67–69.

Bateson, G., Jackson, D.D., Haley, J. & Weakland, J.H. (1956). Toward a theory of schizophrenia. *Behavioral Science, 1,* 251–264.

Beels, C.C. & McFarlane, W.R. (1982). Family treatment of schizophrenia: Background and state of the art. *Hospital and Community Psychiatry, 33*(7), 541–550.

Bernheim, K.F. (1982). Supportive family counseling. *Schizophrenia Bulletin, 8,* 634–640.

Bleuler, E. (1908). Die prognose der dementia praecox (schizophrenien gruppe). *Allgemeine Zeitschrift Psychiatrie, 65,* 436.

Bleuler, E. (1911). *Dementia praecox oder die gruppe der schizophrenien.* In hrsg. von G. Aschaffenburg, Hanbuch der Psychiatrie, Leipzig, Deuticke.

Bleuler, M. (1978). *Die schizophrenen geistesstorungen im lichte langjahriger kranken— und familiengeschicten.* Stuttgart: George Thieme Verlag 1972: (New York: Intercontinental Medical Book Corp, *The schizophrenic disorders: Long-term patient and family studies.* Translated by Clemens SM. New Haven: Yale University Press.

Breier, A. & Strauss, J.S. (1983). Self-control of psychotic disorders. *Archives of General Psychiatry, 40,* 1141–1145.

Brown, G.W., Birley, J.L.T. & Wing, J.K. (1972). Influence of family life on the course of schizophrenic disorder: A replication. *British Journal of Psychiatry, 121,* 241–258.

Campbell, J. & Schraiber, R. (1989). *The well-being project: Mental health consumers speak for themselves.* Sacramento, CA: California Dept. of Mental Health.

Chadwick, P.D.J. & Lowe, C.F. (1990). Measurement and modification of delusional beliefs. *Journal of Consulting and Clinical Psychology, 58*(2), 225–232.

Ciardello, J.A. (1981). Job placement success of schizophrenic clients in sheltered workshop programs. *Vocational Evaluation and Work Adjustment Bulletin,* Fall, 125–128.

Ciompi, L. (1980). Catamnestic Long-term study on the course of life and aging of schizophrenics. *Schizophrenia Bulletin, 6,* 606–618.

Ciompi, L. & Müller, C. (1976). *Lebensweg und alter der scizophrenenen: Eine katamnestische lonzeitstudies bis ins senium.* Berlin: Springer Verlag.

Cohen, P. & Cohen, J. (1984). The clinicians illusion. *Archives of General Psychiatry, 41,* 1178–1182.

Coursey, R.D., Keller, A.B. & Farrell, E.W. (1995). Individual psychotherapy and persons with serious mental illness: The client's perspective. *Schizophrenia Bulletin, 21*(2), 283–301.

Coursey, R.D., Farrell, E.W. & Zahniser, J.H. (1991). Consumers attitudes toward psychotherapy, hospitalization. and aftercare. *Health and Social Work, 16*(3), 155–161.

Coursey, R.D. (1989). Psychotherapy with persons suffering from schizophrenia. *Schizophrenia Bulletin, 15,* 349–353.

Cousins, N. (1979). *Anatomy of an illness as perceived by the patient: Reflections on healing and regeneration.* New York, Norton.

Desisto, M.J., Harding, C.M., McCormick R.V., Ashikaga, T. & Gautum, S. (1995a). The Maine-Vermont three decades studies of serious mental illness: Matched comparison of cross-sectional outcome. *British Journal of Psychiatry, 167,* 331–338.

Desisto, M.J., Harding, C.M., McCormick R.V., Ashikaga, T. & Gautum, S. (1995b). The Maine-Vermont three decades studies of serious mental illness: Longitudinal course of comparisons. *British Journal of Psychiatry, 167,* 338–342.

Diamond, R.J. (1984). Increasing medication compliance n young adult chronic psychiatric patients. *New Directions in Mental Health Services, 21,* 59–69.

Engel, G. (1980). The clinical application of the biopsychosocial model. *American Journal of Psychiatry, 137*, 535–544.

Falloon, I.R.H. (1988). Prevention of morbidity in schizophrenia. In I.R.H. Falloon (Ed.), *Handbook of behavioral family therapy.* New York: Guilford.

Falloon, I.R.H., Boyd, J.L. & McGill, C.W. (1985). *Family management of schizophrenia.* Baltimore: Johns Hopkins University Press.

Goldstein, M. & Doane, J.A. (1982). Family factors in the onset, course, and treatment of schizophrenic spectrum disorders: An update on current research. *Journal of Nervous and Mental Disability, 170,* 692–700.

Green, M.F. (1993). Cognitive remediation in schizophrenia: Is it time yet? *American Journal of Psychiatry, 150*(2), 178–187.

Harding, C.M., Zubin, J. & Straus, J.S. (1992). Chronicity in schizophrenia revisited. *British Journal of Psychiatry, 161* (Suppl. IX), 27–37.

Harding, C.M., Brooks, G.W., Ashikaga, T., Strauss, J.S. & Breier, A. (1987a). The Vermont longitudinal study of persons with severe mental illness: 1. Methodology, study sample, and overall status 32 years later. *American Journal of Psychiatry, 144* (6), 718–726.

Harding, C.M., Brooks, G.W., Ashikaga, T., Strauss, J.S. & Breier, A. (1987b). The Vermont longitudinal study II. Long-term outcome of subjects who retrospectively met DSM III criteria for schizophrenia. *American Journal of Psychiatry, 144* (6), 727–725.

Harding, C.M., Strauss, J.S., Hafez, H. & Lieberman, P. (1987). Work and mental illness: I. Toward an integration of the rehabilitation process. *Journal of Nervous and Mental Disability, 175*(6), 317–327.

Harding, C.M., Zubin, J. & Strauss, J.S. (1987). Chronicity in schizophrenia: Fact, partial fact, or artifact? *Hospital and Community Psychiatry, 38*(5), 477–486.

Heinrichs, D.W. (1986). The psychotherapy of schizophrenia. In G. D. Burrows, T. R. Norman, G. Rubenstein (Eds.), *Handbook of studies in schizophrenia—Part 2.* New York: Elsevier.

Herth, K. (1990). Fostering hope in terminally ill people. *Journal of Advanced Nursing, 15,* 1250–1259.

Huber, G., Gross, G. Schuttler, R. & Linz, M. (1980). Longitudinal studies of schizophrenic patients. *Schizophrenia Bulletin, 6,* 592–605.

Huber, G., Gross, G. & Schuttler, R. (1979). Schizophrenie: Verlaufs und sozialpsychiatrische langzeituntersuchungen an den 1945 bis 1959 in Bonn hospitalisierten schizophrenen. Kranken: *Monographien aus dem Gesametgebiete der Psychiatrie. BD 21.* Berlin Springer Verlag.

Kanas, N. (1991). Group therapy with schizophrenic patients: A short-term, homogenous approach. *International Journal of Group Psychotherapy, 41,* 33–48.

Kanas, N. (1986). Group therapy with schizophrenics. *International Journal of Group Psychotherapy, 36,* 339–351.

Kanter, J., Lamb, H.R. & Loeper, C. (1987). Expressed emotion in families: A critical review. *Hospital and Community Psychiatry, 38,* 374–380.

Kendler, K.S. & Eaves, L.J. (1986). Models for the joint effect of genotype and environment on reliability to psychiatric illness. *American Journal of Psychiatry, 143*(3), 279–89.

Krapelin. (1902). *Dementia praecox, in clinical psychiatry: A textbook for students and physicians. 6th ed.* Translated by Diefendorf AR. New York: Macmillan.

Legatt, M. (1986). Schizophrenia: The consumer's viewpoint. In G. D. Burrows, T. R. Norman, G. Rubinstein, *Handbook of studies in schizophrenia—Part 2.* New York: Elsevier.

Leff, J., Kuipers, L. Berkowitz, R. et al. (1982). A controlled trial of social intervention in the families of schizophrenic patients. *British Journal of Psychiatry, 141,* 121–134.

Lefley, H.P. (1992). Expressed emotion: Conceptual, clinical, and social policy issues. *Hospital and Community Psychiatry, 43*(6), 591–598.

Liberman, R.P., Mueser, K.T. & Wallace, C.J. (1986). Social skills training for schizophrenic individuals at risk for relapse. *American Journal of Psychiatry, 143, 523–526.*

Lidz, T. (1973). *The origin and treatment of schizophrenic disorders.* New York: Basic Books.

Lovejoy, M. (1982). Expectations and the recovery process. *Schizophrenia Bulletin, 8* (4), 605–609.

McCrory, D.J. (1988). The human dimension of the vocational rehabilitation process In M. D. Bell & J. A. Ciardello (Eds.), *Vocational rehabilitation of persons with prolonged psychiatric disorders,* p 208–218, Baltimore: Johns Hopkins University Press.

Meyer, A. (1951). The life chart and the obligation of specifying positive data in the psychopathological diagnosis. In Hoeber (1919), *Contributions to medical and biological research, Vol. 2.* Reprinted in E.E. Winters (Ed.), *The collected papers of Adolf Meyer.* Baltimore: Johns Hopkins Press.

Mosher, L.R. & Burti, L. (1989). *Community mental health: Principles and practice.* New York: W. W. Norton & Co.

Moyers, B. (1993). *Healing and the mind.* New York: Doubleday.

Neligh, G.L. & Kinzie, J.D. (1983). Therapeutic relationships with the chronic patient. In D. L. Culture (Ed.), Effective aftercare for the 1980s. *New Directions for Mental Health Services.* San Francisco: Jossey-Bass.

Rotelli, F. & Dell Aqua, G. (1991). La storia della psichiatria Triestina. *Il Lanternino, XVI* (4) Prog. 92: 1–36.

Ruocchio, P.J. (1989). How psychotherapy can help the schizophrenic patient. *Hospital and Community Psychiatry, 40,* 180–190.

Seeman, M.V. & Lang, M. (1990). The role of estrogens in schizophrenia: gender differences. *Schizophrenia Bulletin, 16*(2), 185–194.

Siegel, B. (1986). *Love, medicine, and miracles.* New York: Harper & Row.

Stein, G. (1934). *Sacred Emily in portraits in prayer.* New York: Random House.

Strauss, J.S., Hafez, H., Lieberman, P. & Harding, C.M. (1985). The course of psychiatric disorder: III. Longitudinal principles. (special article). *American Journal of Psychiatry, 142*(3), 289–296.

Strauss, J.S. & Carpenter, W.T. (1974). Characteristic symptoms and outcome in schizophrenia. *Archives of General Psychiatry, 30*(30), 429–434.

Strauss, M.B. (1968). (Ed.) *Familiar medical quotations.* Boston: Little Brown, p. 663.

Test, M.A. & Stein, L.L. (1978). Community treatment of the chronic patient: research overview. *Schizophrenia Bulletin, 4*(3), 350–364.

Tsuang, M.T., Woolson, R.F. & Fleming, J.A. (1979). Long-term outcome of major psychoses. 1: Schizophrenia and affective disorders compared with psychiatrically symptom-free surgical conditions. *Archives of General Psychiatry, 36,* 1295–1301.

Vaillant, G. (1980). Adolf Meyer was right: Dynamic psychiatry needs the life chart. *Journal of the National Association of Private Psychiatric Hospitals, 11,* 4–14.

Wynne, L.C. & Singer, M. (1977). Thought disorder and family relations. *Archives of General Psychiatry, 9,* 199–206.

Zubin, J. & Spring, B. (1977). Vulnerability—A new view of schizophrenia. *Journal of Abnormal Psychology, 86,* 103–126.

## Open Doors

*John S. Caswell*

In 2002, when working with Next Step Peer Support Center, John Caswell was honored with the Indomitable Service Award from Next Step. In 2003 he received the Outstanding Consumer Empowerment Leader Award presented by NAMI, NH. He is currently at Granite Steps Publications, W. Lebanon, NH.

This article was previously published in the *Psychiatric Rehabilitation Journal*, 2003, 27(2), and is reprinted with permission.

Hello, my name is John. I have a 17-year history of drug and alcohol abuse but gave up drugs and alcohol in 1987. I have since been diagnosed with a mental health disorder, "chronic paranoid schizophrenia." Although I had experienced a psychotic episode in 1979 and found myself on the mental health ward a number of times following my first episode, it was not until 1990 that I was diagnosed with schizophrenia, 3 years after giving up drugs and alcohol.

When an individual is diagnosed with a mental health disorder it is the whole life of the individual that has become disordered. Severe mental illness most often affects every aspect of the individual's life including but not limited to, housing, employment and finances, personal and social relationships and one's ability to carry out the daily activities necessary to take care of oneself. Having been diagnosed with a severe mental illness I was eligible to receive payments through our federal government and the Social Security Disability Insurance program because I was unable to work and support myself. Shortly after being assigned my "mental health label" I left the New England area to live with my brother and his family in Salt Lake City, Utah.

The house in Salt Lake was rather small so I slept in the camper trailer in the back yard. My brother drank alcohol and would, from time to time, invite friends into his home to party. I was trying to stay clean so most of my time was spent in the camper.

Although there was a television in the camper and I did a lot of reading, I was having very little interaction with other people. Oh, I would go into the house two or three times a day, but the people there were always the same, unless there was a party going on. It began to seem as if each day was the same as the day before. I felt what I needed was to see new faces and to interact with different people. After all, we humans are by nature, social beings.

I soon found myself going out to the bars with my brother and his friends. At first I would just drink juice and I was in fact, for a time, their designated driver. But before long I started going to the bars alone and eventually reached a point in which I thought it would be okay to drink "just one beer." As those of us who share this problem with alcohol know, one beer is too many and a dozen are not enough. Within 3 months I found that I was facing a driving while intoxicated charge.

When I went to court I told the judge that I was guilty as charged and that I should have known better than to drink and drive. I was ordered to pay a fine and to perform 40 hours of community service. I had refused to take an alcohol sensor test the night I had been arrested, therefore my license was suspended for a year. I paid the fine and performed the community service. I also attended the impaired driver education course that was required to get my license back although it would be a year before driving would be a reality for me. Then I flew home to New England.

I could not afford an apartment of my own when I first returned to New England so I moved in with two other people. One of the individuals I lived with would, from time to time, drink alcohol and although they knew of my problem, they kept it in the house. This was very hard for me. After all, although I was in the process of recovery from a 17-year history of substance abuse and had managed to stay clean for 3 years, I had recently relapsed into alcohol. As you have already read, that relapse ended in a very bad way.

Trying to give up alcohol while living with someone who drinks is not easy. It seemed as if each time I opened the refrigerator to get a glass of milk or a snack I would be confronted with the temptation of alcohol. There was also one cupboard in the apartment where I had discovered a stash of hard liquor. After learning of the stash I never opened that cupboard door again. The temptation was very hard to deal with but I somehow managed to overcome. Each time I was confronted with the temptation of alcohol I made a conscious decision and/or choice not to drink. I had finally learned where "just one drink" could lead and I had had enough. I was determined not to give in.

The mood swing of people who drink can be very unpredictable even during times when they haven't been drinking. This is rather hard to explain but can be understood by those of us who have had the personal experience of living with an individual who drinks. I never knew what type of mood the individual I was living with would be when they came through the door so I made it a point to be in my room before they came home from work. I sometimes refer to this as "self-imposed isolation" but in reality, I was isolating for reasons that at the time were beyond my control.

Another fact that needs to be considered in regard to my isolation is that I was taking the antipsychotic medication Haldol. Haldol helped with some of the symptoms of my mental illness (schizophrenia); however, I always felt a little "disconnected," "out of sorts," and "paranoid" while taking it. Therefore, I didn't like to be around other people. I was afraid I would do something out of the ordinary or that I would upset someone.

Although I had reconnected with our local mental health agency and had tried to the best of my ability, I just couldn't land a job. The guilt I experienced through knowing that other members of the household went to work each day while I was in fact unemployed is another reason I would go to my room before they came home from work. I began to experience guilt over the fact that I was receiving a check from the government when in fact I was unemployed. The more I thought about these things the more depressed I became and the more I isolated.

As I have already stated, we humans are, by nature, social beings. We live to have contact, personal interaction and to share "new life experiences" with other beings of our kind. The isolation I was experiencing may in some ways be similar to that experienced by an individual who is in prison. My bedroom had in fact become my prison and I had sentenced myself to solitary confinement.

I don't know if an individual in solitary confinement is allowed to write or read, but if not, what is there to live for? If not allowed to read the only thing the individual has to live for are memories of the past and the hope that one day soon the isolation will end. Early on in the period of isolation I had experienced while in Salt Lake City I had been able to find comfort in reading; however, during this period, the thought of reading didn't even enter my mind.

As time passed and I continued to isolate I began to think of the things that had led up to my isolation. I didn't think of the person I lived with who kept alcohol in the house, but rather of my past use of drugs and alcohol and of past misdeeds I had committed. This too contributed to the depression and isolation I was experiencing. I began to believe that I was undeserving and unworthy of meaningful relationships with others.

The solitary confinement I was experiencing was different than that experienced by an individual in prison. I was able to leave my room and in fact was afforded all the rights and freedoms of any citizen of our great nation who abides by our laws and respects the rights of others. Through circumstances that I thought were beyond my control I had restricted myself from exercising these basic rights and freedoms.

Another difference is that there was a television in the apartment and early on I would leave my room and watch television while other members of our household were at work. Television can help alleviate feelings of isolation, as can radio, but these are just a temporary fix, in effect a Band-Aid for an ailment that can only be overcome through personal interaction with others and the sharing of new life experiences. After all, have you ever noticed how many reruns are played on television? And if you watch the news on television or listen to it on the radio it can become rather depressing. Although from time to time the news does report a story with a positive outcome, seldom is there a report that helps one to continue to have faith in human nature.

Isolation can lead to depression simply by the lack of contact and interaction with other human beings. This was the 20th century. Most people who could afford a telephone owned one. Through the telephone people are able to communicate with other members of their community, but as I began to isolate I was forced to call the same people over and over again. And because most of my old friends still used drugs and alcohol there were very few people whom I could call. This is due solely to the fact that I was isolating and thereby not creating for myself the opportunity to meet new people and share new life experiences. Early on, before I was deep into my isolation, I couldn't wait to call friends and learn of new and exciting things that were going on in their life. While isolating I seldom had much to contribute to the conversation simply because I was not experiencing anything new and exciting myself. When asked about my day or life I often reported, "Oh, just another day," or "Nothing new," then I would go on to ask, "What's up with you?" As the isolation become more intense I reached a point in which I stopped calling my friends altogether. I was unaware I had done this.

Finding myself trapped in this "prison of isolation" I eventually reached a point at which I couldn't help but think of "breaking free," and/or "putting an end to it." This had just become too much. There has to be more to life than this. I began to realize that what I needed was to find a way to somehow create and experience some degree of continual change that included sharing new life experiences with other people.

So how was I able to "break free" and begin to feel comfortable outside of my prison and out in the community? I was very lucky in that at the time there was an F. W. Woolworth store located in the city about 5 miles from my home. When the isolation reached a point at which I could no longer stand it, I left my room, took a shower, dressed in warm clothes because it was winter and took the bus to the city. Once there, I stood in front of the Woolworth store and as people entered or exited the store I held the door open for them. Most people would thank me for doing this. Shortly after starting this act of kindness I began to take notice of and count each time someone said "Thank you" to me. I also made a point of saying, "You're welcome." When I needed a break from the winter weather I would go to the coffee shop in Woolworth's and have a cup of coffee. In taking those breaks I got to know the people who were working behind the counter of the coffee shop as well as some of the customers. I never mentioned the fact that I was their doorman, but if I recall correctly others may have brought up the subject once or twice.

I'm not sure what I felt while holding the door open on that first day but I can't help but to think that hearing the words, "Thank you" repeatedly throughout the day helped me to begin to change. In the beginning I would just say, "You're welcome" as people gave me thanks, but eventually I would also smile and say, "Have a great day!"

With the approach of spring I had reached a point at which I would go to Woolworth's and hold the doors open almost every weekday. I was no longer trapped in my self-imposed prison; I had "broken free." I now had purpose and meaning in my life. I was contributing to society and bringing at least a little joy to my fellow human beings. I now had a reason to leave my room and I began to feel better about myself. If I took a day off from opening the doors when I returned to Woolworth's, people would ask where I had been. This too contributed to my wellness because I began to feel as though people missed and cared about me.

I believe it was April of that year when our local mental health agency secured the cleaning contract with the local research and engineering laboratory. I gave up my doorman's job and went to work as a custodian.

Although I really didn't like the type of employment that I now found myself doing, I did in fact begin to feel better about myself because I was now employed. I had been told by people who work for the mental health agency that this would be a temporary position but they did not put any limits on the length of time I would be allowed to work for them. Although my vocational counselor had told me that she thought I could pass the GED test and had encouraged me to take it, at the time I had very little confidence in my ability and kept coming up with excuses as to why I wouldn't take the test. Once I started work as a custodian I don't believe she mentioned the test again until after I quit my job.

When I started working as a custodian I worked 4 hours a day, 5 days a week. I was told that I was working over what our Social Security Administration considered to be "Substantial Gainful Activity" and if I continued to do so I would lose my Social Security Disability check. This did not concern me because there was a new building being built at work and I would be allowed to work full time when the building was complete. When the building was completed I started working full time and soon thereafter became the lead person. My new duties included giving support and encouragement to other consumer/employees and making sure the work got done when someone was out sick.

It seemed that there was at least one person out almost every day. In the beginning I didn't mind this because I had no problem filling in for individuals who were out. The problem began when my boss went on vacation. When the other employees learned the boss was going to be out they started taking time off. They didn't understand that he would learn how much time they had taken off when he returned from vacation. During the ten workdays he was away I had to cover fourteen shifts in which people had taken time off and repeated shifts for one person who had in fact quit her job. As this was my first experience as a supervisor I took it upon myself to do the work of others when they were out. I had yet to learn to delegate and share responsibility.

I was still taking the antipsychotic medication Haldol and in fact with the support and guidance of my doctor was in the process of reducing my dose. At one point I had been taking 10 mg per day but because of the side effects I had only taken it intermittently. I just couldn't stand the side effects. With the assistance of my doctor I reduced my dose to 5 mg and may have even gone as low as 2.5 mg, although the total amount I reduced has slipped from my memory. While taking the full dose I believe I had been meeting with my doctor every month, but as we reduced my dose I began meeting with him once every 3 months. Although while taking 10 mg I had taken it only intermittently, while reducing my dose I took it as prescribed.

Things had gone well at work for a while, but when my boss had taken vacation and all those people took time off I began to feel overwhelmed and reached a point in which I hated going to work. I never knew how many people would be out sick.

Although I don't remember when the conversation took place, at one point during my employment journey I had told my supports manager I wanted to give up my job and go to college and become a substance abuse counselor. I don't at this time remember what her response had been, but I remember it to have been very discouraging, so I didn't mention it again, to anyone.

When I started work as a custodian I felt a little better about myself because I was employed and was in fact contributing to my household. I was surviving without my SSDI check and I was contributing to my community. Although I had been taking an antidepressant, I was still experiencing depression and it was now intensifying.

My living situation had not changed and I continued to feel isolated while at home. I was taking the bus to work because I didn't own a car. I was trying to save money for a car and in fact bought one for $650 only to learn it would cost about $900 to get it through inspection. I sold the car for $300 and continued to take the bus to work. The bus was seldom on schedule and it seemed that I was always waiting for it. To insure I arrived at work on time

I took the early bus and usually reported to work about half an hour early. Reliable transportation would have been helpful.

Another aspect of my life in which a car would have been helpful is that I'm divorced and have two children who lived about 25 miles from my home. Although their mother brought them to town from time to time so they could visit and my mother had on occasion picked them up, it was seldom that they got to see their dad. When we did get to see each other, I really didn't know how to act. I was experiencing side effects of my medication and I was depressed. Although I tried to the best of my ability to act like a "normal person and dad" I do not believe I was very successful at this. I felt very guilty because I was behind in my child support payment and over the fact that my children seldom had the opportunity to spend time with their dad. I also missed them.

The day came in which my mother gave me a ride to pick up my children for a visit and although I had called before leaving my apartment and learned that their phone was no longer in service, we made the drive. I was concerned about my children. When we arrived at their home I found the house to be empty. They had moved.

It took about 3 months to locate them at which time I learned they were living in a state located about 2,000 miles away. After learning their phone number I called their home. My ex-wife asked how I had found their number and why I was calling. Over the years she would most often ask why I had called each time I tried to get in touch with our children. Although I called often, they did not have an answering machine and had no way of knowing that I was trying to get in touch with them. It was rare that we had an opportunity to speak with one another. I wrote letters and did in fact receive a few in return, but we eventually stopped writing. I mailed each of my children self-addressed, stamped post cards at the suggestion of my supports manager; to the best of my knowledge they still have them. I sent them cameras and film and have yet to receive my first picture. I asked my ex-wife to send me copies of their report cards and she sent a few, but this too eventually ended. I had tried to the best of my ability to build a meaningful relationship with my children and I didn't know what else I could do short of moving to the state in which they now lived. I was learning the difficulty of trying to maintain a long-distance relationship and it just wasn't working. During this time they had moved again and there was a time in which we had no contact; therefore, after finally getting in touch with them again it took time to reestablish our relationship. All of these things were repeatedly being mulled over and over in my mind and I became very depressed and confused.

During the time my doctor and I were in the process of cutting down my medication, I had a lot of Haldol in my bedroom. I'm not sure, but because my income was low, I may have been granted a scholarship from the pharmaceutical company. I do know that at one point I did in fact have a scholarship and was receiving my medication in bottles of 100 tablets.

Upon arriving home from a very hard day of work I had just had enough. I went to my bedroom and got my medication. Then I went to the kitchen sink, filled a glass with water and attempted suicide by overdosing on Haldol. I'm not sure how many pills I took, but I guess the number to be around 150. Then I went back into my bedroom and tried to go to sleep, but I couldn't. My mind was full of all the reasons for which I wanted to end my life and the thoughts played over and over.

As the night progressed I thought more about my children and mother and how my suicide would affect them. I eventually reached a point in which I felt guilty about attempting to take my life. I no longer wanted to die, but the effects of the Haldol were beginning to take their toll. My sinuses were so dry that I was afraid they would split open, my head hurt and my stomach was upset, all of my muscles ached, and my entire body felt strange. It seemed as if my mind was disconnected from my body. I no longer wanted to die, but I didn't want the people I was living with to know I had attempted suicide so I stayed in my room until I was sure they had gone to sleep for the night. While I was waiting I felt terrible over what I had done.

I think it was around midnight that I left my room, walked downtown, and called a taxi. When the taxi arrived I asked the driver to take me to the hospital. As we approached the hospital the driver asked if I wanted to go to the main entrance or the emergency room. I asked him to drop me off at the main entrance.

When we arrived I got out of the taxi, entered the hospital and sort of paced in the main lobby. Before long I started to hear a familiar sound. Someone was vacuuming the hall. As time passed the sound became louder and louder and before I knew it a custodian came around the corner with a vacuum cleaner that was the same brand and color as those I use at work. This was just too much. I left the hospital and sat down on a bench out front. While outside I smoked a couple of cigarettes and vomited twice. Then I went back into the hospital, called a taxi, and went home.

The next day was Friday. I did not go to work. I just didn't want to face any people. I felt physically ill and I was still upset emotionally. I felt terribly guilty. After the people I was living with went to work I went upstairs and paced in one of the bedrooms. I went downstairs before they came home and went out on the back porch and smoked a cigarette. There was a note from two of my counselors stuck to the door.

They had stopped by because they were concerned that I had not called in sick and had not shown up for work. I had never done that before.

I spent most of the weekend in my bedroom and on Monday I met with my doctor and the person who oversaw the custodians. I told them I wanted to quit my job and go to college and become a counselor. They told me that rather than give up my job I could take a leave of absence and they would hold my job for me. While discussing this, I eventually had to tell them that they just didn't understand that I didn't want to work as a custodian any longer. I had been employed as a custodian for 2 ½ years, although at the start of my employment, I had been told that the job would be temporary.

A short time following my suicide attempt I told my doctor I had overdosed by taking 150 tablets of Haldol the Thursday night before I quit my job. If I recall correctly his response was that if it had been a different medication I might not have been able to tell him about the overdose. I don't believe we ever discussed the reason for the overdose nor do I recall him recommending that I see a therapist.

Following my suicide attempt my doctor put me on the newer antipsychotic medication, Risperdal, and it seems to work rather well, although in times of stress I have to increase my dose. I have not attempted to take my life since changing medication in 1995.

When my vocational counselor learned that I wanted to go to college she told me the first step would be to get my GED. I told her I had just quit my job and that I had no money. She was able to get the mental health agency to pay for the test. When I told her I had no way to get to the testing facility she said she would give me a ride. True to her word she brought me to the testing facility both nights that it took me to complete the required tests. She did this although the tests were held at night after her regular work hours and in spite of the fact that it snowed both nights. I took the test in December of 1995 and learned of the results in January of 1996. I had passed the test.

Another thing my vocational counselor did for me was to connect me with the State of New Hampshire Department of Vocational Rehabilitation. My voc rehab counselor had me take a vocational assessment to learn if my career choice would be a good match and/or fit. When I got the results of the assessment I learned that a career in human services would in fact be a good match for me. When I left the voc rehab office that day I took it upon myself to walk directly across the mall and take the elevator to the office of Lebanon College.

When I walked into the office I asked the receptionist if the college was offering any courses in English. I was told that a course in English Grammar would be offered the next semester. I was also informed that the course would cost $235. When I told her I had no money she let me know that the Greater Lebanon Chamber of Commerce was just starting a scholarship program and she gave me an application. I filled out the application and wrote the required essay. Then I mailed the application and essay to the Chamber of Commerce. The essay I wrote is titled, "Why I Want to Become a Substance Abuse Counselor" and is published in my book, *Reflections of Reality.*

Within a very short time I was invited into the Chamber office for an interview. By the end of the interview I had learned that I would soon receive a letter from the Chamber that would explain their decision in regard to my scholarship. Very shortly after that I received a letter with an enclosed check for $200. I paid the remaining $35 for the course and $15 for the required workbook. I passed that course with a grade of A-.

In taking that first college course and in doing so on my own initiative, I think I was able to prove to my voc rehab counselor that I was serious in respect to my educational goal. After sharing my grade with him he asked if I would like to attend a more challenging school. I welcomed the opportunity and he paid for a course in Critical Thinking at the College for Lifelong Learning (CLL).

During the time that I took my first college course I moved into an apartment the mental health agency used as transitional housing. The apartment was close enough to Lebanon College that I could walk to class. When I stated attending CLL I arranged for a taxi to pick me up both before and after class.

I think there was only one night in which the taxi didn't pick me up for class. That night I walked. The problem was getting home, not only on that night, but on other nights as well. One night my instructor gave me a ride home. Another night after standing in the cold, dark, snowy parking lot for better than half an hour waiting for my taxi, I accepted a ride home from a lady who had driven by, seen me standing there and turned around to see that I was okay. There were also a number of nights in which I had to walk home after class. I passed that course with a grade of B.

Next my voc rehab counselor had me apply for student loans and register for classes with New Hampshire Technical Institute (NHTI), located in Concord, NH some 65 miles south of my home in Lebanon. I was able to register with the college through the mail, and my mother agreed to give me a ride to Concord for orientation because I did not own a car. It was on the way home from Concord that my mother told me how proud she was of me.

My voc rehab counselor told me the State of NH would not pay for a car for me so I went back to work as a custodian. In 3 months time I was able to save about $1000 and buy a used car. Voc rehab paid my car insurance, bought my books and supplies and paid some of my tuition. During the time I was taking the class at Lebanon College, but before I moved into the apartment owned by the mental health agency, a couple of friends stopped by and asked if I would be willing to help them move some furniture. The furniture was to be used for a peer support center in Lebanon. I helped them load a U-haul truck with furniture donated by Dartmouth College. Then we unloaded the truck at a friend's house.

By the time I was able to buy a car, Next Step, our peer support center, had been open for a while and I began to stop in. In the beginning I was rather quiet and would stay at the center for only a few minutes, but eventually I began to share positive things about my educational journey and spend more time there. As I began to get to know people I also shared my poetry and in doing so they learned I was receiving services through the local mental health agency. They also learned that I was in the process of recovery from a history of substance abuse.

Through Next Step I began to meet people who had been through and were sharing life experiences similar to those I had experienced. It was through this sharing that I began to feel that I was not alone. I was overcoming my substance abuse and had been clean for a number of years and the more I shared the more comfortable I felt. It also seemed the more I was willing to share the more others shared about themselves. Members of Next Step did not judge me for my past use of drugs and alcohol or my mental illness, but I believe they may have been impressed by the fact that I was overcoming my past and even attending college. I began to feel accepted as well as respected.

While attending the Technical Institute I had an opportunity to move into an apartment that is not considered transitional and have lived there for 4 years. I do not allow alcohol in my home or my car and I try not to put myself in vulnerable situations where people are drinking. I have not had a drink of alcohol since before leaving Salt Lake City, and October of 2002 marked 12 years of clean time for me.

About mid-way through my educational journey the mental health agency assigned a new vocational counselor to work with me. She was a great support during the rest of my educational journey. We also traveled to Concord to attend the state benefits planners meetings and together we became quite knowledgeable in both federal and state benefits. She was also a great support as I started working at our peer support center at a time in which the center experienced a number of leadership changes. She also supported and assisted other members of the center in many ways.

In May of 2000, I graduated from New Hampshire Technical Institute with high honors and an Associates Degree in Human Services with Specialization in Alcohol and Drug Abuse Counseling. I am currently employed as a Peer Support Specialist with Next Step and have been working in that capacity for over 2 years.

Through our peer support center I have found a place where I feel safe, welcome, accepted and respected, as well as challenged. I can also rest assured that I will continue to receive the support I need as I face new life challenges. This is evident in the genuine, sincere support I received when I told the Next Step community of my most recent challenge, a diagnosis that I have been infected with the Hepatitis C Virus.

With the assistance of one of our members I was able to develop my own Wellness Recovery Action Plan based on the work of Mary Ellen Copeland. I don't look at my plan every day but I do from time to time review and revise it as I become more self-aware and learn of more effective coping strategies.

A year after starting work with Next Step I wrote a paper titled "How Peer Support Can Work for You." Although I believe each of us is entitled to our own definition of peer support, I sometimes share my paper with new members to sort of give them a baseline for defining how peer support can work for them. The paper is posted on the wall of the center and I feel good about that. I have contributed something that will hopefully live on long after my journey as I now know it is over.

I continue to open doors for others and I make a point of saying "you're welcome" as they give me thanks. I also try to remember to say "thank you" to people who show me acts of kindness. And I have written a poem titled "My Thank You Bank" that I have published in my book, *Reflections of Reality*.

A while ago I told my supports manager that my recovery could have progressed faster and more smoothly had I had a therapist on my team. At that time he asked if I would like a therapist. I told him I had made it this far without one and that I would think about it. The subject has been re-explored with my new supports manager. To the best of my knowledge, this is the eighth supports manager I've been assigned since 1991 when I reconnected with our local mental health agency.

Although it is important not to dwell on the past, it is equally important to come to terms with it and to keep it in perspective. I am coming to terms with my past by writing about it and sharing my writing with other people. I am able to do this through our Peer Support Center where I am accepted and respected for the person I have become as opposed to being judged for a past for which I am not particularly proud.

I'm now experiencing a richer, fuller life that is better than I could have imagined while caught up in the world of addictions, isolation, depression, and early recovery. Through our peer support center, I share my life with others in hope that they too may meet and overcome challenges that are similar to those I have overcome. I like to believe I'm "opening doors" that will allow others to move forward in their journey of recovery and that will assist them in improving the quality of their lives.

Today, thanks to our peer support center, my life includes many meaningful personal and social relationships and the sharing of numerous "new life experiences." For this I am extremely grateful.

**Chapter 2  Then What Happens to People Over Time?**

## Introduction to Chapter 2

*Courtenay M. Harding*

This chapter continues the discussion about the possibility of recovery. These papers describe the impact of time on symptoms, functioning, and quality of life. Instead of the expected downward trajectory for the worst case scenario (schizophrenia), the contemporary longitudinal studies found that more than one half significantly improved or recovered. These studies, which were 2 to 3 decades in length, followed intact cohorts whether or not they were still in treatment. Such a strategy significantly rebalances the picture of what is possible for such patients—even the most chronic and most disabled persons.

The first paper by Carpenter and Kirkpatrick (1988) reveals that variability amongst people who eventually become ill starts with the personalities that they bring to the process and the variability in the presentation of prodromal configurations, and it continues through the onset, course, and outcome epochs. These authors present cogent arguments suggesting strongly that investigators need to focus on such epochs to better understand the underlying heterogeneity that serve to hide signals and confuse our understanding about such complex disorders.

The chapter continues to present the base papers of the now classic Vermont Longitudinal Study that examined the course of serious mental illness with the worst cases of chronic disability and severity of illness (Harding et al., 1987a,1987b). After a comprehensive biopsychosocial rehabilitation program, two thirds of these people who were once called "the hopeless cases" and expected to die in the hospital, reclaimed their lives. This NIMH study followed people at the average of 32 years after first admission, with 97% of the people found. The model of care in Vermont was "rehabilitation, community integration, and self-sufficiency."

The sister longitudinal study, The Maine-Vermont Comparison Study (DeSisto et al, 1995), follows and is the only one of its type in the world literature. The Maine team matched each Vermont subject on age, sex, DSM-III diagnosis and length of hospitalization. They matched catchment areas on health and census data, used the same protocols and same treatment eras, and performed interrater trials between teams. At an average of 35 years after first admission, 94% of the Mainers were studied. The primary difference was the lack of rehabilitation for the Maine patients. Findings revealed that there were significant differences between Vermont and Maine subjects on variables such as community functioning, work, and symptoms. These studies underpin the finding that participation in rehabilitation can and does make a difference in the lives of people struggling to recover. They also revealed that decisions made at the top of a system can affect the outcomes of the very people the system is trying to serve. Further, the research team concluded that there was a probability of neuroplasticity with the brain trying to recalibrate itself across time.

Additional evidence outlining the Swiss study conducted in Lausanne and others in Europe is presented by Luc Ciompi (1980). He describes a "life process" in the longest follow-up study in the world literature. He quotes and agrees with Manfred Bleuler (1982) who conducted the first contemporary study in Zurich. Bleuler outlined 3 principles of care to promote improvement and recovery processes: 1) relating to the healthy part of the person; 2) mobilizing hidden resources with sudden changes; and 3) using the "calming" influences of talking therapy and medications.

In the next paper, Davidson and McGlashan (1997) suggest that affective symptoms, later and acute onsets, and response to medication can predict a better chance to improve—a finding considered sacrosanct for decades but challenged by Harding et al. (1993) and Vaillant (1978) in their long-term studies. These investigators re-emphasized two major barriers to improvement, cognitive deficits and negative symptoms, and issued a call for early intervention.

The UCLA team, of Liberman et al. (2002), present a multi-dimensional scheme to measure recovery in a meaningful way using both symptom reduction and functional improvement and "possible facilitators" to enable future investigators to generate and test hypotheses. Also, it should be noted that all the Ciompi, Harding, and DeSisto papers outline a wide selection of factors that go into a recovery analysis.

A previously unpublished paper from Torgalsbøen in Norway offers a way to differentiate between process and outcome, cure and healing, control and empowerment, and the importance of connection and meaning in the recovery model. The Low Turning Point article by Rakfeldt et al. (1988) forms the basis for many evidence-based cognitive-behavioral strategies (e.g., Dialectical Behavior Therapy (DBT) and the Wellness Recovery Action Planning (WRAP) techniques) used today in so many recovery-oriented approaches.

And lastly, a first-person account by Twombly (1999) conveys her frustration in trying to secure adequate care and her emerging self-acceptance as she learns more about herself and her illness and gains support and encouragement from others. She shows what perseverance, insight, and time can do in the evolution of reclaiming a life after serious illness.

# The Heterogeneity of the Long-Term Course of Schizophrenia

*William T. Carpenter, Jr., and Brian Kirkpatrick*

At the time of original publication, William T. Carpenter, Jr., MD, was Director at the Maryland Psychiatric Research Center, and Professor of Psychiatry, University of Maryland School of Medicine, Baltimore, MD; and Brian Kirpatrick, MD, was Research Assistant Professor at the Maryland Psychiatric Research Center, Baltimore, MD.

This article originally appeared in the *Schizophrenia Bulletin*, 1988, 14, 645–652, and is reprinted with permission.

**Abstract:** Research has demonstrated considerable heterogeneity in the long-term course of schizophrenia. In the period preceding the onset of frank psychosis (onset), patients vary relative to the rapidity of onset, the presence or absence of asociality, and the presence or absence of semipsychotic symptoms. Following the onset of psychosis (middle course), patients may suffer from episodic or unremitting psychosis, and may or may not exhibit the deficit syndrome. In late adult life (late course), patients vary relative to the presence or absence of an improvement in psychosis and social capability. The usual approach to the study of putative course subtypes is to define a subtype by a number of features; they may include features of more than one epoch. In addition, the course of psychosis has not been distinguished from enduring personality impairments in these subtypes. Another approach to defining putative course subtypes would be based on dichotomizing patients' according to the presence or absence of a particular feature of a single epoch. This second approach has important advantages: the availability of larger study populations and a diminished liability for confounding due to the correlates of features other than those under scrutiny.

It is very likely that schizophrenia is a clinical syndrome rather than a single disease entity (Kendell, 1975; McHugh & Slavney, 1983; Carpenter, 1987). Clinical observation has documented the marked variation among cases in all aspects of psychopathology. Factors such as age of onset, rate of onset, early morbid or premorbid picture, symptoms and signs, inter-episode residual impairments, long-term outcome, late course improvement, treatment response, and distribution of risk factors show so much difference among patients that each may prove useful as a categorical variable for the purpose of subdividing the syndrome of schizophrenia. Furthermore, many other variables (e.g., pattern of familial interaction, performance on cognitive or neuropsychological tests, biochemical assessments, and brain imaging) reveal such a range of values as to question the concept of schizophrenia as a single disease entity.

Relative homogeneity in long-term course has been the prevailing concept of schizophrenia, although it has been frequently refuted; and alternative diagnostic classes have been defined for patients with more benign course and outcome. In *DSM-III* and *DSM-III-R* (American Psychiatric Association 1980, 1987), this approach has given way to the tautology of distinguishing putative disease entities by their duration, per se, and by an accompanying acceptance of a greatly increased heterogeneity of affective disorders; the latter include many forms of atypical psychoses and cases with mood-incongruent psychotic features. Other DSM-III and DSM-III-R psychoses, such as brief reactive psychosis, atypical psychosis, schizoaffective disorder, and schizophreniform psychosis, have doubtful validity and clinical utility.

However, even in the relatively chronic category of DSM-III schizophrenia, considerable variability of course is observed. Angst (1988) and McGlashan (1988) document this in their reviews of European and North American follow-up studies, and Harding (1988) describes interesting variability observed during the course of illness. Taken together, these studies belie a single disease construct to the extent that the construct is dependent on a relatively homogeneous long-term course. Since the pathophysiology of psychoses is enigmatic, similarities in onset, symptoms, and course have been used to define disease entities. Clinical heterogeneity does not exclude the possibility of etiological homogeneity; general paresis of the insane is such an example.

This variability in clinical course is of relevance for the design of future studies. It is important to devise methods to reduce the apparent heterogeneity of schizophrenia to define the most appropriate study cohorts and to provide optimal circumstances for replication studies. Too often, when a study fails to confirm a hypothesis or replicate a previous study, it cannot be ascertained whether the failure is due to a lack of validity of the hypothesis or to an inability to construct a suitable study population for testing. In this regard, the course of schizophrenia (i.e., the nature of onset of episodes and remissions, and the nature of the illness late in its course) provides a promising criterion for reducing the heterogeneity of study populations.

As is documented in this issue, the research on the long-term course of schizophrenia leads to a number of conclusions that can be stated with confidence. This body of research also suggests important reconceptualizations of how to conduct research on schizophrenia, some of which we discuss here.

### THE CONCEPT OF COURSE OF SCHIZOPHRENIA

There have been several attempts to define subtypes of schizophrenia based on long-term course. Huber et al. (1975, 1980) described 12 patterns of course of illness, while Bleuler (1968, 1978) described 7 patterns and Ciompi (1980a, 1980b)) described 8 patterns. There is extensive overlap in these descriptions, encouraging the view that a relatively small number of patterns may characterize the onset and course of illness for the vast majority of patients. In addition, Harding (1988) was able to categorize the patients in the Vermont study into the eight course patterns of Ciompi. These patterns incorporate observations about the nature of onset, the pattern of psychotic episodes, psychopathology between episodes, and the presence or absence of recovery late in the illness. There is a body of follow-up literature suggesting that even the progressive forms of illness tend to plateau within 5 to10 years, making it feasible to classify most cases without waiting for long-term follow-up or ultimate outcome of illness (Bleuler, 1978; Ciompi, 1980a, 1980b; Huber et al., 1980; Engelhardt et al., 1982; Pfohl & Winokur, 1982, 1983; Dube et al., 1984; McGlashan, 1984; Achté et al., 1986).

Relative to reducing the heterogeneity of schizophrenia, one can delineate two approaches to using pattern of course. The first is to regard each distinctive pattern as a putative disease entity. Eight patterns are generated by the dichotomization of onset (insidious and acute), psychotic episodes (chronic or episodic), and late course pattern (deteriorated or improving) (Bleuler, 1968, 1978; Flekkoy, et al., 1975; Huber et al., 1975, 1980; Ciompi, 1980a, 1980b; Harding et al., 1987a, 1987b; McGlashan, 1987). This approach, depicted in Figure 1 and Table 1, has been useful in summarizing descriptive course data. However, the approach is difficult to implement in defining putative disease entities, because each epoch embraces multiple factors. Insidious onset may, for instance, refer to a gradually emerging psychosis or may refer to an early morbid pattern of emotional withdrawal and negative symptoms. And how is a late course patient with improving psychosis and a persevering deficit syndrome to be classified? If these psychopathological domains are to be separated, the dichotomization within each epoch of onset, middle and late course, results in four or more subgroups, not two. Rather than eight resultant patterns defining putative disease entities, two dichotomizations per epoch would result in dozens of patterns. An alternative approach is therefore more practical.

The second approach is similar but is based on a *dichotomization* of patients according to the particular period of clinical course, or course epoch, of interest. These three epochs are onset, middle course, and late course. Within this approach, instead of presuming that, for instance, the combination of insidious onset, prolonged psychosis, and personality deterioration defines a disease entity, one could view each of these factors as an important dichotomizing tool that may represent a lesion or disease process; one would make no a priori assumption about the relationship of each feature to those other epochs. This approach has the practical advantage for most investigators of dividing a study acute cohort into two groups (e.g., acute onset vs. insidious onset of psychotic symptoms) rather than the large number of groups (see Table 1) required by combining observations from the three course epochs.

**Table 1. A Summary of Patterns of Course in Schizophrenia**

| Pattern | Onset | Nature of Psychotic Episodes | Improvement Late in Life |
|---------|-------|------------------------------|--------------------------|
| 1 | Insidious | Chronic | Present |
| 2 | Insidious | Chronic | Absent |
| 3 | Insidious | Episodic | Present |
| 4 | Insidious | Episodic | Absent |
| 5 | Acute | Chronic | Present |
| 6 | Acute | Chronic | Absent |
| 7 | Acute | Episodic | Present |
| 8 | Acute | Episodic | Absent |

*Note.* This table summarizes the patterns of course of illness found in the classic long-term followup studies. Compare these patterns to those of Ciompi in figure 1.

**Table 2. Dichotomization of Research Populations on the Basis of Epochs**

| Epoch | Basis of Dichotomization | Study Group 1 | Study Group 2 |
|-------|--------------------------|---------------|---------------|
| Onset | A. Psychotic symptoms | Insidious onset | Acute onset |
|       | B. Nonpsychotic impairments | Present before onset of psychosis | Absent |
| Middle course | A. Psychotic symptoms | Chronic | Episodic |
|       | B. Nonpsychotic impairments | Present | Absent |
| Late course | A. Psychotic symptoms | Persistent | Improved |
|       | B. Nonpsychotic impairments | Persistent | Improved |

Note. This table summarizes an approach to research into the heterogeneity of schizophrenia. One would categorize patients in a study population into 2 groups, based on 1 of the features above, and then contrast the groups relative to correlates such as neuroendocrinological or genetic variables. Within each epoch there may be many bases for dichotomization. Each such dichotomization should be based on either a psychotic or nonpsychotic impairment, but not on both. Future research would help determine which are the most fruitful variables for dichotomization.

A definition of these epochs requires clarification of an issue relating to long-term course and the definition of putative subtypes that has frequently not been clear in previous research. Too often, psychotic and nonpsychotic

**Figure 1. Course Subtypes Found in Long-Term Studies**

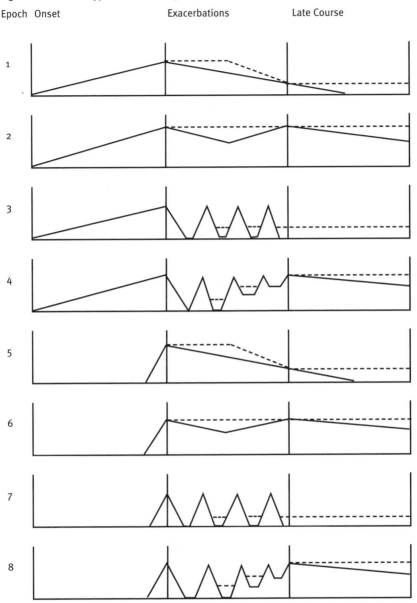

*Note.* This figure summarizes the course subtypes found in the classic long-term studies of Ciompi, Huber and M. Bleuler and replicated by Harding (1988). It is adapted from Ciompi (1980). Although derived from these studies, the subtypes also represent the 8 possible combinations of dichotomizing the 3 course epochs. The subtypes are presented in the same order as those in Table 1. within each of the 8 course subtypes, the X axis represents time and the Y axis represents severity.

impairments have not been clearly distinguished. The first epoch (onset) includes both the beginning of psychotic symptoms (e.g., hallucinations and delusions) and the nonpsychotic personality abnormalities such as childhood asociality that often precede the clearcut appearance of psychotic symptoms. The second epoch (middle course) includes periods of active (episodic or unremitting) psychosis and the nonpsychotic (personality) impairments present between episodes such as sustained inappropriate affect or the deficit syndrome. The third epoch refers lo late course and outcome. A pattern of improvement or recovery in psychosis is observed in some patients, and a pattern of persistence or worsening is seen in others. The same variability may be found in nonpsychotic impairments such as the deficit syndrome (Bleuler, 1968, 1978; Ciompi, 1980a, 1980b; Harding et al., 1987a, 1987b; McGlashan, 1987). Table 2 summarizes this approach to the definition of study groups.

### The Onset Epoch

There is a long tradition of dividing the schizophrenic syndrome according to premorbid, early morbid, and onset characteristics. The dichotomies of good versus poor premorbid, reactive versus process schizophrenia, and acute versus insidious onset are examples of putative entities defined by the features of the epoch of onset. These dichotomies have been validated by assessing short- and long-term outcome, association with precipitating stressors, prediction of treatment response, prediction of familial distribution of schizophrenia spectrum cases, and, with less consistency, age of onset, psychophysiological and biochemical markers, and structural alterations in the brain (Vaillant, 1962; Stephens,1978; Strauss & Carpenter, 1979; Shelton & Weinberger, 1986; Andreasen, 1987).

Within this epoch, it is important to choose with care the aspect of psychopathology used to define cohorts. Some workers have focused on the rate of evolving psychosis (i.e., acute vs. insidious), while others have viewed impairment in personality development as critical (e.g., asocial vs. social, process vs. reactive). Predictive power is no doubt enhanced by combining features of both psychotic and non-psychotic features, and clinicians routinely base prognosis on data from developmental history and onset of psychosis. However, for purposes of reducing heterogeneity to study specific psychopathological processes, it is useful and probably valid to consider personality pathology separately from psychosis and its rate of onset (Kety el al., 1968; Kendler, et al., 1986; Gottesman, et al., 1987).

### The Epoch of Middle Course

All currently accepted diagnostic criteria for schizophrenia include positive symptoms of psychosis (e.g., hallucinations and delusions); the course of this psychosis is quite variable. Terms in the literature such as "chronic," "treatment-refractory," "residual symptoms," and "poor functioning" usually fail to make clear the extent to which the relevant dichotomization is based on inter-episode personality pathology or on the persistence of psychosis per se. At our present state of knowledge, it is important to allow for the possibility that factors involved in the pathogenesis of psychotic symptoms (hallucinations, delusions, and marked formal thought disorder) may be different from factors involved in the pathogenesis of longstanding inter-episode impairments of personality. Family aggregation studies confirm this view (Heston, 1966; Kendler et al., 1986).

### The Late Course Epoch

Those who have viewed schizophrenia as a chronic, deteriorating illness have sometimes proposed long-term outcome as a definitive diagnostic and dichotomizing tool. Recovery or very substantial improvement disallowed the diagnosis of schizophrenia, and diagnoses such as schizophreniform psychosis were introduced for the nonprogressive cases (Kleist, 1960; Leonhard, 1966; Langfeldt, 1969).

Work from around the world has now documented variability in course, regardless of diagnostic criteria (Bleuler, 1968, 1978; Flekkoy et al., 1975; Hawk et al., 1975; Brockington et al., 1978; Kendell et al., 1979; Ciompi, 1980a, 1980b); Angst, 1988; Harding, 1988; McGlashan, 1988). A substantial number of patients with schizophrenia show sustained and substantial improvement in psychopathology late in the course of illness, the proportion of such cases depending on diagnostic criteria and perhaps on treatment and cultural/environmental circumstances as well (Lin and Kleinman, 1988). This improvement can apparently involve decreased intensity of psychosis or improvement in nonpsychotic impairments. Predictors of late course improvement have not yet been well validated, but McGlashan (1987) examined 100 clinical and demographic variables from patients' distant past and found only five variables predictive of late improvement at the $p = .05$ level. All five may be chance findings, but family closeness ($p = 0.1$) and schizotypal personality ($p = .02$) merit further study.

Some conceptual distinctions will assist in the investigation of late course processes:

1) We suggest that study groups should be differentiated according to whether improvements occur in psychotic or nonpsychotic aspects of illness, or both.

2)   Of those patients with the deficit syndrome (one form of nonpsychotic impairment), it may prove very interesting to differentiate between early onset (i.e., early deficit morbidity before psychosis) cases and those cases in which the deficit syndrome developed only after the appearance of psychosis.

### USING EPOCHS FOR RESEARCH: THE DOMAINS APPROACH

We have argued elsewhere that schizophrenia is a clinical syndrome defined by combining quite divergent aspects of psychopathology (Carpenter et al., 1985). In the absence of valid disease entities, it is useful conceptually to identify domains of psychopathology, such as positive symptoms or the deficit syndrome, for independent scrutiny (Carpenter & Buchanan, 1989). Course patterns may also depend on distinct pathophysiological processes and, thus, are also candidates for this approach. For each epoch, we give below an example of a hypothesis relating to a dichotomy within that epoch.

Concerning the *first epoch* (onset), there is evidence that chronic schizophrenia is genetically linked to the schizophrenia spectrum and that acute schizophrenia is not (Kety et al., 1968). The clinical features that define chronicity have not been teased apart, so the basis for the excess of the schizophrenia spectrum in biological relatives of chronic schizophrenic probands is not known. Defining cohorts using first epoch patterns may clarify this important issue. One could replicate the finding that a high prevalence of schizophrenia spectrum relatives is associated with childhood asociality in schizophrenic probands (Kendler et al., 1982) by subdividing a cohort of schizophrenic probands according to the presence or absence of this feature and determining the prevalence of the schizophrenia spectrum among biological relatives of the two schizophrenic cohorts (and appropriate controls). Such a design would be strengthened if the two proband cohorts were similar in rate of onset of psychosis and the features of the other epochs, thus increasing the likelihood that nonpsychotic childhood impairment would be the crucial variable.

Concerning the *second epoch* (middle course), a question of prime importance is the pathophysiological mechanism that underlies persistent as opposed to remitting psychosis. To help isolate this factor in a study design, patients with schizophrenia could be dichotomously categorized on the basis of persistent and remitting psychoses. To avoid a confounding effect, the two study cohorts must be similar relative to the features of the first epoch. We would hypothesize that the pathophysiological difference in these two patterns of psychosis is based on a failure of a homeostatic mechanism in mesocortical or mesolimbic dopaminergic systems in patients with persistent psychosis. Studying the responses of various dopaminergic systems to pharmacologic probes, using variables such as prolactin, homovanillic acid, and in vivo dopamine receptor imaging, could be informative if the comparative cohorts were similar in onset and psychotic state at time of study but differed relative to persistence or remission of psychosis. Again, more specific conclusions can be achieved by shifting from the acute/chronic dichotomy to a discrete pattern of pathology within a specified epoch.

Concerning the *third epoch* (late course), it will be important to discover the mechanisms that lead to late improvement in a subgroup of patients. Here one might hypothesize that an amelioration of psychosis is associated with an age-related decrease in the number of neurons in dopaminergic systems, and that patients vary considerably in the age of occurrence and in the rate and extent of these neuronal changes. Using variables that permit inferences about this neuronal mechanism hypothesis, the investigator would define cohorts distinguished by late improvement versus nonimprovement in psychosis, but which are otherwise comparable.

## DISCUSSION

Certain assumptions underlie the epoch-based research strategy outlined above:

1) There are a variety of psychopathological domains within schizophrenia;

2) These domains differ in their pathophysiology and associated risk factors; and

3) These pathological processes can occur independently and can be observed in attenuated form (e.g., schizoid traits and subtle thought disorder).

Although an underlying biological heterogeneity of schizophrenia is not unequivocally established, it is certainly heuristic to hypothesize etiological and pathogenetic heterogeneity (Carpenter & Buchanan,1989). If schizophrenic patients suffer from diverse pathophysiological processes, studying heterogeneous groups will obscure these processes; whereas if there is a unitary pathophysiology underlying schizophrenia, studying more homogeneous subgroups will not undermine the elucidation of that single process.

Dichotomizing study populations on the basis of individual epochs as described here has important advantages relative to the "disease entity" approach that was summarized earlier. There is first the practical advantage that the researcher needs only to contrast two groups, rather than to define a number of putative disease entities. If the psychopathological domains model is a valid one, then there is another important advantage having to do with the interpretation of study results. For instance, suppose a biological marker distinguished classic "process" schizophrenic patients (with an insidious onset and unremitting psychotic symptoms) from classic "good prognosis" patients (with an acute onset and an episodic course of psychotic symptoms). It would be difficult to interpret such a finding, as the marker could be associated with the prepsychotic abnormality or with the pattern of course of the psychotic symptoms. However, if the two study groups differed in the nature of their onset but not relative to the course of their psychotic symptoms, a correlation with a marker would have a more specific interpretation. The latter design would be clearly mandated by the epochs approach.

There is already extensive evidence supporting the value of subdividing the schizophrenia syndrome by course pattern or domain of pathology. Distinctions such as acute/chronic, Kraepelinian/non-Kraepelinian or type I/II have already been productive (Kety et al., 1968, Crow, 1985; Losonczy et al., 1986). The power of such dichotomies will be increased by explicit attention to the domain of pathology and phase of illness upon which the subtypes are being delineated. Long-term follow-up studies provide a strong basis for examining these three epochs, and Harding (1988) and McClashan (personal communication) have demonstrated an ability to apply similar criteria to new study-cohorts.

This conceptual approach may guide the investigator in several crucial tasks:

- The elucidation of the many pathological processes which, in various combinations, lead to the heterogeneous clinical syndromes that currently define schizophrenia.

- The clarification of those pathological processes which are shared across nosological classes and those which are specific to schizophrenia

- The identification of areas neglected by previous research (e.g., neuroleptic effects in the third epoch).

It is to be anticipated that new data generated within this conceptual framework will provide the scientific basis for advances in nosology of relevance to *DSM-IV* and ICD-10. Application of the course typology in psychosis other than schizophrenia may even provide a basis for a new division of the psychoses. For instance, almost 20% of major affective disorder patients have a chronic course (Rennie, 1942; Keller and Shapiro, 1982; Keller et al., 1983). Do many of these patients have insidious onset or late course deficits? If so, does this subgroup share a pathophysiological process with some chronic schizophrenic patients? A focus on epochs may clarify whether similar causal mechanisms are involved in discrete aspects of several entities we now consider independent diseases.

## REFERENCES

Achté, K., Lonnqvist, J., Kuusi, K., Piirtola, O. & Niskanen, P. (1986). Outcome studies on schizophrenic psychoses in Helsinki. *Psychopathology, 19,* 60–67.

American Psychiatric Association. (1987). *DSM-III: Diagnostic and statistical manual of mental disorders. 3rd ed., revised.* Washington, DC: The Association.

Andreasen, N.C. (1987). The diagnosis of schizophrenia. *Schizophrenia Bulletin, 13,* 9–22.

Angst, J. (1988). European long-term followup studies of schizophrenia. *Schizophrenia Bulletin, 14,* 501–513.

Bleuler, M. (1968). A 23-year longitudinal study of 208 schizophrenics and impressions in regard to the nature of schizophrenia. In D. Rosenthal, & S.S. Kety, (Eds.), *The transmission of schizophrenia* (pp. 3–12). New York: Pergamon Press.

Bleuler, M. (1978). *The schizophrenic disorders.* Translated by S.M. Clemens. New Haven: Yale University Press.

Brockington, I.F., Kendell, R.E., & Leff, J.P. (1978). Definition of schizophrenia: Concordance and prediction of outcome. *Psychological Medicine, 8,* 387–398.

Carpenter, W.T., Jr. (1987). Approaches to knowledge and understanding of schizophrenia. *Schizophrenia Bulletin, 13,* 1–8.

Carpenter, W.T., Jr., & Buchanan, R.W. (1989). Domains of psychopathology relevant to the study of etiology and treatment of schizophrenia. In S.C. Schulz, & C.A. Tamminga, (Eds.), *Schizophrenia: A scientific focus.* New York: Oxford University Press.

Carpenter, W.T., Jr., Heinrichs, D.W., & Wagman, A.M.I. (1985). On the heterogeneity of schizophrenia. In M. Alpert, (Ed.), *Controversies in schizophrenia* (pp. 25–37). New York: Guilford Press.

Ciompi, L. (1980a). Catamnestic long-term study of the course of life and aging of schizophrenics. *Schizophrenia Bulletin, 6,* 606–618.

Ciompi, L. (1980b). Three lectures on schizophrenia. *British Journal of Psychiatry, 136,* 413–420.

Crow, T.J. (1985). The two-syndrome concept: Origins and current status. *Schizophrenia Bulletin, 11,* 471–486.

Dube, K.C., Kumar, N., & Dube, S. (1984). Long-term course and outcome of the Agra cases in the International Pilot Study of Schizophrenia. *Acta Psychiatrica Scandinavica, 70,* 170–179.

Engelhardt, D.M., Rosen, R., Feldman, J., Engelhardt, J.A.Z., & Cohen, P. (1982). A 15-year follow-up of 646 schizophrenic outpatients. *Schizophrenia Bulletin, 8,* 493–503.

Flekkoy, K., Lund, I., & Astrup, C. (1975). Prolonged clinical and experimental followup of hospitalized schizophrenics. *Neuropsychobiology, 1,* 47–58.

Gottesman, I.I., McGuffin, P., & Farmer, A.E. (1987). Clinical genetics as clues to the "real" genetics of schizophrenia (A decade of modest gains while playing for time). *Schizophrenia Bulletin, 13,* 23–47.

Harding, C.M. (1988). Course types in schizophrenia: An analysis of European and American studies. *Schizophrenia Bulletin, 14,* 633–643.

Harding, C.M., Brooks, G.W., Ashikaga, T., Strauss, J.S., and Breier, A. (1987a). The Vermont longitudinal study of persons with severe mental illness: I. Methodology, study sample, and overall status 32 years later. *American Journal of Psychiatry, 144,* 718–726.

Harding, C.M., Brooks, G.W., Ashikaga, T., Strauss, J.S., and Breier, A. (1987b). The Vermont longitudinal study of persons with severe mental illness: II. Long-term outcome of subjects who restrospectively met DSM-III criteria for schizophrenia. *American Journal of Psychiatry, 144,* 727–735.

Hawk A.B., Carpenter, W.T., Jr., & Strauss, J.S. (1975). Diagnostic criteria and 5-year outcome in schizophrenia: A report from the International Pilot Study of Schizophrenia. *Archives of General Psychiatry, 32,* 343–347.

Heston, L.L. (1966). Psychiatric disorders in foster home reared children of schizophrenic mothers. *British Journal of Psychiatry, 112,* 819–825.

Huber, G., Gross, G., & Schüttler, R. (1975). A long-term follow-up study of schizophrenia: Psychiatric course of illness and prognosis. *Acta Psychiatrica Scandanivica, 52,* 49–57.

Huber, G., Gross, G., Schüttler, R., & Linz, M. (1980). Longitudinal studies of schizophrenic patients. *Schizophrenia Bulletin, 6,* 592–605.

Keller, M.B., Lavori, P.W., Endicott, J., Coryell, W., & Klerman, G.L. (1983). "Double depression": Two-year follow-up. *American Journal of Psychiatry, 140,* 689–694.

Keller, M.B., & Shapiro, R.W. (1982). "Double depression": Superimposition of acute depressive episodes on chronic depressive disorders. *American Journal of Psychiatry, 139,* 438–442.

Kendell, R.E. (1975). *The role of diagnosis in psychiatry.* Oxford, Blackwell.

Kendell, R.E., Brockington, I.F., & Leff, J.P. (1979). Prognostic implications of six alternative definitions of schizophrenia. *Archives of General Psychiatry, 35,* 25–31.

Kendler, K.S., Gruenberg, A.M., & Strauss, J.S. (1982) An independent analysis of the Copenhagen sample of the Danish adoption study of schizophrenia: V. The relationship between childhood social withdrawal and adult schizophrenia. *Archives of General Psychiatry, 39,* 1257–1261.

Kendler, K.S., Gruenberg, A.M., & Tsuang, M.T. (1986). A DSM-Ill family Study of the nonschizophrenic psychotic disorders. *American Journal of Psychiatry, 143,* 1098–1105.

Kety, S.S., Rosenthal, D., Wender, P.H., & Schulsinger, F. The types and prevalence of mental illness in the biological and adoptive families of adopted schizophrenics. In D. Rosenthal, and S.S. Kety, (Eds.) *The transmission of schizophrenia* (pp. 345–362). Oxford: Pergamon Press.

Kleist, K. (1960). Schizophrenic symptoms and cerebral pathology. *Journal of Mental Science, 106,* 246–253.

Langfeldt, G. (1969). Schizophrenia: Diagnosis and prognosis. *Behavioral Science, 14,* 173–182.

Leonhard, K. (1966). The question of prognosis in schizophrenia. International *Journal of Psychiatry, 2,* 633–635.

Lin, K. M., & Kleinman, A.M. (1988). Psychopathology and clinical course of schizophrenia: A cross-cultural perspective. *Schizophrenia Bulletin, 14,* 555–567.

Losonczy, M.F., Song, I.S., Mohs, R.C., Small, N.A., Davidson, M., Johns, C.A., & Davis, K.L. (1986). Correlates of lateral ventricular size in chronic schizophrenia: I. Behavioral and treatment response measures. *American Journal of Psychiatry, 143,* 976–981,

McGlashan, T.H. (1984). The Chestnut Lodge follow-up study: II. Longterm outcome of schizophrenia and the affective disorders. *Archives of General Psychiatry, 41,* 586–601.

McGlashan, T.H. (1987). Late onset improvement in chronic schizophrenia: Characteristics and prediction. In N.E. Miller, and G.D. Cohen (Eds.), *Schizophrenia and aging* (pp.61–73). New York: Guilford Publications, Inc.

McGlashan, T.H. (1988). A selective review of recent North American long-term followup studies of schizophrenia. *Schizophrenia Bulletin, 14,* 515–542.

McHugh, P.R., & Slavney, P.R. (1983). *The perspectives of psychiatry.* Baltimore: The Johns Hopkins University Press.

Pfohl, B., & Winokur, G. (1982). The evolution of symptoms in institutionalized hebephrenic/catatonic schizophrenics. *British Journal of Psychiatry, 141,* 567–572.

Pfohl, B., & Winokur, G. (1983). The micropsychopathology of hebephrenic/catatonic schizophrenics. *Journal of Nervous and Mental Disease, 171,* 296–300.

Rennie, T.A.C. (1942). Prognosis in manic-depressive psychoses. *American Journal of Psychiatry, 98,* 801–814.

Shelton, R.C., & Weinberger, D.R. (1986). X-ray computerized tomography studies in schizophrenia: A review and synthesis. In D.R. Weinberger, and H.A. Nasrallah, (Eds.), *Handbook of schizophrenia: The neurology of schizophrenia, vol. 1.* (pp. 207–250). New York: Elsevier Science Publishers.

Stephens, J.H. (1978). Long-term prognosis and followup in schizophrenia. *Schizophrenia Bulletin, 4,* 25–47.

Strauss, J.S., & Carpenter, W.T., Jr. (1979). The prognosis of schizophrenia. In L. Bellak, (Ed.), *Disorders of the schizophrenic syndrome* (pp. 472–491). New York: Basic Books.

Vaillant, G.E. (1962). The prediction of recovery in schizophrenia. *Journal of Nervous and Mental Disease, 35,* 534–543.

# The Vermont Longitudinal Study of Persons with Severe Mental Illness, I: Methodology, Study Sample, and Overall Status 32 Years Later

*Courtenay M. Harding, George W. Brooks, Takamaru Ashikaga, John S. Strauss, and Alan Breier*

At the time of original publication, the authors were with the Department of Psychiatry, Yale University School of Medicine, New Haven, CT; the College of Medicine and the College of Engineering and Mathematics, University of Vermont, Burlington, VT; and the Clinical Neuroscience Branch, NIMH, Rockville, MD.

Supported by NIMH grants MH-29575, MH-40607, and MH-00340 and by Biomedical grant S0705429 from the College of Medicine, University of Vermont.

This article originally appeared in the *American Journal of Psychiatry*, 1987; 144, 718–726 and is reprinted with permission.

**Abstract:** The authors report the latest findings from a 32-year longitudinal study of 269 back-ward patients from Vermont State Hospital. This intact cohort participated in a comprehensive rehabilitation program and was released to the community in a planned deinstitutionalization effort during the mid-1950s. At their 10-year follow-up mark, 70% of these patients remained out of the hospital but many were socially isolated and many were recidivists. Twenty to 25 years after their index release, 262 of these subjects were blindly assessed with structured and reliable protocols. One half to two thirds of them had achieved considerable improvement or recovery, which corroborates recent findings from Europe and elsewhere.

Understanding of the long-term course and outcome of patients with prolonged psychiatric disorders is often thwarted by patient and clinician mobility (Bachrach, 1984; Community Mental Health Centers and Psychiatrists, 1985), short-term caseloads shaped by academic training and service delivery systems (Neilsen, Stein, Talbott, et al., 1981; Schwartz & Goldfinger, 1981), the magnitude of methodological hurdles (Bachrach,1976; Bellak, 1948; Harding & Brooks, 1984; Langfeldt, 1956; Shapiro & Shader, 1979; Stephens, 1970; Strauss & Carpenter, 1972; Stromgren, 1961; Zubin, Salzinger, Burdock, et al., 1961) and disputes over the classification of the disorders under study (Stephens, 1970; Carpenter, Heinrichs &Wagman, 1985; Vailiant, 1984; Cooper, Kendell, Gurland, et al.,1972). These conditions have produced sporadic, contradictory data and untested assumptions that undercut attempts to clarify the nature of psychiatric illness, erode the ability to target treatment interventions, and muddle efforts toward comprehensive public policies.

It is possible, however, to generate a longitudinal study that overcomes most of these obstacles (Harding & Brooks, 1984, 1980). What is required is an intact cohort of patients, selected for the established chronicity of their illness, who are prospectively followed over many years, with careful record keeping, structured and reliable protocols, operational definitions, and standardized assessments of psychopathology and psychosocial functioning. The Vermont longitudinal study meets these criteria.

Since the early 1950s, members of the Vermont Longitudinal Research Project have been prospectively following the course of an intact cohort of 269 patients from the back wards of Vermont State Hospital (Harding & Brooks, 1984, 1980; Brooks, 1959, 1960, 1961; Brooks & Deane, 1960, 1965; Brooks, Deane, Lagor et al., 1963; Brooks, Deane, & Laqueur, 1970; Chitcick, Brooks, Irons et al., 1961) in much the same manner as the catamnestic studies of Manfred Bleuler at Burgholzli Hospital in Switzerland (1955, 1963, 1968, 1969, 1974, 1978, 1983). Known in the literature as *The Vermont Story* cohort (Chitcick, Brooks, Irons et al., 1961), the majority of these once profoundly ill, severely disabled, long-stay patients came from the sickest group in the hospital and met the DSM-I guidelines for the diagnosis of schizophrenia. They participated in an innovative pioneering rehabilitation program and were released to a hospital run comprehensive community aftercare program between 1955 and 1965 (Chitcick, Brooks, Irons et al., 1961).

Ten years after the inception of the program, we conducted a follow-up study, which indicated that two-thirds of the cohort were not hospitalized but were being maintained by heavy expenditures of clinical effort, time, and money (Deane & Brooks, 1967). Many of these patients were socially isolated while living and working in other institution-like settings. This follow-up period was similar to that charted by many longitudinal studies of similar patient groups, studies that have heavily influenced our ideas about the long-term course and outcome of people with severe and prolonged psychiatric disorders. The Vermont study and other longer studies provide evidence that some psychiatric illnesses require longer time periods to acquire a more complete and accurate picture of course and outcome.

In our effort to reassess the outcome of the Vermont cohort over a longer period of time, we were able to account for all but seven members of the original cohort (97%) in the early 1980s. This situation gave us the opportunity to find out whether these subjects were still as disabled as they had been 20 or more years earlier. We conducted both a structured cross-sectional assessment of the subjects' current status across a wide range of characteristics and a retrospective documentation of what had happened to members of this cohort in the intervening years. Adding these new data to the prospectively gathered information from the earlier hospitalization and rehabilitation program, we have been able to provide a more comprehensive picture of the long-term course of schizophrenia and other severe psychiatric disorders.

The specific focus of this report from the Vermont Longitudinal Research Project is a description of the sample, methodology, and design of the project and documentation of the long-term outcome for the cohort as a whole. A companion paper examines the long-term outcome of those subjects within the larger cohort who were rediagnosed as meeting the newer DSM-III criteria for schizophrenia (Harding, Brooks, Ashikaga et al., 1987).

## HISTORY OF THE PROJECT

### Phase I: The Rehabilitation Program in the 1950s

In the early 1950s, one of us (G.W.B.) began to study the efficacy of the then-new drug chlorpromazine (36). The back-ward "hopeless cases" were chosen as subjects. Some patients responded well and were eventually released. Other patients did not respond as well, but the effect of the releases was to give fresh hope to both the staff and the patients. In 1955 a multidisciplinary clinical team, sponsored by the Vermont State Hospital and the Vocational Rehabilitation Division of the Vermont State Department of Education, initiated a program of comprehensive rehabilitation and community placement for those back-ward patients who had not improved sufficiently with chlorpromazine. From January 1955 to December 1960, 269 patients who were considered among the most severely disabled and chronically mentally ill in the hospital were referred to the program (Chittick, Brooks, Irons et al., 1961). After the re-education of the staff, a program was constructed in collaboration with the patients that consisted of drug treatment, open-ward care in homelike conditions, group therapy, graded privileges, activity therapy, industrial therapy, vocational counseling, and self-help groups.

In the community treatment component, the same clinical team went into the community and established halfway houses and outpatient clinics, found job openings, made job placements, and linked patients to natural support networks. In that era of custodial care, before the advent of community mental health centers and the later deinstitutionalization movement, this comprehensive program was considered unusual and innovative.

The average age of the subjects was 40 years. The group was described by their clinical team in *The Vermont Story* as follows:

> At the time of selection, the group averaged 16 years' duration of illness with an average of 10 years of total disability and 6 years of continuous hospitalization. The group members had from one to ten hospitalizations, with a median of about two hospitalizations each. They had com-

pleted from none to 16 years of schooling, with a median of about nine grades. Nearly all had been declared financially incapable of paying anything for their own care, and were committed to the hospital at State expense. The group was, in other words, quite characteristic of the schizophrenic group as outlined by Hollingshead and Redlich (1958). They were middle-aged, poorly educated, lower-class individuals further impoverished by repeated and prolonged hospitalizations. In addition, this group had little social support. About five out of six were single, divorced, widowed, or separated. They were seldom visited by friends or relatives, and received very few packages or letters. (Chittick, Brooks, Irons et al., 1961, p. 30)

At the time the subjects were selected, the research team also described their presenting disabilities and impairments:

The patients, as a group, were very slow, concentrated poorly, seemed confused and frequently had some impairment or distortion of recent or remote memory. They were touchy, suspicious, temperamental, unpredictable, and over-dependent on others to make minor day-to-day decisions for them. They had many peculiarities of appearance, speech, behavior, and a very constricted sense of time, space, and other people so that their social judgment was inadequate. Very often they seemed to be goalless or, if they had goals, they were quite unrealistic. They seemed to lack initiative or concern about anything beyond their imme-diate surroundings. Because of their very low socioeconomic level and prolonged illness, they suffered from profound poverty, inadequate educational opportunities, and a very limited experience in the world.

These patients also suffered a high incidence of chronic physical disabil-ities. Their psychomotor performance in a wide variety of tests was impaired so that their reaction times were prolonged and their ability to perform any type of skilled or precise activity was impaired. They suf-fered an increased incidence of many degenerative and chronic dis-eases, including tuberculosis and malignant tumors.

There was a very high incidence of needs in such areas as dental care, visual corrections, and hearing aids. Many patients, especially after pro-longed phenothiazine treatment, were obese. Care of the feet had been neglected. In our experience, there also seemed to be a high incidence of chronic skin disorders including eczema-dermatitis, tinea, and psori-asis. (Chittick, Brooks, Irons et al., 1961, p. 31)

### Phase II. The 1965 Follow-Up Study

In 1965, after 5 years of the hospital-based rehabilitation program and 5 years during which the primary focus was the community component, Deane and Brooks (1967) conducted a follow-up study of these patients. They found that two-thirds of the cohort could be maintained in the community, if sufficient transitional facilities and adequate aftercare were provided. Seventy percent of the subjects were out of the hospital at that follow-up: 30% had been discharged and had never returned, and 40% had been readmitted at some time but had been discharged again. Of the 30% of the subjects who were in the hospital at follow-up, 20% had been readmitted and had stayed, and 10% had never been discharged. The average number of readmissions for the recidivists' in the cohort was 1.98.

Other findings indicated that being female, schizophrenic, chronically ill, and married during some part of one's life were important predictors of good functioning at follow-up. Age at first admission did not predict which patients would do better. At the 1965 follow-up, most, subjects were single (60%), used community care facilities primarily for socializing, had a tendency to replace the institution with sheltered employment (e.g., a job as a cook in a nursing home, with bed and board), and maintained substantial contact with rehabilitation workers.

Thus, 5 to 10 years after release from the rehabilitation program, 70% of the patients were out of the hospital, which was considered remarkable at the time because they had been expected to live out their lives in the hospital. However, the study concluded with a warning:

> Implicit in our findings is the fact that any plan for rehabilitation of the chronic patient be conceived as long term, since all of our evidence suggests that the commitment necessary to the chronic mental patient has no foreseeable end, and that unless constant attention be given to the chronic patient, the end result may be simply that he is out of the hospital, but operating at a high level of inadequacy and a low level of employment. (Deane & Brooks, 1967, pp. ii, iii)

It is at this point that most follow-up studies stop and most programs are discontinued. Thus, most of our understanding of the long-term outcome for severe mental disorder is derived from such shorter-term data. The question asked in the present study was, Do these patients still continue to display such impairment and disabilities 20 to 25 years later, as predicted earlier by our own research team?

**Phase III: The 20- to 25-Year Follow-Up Study**

We recently completed our latest follow-up of the original 269 subjects. We have follow-up data on the 22 subjects with organic disorders but removed them from our ongoing analyses to make our study comparable to others in the field. Table 1 reveals the cohort's current status.

**Table 1. Status at 20- to 25-Year Follow-up of 269 Chronic Psychiatric Patients in the Vermont Study**

| Subjects' Follow-Up Status | Total Group | Subjects Remaining After Exclusion of 22 with Organic Disorders ($N = 247$)[a] | |
|---|---|---|---|
| | | N | % |
| Alive and interviewed | 178 | 168 | 68 |
| Deceased, family interviewed | 71 | 61 | 25 |
| Alive; refused participation[b] | 13 | 11 | 4 |
| Could not be located | 7 | 7 | 3 |

[a] Twenty-two subjects classified as having organic disorders according to DSM-III criteria at the index admission were excluded from the data analyses.

[b] Most of these subjects were interviewed and gave considerable information, but they refused to sign the forms permitting use of their data.

The catamnestic period of the subjects ranges from 22 to 62 years, with an average of 32 years, which makes this study one of the longest ever conducted. The subjects who were still alive at follow-up ($N = 168$) were divided nearly evenly between the sexes (81 men and 87 women). The mean age was 59 years (range = 38–83 years), with two-thirds of the group 55 years old or older. The year of birth of the subjects ranged from 1897 to 1942.

The remainder of this report focuses on the method and results of the long-term follow-up study of the subjects who were still alive and could be interviewed.

**METHOD**

**Measures**

Batteries of structured instruments were used for collecting data. They included interview schedules and record abstraction protocols.

The Vermont Community Questionnaire (VCQ) was a battery of interview instruments designed to document and assess a subject's history and functioning in a wide variety of areas across time. Fifteen established scales were combined to create the VCQ and to acquire such a database (Harding & Brooks, 1984). The field interviewers were blind to hospital records and diagnostic information about each subject.

The VCQ consisted of two structured interviews, each with standardized probes, ratings, and computer coding. The VCQ-cross-sectional interview (VCQ-C) assessed current status; the VCQ-longitudinal interview (VCQ-L) documented retrospective data over the preceding 20 to 25 years.

The major areas of functioning covered by the VCQ-C were residence, work, finances, intimate relationships, family information, social support system, typical weekly activities, basic self-care, utilization of treatment/social services, contact with the criminal justice system, community involvement, degree of satisfaction, environmental stressors, competence, and psychopathology. Approximately 1 hour and 15 minutes were required to administer the interview's 135 questions. The rater section of the interview battery contained 98 additional items based on observation and other information gathered from the subjects and their environment.

The second interview (the VCQ-L) required 75 minutes and was held within 1 week of the first. The VCQ-L had 156 questions that documented status and events during the preceding 20 years in a year-by-year follow-back procedure utilizing a modified Meyer/ Leighton Life Chart (Leighton, Leighton & Gregorio, 1949). This chart provided a graphic overview of each subject's life and was completed with a set of structured probes, codes, and protocols created for this project. The Life Chart was a large, lined sheet of paper vertically separated into years, from 1982 at the top to 1955 at the bottom, and horizontally separated into 10 outcome areas. These domains included residence, hospitalization, work, source of income, important personal relationships, deaths of important people, other life events, use of community support systems, physical health, and medications. A Life Chart was completed for each subject, who worked with the interviewer on the chart spread out on a table.

Each of the field interviewers had had 5 to 8 years of previous clinical experience with a range of clients who were deinstitutionalized and labeled "chronic patients" by their community mental health clinics.

A small instrument called the Verinform was designed to verify the interview information by asking a variety of informants about the subjects' current status and historical data. The Verinform was used for interviews with general practitioners, aftercare or vocational rehabilitation counselors, family, or friends whoever knew the subject well.

The Hospital Record Review Form was designed to provide a standardized method for recording data from Vermont State Hospital records. The interview instrument known as the Psychiatric and Personal History Schedule from the World Health Organization (WHO) Collaborative Project on Determinants of Outcome of Severe Mental Disorders (World Health Organization, 1978) was converted from an interview format to a standardized form for abstracting record information on psychiatric history in a systematic and structured manner. The new format maintained the coded answers but assigned them to document five different time periods: first admission, episodes between first and index admission, index admission (the admission preceding entry into the rehabilitation program—the only common denominator across all subjects and designated arbitrarily as index for research definition purposes), life history, and episodes during the years in the community after index release. In addition, the WHO signs and symptoms checklist was augmented with Strauss's Case Record Rating Scale (Strauss & Harder, 1981), the Strauss-Carpenter Prognostic Scale (Strauss & Carpenter, 1977), and the Global Assessment Scale (Endicott, Spitzer & Reiss, 1976). The record reviewer was blind to all outcome and interview data. She was a clinical psychologist with several years of experience with Vermont State Hospital records.

The component instruments in each battery that used the work of others had been tested extensively for reliability and validity by their originators. However, groups of individual questions from each classic scale were taken from their original context and interwoven with questions from other instruments (e.g., the questions on social relationships from all instruments were put together to make a more natural interview sequence); therefore, reliability studies of the entire VCQ and Hospital Record Review Form batteries were deemed essential.

Initially, the VCQ-C and VCQ-L interviews were each field-tested with a wide range of community people matched in age to the cohort. These consultants critiqued the appropriateness of the questions vis-à-vis their life experiences and suggested that we add questions about powerlessness, disability income, medication compliance, and the increasing number of deaths of people in their personal support systems. This strategy led to improvement in the battery's ability to tap relevant issues for people in the age ranges to be assessed and improvement in its construct validity. Changes and deletions of items honed it to the size used in the follow-up study.

Each field battery was then subjected to two sets of inter-rater trials (trial 1, $N = 21$ pairs; trial 2, $N = 18$ pairs). The sets were completed 6 months apart to test for the degree of change in raters' assessments during the intervening time period. Both raters attended a cross-sectional and a longitudinal interview for each of the test subjects. Each rater scored the interview independently, and the pairs of ratings were then compared for concordance. The kappa coefficients from the first and second sets of trials are shown in Table 2.

The Hospital Record Review, with 1,800 items, was divided into its five subsections and also subjected to trials of inter-rater agreement between the one reviewer who left the team and the one who subsequently joined the project. Kappa coefficients ranged from .40 ($p < .01$) to .95 ($p < .001$), and all were significant.

In summary, on the basis of the evidence presented, we rendered the conclusion that these instruments were moderately reliable and contained an acceptable degree of face and construct validity.

**Table 2. Kappa Levels for Inter-rater Agreement on Trials of Instrument Batteries Given to Vermont Study Subjects**

| | Kappa | |
|---|---|---|
| Instrument | First Trial | Second Trial |
| Field instruments | | |
| Vermont Community Questionnaire | | |
|   Cross-sectional | | |
|     Interview | .96[a] | .97[a] |
|     Rater section | .50[b] | .70[b] |
|   Longitudinal | | |
|     Interview | .96[a] | .96a |
|     Rater section | .64[b] | .59b |
| Hospital Record Review Form | | |
|   First admission | .41[b] | |
|   Episodes between first and index admission | .95a | |
|   Index admission | .40[b] | |
|   Episodes after discharge | .94[b] | |
|   Topical life history | .67[b] | |
| Life Chart (experimental) | .98[a] | .78[b] |

[a] $p < .001$.
[b] $p < .01$.

**Procedure**

Each subject still living at the time of follow-up, who was willing to participate, was given two interviews (approximately 1 week apart) at his or her place of residence by one of the two interviewers. In addition, two or three people who knew the subject well were interviewed in a structured protocol to verify current status and historical data. These people included relatives, general practitioners, counselors, clinicians, and friends. All but 17 subjects (10%) resided in Vermont. The subjects who lived elsewhere were interviewed with the same protocol. Strict attention was paid to the protection of patients' rights such as privacy, confidentiality, refusal, and informed consent.

Relatives, friends, and caregivers of the deceased members of the original cohort were also interviewed. A structured protocol documented the lives and the levels of functioning of these subjects until the time of their deaths. The inclusion of these data provided a more balanced view of the long-term course of severe psychiatric disorders than has been available in past studies, which have relied on data from survivors only. A separate report will be devoted to the deceased subjects.

### RESULTS

This group of back-ward patients represented the most severely ill group from Vermont's only state hospital. Two to three decades after a comprehensive rehabilitation program and a planned deinstitutionalization, one-half to two-thirds of these patients were rated as considerably improved or recovered. The findings also showed a wide variation in many areas of functioning for these patients.

#### Demographic Data for the Cohort at Follow-Up

Fifty-one percent of the 168 subjects who were alive, did not have an organic disorder, and were interviewed had not completed high school. However, an eighth grade education was considered to be the norm before the 1940s in Vermont (Bureau of the Census, 1945).

Nineteen percent ($N = 32$) of the 168 subjects were currently married, and 7% ($N = 11$) were widowed. Fifty-one percent ($N = 86$) were still single, and 23% ($N = 39$) were divorced or separated.

Eighty-eight percent of the subjects ($N = 148$) lived in residential and rural neighborhoods rather than industrial or commercial areas. Fifty percent ($N = 81$) lived in independent housing (house, apartment, mobile home, or rooming house), and 40% ($N = 64$) lived in boarding homes. (This information was coded for an $N$ of 161.) Five single middle-aged men were currently in the hospital, seven were in level II nursing homes (institutions for individuals, including the mentally retarded, who do not require 24-hour nursing care but who do require care above the level of room and board), and four were in other settings. Of the subjects receiving boarding home care, seven seemed capable of living independently, often assisting the boarding home operator and taking responsibility for management of the home. An additional 23 were actively involved in activities within the house, at the local community mental health center or in the community and were self-motivated. Longitudinal patterns of residence revealed an average of two readmissions for the group since release from the index hospitalization. The average total length of stay was 2 years or less.

Twenty-six percent ($N = 44$) of the 168 subjects were employed; half of them were classified as working in unskilled jobs. Thirty-three percent ($N = 56$) were unemployed, 8% ($N = 14$) were volunteers, and 5% ($N = 8$) were housewives. Due to the advanced ages in the sample, an additional 26% ($N = 44$) were classified as elderly, widowed, or retired. Solid information was unavailable on four (2%) of the subjects for this rating.

Our findings also indicated that 85% of the sample had a gross income of less than $10,000 a year. In 1982 Vermont ranked 36th in the nation for per capita income, with an average of $9,979 (Summary of US Census Data for Vermont Cities and Towns, 1982). Using an assessment from the Community Care Schedule by Schwartz, Miller & Spitzer et al. (1977) and budget sheets outlining expenses and income, we rated 77% of the subjects as having an adequate income; the schedule's definition of adequate was that the "amount of money received will cover the subject's basic needs comfortably."

### Overall Psychological and Social Functioning

The Global Assessment Scale (GAS) (Endicott, Spitzer & Reiss, 1976) was chosen to provide a single score that would capture the essence of the subjects' psychological and social functioning. Scores on this scale showed that 68% ($N$ = 114) of the study sample were functioning above the cutoff point of 61 designated by the authors as "some mild symptoms (e.g., depressive mood or mild insomnia) or some difficulties in several areas of functioning, but generally functioning pretty well, has some meaningful relationships and most untrained people would not consider him sick." A 2X2 (GAS by Sex) chi-square test with Yates' correction revealed no significant differences between the sexes in level of functioning ($\chi^2$ = 0.13, $df$ = 1, $p$ = .72), but it should be noted that 68% of those with a GAS score between 31 and 70 were men, while 62% of those with a GAS score between 71 and 90 were women (see Figure 1).

In order to describe more of the individual components that went into the assessment of overall functioning, the Levels of Function Scale (Strauss & Carpenter, 1977) was used. On this scale, subjects are scored from 0 (poor) to 4 (best) on nine items of interest; the reliability of the scale has been demonstrated. A product-moment correlation revealed that the overall total score was highly correlated ($r$ = .88) with the GAS score just reported. Table 3 summarizes the findings from the Levels of Function Scale. Individual areas of functioning were restored for one-half to four-fifths of this group. Because of the wide variation in outcome functioning at follow-up within specific subjects, the global rating of slight or no impairment was given to only 55% ($N$ = 92) of the cohort. No impairment was rated for subjects who were asymptomatic and living independently, had close relationships, were employed or were otherwise productive citizens, were able to care for themselves, and led full lives in general. Other subjects did well in some areas of functioning but not so well in others. Theirs was a very mixed picture on a continuum weighted toward dysfunction.

## Figure 1. Global Assessment Scale Scores of 168 Subjects in the Vermont Study Who Were Alive and Were Interviewed at Follow-Up

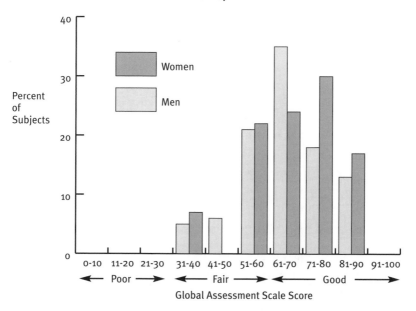

## Table 3. Results From the Strauss-Carpenter Lewis of Function Scale for the 168 Subjects of the Vermont Study Who Were Alive and Interviewed

| Area of Functioning | N | % |
|---|---|---|
| Not in hospital in past year | 140 | 83 |
| Met with friends every week or two | 111 | 66 |
| Had one or more moderately to very close friends | 128 | 76 |
| Employed in past year[a] | 79 | 47 |
| Displayed slight or no symptoms | 121 | 72 |
| Able to meet basic needs | 133 | 79 |
| Led moderate to very full life | 128 | 76 |
| Slight or no impairment in overall function | 92 | 55 |

[a] Quality of work could not be rated; issues of confidentiality prevented visits to subjects' work sites.

### DISCUSSION

Current assumptions about the long-term course of schizophrenia and other severe mental illnesses include the idea that people with repeated episodes are at best likely to achieve marginal levels of functioning over time. Heterogeneity of outcome is expected, with a dichotomized split between "process" and "reactive" patients (Garmezy, 1965), good premorbid and poor premorbid functioning (Phillips, 1953), or type I and type II illness (Crowe, 1980), or the familiar breakdown into "one-third get better, one-third stay the same, and one-third get worse." The findings from the Vermont cohort, drawn from the most chronically ill patients (the lowest third of the hospital), revealed that over one-half of these once profoundly ill, long-stay patients had achieved a much higher level of functioning than had been predicted by our own research team during the early days of the patients' community tenure. Their achievement is even more remarkable given their original levels of chronicity.

These findings hold for other subsets of the cohort as well. For example, our companion paper in this issue (Harding, Brooks, Ashikaga et al., 1987), about the subjects who were rediagnosed as meeting the DSM-III criteria for schizophrenia, describes similar proportions of restored and heterogeneous functioning, as does our forthcoming paper about the outcome of the deceased subjects before they died. Another paper will delineate the reduction by 46% of the number of individual subjects who currently use the public mental health system in Vermont. It appears that they have left the formal system and turned to natural community supports over time.

Our findings of heterogeneity of outcome, with significant improvement or recovery for half the cohort, corroborate the results of four other long-term follow-up studies conducted within the last 15 years: Manfred Bleuler's 23-year study of 208 patients at Burgholzli Hospital in Zurich (1978), Ciompi and Muller's 37-year study of 289 patients in Lausanne (1976), Huber and colleagues' 22-year follow-up study of 502 subjects in Bonn (1979), and the "Iowa 500" study by Tsuang, Woolson, & Fleming, (1979). The studies from Europe have not been seriously regarded by some investigators because of such methodological difficulties as the lack of reliable diagnostic criteria, the number of deceased and missing subjects at follow-up (especially in the Lausanne and Bonn studies), and the use of less structured clinical interviews to assess psychopathology and acquire outcome data (Shapiro & Shader, 1979). However, the Iowa and Vermont studies have improved on many of these methodological deficiencies, and the findings are nearly identical to those of the European studies.

Thus, of the 1,300 subjects in the five studies who were assessed two or three decades later, more than one-half were found to have considerably improved or recovered (Harding, Zubin & Strauss, 1987). Such similarities in the findings across studies seem to override the differences. Together, the data give evidence that, contrary to the expected downward and deteriorating course for schizophrenia or for other severe and chronic psychiatric disorders, symptoms can be ameliorated over time and functioning can be restored. Further support for the heterogeneity of patients' outcome functioning is supplied by many other shorter follow up studies as well (Strauss & Carpenter, 1977; Ciompi & Miller 1976; Gardos, Cole & LaBrie,1982; Strauss, Kokes, Ritzler, et al., 1978; World Health Organization, 1973).

Although the Vermont Longitudinal Research Project achieved a more rigorous design than many earlier efforts, the study still has several shortcomings. In 1955, the original selection of the subjects depended on referrals of patients by the staff to the rehabilitation program. The original investigators then restricted entry into the research cohort to the most chronic patients only.

The project was primarily aimed toward establishing a treatment program to deinstitutionalize the patients remaining in the back wards. This program represented one of the first attempts at deinstitutionalization in the United States and was one of the few that was carefully planned. The study became a follow-up study as time and contacts continued. The standardization of assessments and the structured protocols were instituted as the study proceeded. Thus, the study was not initially planned as a 32-year follow-up but ended up as such.

There were no subjects who could become a control group in the Vermont State Hospital, inasmuch as the entire most severely ill third of the patients in the state's only hospital (excluding the geriatric population) was selected to participate in the program. For years an appropriate comparison sample was sought, and recently a study was undertaken in the state of Maine that matched each of the Vermont study's subjects by age, sex, diagnosis, and level of chronicity with a patient from the Augusta Mental Health Institute. These new subjects are being interviewed with the same protocols and instruments to determine their life courses and illness trajectories. The primary difference between the two samples is the presence or absence of rehabilitation efforts. It is hoped that the difference in outcome between rehabilitated and nonrehabilitated subjects will be helpful in the study of mediating factors in long-term course.

As we have noted, the Vermont subjects were selected from the most disabled patients in the hospital. We have portrayed the severity of their handicaps, the length of their institutionalization, their lack of response to phenothiazines after an average of 2½ years of psychotropic treatment, the back-ward hopeless atmosphere in which they had lived for years, the broken ties with family and community, as well as impoverished financial and educational backgrounds. In addition, many subjects behaved violently or in other unacceptable ways in their communities and were often brought to the hospital by local police. Few of these subjects used street drugs, but some abused alcohol.

Our findings should be generalizable to similar long-stay patients, estimated by Minkoff (1978) and others to number about 1.1 million in the United States. The results of the study could be considered conservative for the long-term course of severe mental illness because anyone who is less severely ill, who has spent less time institutionalized, and who is less severely handicapped may have a better chance of long term recovery. However, the use of street drugs, multiple short-term hospitalizations, and the predominance of DSM-III axis II diagnoses add new complexities to the current picture of prolonged psychiatric disorder, especially schizophrenia, for subgroups of younger patients; these are currently being assessed in the elegant studies of Test, Knoedler and Allness (1985) in Wisconsin.

Another aspect of the question of generalizability is whether our subject's improvement was an artifact of the quiet, benign rural environment. Zubin (1985) pointed out, "Where in the world would you get the natural history of schizophrenia if not under the best circumstances? You wouldn't want to go to the ghetto, where people are suffering from a lot of other sources of distress, to see whether the outcome is good there. You want to go to the best place, where triggering mechanisms are at a minimum" (p. 407).

The impact of rural life on the course of illness is very complex. In 1982 Vermont was a community of 518,846 people scattered in clumps across 9,273 square miles (Bureau of the Census, 1984; Arnold, 1982), with a density of 56 people per square mile. Vermonters tend to pride themselves on Yankee individuality and independence (Hill, 1960; Merrill, 1975); therefore it is possible to regulate one's social distance and to find a niche sometimes for people with eccentric behaviors. Despite its ecological niches and visual beauty, however, Vermont registers fairly high rates of suicide (Burlington, Vermont State Health Department, 1992), alcoholism, and incest (Division of Planning and Rehabilitation Services, 1982), as well as unemployment, poverty, and long, difficult winters. Families and patients alike experience the pain of stigma and social rejection. Therefore, it is not clear whether the primary environment has been the deciding factor in the improvement process, but perhaps the secondary effects of a rural environment, such as small numbers and stability, have been helpful. As we said earlier in describing phase I of the project's history, the same five members of the clinical research team went with patients to the community and were available for support and clinical care over a 10-year period when the subjects were both in and out of the hospital. This continuity of contact persisted during the second 10 years, as people changed their roles from clinicians and patients to friends and neighbors. (It also may explain the 97% rate of original subjects found and the 5% refusal rate.)

Further, in any discussion of the effect of rural life, it is important to point out that the data from the Bonn and Zurich studies came from industrialized cities and that Lausanne is a medium-sized city. Only Iowa and Vermont are clearly rural localities, but the trends in the data across all five studies with different environments are similar.

The knowledge gained from our study and others that there is a wide range of long-term outcomes provides an impetus to continue the search, begun by the investigators in the three European studies, for longitudinal patterns of course of illness demonstrated by subgroups of patients who achieve considerable improvement or recovery and those who do not. Additional questions to be asked now are: When in the course of their illness did those patients who improved begin to do so? Are there any predictors of future outcome status? Many older concepts of predictors have not been as strong as once thought (Bleuler, 1978; Strauss & Carpenter, 1977; Ciompi, 1980; Huber, Gross, Schuttler et al., 1980; Valliant, 1978, and our companion paper, 1987), and we have begun investigations into these important questions.

The answers will begin to reshape our psychological and biological concepts of severe mental illness and the way in which service delivery systems and treatments are designed.

### Acknowledgments
The following people contributed to this phase of the project design and methodology—Brendan Maher, PhD; the late Robert Shapiro, MD; Bonnie Spring, PhD; Joseph L. Fleiss, PhD; Jane Murphy, PhD; Joseph M. Tobin, MD; Lee Robins, PhD; Leona Bachrach, PhD; Edward Zigler, PhD; Stanley Herr, JD; and Jon Rolf, PhD; additional aid with instrumentation—William Woodruff, MD; Alan Gelenberg, MD; Gerard Hogarty, MSW; Paula Clayton, MD; Janet Mikkelsen, MSW; and Thomas McGlashan, MD; data collection—Paul D. Landerl, MSW; Carmine M. Consalvo, PhD; Janet Wakefield, PhD; William Deane, PhD; Barbara Curtis, RN; and Robert Lagor, BA; data management—Susan Childers, ACSW Lori Witham; Mary Ellen Fortini, PhD; Sandi Tower; Andrea Pierce; Mary Noonan; Dorothy Myer; and Joanne Gobrecht; manuscript review—Luc Ciompi, Prof Dr Med; Prof John Cooper; Boris Astrachan, MD; Malcolm B. Bowers, Jr., MD; Richard Musty, PhD; George Albee PhD; Thomas Achenbach, PhD; Paul Carling, PhD; Lawrence Gordon, PhD and Frederick Schmidt, PhD; and manuscript preparation—Nancy L. Ryan.

**REFERENCES**
American Psychiatric Association and National Council of Community Mental Health Centers. (1985). *Community mental health centers and psychiatrists*. Washington, DC, and Rockville, MD: Author.

Arnold, T.W. (1982). *Land area and population history in Vermont Data Series*. Burlington: University of Vermont, Center for Rural Studies.

Bachrach L.L. (1984). The concept of young adult chronic psychiatric patients: Questions from a research perspective. *Hospital and Community Psychiatry, 35,* 573–580.

Bachrach, L.L. (1976). A note on some recent studies of released mental hospital patients in the community. *American Journal of Psychiatry, 133,* 73–75.

Bellak, L. (1948). *Dementia praecox.* New York: Grune & Stratton.

Bleuler, M. (1955). Research and changes in concepts in the study of schizophrenia, 1941–1950. *Bull Isaac Ray Medical Library, 3,* 1–132.

Bleuler, M. (1963). Conception of schizophrenia within the last fifty years and today. *Proceedings of the Royal Society of Medicine, 56,* 945–952.

Bleuler, M. (1968). A 23-year longitudinal study of 208 schizophrenics and impressions in regard to the nature of schizophrenia. In D. Rosenthal & S.S. Kety (Eds.), *The transmission of schizophrenia.* Oxford, England: Pergamon Press.

Bleuler, M. (1969). The genesis and nature of schizophrenia. *Psychiatry Digest, 30,* 17–26.

Bleuler, M. (1974). The long-term course of the schizophrenic psychoses. *Psychological Medicine, 4,* 244–254.

Bleuler, M. (1978). *The schizophrenic disorders: Long-term patient and family studies.* Translated by S. M. Clemens. New Haven: Yale University Press.

Bleuler, M. (1983). Schizophrenic deterioration. *British Journal of Psychiatry, 143,* 78–79.

Brooks, G.W. (1956). Experience with the, use of chlorpromazine and reserpine in psychiatry. *New England Journal of Medicine, 254,* 1119–1123.

Brooks, G.W. (1959). Opening a rehabilitation house. In M. Greenblatt & B Simon (Eds.), *Rehabilitation of the mentally ill.* Washington, DC: American Association for the Advancement of Science.

Brooks, G.W. (1960). Rehabilitation of hospitalized chronic schizophrenic patients. In I. Appleby, J. Scher & J. Cumming (Eds.), *Chronic schizophrenia.* Chicago: Free Press.

Brooks, G.W. (1961). Motivation for work in psychiatric rehabilitation. *Diseases of the Nervous System, 22,* 129–132.

Brooks, G.W. (1961). Rural community influences and supports in a rehabilitation program for state hospital patients. In M. Greenblatt, D. J. Levinson & G. L. Klerman, (Eds.), *Mental patients in transition.* Springfield, IL: Charles C Thomas.

Brooks, G.W., & Deane, W.N. (1960). Attitudes of released chronic schizophrenic patients concerning illness and recovery as revealed by a structured post-hospital interview. *Journal of Clinical Psychology, 16,* 259–264.

Brooks, G.W., & Deane, W.N. (1965). The chronic mental patient in the community. *Diseases of the Nervous System, 26,* 85–90.

Brooks, G.W., Deane, W.N., Lagor R.C. et al. (1963). Varieties of family participation in the rehabilitation of released chronic schizophrenic patients. *Journal of Nervous and Mental Disease, 136,* 432–444.

Brooks, G.W., Deane, W.N., & Laqueur HP. (1970). Fifteen years of work therapy. *Diseases of the Nervous System (Suppl), 31,* 161–165.

Carpenter, W.T., Heinrichs, D.W., & Wagman, A.M.I. (1985). On the heterogeneity of schizophrenia. In M. Alpert (Ed.), *Controversies in schizophrenia: Changes and constancies.* New York: Gilford Press.

Chittick, R. A., Brooks, G. W., Irons, F. S., et al. (1961). *The Vermont Story.* Burlington, VT: Queen City Press.

Ciompi, L. (1980). Catamnestic long-term study on the course of life and aging of schizophrenics. *Schizophrenia Bulletin 6,* 606–618.

Ciompi, L., & Müller, C. (1976). *Lebensweg und alter der schizophrenen. Eine katamnestische longzeitstudie bis ins senium.* Berlin: Springer-Verlag.

Cooper, J.E., Kendell, R.E., Gurland, B.J., et al. (1972). *Psychiatric diagnosis in New York and London: A comparative study of mental hospital admissions.* New York: Oxford University Press.

Crowe, T. (1980). Molecular pathology of schizophrenia: more than one disease process? *British Medical Journal, 12,* 16–68.

Deane, W.N, & Brooks, G.W. (1967). *Five-year follow-up of chronic hospitalized patients.* Waterbury, VT: Vermont State Hospital.

Division of Planning and Rehabilitation Services. (1982). *Statistics.* Waterbury, Vermont Department of Human Services.

Endicott, J., Spitzer, R.L., & Reiss, J.I. et al. (1976). The Global Assessment Scale: A procedure for measuring overall severity of psychiatric disturbance. *Archives of General Psychiatry, 31,* 766–771.

Gardos, G., Cole, J.O., & LaBrie, R.A. (1982). A 12-year follow-up study of chronic schizophrenics. *Hospital and Community Psychiatry, 33,* 983–984.

Garmezy, N. (1965). Process and reactive schizophrenia: some conceptions and issues. In M. M. Katz, J. Cole, W. E. Barton, *The role and methodology of classification in psychiatry and psychopathology* (NIMH Public Health Service Publication 1584). Washington, DC: Government Printing Office.

Harding, C.K., & Brooks, G.W. (1980). Longitudinal assessment for a cohort of chronic schizophrenics discharged twenty years ago. *Psychiatric Journal of the University of Ottawa, 5,* 274–278.

Harding, C.M. & Brooks, G.W. (1984). Life assessment of a cohort of chronic schizophrenics discharged twenty years ago. In S. Mednick, M. Harway, K. Finello (Eds.), *The handbook of longitudinal research, vol. 11.* New York: Praeger.

Harding, C.K., Brooks, G.W., Ashikaga, T., et al. (1987). The Vermont longitudinal study of persons with severe mental illness, II: Long-term outcome of subjects who retrospectively met DSM-III criteria for schizophrenia. *American Journal of Psychiatry, 144,* 727–735.

Harding, C. M., Zubin, J., & Strauss, J.S. (1987) Chronicity in schizophrenia: fact, partial fact, or artifact? *Hospital and Community Psychiatry, 38*(5), 477–486.

Hill, R.N. (1960). *Yankee Kingdom: Vermont and New Hampshire.* New York: Harper & Brothers.

Hollingshead, A.B., & Redlich, F.C. (1958). *Social class and mental illness: A community study.* New York: John Wiley & Sons.

Huber, G., Gross, G., & Schüttler R. (1980). Longitudinal studies of schizophrenic patients. *Schizophrenia Bulletin, 6,* 592–605.

Huber, G., Gross, G., & Schüttler, R. (1979). Schizophrenie: Verlaufs und sozialpsychiatrische Langzeit unter suchfigen an den 1945 bis 1959 in Bonn hospitalisierten schizophrenen Kranken. *Monographien aus dem Gesamtgebiete der Psychiatrie. Bd. 21.* Berlin: Springer-Verlag.

Langfeldt, G. (1956). The prognosis in schizophrenia. *Acta Psychiatrica Neurologica Scandinavica (Suppl), 110.*

Leighton, A.K. & Leighton, D.C. (1949). *Gregorio, the hand-trembler: A psychobiological personality study of a Navaho Indian.* Peabody Museum Papers. Cambridge, MA: Harvard University Press.

Merrill, P.H. (1975). *Vermont under four flags: A history of the Green Mountain state (1635–1975).* Barre, VT: Northlight Studio Press.

Minkoff, K. (1978). A map of chronic patients. In J. A. Talbott (Ed.), *The chronic mental patient.* Washington, DC: American Psychiatric Association.

Montpelier, Agency of Development and Community Affairs, State of Vermont (1982). *Summary of US Census Data for Vermont Cities and Towns.*

Neilsen, A.C., III, Stein L.I., Talbott J.A. et al. (1981). Encouraging psychiatrists to work with chronic patients: opportunities and limitations of residency education. *Hospital and Community Psychiatry, 32,* 767–775.

Phillips, L. (1953). Case history data and prognosis in schizophrenia. *Journal of Nervous and Mental Disease, 117,* 515–525.

Schwartz, C., Miller, C., Spitzer, R.I. et al. (1977). *Community Care Schedule (CCS).* New York: New York State Psychiatric Institute.

Schwartz, S.R., & Goldfinger S.M. (1981). The new chronic patient: clinical characteristics of an emerging subgroup. *Hospital and Community Psychiatry, 32,* 470–474.

Shapiro, R., & Shader, R. (1979). Selective review of results of previous follow-up studies of schizophrenia and other psychoses, In *World Health Organization, Schizophrenia: An international follow-up study.* New York: John Wiley & Sons.

Stephens, J.H. (1970). Long-term course and prognosis in schizophrenia. *Seminars in Psychiatry, 2,* 464–485.

Strauss J.S., & Carpenter, W.T. (1972). The prediction of outcome in schizophrenia, I: Characteristics of outcome. *Archives of General Psychiatry, 27,* 739–746.

Strauss J.S., & Carpenter, W.T. (1977). Prediction of outcome in schizophrenia, III: Five-year outcome and its predictors. *Archives of General Psychiatry, 34,* 159–163.

Strauss J.S., & Harder, D.W. (1981). The Case Record Rating Scale. *Psychiatry Research, 4,* 333–345.

Strauss J.S., Kokes, R.F., Ritzler, B.A., et al. (1978). Patterns of disorder in first admission psychiatric patients. *Journal of Nervous and Mental Disease, 166,* 611–625.

Stromgren, E. (1961). Recent studies of prognosis and outcome in mental disorders. In P. Hoch & J. Zubin, *Comparative epidemiology of the mental disorders*. New York: Grime & Stratton.

Test, M.A., Knoedler, W.H. & Allness, D. J. (1985). The long-term treatment of young schizophrenics in a community support program. *New Directions for Mental Health Services, 26*, 17–27.

Tsuang, M.T., Woolson, R.F., & Fleming, J.A. (1979). Long-term outcome of major psychoses, I: Schizophrenia and affective disorders compared with psychiatrically symptom-free surgical conditions. *Archives of General Psychiatry, 36*, 1295–1301.

US Department of Commerce, Bureau of the Census. (1945). *Statistical abstracts of the United States (1944–1945)*. Washington, DC: Author, pp, 223, 231.

US Department of Commerce, Bureau of the Census. (1984). *Local population estimates—Vermont (1982). (Current population reports, Series P-26, Number 82-45-SC)*. Washington, DC: US Government Printing Office.

Vaillant, G.E. (1978). A 10-year follow-up of remitting schizophrenics. *Schizophrenia Bulletin, 4*(11), 78–85.

Vaillant, G.E. (1984). The disadvantages of DSM-III outweigh its advantages. *American Journal of Psychiatry, 141*, 542–545.

Vermont State Health Department. (1992). *Statistics*. Burlington,VT: Author.

World Health Organization (1973). *The international pilot study of schizophrenia*. Geneva: Author.

World Health Organization (1978). *Collaborative project on determinants of outcome of severe mental disorders (1977–1979): Research protocols*. Geneva: Author.

Zubin, J. (1985). *General discussion, controversies in schizophrenia: Changes and constancies*. Edited by M. Alpert. New York: Guilford Press.

Zubin, J., Salzinger, S., Burdock, E.L. et al. (1961). A biometric approach to prognosis in schizophrenia. In P. Hoch & J. Zubin, *Comparative epidemiology of the mental disorders*. New York: Grime & Stratton.

# The Vermont Longitudinal Study of Persons with Severe Mental Illness, II: Long-Term Outcome of Subjects Who Retrospectively Met DSM-III Criteria for Schizophrenia

*Courtenay M. Harding, George W. Brooks, Takamaru Ashikaga, John S. Strauss, and Alan Breier*

At the time of original publication, the authors were with the Department of Psychiatry of Yale University School of Medicine, New Haven, CT; the College of Medicine and the College of Engineering and, Mathematics, University of Vermont, Burlington, VT; and the Clinical Neuroscience Branch, NIMH, Rockville, MD.

Supported by NIMH grants MH-29575, MH-40607, and MH-00340 and by Biomedical grant S0705429 from the College of Medicine, University of Vermont.

This article originally appeared in the *American Journal of Psychiatry*, 1987, 144, 727–735 and is reprinted with permission.

**Abstract:** The authors present the findings from a long-term follow-up study of 118 patients from Vermont State Hospital who, when rediagnosed retrospectively, met DSM-III criteria for schizophrenia at their index hospitalization in the mid-1950s. The patients were studied with structured, reliable, multivariate, instrument batteries by raters who were blind to information in their records. The rediagnostic process is described, and results of the follow-up are presented. Outcome varied widely, but one half to two thirds of the sample had achieved considerable improvement or recovered, in contrast to statements in *DSM-III* that predict a poor outcome for schizophrenic patients.

The third edition of the *Diagnostic and Statistical Manual of Mental Disorders (DSM-III)* of the American Psychiatric Association both reflects and shapes current American thinking about the course and outcome of schizophrenia. Heavily based on the Feighner criteria (1972) and the Research Diagnostic Criteria (Spitzer, Endicott & Robins, 1978), *DSM-III* pictures the schizophrenic patient as a person with increasing residual impairment.

A complete return to premorbid functioning is unusual—so rare, in fact, that some clinicians would question the diagnosis. However, there is always the possibility of full remission or recovery, although its frequency is unknown. The most common course is one of acute exacerbations with increasing residual impairment between episodes. (*DSM-III*, p. 185)

These impairments are said to include flattened affect, persisting delusions and hallucinations, and increasing inability to carry out everyday functions such as work, social relationships, or basic self-care. Such assumptions influence concepts of etiology (Crow, 1983) and course and outcome (Garmezy, 1965); in addition, they shape decisions about treatment

(Stephens & Astrup, 1965), program implementation (Kirk & Therrien, 1975), economic planning (Lamb & Edelston, 1976), and social policy for mental health service delivery systems (Talbott, 1979).

The advent of *DSM-III* has been seen by many clinicians and investigators as a major change in a field heretofore severely hampered in research and treatment relevant to schizophrenia by the lack of reliable definitions of diagnostic categories (Cooper, Kendell & Gurland, 1972; Fenton, Mosher & Matthews, 1981; Romano, 1977). With such a system in place (Spitzer, Forman & Nee, 1979) it is now possible to reaffirm or disconfirm the prevalent notions about the long-term course of schizophrenia.

This paper reports findings from the fifth very long-term follow-up study of schizophrenia conducted within the last decade (Ciompi & Müller, 1976; Huber, Gross & Schüttler, 1979; Bleuler, 1978) and the second such endeavor recently completed in the United States (Tsuang, Woolson & Fleming, 1979). It is the only study to date that has examined the long-term outcome of subjects rediagnosed as meeting the DSM-III criteria for schizophrenia.

The Vermont Longitudinal Research Project was a 32-year prospective follow-along study of a clinical research cohort (Brooks, 1959,1960,1961a, 1961b; Brooks & Deane, 1960, 1965; Brooks, Deane & Lagor, 1963; Brooks, Deane & Laquer, 1970; Chittick, Brooks, Irons et al., 1961; Harding & Brooks, 1980, 1984). The prospectively gathered material has been combined with a systematic retrospective follow-back to document the lives of 97% ($N = 262$) of the 269 original subjects.

In the mid-1950s, when they became subjects in the study, these patients were "middle-aged, poorly educated, lower-class individuals further impoverished by repeated and prolonged hospitalizations" (Chittick, Brooks, Irons et al., 1961, p. 29). Demographic, illness, and hospitalization characteristics of this cohort have been extensively described elsewhere (Chittick, Brooks, Irons et al., 1961; Harding & Brooks, 1980, 1984; Harding, Brooks, Ashikaga et al. 1987a; Harding & Strauss, 1985; Harding, 1984; Harding, Brooks, Ashikaga et al. 1987b).

The subjects were originally chosen for a rehabilitation program from the back wards of Vermont State Hospital because of their chronic disabilities and resistance to treatment. The chronicity criterion required subjects to have been disabled for 1 year before entry into the rehabilitation program. The term "disabled" was defined as inability to function in ordinary day-to-day role capacities. Members of this cohort had been ill for an average of 16 years, totally disabled for an average of 10 years, and continuously hospitalized for 6 years. In addition, most patients had been given phenothiazines for 2½ years without enough improvement to warrant discharge. They were provided with a comprehensive rehabilitation program and released to the community during the mid-to-late 1950s in a planned deinstitutionalization effort (Brooks, 1959,1960,1961a, 1961b; Brooks & Deane, 1960, 1965; Brooks, Deane & Lagor, 1963; Brooks, Deane & Laquer, 1970; Chittick, Brooks, Irons et al., 1961; Harding, Brooks, Ashikaga et al., 1987b).

In the follow-up data collection period (1980–1982), 97% of the original cohort was intensively studied in a structured and reliable manner (Harding, 1984; Harding, Brooks, Ashikaga et al. 1987b). The catamnestic period for these patients ranged from 22 to 62 years. More detailed descriptions of the methodology, the study sample, and the overall status of the cohort at follow-up may be found in our companion paper in this issue.

Initial results for these subjects, whose original diagnoses had been made according to DSM-I criteria, indicated that from one-half to two-thirds of the cohort had significantly improved or recovered (Harding, Brooks, Ashikaga et al., 1987a; Harding, 1984). These findings were at odds with the prevailing assumptions about the long-term course of schizophrenia. It was possible, however, that this discrepancy had been generated by the use of the loosely formulated DSM-I diagnostic guidelines. Therefore, with the publication of *DSM-III* while we were in the midst of our study, we undertook the task of giving a retrospective rediagnosis from cast records for each of the 269 patients in order to determine what their DSM-III status would have been at the time they were selected for the study.

The present paper examines the process of rediagnosis and assesses the long-term outcome achieved by the group who met the DSM-III criteria for schizophrenia at selection. The two hypotheses involved in this aspect of the study were statements of common conceptions about schizophrenia:

1) Members of this cohort diagnosed as having met the DSM-III criteria for schizophrenia at index hospitalization would still have signs and symptoms of schizophrenia at follow-up.

2) Members of this cohort diagnosed as having met the DSM-III criteria for schizophrenia at index hospitalization would have uniformly poor outcomes in critical areas of functioning such as work, social relations, and self-care at follow-up.

Confirmation of these hypotheses would lend support to the validity of the statements about the long-term course and outcome of schizophrenia that are made in *DSM-III*.

### REDIAGNOSIS OF PATIENTS AT INDEX HOSPITALIZATION

Originally, 213, or 79%, of the 269 subjects had been given a diagnosis of schizophrenia according to DSM-I guidelines. Table 1 presents a breakdown by age, sex, and diagnosis of the entire cohort at entry into the study in the mid-1950s.

**Table 1. DSM-I Diagnoses of 269 Chronic Psychiatric Patients at Entry Into the Vermont Study in the Mid-1950s**

| Diagnostic Category | Mean Age (years) | Subjects with Diagnosis (N = 269) | |
|---|---|---|---|
| | | N | % |
| Schizophrenia | | 213 | 79 |
| Hebephrenic | | | |
| Men | 36 | 13 | |
| Women | 41 | 9 | |
| Catatonic | | | |
| Men | 38 | 26 | |
| Women | 43 | 39 | |
| Paranoid | | | |
| Men | 43 | 48 | |
| Women | 45 | 59 | |
| Undifferentiated | | | |
| Men | 34 | 8 | |
| Women | 37 | 11 | |
| Affective disorders | | 34 | 13 |
| Men | 39 | 16 | |
| Women | 38 | 18 | |
| Organic disorders | | 22 | 8 |
| Men | 36 | 14 | |
| Women | 44 | 8 | |

We instituted several methods to achieve the retrospective rediagnosis. First, the two raters selected (J.S.S. and A.B.) were new to the project and blind to the outcome of each subject. The raters participated in two sets of inter-rater trials on 40 randomly selected cases (15% of the 269 subjects), which were independently assessed in a straight series without any discussion between raters. The case records and standardized record review abstracts from the time of the patient's entry into the study were stripped of all previous diagnostic assignments as well as any information about future episodes, hospitalizations, and other outcome information after index admission. (Index hospitalization was designated as the hospitalization during the 1950s during which transfer to the rehabilitation program occurred.) The DSM-III criteria were strictly applied.

The hospital records had been abstracted, as part of the overall goals of the larger project, in a structured and systematic manner by means of a battery of instruments known as the Hospital Record Review Form. This battery contained forms for extracting data about family and early life history, prodromal signs, and all hospital admissions. Inter-rater trials had revealed it to be a reliable instrument battery (Harding, 1984; Harding, Brooks, Ashikaga et al. 1987b).

For a signs and symptoms checklist, we used Strauss's Case Record Rating Scale (Strauss & Harder, 1981) and ratings from the World Health Organization's (WHO) Psychiatric and Personal History Schedule (Who Health Organization, 1978). This combination battery recorded behavioral descriptors and symptom dimensions noted by the clinician in recounting his or her impressions of the patient at the time of the original assessment. Case summaries and copies of the original chart information, such as admission and discharge summaries with ward notes but with all references to diagnosis deleted, were included in each diagnostic packet. Structured DSM-III diagnostic checklists from WHO and the Chestnut Lodge Follow-Up Study (McGlashan, 1984) were used by those making the rediagnoses to systematically summarize all the evidence for each diagnosis to be assigned.

Concerns about the quality of the records might be raised, because throughout the United States records from most state hospitals are considered to be poor. Vermont State Hospital's records, however, were remarkably complete. Since most of our subjects had also been the subjects of early phenothiazine drug trials before their entry into the rehabilitation program, the records tended to be of good research quality both before and during the institution of the federally funded rehabilitation program in 1957. The records described the evolution of symptoms by using statements from the patients themselves and gave examples of behaviors to illustrate the presence of hallucinations, delusions, catatonic waxy flexibility, and ocher symptoms. Such clinical notes were entered often by psychiatrists, residents, and other members of the treatment team. There were also mental status reports, past medical histories, results of current physical examinations, medication charts, treatment plans, progress notes, and admission and discharge summaries. In addition, social workers had collected systematic family and personal histories.

We conducted two sets of inter-rater trials. Complete agreement was achieved on 57% of the first 21 cases. In an analysis of the cases about which there was disagreement, it was found that 56% of the time, the second diagnosis proposed by one rater agreed with the first diagnosis selected by the other rater. Each rater agreed with the eventual consensual diagnosis 71% of the time overall and 75% of the time for schizophrenia. In assessing the level of inter-rater agreement, after collapsing the data into four diagnostic categories (schizophrenia, schizoaffective disorder, affective disorders, and "other" disorders), we generated an overall kappa coefficient (Fleiss, 1973) for the first trial of .40 ($p = .001$) and a kappa of .40 ($p = .02$) for schizophrenia alone. In the second trial set of 19 cases, an overall kappa of .65 ($p$ <.0001) was generated; the kappa for schizophrenia was .78 ($p$ < .0007). Clearly, there was an improvement in levels of agreement after the raters had further experience with the records and the diagnostic system. On the basis of the variation in the observed statistic, we concluded that the kappa value fell within the range observed by Spitzer et al. (36).

After application of the DSM-III criteria to the entire set of cases, 118 subjects received a diagnosis of schizophrenia (see Table 2).

Fifty-four percent (114 of 213) of those who were diagnosed as having schizophrenia according to the DSM-I guidelines retained the same diagnosis with the DSM-III criteria. (An additional four members of the DSM-III schizophrenia group were shifted from the DSM-I affective disorders category.) The primary shift from the DSM-I category of schizophrenia occurred to the DSM-III categories of schizoaffective disorder and atypical psychosis, not to the affective disorders category as expected from the experience of previous investigators.

The process of rediagnosis provided subtype categories for this subsample. The paranoid subtype predominated in both the DSM-I (50%, or 107 of 213) and DSM-III (61%, or 50 of 82) classification systems. The remaining subtypes included undifferentiated (17%, or 14 of 82), catatonic (13%, or 11 of 82), and disorganized (9%, or seven of 82).

## METHOD

Of the 118 subjects who met the DSM-III criteria for schizophrenia, at follow-up 70% ($N$ = 82) were alive and were interviewed, 24% ($N$ = 28) were deceased, 3% ($N$ = 4) refused to participate, and 3% were lost to follow-up. It should be noted that these figures are nearly identical to those reported for the larger cohort in our companion paper (see Table 1 in the previous article).

The present paper focuses on the long-term outcome of the 82 subjects who were alive and were interviewed 20 to 25 years after their entry into the project, because their data were the most reliable. The catamnestic period for these subjects ranged from 22 to 59 years.

Forty-five percent of the 82 subjects who met the DSM-III criteria for schizophrenia at index hospitalization had been hospitalized for more than 6 years before being transferred to the rehabilitation program in the 1950s. Twenty-four percent had been in the hospital from 2 to 6 years, and 31% had been hospitalized less than 2 years.

Demographic analysis of these 82 subjects produced the following information. The group was split evenly between the sexes (41 men and 41 women). Their ages (as of July 1, 1981, which was the midpoint in the data collection period) ranged from 41 to 79 years. It should be noted that 91% ($N$

**Table 2. Follow-Up Status by DSM-III Category of 269 Chronic Psychiatric Patients in the Vermont Study Who Were Rediagnosed Retrospectively**

| Subjects' Follow-Up Status | Number of Subjects in Diagnostic Category | | | | | | Total | |
| --- | --- | --- | --- | --- | --- | --- | --- | --- |
| | Schizophrenia | Schizoaffective Disorder | Affective Disorders | Atypical Psychosis | Other | Organic Disorders | N | % |
| Alive and interviewed | 82 | 25 | 29 | 13 | 19 | 10 | 178 | 66 |
| Alive; refused participation | 4 | 1 | 1 | 0 | 5 | 2 | 13 | 5 |
| Could not be located | 4 | 1 | 1 | 0 | 1 | 0 | 7 | 3 |
| Deceased | 28 | 4 | 16 | 5 | 7 | 10 | 70[a] | 26 |
| Total N | 118 | 31 | 47 | 18 | 32 | 22 | 268[a] | |
| Total % | 44 | 12 | 17 | 7 | 12 | 8 | | 100 |

[a] For one patient there was not enough information to make adequate ratings.

= 75) were above the age of 50; the average age for the group was 61 years. Fifty-five percent (*N* = 45) of the subjects had not completed high school. Sixty-two percent (*N* = 51) had never married, and only 10% (*N* = 8) had remained married. Seventy-six, or 93 %, were living in Vermont.

**Table 3. Psychiatric Status at Follow-Up of 82 patients in the Vermont Study Originally Diagnosed as Schizophrenic and Rediagnosed According to the RDC**

| Diagnostic Category | Subjects with Diagnosis (*N* = 82) | |
|---|---|---|
| | N | % |
| No symptoms | 37 | 45 |
| Schizophrenia | | |
| Positive symptoms | | |
| Definite | 1 | 1 |
| Probable | 7 | 9 |
| Possible | 0 | 0 |
| Negative symptoms | | |
| Definite | 7 | 9 |
| Probable | 7 | 9 |
| Possible | 0 | 0 |
| Affective disorders | | |
| Definite | 1 | 1 |
| Probable | 8 | 10 |
| Possible | 0 | 0 |
| Organic disorders | | |
| Definite | 1 | 0 |
| Probable | 9 | 11 |
| Possible | 0 | 0 |
| Alcoholism | | |
| Definite | 0 | 0 |
| Probable | 1 | 1 |
| Possible | 0 | 0 |
| Not enough information to rate | 4 | 4 |

To carry out the follow-up study, our raters conducted two structured and reliable field interviews with each subject to ascertain current status and longitudinal patterns of community tenure. The raters were blind to previously recorded information about the subjects. Additional informants who knew each subject well were also interviewed, and ratings were verified. The six subjects who were not living in Vermont were interviewed with the same protocols. Another structured protocol (the Hospital Record Review Form, described at length elsewhere [Harding, Brooks, Ashikaga et al. 1987b]) was used by a rater blind to all field information to abstract hospital and vocational rehabilitation records.

We used two structured interview batteries from the Vermont Community Questionnaire (Harding, 1984; Harding, Brooks, Ashikaga et al.

1987b), which included 15 standard scales and schedules, to assess the subjects' levels of functioning in a variety of areas at follow-up and to discern longitudinal shifts and patterns across the 20 to 25 years since the rehabilitation program began. All batteries were subjected to two sets of inter-rater trials 6 months apart and were found reliable (Harding, 1984; Harding, Brooks, Ashikaga et al. 1987b).

As part of the assessment, the two interviewers, who were new to the project and who had 5 to 8 years of clinical experience each, made ratings that provided a current clinical profile for each subject. The interviewers were blind to diagnostic record information when they made these symptom ratings, after the third hour of contact with each subject. The interviewers used the Research Diagnostic Criteria Screening Interview (Spitzer, Endicott & Robins, 1977, NY State Psychiatric Institute, Department of Psychophysiology), the Brief Psychiatric Rating Scale (Overall & Gorham, 1962), and a reduced version of the Mini-Mental State examination (Folstein, Folstein & McHugh, 1975) to make their assessments. This assessment package was designed to replace the Schedule for Affective Disorders and Schizophrenia (SADS) (Endicott & Spitzer, 1978), proposed in our original design (Harding & Brooks, 1984), because the extra time and costs required for the SADS interview were not funded.

In addition, the Global Assessment Scale (GAS) (Spitzer, Gibbon & Endicott, 1975; Endicott, Spitzer & Fleiss, 1976) provided a single score (from 0 to 100) based on level of symptoms and social functioning. The scale's developers divided scores on the instrumentation into three categories (0–30 = poor, 31–60 = fair, 61–100 = good functioning). The inter-rater trials generated a Pearson coefficient of .85 ($p < .0001$) for the first set ($N = 20$) and .93 ($p < .0001$) for the second set ($N = 20$) on this scale alone.

The Strauss-Carpenter Levels of Function Scale (Strauss & Carpenter, 1977) was used to identify some of the-major components that constitute the overall level of functioning assessed by the GAS. Each of the nine items is scored from 0 (poorest) to 4 (best); they include hospitalizations, symptoms, amount and quality of friendships, amount and quality of work, ability to meet basic needs, fullness of life, and overall level of functioning. (We excluded quality of work because unlike all the other assessments it could not be cross-checked by separate informants. A visit to each subject's work site was not deemed to be in the best interests of our subjects, most of whose employers might have been unaware of their early history as state hospital patients.) The results of inter-rater trials on this instrument alone generated Pearson coefficients of .92 ($p < .0001$) on the first set ($N = 21$) and .92 ($p < .0001$) on the second set ($N = 18$).

### RESULTS

For one half to two thirds of these subjects who retrospectively met the DSM-III criteria for schizophrenia, long-term outcome was neither downward nor marginal but an evolution into various degrees of productivity, social involvement, wellness, and competent functioning. The more stringent DSM III diagnostic criteria for schizophrenia failed to produce the expected uniformly poor outcome.

The combined data from the structured instrument battery described earlier, as well as all of the clinical observations obtained in the 3-hour interview sequence, indicated that 68% of the 82 subjects who met the DSM-III criteria for schizophrenia at index hospitalization did not display any further signs or symptoms (either positive or negative) of schizophrenia at follow-up. Forty-five percent of the sample displayed no psychiatric symptoms at all. For another 23%, symptoms had shifted to probable affective or organic disorders. One person was rated as a probable alcohol abuser (see Table 3).

Eighty-four percent of the 82 subjects had had psychotropic medications prescribed for them; 75% of these in a low to medium dose range (in chlorpromazine equivalents). Seventy-five percent of the subjects stated they were complying with their regimes, but field interviewers were eventually told, after hours of interview time had elapsed, that the actual compliance pattern was closer to the following: about 25% of the subjects always took their medications, another 25% self-medicated when they had symptoms, and the remaining 34% used none of their medications. Adding the 34% who were noncompliers to the 16% who were currently not receiving any prescriptions for psychotropics means that 50% of the cohort was not using such medication.

A single score for psychological and social functioning was assigned each subject on the basis of the GAS. Figure 1 compares outcome scores of the subjects who met the DSM-III criteria for schizophrenia at index hospitalization with the scores of the subjects who met the DSM-I guidelines for schizophrenia at index hospitalization. Sixty percent or more of the subjects diagnosed as schizophrenic by both diagnostic systems scored over 61, designated by the developers of the scale as good functioning. No one scored in the poor functioning category (score of 30 or less). It should be noted that all but four subjects who met the DSM-III criteria for schizophrenia came from the pool of subjects diagnosed as meeting the DSM-I criteria for schizophrenia.

Figure 2 shows the GAS scores of the 82 subjects who met both DSM-I and DSM-III criteria for schizophrenia (including 4 subjects who were in other categories of DSM-I but who met DSM-III criteria for schizophrenia) and of the subjects who met DSM-I criteria but who were reclassified as fit-

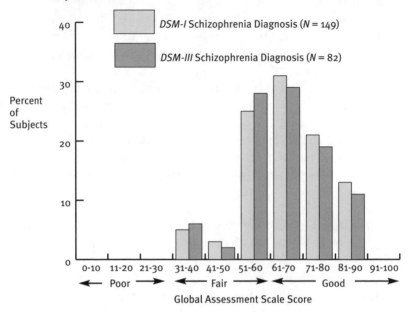

Figure 1. Global Assessment Scale Scores of Subjects in the Vermont Study Who Met DSM-I Criteria and Those Who Met DSM-III Criteria for Schizophrenia at Index Hospitalization

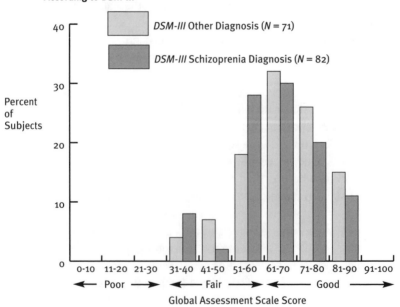

Figure 2. Global Assessment Scale Scores of Subjects in the Vermont Study Who Met DSM-I Criteria and Those Who Met DSM-III Criteria for Schizophrenia and Subjects Diagnosed as Schizophrenic by DSM-I Who Had Other Diagnoses According to DSM-III

**Table 4. Results From the Strauss-Carpenter Levels of Function Scale at Follow-Up for Vermont Study Subjects Diagnosed as Schizophrenic by DSM-I and Rediagnosed by DSM-III**

| Area of Functioning | Patients with DSM-I Schizophrenia (N = 149) | | Patients with DSM-I and DSM-III Schizophrenia (N = 82)[a] | | Patients with DSM-I but Not DSM-III Schizophrenia (N = 71) | | $\chi^2$ (df = 1)[b] | p |
|---|---|---|---|---|---|---|---|---|
| | N | % | N | % | N | % | | |
| Not in hospital in past year | 125 | 84 | 67 | 82 | 61 | 86 | 0.23 | .63 |
| Met with friends every week or two | 97 | 65 | 50 | 61 | 51 | 72 | 1.54 | .21 |
| Had one or more moderately to very close friends | 113 | 76 | 56 | 68 | 61 | 86 | 5.62 | .02 |
| Employed in past year[c] | 66 | 44 | 33 | 40 | 37 | 52 | 1.71 | .19 |
| Displayed slight or no symptoms | 104 | 70 | 56 | 68 | 52 | 73 | 0.24 | .62 |
| Able to meet basic needs | 119 | 80 | 66 | 81 | 57 | 80 | 0.00 | 1.00 |
| Led moderate to very full life | 113 | 76 | 60 | 73 | 57 | 80 | 0.71 | .40 |

[a] Includes four subjects who were not schizophrenic according to DSM-I but who were given a DSM-III diagnosis of schizophrenia.

[b] Chi-square with Yates' correction for the comparison between the group diagnosed as schizophrenic by both DSM-I and DSM-III and the group with DSM-I schizophrenia only (now DSM-III other categories).

[c] Does not account for subjects who were widowed, retired, or elderly.

ting some category other than schizophrenia by DSM-III criteria ($N$ = 71). A t-test for the means of the two groups revealed no significant differences between them ($t$ = 1.44, $df$ = 149, n.s.).

Table 4 shows the findings from the Levels of Function Scale for living subjects originally diagnosed as meeting the DSM-I guidelines for schizophrenia, those for subjects who met the DSM-III criteria for schizophrenia, and those for subjects who met the DSM-III criteria for other categories. For most outcome variables in either diagnostic system, for any of the three groups, two-thirds to four-fifths of the subjects were found to be significantly improved.

The only exception to the high levels of functioning across all diagnostic categories was the rating for employment which was scored for one-half or fewer of the subjects. However, this rating did not take into account subjects who were retired or elderly.

The major difference between the subjects who met the DSM-III criteria for schizophrenia and those who met the DSM-III criteria for other diagnoses was fewer close friendships for the DSM-III schizophrenia subsample (68% versus 86%) ($\chi^2$ = 4.89, $df$ = I, $p$ = .03).

We compared these two groups by using a 2X2 chi-square test with Yates' correction. A small number of cases with missing values were included in the analysis category that reflected the least positive outcome. No significant differences in results were observed when we used this approach and when we used the standard method of excluding cases with missing values.

### DISCUSSION

Members of the Vermont cohort were once profoundly ill, back-ward, chronic patients who were provided with a comprehensive rehabilitation program and released to the community 20 to 25 years ago. The 5- to 10-year follow-up study found that two thirds of these patients were out of the hospital but were expected to require continuous support by the mental health system in order to remain in the community (Deane & Brooks, 1967). Further, the subsample of this group rediagnosed as having met the DSM-III criteria for schizophrenia at index hospitalization would be expected according to that system's description of schizophrenia, to have a course with "increasing residual impairment between episodes" (*DSM-III*, p. 185), including continued symptoms, unemployment, social isolation, and inability to care for themselves.

Data from the present study demonstrated that these predictions were inadequate for the majority of subjects. Widely heterogeneous patterns of social, occupational, and psychological functioning evolved over time for these once schizophrenic patients. The more stringent diagnostic criteria of

*DSM-III* failed to predict any better than the more loosely formulated DSM-I guidelines the true outcome for these schizophrenic patients.

Although these findings show some robustness, they come from a study that suffers from numerous flaws (see previous article). Although it was one of the more rigorously designed research studies of its type, the selection was biased toward the long-term institutionalized patient. The use of reliable, structured instrument batteries was a significant advance over many earlier studies, but the DSM-III diagnoses had to be made retrospectively. The updating of subjects' diagnoses to meet current diagnostic criteria is a problem common to all longitudinal studies. It is always a trade-off to try to second-guess the original clinician, who was able to see and interact with the patient. The original clinicians were apt to neglect noting signs and symptoms that were not present and to present data to substantiate their own diagnostic decisions. We were fortunate to have excellent records rich in descriptive passages of actual conversations and behaviors to aid in our own rediagnostic work, but we did not see the patients in person then.

The structured battery that determined the subjects' current functional status was solidly reliable. The two interviewers each had 5 to 8 years of clinical experience with caseloads of chronic patients before these investigations, and they spent several hours with each subject as well as with a variety of other informants (including other clinicians) who knew these clients or family members well.

Our findings of heterogeneity in functioning at outcome corroborate similar results from the four other long-term studies of schizophrenia that we have mentioned: the three European studies by Bleuler (1978), Ciompi and Muller (1976), and Huber et al. (1979) and the Iowa 500 study (Tsuang, Woolson & Fleming, 1979). These studies have been extensively analyzed by us elsewhere (Harding, Zubin & Strauss, 1987). Diverse levels of functioning have been found also in shorter-term studies such as the WHO International Pilot Study of Schizophrenia (1978; 1973), the Rochester First Admission Study (Strauss, Kokes & Ritzler, 1978), the Boston State Hospital 12-Year Follow-Up Study (Gardos, Cole & LaBrie, 1982), and the New York State Psychiatric Institute Diagnostic Study (Endicott, Nee, Cohen et al., 1986).

It has been argued that the more stringent the criteria, the better a sample will reflect "true" or "core" schizophrenia (Langfeldt 1937, 1939), and that core schizophrenia has a uniformly poor outcome (Stephens & Astrup, 1965; Achte, 1967; Astrup & Noreik, 1966; Eitinger, Laane, & Langfeldt, 1958). The rigorous inclusion/exclusion criteria of the DSM-III classification were designed to select for core schizophrenia, but since the findings of this study revealed outcome to be heterogeneous, the DSM-III criteria did not predict long-term outcome as well as expected. This finding was recently duplicated for prediction of very short-term outcome as well. (Endicott, Nee, Cohen et al., 1986).

Hawk and associates (1975) also found that narrowness of criteria did not predict homogeneous outcome functioning when they compared subjects rediagnosed according to four diagnostic systems, i.e., Langfeldt's criteria (1939), Schneider's first-rank symptoms (1959), DSM-II, and the Flexible System (Carpenter, Strauss & Bartko, 1973).

The focus on strictness of criteria evolved from the Kraepelinian notion that prognosis confirmed diagnosis (Kraepelin, 1902). This theory stated that poor outcome reflected a unifying common denominator for clustering several differently expressed types of mental disorders under one umbrella, dementia praecox. If the patients recovered or improved, they had obviously been misdiagnosed, and another label was applied such as reactive psychosis (Jaspers, 1963), schizophreniform states (Langfeldt, 1939), or cycloid psychoses (Leonhard, 1966; Vaillant, 1964). In pursuing this argument further, Vaillant (1964) cited 16 major attempts to reclassify "remitting schizophrenics" and concluded that most investigators were describing a blend known as Kasanin's schizoaffective disorder (1933). Thus, there was no definitive system to describe schizophrenic patients who improved without recategorizing them as having another disorder.

A decade later, in 1975, Vaillant himself completed a 10- to 15-year follow-up of 51 patients who exhibited the classical profile of remitting schizophrenia, as cited from the literature by Stephens (1970) and others. This profile included a positive family history of affective disorders, sudden onset with the patient reacting to a clear precipitant, bipolar-like symptoms, and remission within the first 2 years. Thirty-nine percent of the 51 study subjects developed a chronic course. Vaillant found no factors that could differentiate between the patients who would relapse and those who were later rediagnosed as having an affective disorder (1978). He concluded that "diagnosis and prognosis should be treated as different dimensions of psychosis" (1975).

In the current study, it should be noted that the 25 interviewed patients who were rediagnosed as schizoaffective, the three who had schizophreniform disorders, and the 13 who had atypical psychoses were all eliminated from the analyses that were done to determine the long-term outcome of "core" schizophrenia. These patients were considered to have a much better chance for a good long-term outcome. Despite this very stringent approach, there were still "core schizophrenics" who remitted—a finding that supports Vaillant's concept of the separate contributions of diagnosis and prognosis to long-term outcome (1975, 1978).

In addition to incorporating the Kraepelinian idea that future course validates the original diagnosis, *DSM-III* was based on the Feighner, or St.

Louis, criteria (1972), which established the validity of a diagnosis by requiring deterioration from a previous level of functioning as well as a 6-month duration of illness with or without prodrome. Thus, in the *DSM-III* attempt to select out reactive, schizophreniform and cycloid types, subjects are required to have been functioning poorly before they are entered into the classification and are expected to be functioning poorly at follow-up. Strauss and Carpenter (1974) pointed out the tautology of such a scheme. They suggested that finding an outcome of chronic illness may be primarily related to the original selection of patients with a longstanding disorder as the entry criterion. However, the Vermont subjects were selected for their strong indications of chronicity (e.g., at selection these subjects had had an average of 6 years of continuous psychiatric hospitalization and 16 years of illness before entering the rehabilitation program). Despite this status, many of these very chronic patients appear to have recovered or improved considerably. This finding clearly supports those of the Bonn, Lausanne, Iowa, and Burghölzli studies, which found improvement or recovery two to three decades later (Ciompi & Müller, 1976; Huber, Gross & Schüttler, 1979; Bleuler, 1978; Tsuang, Woolson & Fleming, 1979).

One of the complications in analyzing data across earlier studies was the fact that those studies often used the criteria "recovered" or "improved" without defining either concept and commonly used only a single measure of outcome, such as "hospitalized" or "discharged" (see Shapiro and Shader [1979] for a discussion). However, the work of Strauss and Carpenter (1977, 1972, 1974) and many others has clearly demonstrated the partial independence in level of functioning at outcome in a variety of areas such as work, social relationships, symptoms, and hospitalization. In Strauss and Carpenter's "open-linked systems" approach (1974) to analyzing the course of disorder, the best predictor of follow-up functioning was pre-episode functioning in the same area (e.g., previous levels of work predicted current levels of work-a finding also supported by Brown et al. [1966] and Monck [1963]). Strauss and Carpenter pointed to the need for separate measurements of functioning in a wide variety of areas.

The Vermont Longitudinal Research Project found evidence to support this strategy. Within the middle range of outcome, there were subjects in the sample who were considered to be functioning well (e.g., working, with good family relationships and friends) but who still had delusions or hallucinations. Many subjects had learned either to devise ways of controlling their symptoms—ability reported also by Breier and Strauss (1983)—or had learned not to tell anyone about them anymore. Other subjects were working but were otherwise socially isolated. Some subjects had warm and extensive social networks but did not work. The picture was a complex and heterogeneous one.

Because narrowness of diagnostic criteria seems not to predict outcome, attention might be refocused on an analysis of this hidden underlying heterogeneity within samples (Harding, Brooks & Ashikaga, 1987a, Hogarty, 1977) in order to sort out other possible predictors of long-term outcome.

The implications of the findings from the Vermont cohort are many and varied. The present study provides strong evidence for the limited usefulness of the current diagnostic classification systems in predicting accurately the long-term outcome for people who meet the criteria for schizophrenia. Further, in each of the five major studies conducted in the past decade that assessed the long-term outcome of schizophrenia, one half or more of the subjects had recovered or considerably improved in their functioning. Together, these findings offer an argument for a shift in our thinking about the proportions of schizophrenic patients who are able to achieve a better outcome than has heretofore been expected.

Acknowledgments

The following people contributed to this phase of the project: design and methodology—Brendan Maher, PhD; the late Robert Shapiro, MD; Bonnie Spring, PhD; Joseph L Fleiss, PhD; Jane Murphy, PhD; Joseph M. Tobin, MD; Lee Robins, PhD; Leona Bachrach, PhD; Edward Zigler, PhD; Stanley Herr, JD; and Jon Rolf, PhD; additional aid with instrumentation—William Woodruff, MD; Alan Gelenberg, MD; Gerard Hogarty, MSV; Paula Clayton, MD; Janet Mikkelsen, MSW; and Thomas McGlashan, MD; data collection—Paul D. Landerl, MSW; Carmine M. Consalvo, MEd; Jana Wakefield, PhD; William Deane, PhD; Barbara Curtis, RN; and Robert Lagor, BA; data management—Susan Childers, ACSW; Lori Witham; Mary Ellen Fortini, PhD; Sandi Tower; Andres Pierce; Mary Noonan; Dorothy Myer; and Joanne Gobrecht; manuscript review—Luc Ciompi, Prof Dr Med; Prof John Cooper; Boris Astrachan, MD; Malcolm B. Bowers, Jr., MD; Richard Musty, PhD; George Albee, PhD; Thomas Achenbach, PhD; Paul Carling, PhD; Lawrence Gordon, PhD; and Frederick Schmidt, PhD, and manuscript preparation—Nancy L Ryan.

**REFERENCES**

Achte, K.A. (1967). On prognosis and rehabilitation in schizophrenia and paranoid psychoses. *Acta Psychiatrica Neurologica Scandinavica (Suppl),196*.

Astrup, C., & Noreik, K. (1966). Functional psychoses: diagnostic and prognostic models. Springfield, Ill: Charles C Thomas.Bleuler, M. (1978). *The schizophrenic disorders: Long-term patient and family studies*. Translated by S. M. Clemens. New Haven: Yale University Press.

Breier, A, & Strauss, J.S. (1983). Self-control of psychotic disorders. *Archives of General Psychiatry, 40,* 1141–1145.

Brooks, G.W. (1959). Opening a rehabilitation house. In M. Greenblatt & B Simon (Eds.), *Rehabilitation of the mentally ill.* Washington, DC: American Association for the Advancement of Science.

Brooks, G.W. (1960). Rehabilitation of hospitalized chronic schizophrenic patients. In I. Appleby, J. Scher & J. Cumming (Eds.), *Chronic schizophrenia.* Chicago: Free Press.

Brooks, G.W. (1961). Motivation for work in psychiatric rehabilitation. *Diseases of the Nervous System, 22,* 129–132.

Brooks, G.W. (1961). Rural community influences and supports in a rehabilitation program for state hospital patients. In M. Greenblatt, D. J. Levinson & G. L. Klerman, (Eds.), *Mental patients in transition.* Springfield, IL: Charles C Thomas.

Brooks, G.W., & Deane, W.N. (1960). Attitudes of released chronic schizophrenic patients concerning illness and recovery as revealed by a structured post-hospital interview. *Journal of Clinical Psychology, 16,* 259–264.

Brooks, G.W., & Deane, W.N. (1965). The chronic mental patient in the community. *Diseases of the Nervous System, 26,* 85–90.

Brooks, G.W., Deane, W.N., & Laqueur H.P. (1970). Fifteen years of work therapy. *Diseases of the Nervous System (Suppl), 31,* 161–165.

Brooks, G.W., Deane, W.N., Lagor R.C. et al. (1963). Varieties of family participation in the rehabilitation of released chronic schizophrenic patients. *Journal of Nervous and Mental Disease, 136,* 432–444.

Brown, G.W., Bone, M., Dalison, B., et al. (1966). *Schizophrenia and social care.* London: Oxford University Press.

Carpenter, W.T., Jr, Strauss, J.S., & Bartko, J.J. (1973). A flexible system for the identification of schizophrenia: A report from the International Pilot Study of Schizophrenia. *Science, 182,* 1275–1278.

Chittick, R. A., Brooks, G. W., Irons, F. S., et al. (1961). *The Vermont Story.* Burlington, VT: Queen City Press.

Ciompi, L., & Müller, C. (1976). *Lebensweg und alter der schizophrenen. Eine katamnestische longzeitstudie bis ins senium.* Berlin: Springer-Verlag.

Cooper, J.E., Kendell, R.E., Gurland, B.J., et al. (1972). *Psychiatric diagnosis in New York and London: A comparative study of mental hospital admissions.* New York: Oxford University Press.

Crow, T. (1983). Schizophrenic deterioration. *British Medical Journal, 143,* 80–81.

Deane, W.N, & Brooks, G.W. (1967). *Five-year follow-up of chronic hospitalized patients.* Waterbury, VT: Vermont State Hospital.

Eitinger, L., Laane, C.L., & Langfeldt, G. (1958). The prognostic value of the clinical picture and the therapeutic value of physical treatment in schizophrenia and the schizophreniform states. *Acta Psychiatrica Neurologica Scandinavica, 33,* 33–53.

Endicott, J., & Spitzer, R.L. (1978). A diagnostic interview: The schedule for affective disorders and schizophrenia. *Archives of General Psychiatry, 35,* 837–844.

Endicott, J., Nee, J., Cohen, J.L., et al. (1986). Diagnosis of schizophrenia. *Archives of General Psychiatry, 43,* 13–19.

Endicott, J., Spitzer, R.L., Fleiss, J.L., et al. (1976). The Global Assessment Scale: A procedure for measuring overall severity of psychiatric disturbance. *Archives of General Psychiatry, 33,* 766–771.

Feighner, J. P., Robins, E., Guze, S. B., et al. (1972). Diagnostic criteria for use in psychiatric research. *Archives of General Psychiatry, 26,* 57–63.

Fenton, W.S., Mosher, L.R., & Matthews, T.M. (1981). Diagnosis of schizophrenia: A critical review of current diagnostic systems. *Schizophrenia Bulletin, 7,* 452–476.

Fleiss, J. (1973). *Statistical methods for rates and proportions.* New York: John Wiley & Sons.

Folstein, M.F., Folstein, S.E., & McHugh, P.R. (1975) "Mini-Mental State": A practical method for grading the cognitive state of patients for the clinician. *Journal of Psychiatric Research, 12,* 189–198.

Gardos, G., Cole, J.O., & LaBrie, R.A. (1982). A 12-year follow-up study of chronic schizophrenics. *Hospital and Community Psychiatry, 33,* 983–984.

Garmezy, N. (1965). Process and reactive schizophrenia: some conceptions and issues. In M. M. Katz, J. Cole, W. E. Barton, *The role and methodology of classification in psychiatry and psychopathology* (NIMH Public Health Service Publication 1584). Washington, DC: Government Printing Office.

Harding, C. M., Brooks, G. W., Ashikaga, T., et al. (1987b). Aging and social functioning in once-chronic schizophrenic patients 22–62 years after first admission: The Vermont story. In N. Miller, G. Cohen, (Eds.), *Schizophrenia and aging.* New York: Guilford.

Harding, C. M., Zubin, J., & Strauss, J.S. (1987) Chronicity in schizophrenia: fact, partial fact, or artifact? *Hospital and Community Psychiatry, 38*(5), 477–486.

Harding, C.K., & Brooks, G.W. (1980). Longitudinal assessment for a cohort of chronic schizophrenics discharged twenty years ago. *Psychiatric Journal of the University of Ottawa, 5,* 274–278.

Harding, C.M. & Brooks, G.W. (1984). Life assessment of a cohort of chronic schizophrenics discharged twenty years ago. In S. Mednick, M. Harway, K. Finello (Eds.), *The handbook of longitudinal research, vol. 11.* New York: Praeger.

Harding, C.M. (1984). *Long-term outcome functioning of subjects re-diagnosed as meeting the DSM-III criteria for schizophrenia* (doctoral dissertation). Burlington: University of Vermont.

Harding, C.M., & Strauss, J.S. (1985). The course of schizophrenia: An evolving concept. In M. Alpert (Ed.), *Controversies in schizophrenia: Changes and constancies.* New York: Guilford Press.

Harding, C.M., Brooks, G.W., Ashikaga, T., Strauss, J.S., & Breier, A. (1987). The Vermont longitudinal study of persons with severe mental illness: I. Methodology, study sample, and overall status 32 years later. *American Journal of Psychiatry, 144,* 718–726.

Hawk A.B., Carpenter, W.T., Jr., & Strauss, J.S. (1975). Diagnostic criteria and 5-year outcome in schizophrenia: A report from the International Pilot Study of Schizophrenia. *Archives of General Psychiatry, 32,* 343–347.

Hogarty, G.E. (1977). Treatment and the course of schizophrenia. *Schizophrenia Bulletin, 3,* 587–599.

Huber, G., Gross, G., & Schüttler, R. (1979). Schizophrenie: Verlaufs und sozialpsychiatrische Langzeit unter suchfigen an den 1945 bis 1959 in Bonn hospitalisierten schizophrenen Kranken. *Monographien aus dem Gesamtgebiete der Psychiatrie. Bd. 21.* Berlin: Springer-Verlag.

Jaspers, K. (1963). *General psychopathoiogy.* Edited and translated by M.W. Hamilton. Chicago: University of Chicago Press.

Kasanin, J. (1933). The acute schizoaffective psychoses. *American Journal of Psychiatry, 90,* 97–126.

Kirk, S.A, & Therrien, M.L. (1975). Community mental health myths and the face of former hospitalized patients. *Psychiatry, 38,* 209–217.

Kraepelin, E. (1902). *Dementia praecox, in clinical psychiatry: A textbook for students and physicians, (6th ed.).* Translated by A.R. Diefendorf. New York: Macmillan.

Lamb, H.R, & Edelson, M.B. (1976). The carrot and the stick: inducing local programs to serve long-term patients. *Community Mental Health Journal, 12,* 137–144.

Langfeldt, G. (1937). The prognosis in schizophrenia and the factor influencing the course of disease. *Acta Psychiatrica Neurologica Scandinavica (Suppl), 13.*

Langfeldt, G. (1939). *Schizophreniform states.* Copenhagen: E Munks-gaard.

Leonhard, K. (1961). Cycloid psychoses: Endogenous psychoses which are neither schizophrenic nor manic depressive. *The Journal of Mental Science, 107,* 633–648.

Leonhard, K. (1966). The question of prognosis in schizophrenia. *International Journal of Psychiatry, 2,* 633–635.

McGlashan, T.H. (1984). The Chestnut Lodge follow-up study: II. Long-term outcome of schizophrenia and the affective disorders. *Archives of Gcncral Psychiatry, 41,* 586–601.

Monck, E.M. (1963). Employment experience of 127 discharged schizophrenic men in London. *British Journal of Preventive and Social Medicine, 17,* 101–110.

New York State Psychiatric Institute, Department of Psychophysiology. (1976). *Research Diagnostic Criteria Screening Interview.* New York: Author

Overall, J.E., & Gorham, D.R. (1962). The Brief Psychiatric Rating Scale. *Psychological Reports, 10,* 799–812.

Romano, J. (1977). On the nature of schizophrenia: Changes in the observer as well as the observed (1932–1977). *Schizophrenia Bulletin, 3,* 532–559.

Schneider, K. (1959). *Clinical psychopathology.* Translated by M.W. Hamilton. New York: Grune & Stratton.

Shapiro, R., & Shader, R. (1979). Selective review of results of previous follow-up studies of schizophrenia and other psychoses. In World Health Organization, *Schizophrenia: An international follow-up study.* New York: John Wiley & Sons.

Spitzer, R.I., Endicott, J, & Robins, E. (1977). *Research Diagnostic Criteria (RDC) for a selected group of functional disorders, 3rd ed.* New York: New York State Psychiatric Institute, Biometrics Research.

Spitzer, R.I., Endicott, J, & Robins, E. (1978). Research diagnostic criteria: Rationale and reliability. *Archives of General Psychiatry, 35,* 773–782.

Spitzer, R.L., Forman, J.B.W., & Nee, J. (1979). DSM-III field trials, I: Initial inter-rater diagnostic reliability. *American Journal of Psychiatry, 136,* 815–817.

Spitzer, R.L., Gibbon, M., & Endicott, J. (1975). *The Global Assessment Scale (GAS).* New York: New York State Psychiatric Institute.

Stephens, J.H. (1970). Long-term course and prognosis in schizophrenia. *Seminars in Psychiatry, 2,* 464–485.

Stephens, J.K., & Astrup, C. (1965). Treatment outcome in "process" and "non-process" schizophrenics treated by "A" and "B" types of therapists. *Journal of Nervous and Mental Diseases, 140,* 449–436.

Strauss J.S., & Carpenter, W.T. (1972). The prediction of outcome in schizophrenia, I: Characteristics of outcome. *Archives of General Psychiatry, 27,* 739–746.

Strauss J.S., & Carpenter, W.T. (1977). Prediction of outcome in schizophrenia, III: Five-year outcome and its predictors. *Archives of General Psychiatry, 34,* 159–163.

Strauss J.S., & Harder, D.W. (1981). The Case Record Rating Scale. *Psychiatry Research, 4,* 333–345.

Strauss J.S., Kokes, R.F., Ritzler, B.A., et al. (1978). Patterns of disorder in first admission psychiatric patients. *Journal of Nervous and Mental Disease, 166,* 611–625.

Strauss, J.S., & Carpenter, W.T. (1974). The prediction of outcome in schizophrenia, II: Relationship between predictor and outcome variables. *Archives of General Psychiatry 31,* 37–42.

Strauss, J.S., & Carpenter, W.T. (1974). Characteristic symptoms and outcome in schizophrenia. *Archives of General Psychiatry, 30,* 429–434.

Talbott, J.A. (Ed). (1979). *The chronic mental patient: problems, solutions, and recommendations for a public policy.* Washington, DC: American Psychiatric Association.

Tsuang, M.T., Woolson, R.F., & Fleming, J.A. (1979). Long-term outcome of major psychoses, I: Schizophrenia and affective disorders compared with psychiatrically symptom-free surgical conditions. *Archives of General Psychiatry, 36,* 1295–1301.

Vaillant, G.E. (1964). Prospective prediction of schizophrenic remission. *Archives of General Psychiatry, 11,* 509–518.

Vaillant, G.E. (1975). Paper presented at the 128th annual meeting of the American Psychiatric Association, Anaheim, CA.

Vaillant, G.E. (1978). A 10-year follow-up of remitting schizophrenics. *Schizophrenia Bulletin, 4*(11), 78–85.

World Health Organization (1973). *The international pilot study of schizophrenia.* Geneva: Author.

World Health Organization (1978). *Collaborative project on determinants of outcome of severe mental disorders (1977–1979): Research protocols.* Geneva: Author.

# The Maine and Vermont Three-Decade Studies of Serious Mental Illness
# I. Matched Comparison of Cross-Sectional Outcome

*Michael J. DeSisto, Courtenay M. Harding, Rodney V. McCormick, Takamaru Ashikaga, and George W. Brooks*

At the time of original publication, author affiliations were as follows: Michael J. DeSisto, PhD, Bureau of Mental Health, State of Maine, Augusta, Maine; Courtenay M. Harding, PhD, Department of Psychiatry, Yale University, New Haven, CT; Rodney V. McCormick, PhD, Takamaru Ashikaga, PhD, Department of Medical Biostatistics; George W. Brooks, MD, Department of Psychiatry, College of Medicine, University of Vermont, Burlington, VT, USA.

This article originally appeared in the *British Journal of Psychiatry*, 1995, 167, 331–338, and is reprinted with permission.

Abstract: *Background.* This study compared long-term outcome of serious mental illness in two states using a matched design to assess psychiatric rehabilitation programs: Vermont subjects participated in a model psychiatric rehabilitation program, while the Maine group received more traditional care. *Method.* Maine and Vermont subjects (*n* = 269) were matched by age, sex, diagnosis, and chronicity. Demographic, Illness, and life history information were abstracted from hospital records by clinicians blind to outcome. DSM-III criteria were applied retrospectively. Outcome was assessed by clinicians blind to history. *Results.* Vermont subjects alive at follow-up (*n* = 180) were more productive (*P* < 0.0009), had fewer symptoms (*P* < 0.002), better community adjustment (*P* < 0.001) and global functioning (*P* < 0.0001) than Maine subjects (*n* = 119). *Conclusions.* Outcome differences may be due to Vermont's model program and a policy of allowing an earlier opportunity for community life.

Long-term studies of serious mental illness have provided a clearer understanding of the wide heterogeneity of outcome that is possible (Huber et al., 1975; Ciompi & Müller, 1976; Bleuler, 1978; Tsuang et al., 1979; Harding et al., 1987a, b). This appreciation has been especially helpful for schizophrenia, which, until recently, had been thought to be defined by a uniformly poor outcome (Kraepelin, 1902; American Psychiatric Association, 1980). However, comparing long-term studies is difficult owing to differences of method concerning for example: diagnostic criteria, outcome definitions, instrumentation, strategies for missing and deceased subjects, protocols for collection of follow-up information, and treatment eras (Strauss & Carpenter, 1972; Angst, 1988; McGlashan, 1988).

To address some of the above issues, this paper compares the long-term outcome of matched groups from two recent long-term studies in the USA.

The average length of follow-up for Vermont and Maine subjects was 32 years (Harding et al., 1987a, b) and 36 years respectively. Identical protocols and instrumentation were used along with reliability studio. The Vermont subjects participated in a model rehabilitation program (Chittick et al., 1961) while the Maine group received traditional inpatient treatment and aftercare (DeSisto et al., 1991). A major aim of the study was to determine the effect of Vermont's rehabilitation program. The study relied on a quasi-experimental design that used group matching and covariance procedures to control for the effect of policy and unmatched group differences.

## BACKGROUND TO THE STUDY

The foundation for this work was established over 30 years ago. Before the policy of deinstitutionalization, mental health centers and entitlement programs, Vermont's State Hospital and the Vocational Rehabilitation Division jointly initiated a pioneering rehabilitation program (Chittick et al., 1961). The program was comprehensive and eclectic (Harding et al., 1987a, b). Concepts from social psychiatry were integrated with those from medicine and vocational rehabilitation. All services were organized around the goal of self-sufficiency. New strategies were used in the hospital which included "blurring of roles," intensified relationships, and new expectations for both patients and staff. Vocational rehabilitation provided new community residences, work options, and case management. Continuity of care across settings was assured as teams of hospital and vocational workers established halfway houses, found job openings, made job placements, and linked patients to natural supports in the community. The program created a comprehensive system of care before the creation of community mental health centers and community support systems.

### The Early 1980s Follow-Up

In the early 1980s, Harding et al., (1987a, b) assessed the long-term outcome of the Vermont cohort at an average of 32 years after first admission. Of the original 269 patients, 262 (97%) were traced. Outcome for the cohort was widely heterogeneous. Of those interviewed, 55% were rated as having little or no social impairment, were asymptomatic, had close relationships, were employed or otherwise productive, and were living independently. Sixty-eight percent were rated as functioning "pretty well," defined as a score over 61 on the Global Assessment Scale (GAS; Endicott et al., 1976). These findings raised questions about whether the favorable outcome was due to the rehabilitation program (Chittick et al., 1961), Vermont's rural environment (Zubin, 1995), or the characteristics of the Vermont sample (McGlashan, 1998, and corrected McGlashan, 1991).

A detailed historical comparison of the evolution of the Maine and Vermont mental health systems revealed that Maine did not develop a comprehensive rehabilitation program that was linked to the depopulation of its hospital. Instead, Maine patients received more "traditional care," in the form of modern drug treatment (beginning in 1955–56) and aftercare (provided first by hospital social workers and then by community mental health centers), with little or no involvement in vocational rehabilitation. Also, the development of alternative residences such as community halfway houses came 16 years after that in Vermont (DeSisto et al., 1991). Since the sociocultural composition of rural Maine and Vermont appeared similar, in order to explore outcome correlates, a cohort in rural Maine matched to Vermont patients by age, sex, diagnosis, and length of hospital stay was followed with the same protocol developed by Harding et al. (1997a).

## METHOD

### Subjects

All of the over 8,000 summary cards for Maine hospital admissions were screened to exclude patients born before 1890, those with organic, drug and alcohol disorders, those on criminal mandates, and those not admitted between 1956 and 1961. This period represented the treatment era during which persons were referred and discharged from the Vermont rehabilitation program.

This strategy resulted in a pool of 1944 possible matches for the Vermont subjects. Exact matching by sex, diagnosis, and age was conducted followed by closest matching on hospital stay (Table 1). In each group there were 125 men and 144 women, and 190 subjects had schizophrenia according to DSM-II criteria (American Psychiatric Association, 1969), 9 had schizoaffective disorder, 20 had affective disorders, and 50 had other disorders.

**Table 1. Comparison of matching variables**

| Variable | Mean | Standard Deviation | Mean difference | t-value | P-value | No. of cases |
|----------|------|--------------------|-----------------|---------|---------|--------------|
| Year of birth | | | | | | |
|   Maine | 1918 | 10.74 | | | | |
|   Vermont | 1919 | 10.81 | -0.08 | -0.54 | 0.59 | 269 |
| Time in hospital to January 1961 (months) | | | | | | |
|   Maine | 88.69 | 68.47 | | | | |
|   Vermont[1] | 90.36 | 84.45 | -1.67 | 0.68 | 0.56 | 267 |

[1] Time in hospital for two Vermont cases (4 and 84) was not available at the time of this analysis.

### Field Work

Vermont's protocols, instrumentation, and standardized procedures were used (Harding et al., 1997a). To assure comparability between states, a Vermont clinician field worker (PL) trained the two Maine field workers in the interview process. Two inter-rater reliability trials were conducted between the Maine clinicians (with 48 subjects) and between the two Maine clinicians and the Vermont clinician (with 20 subjects). The overall kappa (Fleiss, 1973) agreement for the Maine data set was 0.71, while the overall agreement between Maine and Vermont was 0.61.

The clinician field workers, blind to record information, conducted two interviews about one week apart in each subject's place of residence. The first interview involved an assessment of current functioning across outcome domains. The second interview involved a structured year-by-year documentation of domains in a life-chart format (Leighton & Leighton. 1949; Meyer, 1951; Harding et al., 1989). Relatives, friends, and carers of live and deceased subjects were also interviewed. Death certificates validated status. In order to obtain a more balanced view of the long-term course for the entire cohort, a surrogate instrument for deceased subjects was used to document the lives and levels of functioning until the time of death.

### Record Review

Two Maine clinicians, blind to outcome, were trained by a Vermont clinician record reviewer (JF) to extract information for all admissions using Vermont protocols. Each record was reviewed independently and then rated jointly to have a consensus between the clinicians. The reliability of the record review data for Maine was determined using two separate ratings, conducted six months apart, of the index admission and life history sections of the Hospital Record Review Form for 21 randomly selected cases. Kappas were 0.54 for index admission and 0.76 for the life history section.

### DSM-III Rediagnosis

Following the Vermont protocols, primary case records for the index hospital admission, from which all references to diagnosis were deleted, were used by blinded psychiatrists to assign DSM-III (APA, 1980) diagnoses to all Maine patients. Kappa inter-rater reliability for classification of cases as schizophrenia, schizoaffectivc disorder, affective disorder, or other for 40 randomly selected cases was 0.69 for Maine and 0.65 for Vermont. Kappa levels for classification of cases as schizophrenia or not schizophrenia were 0.69 for Maine and 0.78 for Vermont.

### Reliability of Individual Variables

Of the 40 individual variables reported here, 10 (25%) showed very good inter-rater agreement (kappa range 0.81–1.00), 23 (58%) good agreement (kappa range 0.61–0.80), 5 (12%) moderate agreement (kappa range 0.41–0.60), and 2 (5%) only fair agreement (0.21–0.40). Variables showing moderate and fair agreement included: social ratings (frequency of social contacts, number of social relations, degree of interdependence in social relationships); symptom ratings (verifiable delusion or hallucination, symptoms in past month); the person's awareness of any abnormal involuntary movements; and the ratings of number of years the person was compliant with prescribed medication.

### Construction, Internal Consistency, and Reliability

Of the outcome scale battery of interview instruments—the Vermont Community Questionnaire-Cross-sectional (VCQ-C; Harding & Brooks, 1984; Harding et al., 1987a)—was used to assess current functioning. It was constructed by combining 15 established scales described in the literature. The items from these scales were organized across the domains of residence, work, finances, social functioning, social supports, weekly activities, self-care, use of treatment/social services, satisfaction, environmental stressors, competence, and psychopathology.

Outcome scales for self-care ("do-for-self"), "work," "social functioning," and "symptoms" were constructed by adding items after dichotomization. The Appendix summarizes the items used to construct the scales. Cronbach's $\alpha$ coefficients (Cronbach, 1951) demonstrated good internal consistency, with values ranging from 0.74 to 0.89.

In addition to the constructed scales, the GAS was used as a measure of overall functioning, the Community Adjustment Scale (CAS; Harding & Brooks, 1986) was employed to assess adjustment to life in the community, and the Mini-Mental State Examination (MMSE; Folstein et al, 1975) was used to measure overall cognitive functioning.

The reliability of the GAS, CAS, and MMSE, and the constructed scales, was assessed using the interclass correlation coefficient (ICC) (Bartko, 1966). Coefficients between the one Vermont clinician interviewer who trained the Maine team and between each of the two Maine clinician interviewers for ail the outcome scales (20 cases) ranged from 0.75 to 0.98 ($p < 0.0001$).

Regression analysis (Pedhazur, 1982) was used to determine the contribution of differences in important unmatched variables and to make co-variance adjustments. The covariates used included the matching variables, variables listed in Table 3, and the interaction terms of the grouping variable (state) with each covariate. The scores for each covariate were standardized to $z$ scores using the grand means for the combined samples. Since all covariates were transformed to $z$ scores, the regression coefficient for the grouping variable, state, was the difference in the outcome variable adjusted to the grand mean of the covariate.

## RESULTS

### Status of the Cohorts at Follow-Up

Table 2 shows the status of the Vermont and Maine subjects at follow-up. Both cohorts showed attrition by death, more so in Maine because follow-up was 7 years later.

**Table 2. Status of the 269 Maine and 269 Vermont Probands at Follow-up**

|  | Vermont | | Maine | |
|---|---|---|---|---|
|  | N | (%) | N | (%) |
| Interviewed | 180 | (66)[1] | 119 | (44) |
| Deceased: family & significant other interviewed | 71 | (26) | 120 | (45) |
| Alive: refused participation | 11 | (5) | 14 | (5) |
| Not located | 7 | (3) | 16 | (6) |
| Total | 269 | (100) | 269 | (100) |

[1] The data files used in the extensive analysis for this report include date for two Vermont subjects who completed the interviews but who then withdrew from participation in the study. The University of Vermont Institutional Review Board determined that since these persons were not identifiable in any way and had consented to be interviewed, but then withdrew, the data from the interviews could be used in these analyses without harm to the subjects.

The remainder of this report focuses on outcome comparisons of the subjects who were interviewed at follow-up. A separate paper will describe the trajectories for deceased subjects. However, the assumption that the most severely ill subjects died first, leaving a group better suited for recovery, was tested first by comparing the matching variables and covariates of all 299 alive and all 191 deceased subjects.

There were no differences except that the deceased group was almost six years older ($t = -6.34$, $P < 0.0001$) and had more subjects with DSM-III schizophrenia ($t = 2.23$, $P < 0.02$). An analysis of variance with age and diagnosis entered as covariates was then used to compare the GAS and the CAS scores by state (Maine, Vermont) and status (alive, deceased). There was no difference between the live and deceased for the GAS ($F = 0.130$, $P = 0.718$) or the CAS ($F = 0.319$, $P = 0.573$). However, Vermont subjects had higher GAS ($F = 67.64$, $P < 0.0001$) and CAS scores (F=44.67, $P < 0.0001$). There were no significant differences in the survival rates of the cohorts as measured by the Lee-Desu statistic (1.690, $d.f. = 1$, $P = 0.194$).

**Table 3. Comparisons of Matching Variables and Covariates from Interviewed Subjects**

| | Vermont (n = 180) | Maine (n = 118) | t-value | d.f.[1] | p value |
|---|---|---|---|---|---|
| **Hospital stay (months)** | | | | | |
| Mean | 87.7 | 78.6 | 1/06 | 296.0 | 0.29 |
| Standard Deviation | 87.1 | 61.0 | | | |
| **Year of birth** | | | | | |
| Mean | 1921 | 1922 | -1.43 | 258.3 | 0.15 |
| Standard Deviation | 10.3 | 9.9 | | | |
| **Sex[2]** | | | | | |
| Mean | 1.51 | 1.54 | -0.45 | 253.0 | 0.65 |
| Standard Deviation | 0.50 | 0.50 | | | |
| **Diagnosis[3]** | | | | | |
| Mean | 1.54 | 1.64 | -1.73 | 259.0 | 0.09 |
| Standard Deviation | 0.50 | 0.48 | | | |
| **Index year of discharge** | | | | | |
| Mean | 1961 | 1964 | -5.08 | 185.1 | 0.0001 |
| Standard Deviation | 4.6 | 6.9 | | | |
| **Education[4]** | | | | | |
| Mean | 1.84 | 1.34 | 4.89 | 269.2 | 0.0001 |
| Standard Deviation | 0.91 | 0.83 | | | |
| **Urban/rural origin[5]** | | | | | |
| Mean | 3.09 | 2.16 | 6.44 | 262.3 | 0.0001 |
| Standard Deviation | 1.26 | 1.19 | | | |
| **Acute onset[6]** | | | | | |
| Mean | 0.19 | 0.39 | -3.72 | 215.6 | 0.0003 |
| Standard Deviation | 0.40 | 0.49 | | | |
| **Interview year[7]** | | | | | |
| Mean | 1981 | 1988 | -1.56 | 303.0 | 0.0001 |
| Standard Deviation | 0.46 | 0.32 | | | |
| **Father industrial worker[8]** | | | | | |
| Mean | 0.15 | 0.32 | -3.35 | 206.5 | 0.001 |
| Standard Deviation | 0.36 | 0.47 | | | |
| **Economic status[9]** | | | | | |
| Mean | 0.72 | 0.70 | 0.38 | 260.0 | 0.70 |
| Standard Deviation | 0.48 | 0.46 | | | |

1. Fractional d.f. based upon unequal variance t-test
2. 1 = male, 2 = female
3. 1 = DSM-schizophrenia, 2 = not schizophrenia
4. 0 = none, 1 = primary, 2 = secondary, 3 = post-secondary, 4 = college. Data not available for 7 Vermont patients.
5. 1 = metropolitan, 2 = small urban, 3 = farm, 4 = village
6. 0 = no, 1 = yes
7. Not used for matching 1 – 1 overlap
8. 0 = no, 1 = yes
9. 1 = low, 2 = middle, 3 = high. Data not available for 2 Vermont and 1 Maine subjects

### Outcome Comparisons

*Do-for-self.* Younger and better-educated subjects, and subjects discharged earlier, did more for themselves at follow-up in both Maine and Vermont. There was no significant difference between the states in self-care, over and above these covariates ($f = 0.81$, $P = 0.421$).

**Table 4. Maine and Vermont Independent Sample Covariance Analysis[1]**

| | Work | Do-for-Self | Social Functioning | Symptoms | CAS | MMSE | GAS |
|---|---|---|---|---|---|---|---|
| | | | Outcome Variables | | | | |
| Adjusted comparisons | -3.35 | -0.81 | -1.43 | -3.10 | -3.31 | 0.89 | -4.73 |
| 1 = VT, 2 = ME | 0.0009 | 0.421 | 0.153 | 0.0021 | 0.0011 | 0.37 | <0.0001 |
| *Covariates* | | | | | | | |
| Diagnosis | | | 2.12 | | 3.12 | 2.21 | |
| | | | 0.035 | | 0.002 | 0.028 | |
| Sex | | | 2.53 | | | | |
| | | | 0.012 | | | | |
| Hospital stay | | | | -2.45 | -2.80 | 4.69 | -3.28 |
| | | | | 0.015 | 0.0055 | <0.0001 | <0.0012 |
| Year of birth | 4.34 | 3.82 | 4.44 | | | -4.70 | -168 |
| | <0.0001 | 0.0002 | <0.0001 | | | <0.0001 | <0.094 |
| Index year of discharge | -2.43 | -6.58 | -5.05 | -5.59 | -3.61 | | -5.20 |
| | 0.016 | <0.0001 | <0.0001 | <0.0001 | 0.0004 | | <0.0001 |
| Education | 2.38 | 2.33 | 2.18 | | 2.12 | -6.25 | |
| | 0.018 | 0.021 | 0.030 | | 0.035 | <0.0001 | |
| Urban/rural origin | | | | | -2.89 | | -2.40 |
| Acute onset | | | | | 0.0041 | | 0.017 |
| Father industrial worker | | | | | | | |
| Economic status | | | | | | | |
| **Interaction terms** | | | | | | | |
| State year of birth | | | | | | | 2.35 |
| | | | | | | | 0.020 |
| State hospital stay | | | | | | | 2.21 |
| | | | | | | | 0.028 |
| State index year of discharge | | | | | 2.36 | | |
| | | | | | 0.019 | | |
| State acute onset | | | | | 2.82 | | 2.35 |
| | | | | | 0.0052 | | 0.020 |
| **Model statistics** | | | | | | | |
| $R^2$ | 16.9% | 23.8% | 23.1% | 22.2% | 31.1% | 37.5% | 32.2% |
| Error d.f. | 287 | 287 | 285 | 295 | 283 | 238 | 290 |
| F | 14.55 | 22.5 | 14.26 | 28.11 | 15.95 | 28.62 | 17.2 |
| P | | <0.0001 | <0.0001 | <0.0001 | <0.0001 | <0.0001 | <0.0001 |

[1] Maine and Vermont combined into one sample, covariates standardized to z scores, *t* values, and probabilities. The covariates and interaction terms are listed on the left and outcome variables are listed across the top. Model statistics are presented on the bottom. Final state comparisons are displayed in the first row.

*Work.* Younger and better educated subjects and subjects discharged earlier in both states were doing more work at follow-up. However, there was still a "state" effect over and above these covariates ($t = 3.35$, $P < 0.0009$), with more Vermont subjects ($n = 79$, 47%, compared with $n = 31$. 26%, for Maine) working in some capacity at follow-up.

*Social functioning.* In both states, women, DSM-III non-schizophrenic subjects, younger subjects, better-educated subjects, and subjects discharged earlier received higher ratings of social functioning. There was no significant difference in social functioning between the states over and above these covariates ($t = -1.43$, $P = 0.153$).

*Symptoms.* Subjects discharged earlier and those with a shorter hospital stay had fewer symptoms, regardless of state. There was still a significant difference between the states over and above these covariates, with Vermont subjects displaying fewer symptoms at follow-up ($t = -3.10$, $P < 0.002$).

*MMSE.* Younger, better-educated subjects, those with a shorter hospital stay, and those with a DSM-III diagnosis of schizophrenia from both states had better cognitive functioning. There was no significant difference in cognitive functioning between the states over and above these covariates ($f = 0.99$. $P = 0.37$).

*CAS.* Better educated subjects, non-DSM-III schizophrenic subjects, and subjects with a shorter hospital stay showed better community adjustment at follow-up. Overall, subjects discharged earlier had a better community adjustment, but this effect was stronger in Vermont than Maine (state by year of-discharge interaction shows an ordinal relationship. Acute onset was associated with poorer community adjustment in Vermont and better community adjustment in Maine. There was sill a significant difference in community adjustment between the states over and above these covariates ($f = -3.31$, $P < 0.001$), with Vermont subjects displaying better adjustment at follow-up.

*GAS.* Subjects discharged earlier, regardless of state, had better global functioning. In Maine, but not in Vermont, younger subjects had better global functioning (state by year of birth and state by hospital-stay interactions). In Vermont, but not in Maine, subjects with a longer index hospital nay had worse global functioning. In Vermont, acute onset was once again associated with poorer global functioning while in Maine acute onset was associated with better global functioning (state by acute onset interaction). However, then was it significant difference in global functioning between the states, over and above these covariates ($f = -4.73$, $P < 0.0001$). Of the Vermont subjects, 68% (114) were functioning at least "pretty well" (GAS score >61) compared with 49% (59) for Maine.

## DISCUSSION

This study represents the first attempt to conduct at long-term outcome comparison between states using matched samples and the same protocols. Several elements of the method that are keys to interpreting any differences in outcome have been included, such as: sample definitions; operationally defined diagnostic criteria; multiple demographic, predictor and outcome measures; blind ratings of illness and outcome factors; and reliability testing.

However, there am several caveats to consider: a) a distinct bias toward long-stay patients; b) reported moderate response to phenothiazines in Vermont and undetermined response in Maine: c) both present-state and retrospective data elements in Maine and Vermont; d) Clinical referral of known "back-ward" patients to the rehabilitation program in Vermont: and e) computer matching on only a few key variables in Maine. Also, a retrospective, but necessary, modern rediagnosis for both cohorts from clinical records was conducted.

Vermont subjects functioned significantly better at follow-up across all the domains studied except cognitive functioning, which was the same. These initial differences were modulated when differences in unmatched subject variables and the major policy difference between the states, index year of discharge were covaried. After adjustment for these differences, Vermont subjects still displayed greater productivity, better adjustment to the community, and better global functioning.

The regression models for the adjusted comparisons show that different combinations of subject variables were linked to specific outcome domains. For example, subjects with more education had better cognitive and social functioning and better work records. Subjects with more education and less time in hospital had better community adjustment. The goal of this study was not prediction of outcome but instead control of differences in subject variables to determine the effect of the Vermont program on outcome. However, the data support the notion that predictors of outcome vary according to the outcome domain studied (McGlashan, 1966).

The analysis examined the relationship between the original matching variables—age, sex, diagnosis, and length of hospital stay—and the outcome domains studied. Younger subjects from both mates had better cognitive functioning than older subjects. Also, in Maine but not In Vermont, Younger subjects had better global functioning at follow-up. However, follow-up in Maine was seven years later than in Vermont. This allowed the effects of age on functioning to become more pronounced for Maine subjects. Women had better social functioning. This relationship between sex and social outcomes has been found by other investigators (e.g., McGlashan & Bardenstein, 1990). Better-educated and non-schizophrenic subjects and those with less time in hospital showed better community adjustment. Non-schizophrenic subjects in both states displayed better social functioning at follow-up. The better cognitive functioning for subjects with a DSM-III diagnosis of schizophrenia is due to the inclusion of 23 subjects in each state with an organic diagnosis among the non-DSM-III schizophrenic group. These subjects had been removed in the data analysis for Vermont (Harding el al., 1987a, b). Finally, subjects from both states with less time in hospital had fewer symptoms and better community adjustment at follow-up.

Given these findings, what was the effect of the Vermont rehabilitation program on outcome? Can the case be made that the adjusted differences were the result of Vermont's model program, the hallmarks of which were the early opportunity to adapt to living and working in the community and the long-term continuity of care?

First, Vermont subjects had fewer symptoms than Maine subjects at follow-up. The initial impetus for Vermont's model program was the rehabilitation of a group of "back-ward" patients who had made only a modest response to treatment with chlorpromazine (Brooks, 1956). In fact, 178 other patients had responded to the new drug therapy and were released—leaving behind the 269 members of the Vermont cohort. Thus, the Vermont sample was selected clinically, while the Maine sample was selected by computer matching, and thus the drug responsiveness of subjects in Maine was not known beforehand. This sampling difference may have resulted in the difference in symptoms (Vermonter subjects less ill) 30 years later. However, the Maine cohort was also selected from the bottom third (longer-stay) of the hospital population. A controlled look at the question of early drug responsiveness on long-term course and outcome is a question for future studies.

Vermont subjects had a better work outcome. The major policy difference between the states, index you of discharge, was entered by the regression analysis as an adjuster for all domains except work and cognitive functioning. Are the robust differences in work outcome the result of the Vermont program with its emphasis on vocational rehabilitation and the opportunity to work? Are the differences the result of the selection of already good workers for rehabilitation in Vermont (erroneously suggested and corrected by McGlashan, 1991)? Was there a difference in the work ethic between the states, or the availability of jobs and other sociocultural factors? The evidence suggests that the differences in work outcome are not due to differences in sociocultural factors or work ethic between the states. More Vermont subjects came from family farms or small towns and more Maine subjects came from small cities and had fathers who were unskilled or semiskilled industrial workers. However, there was no significant statistical difference in the percentage of the samples that were ever employed before index admission (83%

for Maine and 72% for Vermont). Unskilled industrial or service work accounted for most of the jobs in both states. Further, Vermont subjects worked more in agriculture and skilled clerical or craftsman jobs, therefore, it does not appear that work ethic or opportunity can account for the differences in work outcome. It is possible that in Vermont patient selection was based partly on favorable industrial work in Vermont, but most literature does not support the notion that this form of work therapy has any effect on community work at follow-up (e.g., Kunce, 1970). Even if this were not the case, and although Maine subjects were not selected on the basis of hospital work performance, 82% of them were involved in hospital work with 10% in highly skilled jobs. Perhaps the most convincing evidence against a subject-selection explanation for the observed differences in work outcome is that the difference is mainly the result of a difference in volunteer work and not paid work. The Vermont program specifically targeted boarding home residents for volunteer work. This suggests that there may have been a greater effect of the program on more poorly functioning patients.

To summarize, the results suggest that differences in outcome between the states were the result of several factors. However, even after covariance adjustments, Vermont subjects were more productive, had fewer symptoms, and displayed better overall functioning and community adjustment. While it is always possible that other unknown differences contributed to the differences in outcome it can be argued that the differences in outcome are likely to be attributable to the Vermont program since it provided an opportunity for community adaptation in the context of an array of residential, work, and social opportunities which were all managed to ensure continuity. The analysis of differences in the long-term course trajectories discussed in part II adds further support for this conclusion.

### APPENDIX

#### Listing of Outcome Scale Variables

*Do-for-self.* Get around on own; buy own groceries; cook for self: do own laundry; shop for clothes; housekeeping; manage own money;  independence. Alpha = 0.89 for Maine and 0.85 for Vermont.

*Work.* Volunteer work; hours per week volunteer; hours per week for pay; employment status in past month; quantity of useful work in past year. Alpha = .84 for Maine and 0.74 for Vermont.

*Social functioning.* Interdependence in relationships; degree of social activity; quality of companionship; relations with children; relations with relatives; relations with friends; number of social relations; fullness of life. Alpha = 0.85 for Maine and 0.89 for Vermont.

*Symptoms.* Emotional withdrawal; conceptual disorganization; guilt feelings; mannerisms/posturing; grandiosity; depressed mood, hostility; hallucinatory behavior; unusual thought content; blunted affect; disorientation; auditory hallucinations; rating of degree of psychopathology; valid/verifiable hallucinations or delusions; absence of symptoms in past month. Alpha = 0.76 for Maine and 0.81 for Vermont.

### REFERENCES

American Psychiatric Association (1968). *Diagnostic and statistical manual of mental disorders-II (2nd ed.) (DSM-II).* Washington, DC: Author.

American Psychiatric Association. (1980). *Diagnostic and statistical manual of mental disorders-III (3rd ed.) (DSM-III).* Washington, DC: Author.

Angst, J. (1988). European long-term followup studies of schizophrenia. *Schizophrenia Bulletin, 14,* 501–513.

Bartko, J. J. (1966). The intraclass correlation coefficient as a measure of reliability. *Psychology Reports, 19,* 3–11.

Bleuler, M. (1978). *The schizophrenic disorders: Long-term patient and family studies.* (Translated by S. M. Clemens.) New Haven: Yale University Press.

Brooks, G. W. (1956). Experience with the use of chlorpromazine and reserpine in psychiatry; with special reference to the significance and management of extrapyramidal dysfunction. *New England Journal of Medicine, 254,* 1119–1123.

Chittick, R.A., Brooks, G.W., Irons, F.S., et al. (1961). *The Vermont story.* Burlington, VT: Queen City Press.

Ciompi, L., & Müller C. (1976). *Lebensweg und Alter der Schizophrenen: Eine katamnestische Longzeitstudie bis ins senium.* Berlin: Springer-Verlag.

Cronbach, L. J. (1951). Coefficient alpha and the internal structure of tests. *Psychometrika, 16,* 297-334.

DeSisto, M. J., Harding, C. M., Howard, M. A., et al. (1991). *Perspectives on rural mental health: A comparison of mental health system policy and program development in Maine and Vermont.* Augusta, ME: Kennebec Press.

Endicott, J., Spitzer, R.L., & Fleiss, J.I., et al. (1976). The Global Assessment Scale: A procedure for measuring overall severity of psychiatric disturbance. *Archives of General Psychiatry, 31,* 766–771.

Fleiss, J. (1973). *Statistical methods for rates and proportions.* New York: John Wiley & Sons.

Folstein, M. F., Folstein, F. E. & McHugh, P. R. (1975). Minimental state. *Journal of Psychiatric Residency, 12,* 189–198.

Harding, C.M. & Brooks, G.W. (1984). Life assessment of a cohort of chronic schizophrenics discharged twenty years ago. In S. Mednick, M. Harway, K. Finello (Eds.), *The handbook of longitudinal research, vol. 11.* New York: Praeger.

Harding, C. M. & Brooks, G. W. (1986). Speculations on the measurement of recovery from severe psychiatric disorder and the human condition. *Psychiatric Journal of the University of Ottawa, 11,* 199–204.

Harding, C.M., Brooks, G.W., Ashikaga, T., Strauss, J.S., and Breier, A. (1987a). The Vermont longitudinal study of persons with severe mental illness: I. Methodology, study sample, and overall status 32 years later. *American Journal of Psychiatry, 144,* 718–726.

Harding, C.M., Brooks, G.W., Ashikaga, T., Strauss, J.S., and Breier, A. (1987b). The Vermont longitudinal study of persons with severe mental illness: II. Long-term outcome of subjects who restrospectively met DSM-III criteria for schizophrenia. *American Journal of Psychiatry, 144,* 727–735.

Harding, C. M., McCormick, R. V., Strauss, J. S., et al (1989). Computerised life chart methods to map domains of function and illustrate patterns of interactions in the long-term course trajectories of patients who once met the criteria for DSM-III schizophrenia. *British Journal of Psychiatry, 155* (suppl. 5), 100-106.

Huber, G., Gross, G., & Schüttler, R. (1975). A long-term follow-up study of schizophrenia: Psychiatric course of illness and prognosis. *Acta Psychiatrica Scandanivica, 52,* 49–57.

Kraepelin, E. (1902). *Dementia Praecox, in clinical psychiatry: A textbook for students and physicians, (6th ed.).* Translated by A.R. Diefendorf. New York: Macmillan.

Kunce, J. T. (1970). Is work therapy really therapeutic? *Rehabilitation Literature, 31,* 297–299.

Leighton, A. H. & Leighton, D. C. (1949). *Gregorio, the handtrembler: A psychobiological personality study of a Navajo Indian.* Peabody Museum Papers. Cambridge: Harvard University Press.

McGlashan, T. H. (1986). The prediction of outcome in chronic schizophrenia: IV. The Chestnut Lodge follow-up study. *Archives of General Psychiatry, 43,* 167–176.

McGlashan, T. A. (1988). A selective review of recent North American long-term follow-up studies of schizophrenia. *Schizophrenia Bulletin, 14,* 515–542.

McGlashan, T. A. (1991). A selective review of recent North American long-term follow-up studies of schizophrenia. In S. Martin, J. Goset, S. Grob, (Eds.), *Psychiatric treatment: Advances in outcome research* (pp 61–105). Washington, DC: American Psychiatric Press.

McGlashan, T. H. & Bardenstein, K. K. (1990). Gender differences in affective, schizoaffective, and schizophrenic disorders. *Schizophrenia Bulletin, 16,* 319–329.

Meyer, A. (1951) The life chart and the obligation of specifying positive data in psychopathological diagnosis. Reprinted in *The collected papers of Adolf Meyer* (ed. E. E. Winters), pp. 52–56. Baltimore: Johns Hopkins University Press.

Pedhazur, E. J. (1982) *Multiple regression in behavioral research.* New York: CBS College Publishing.

Strauss J.S., & Carpenter, W.T. (1972). The prediction of outcome in schizophrenia, I: Characteristics of outcome. *Archives of General Psychiatry, 27,* 739–746.

Tsuang, M. T., Woolson, R. F., & Fleming, J. A. (1979). Long-term outcome of major psychoses, I: Schizophrenia and affective disorders compared with psychiatrically symptom-free surgical conditions. *Archives of General Psychiatry, 36,* 1295–1301.

Zubin, J. (1985). *General discussion, controversies in schizophrenia: Changes and constancies.* Edited by M. Alpert, pp 406–407. New York: Guilford Press.

# The Maine and Vermont Three-Decade Studies of Serious Mental Illness
## II. Longitudinal Course Comparisons

*Michael DeSisto, Courtenay M. Harding, Rodney V. McCormick, Takamaru Ashikaga, and George W. Brooks*

At the time of original publication, author affiliations were as follows: Michael J. DeSisto, PhD, Bureau of Mental Health, State of Maine, Augusta, Maine; Courtenay M. Harding, PhD, Department of Psychiatry, Yale University, New Haven, CT; Rodney V. McCormick, PhD, Takamaru Ashikaga, PhD, Department of Medical Biostatistics; George W. Brooks, MD, Department of Psychiatry, College of Medicine, University of Vermont, Burlington, VT, USA.

This paper originally appeared in the *British Journal of Psychiatry*, 1995, 167, 338–341, and is reprinted with permission.

**Abstract:** *Background*. This paper supplements the cross-sectional outcome comparisons of the companion paper by providing a brief account of the longitudinal course of the Maine and Vermont sample across several outcome domains. *Method*. A Life Chart method was used to document changes in individual lives over the domains of residence, work, income source, and use of community resources over a 20-year period. Reliability studies between states were conducted. *Results*. Throughout much of the period, more Vermont subjects lived independently, were working, and were less likely to use community resources compared to Maine subjects. *Conclusions*. Differences in both policies and program contributed to course differences between the groups. System characteristics that may lead to better outcomes are discussed.

The companion paper (previous article) has demonstrated major outcome differences between the Maine and Vermont groups. This paper fills out these statistical outcome differences by providing a more detailed descriptive comparison of the longitudinal courses of the two samples across several outcome domains.

The evolution of developments in each state are also documented to account for policy and program events extraneous to the rehabilitation program (DeSisto et al., 1991). These events are then overlaid with the longitudinal course data for both groups to study the interplay between the natural history of individuals and the systems of care.

### METHODS AND PROCEDURES
A modified version of the Meyer-Leighton Life Chart (Leighton & Leighton, 1949; Meyer, 1951) was used to document retrospectively the yearly course of several life domains for each subject. The entire instrument bat-

tery has been described previously (Harding et al., 1987a). The Life Chart (Harding et al., 1981) documented cohort statuses over a 32-year period in Vermont and a 36-year period in Maine. Outcome domains included work; source of income; residence; hospitalizations; medication; and community resources used. Life-event domains included: presence of significant others; deaths; health; relationships; legal entanglements; finances; and changes in family structure.

A trained clinician interviewer and the subject worked together over a 75- to 90-minute period to complete the Life Chart and other elements of the longitudinal questionnaire. A specific set of probes was asked for each year beginning with the most recent year and working back to earlier years. All data were verified by informants who knew the subject well. For deceased subjects, the Life Chart was completed with family members and significant others. Most subjects and families gave good accounts of their histories, a phenomenon noted earlier by others (Bleuler, 1978; Harding, 1986).

Inter-rater reliability trials resulted in an overall agreement (kappa; Fleiss, 1973) between Maine clinicians of 0.75 ($n$ = 48 cases), between Vermont clinicians of 0.79 ($n$ = 36 cases), and 0.65 ($n$ = 20) between Maine and Vermont clinicians.

Data reduction of the Life Chart was conducted as follows:

*Residence.* Residence categories included: hospital; independent living; rehabilitation or halfway house; and boarding or nursing home. The percentage of any year that a person resided in a category was coded. For example, if in a particular year a subject spent 4 months in the hospital and 8 months living independently, (then "hospital" would be coded as 33% and "independent living" as 67%.

*Work.* The work domain had three categories: full-time (30 hours or more with pay), part-time or unpaid (combining housewife, volunteer, part-time, and volunteer full-time); and unemployed. For a particular year, a subject was classified into one of these categories if it represented their status for more than 6 months.

*Community resources.* Scores reflected receipt of services from any of the following: community mental health centre; vocational rehabilitation (VR); private practitioner.

The status of the Maine and Vermont groups for each outcome domain was compared by determining the percentage of subjects that were in a particular status for each year from 1960 to 1980. A Bonferoni adjusted chi-square comparison of proportions using an alpha = 0.0024 was performed to achieve a nominal 0.05 alpha overall for the 21-year period.

A similar format was used to document the year-by-year developments in mental health policies and programs for each state. The domains included: policy and legal changes; hospital programs; community residential programs; vocational programs; mental health centers; and entitlements. Information about changes in these domains was obtained from a review of state laws, hospital annual reports, published hospital and program histories, and personal interviews with period policy makers and division heads.

## RESULTS

Table 1 briefly summarizes domain and period-specific differences between the Maine and Vermont subjects.

Due to mortality, the total number of Life Charts available from 1960 to 1980 for Maine and Vermont ranged from 224 to 143, and 243 to 173, respectively.

**Table 1. Life Chart Course Comparisons Summary**

| Domain | Years[1] | Maine (%)[2] | Vermont (%)[2] |
|---|---|---|---|
| Residence | | | |
| Hospital | 60–75 | 50.0 | 13.0 |
| Independent | 60–71 | 25.6 | 46.4 |
| Halfway house | 60–63 | 0.3 | 6.2 |
| Boarding home | 63–71 | 3.9 | 14.4 |
| Work | | | |
| Full time | 60–75 | 12.7 | 30.9 |
| Part time | 60 | 1.8 | 7.9 |
| Unemployed | 74, 75, 77–79 | 60.2 | 41.3 |
| Community resources used | | | |
| None | 60–78 | 12.9 | 43.3 |
| Vocational rehabilitation | 60–70 | 0.0 | 16.9 |
| Community Mental Health Center | 62, 64–69 | 11.0 | 2.7 |

1 Years for which significant differences between Maine and Vermont were observed.
2 Average percentage for years where significant differences were observed.

*Residence.* Maine subjects spent significantly more time (50% v. 13%) in the hospital from 1960 through 1975 compared to Vermont subjects. The Vermont residential experience consisted predominantly of more independent living between 1960 and 1971, more residence in halfway houses between 1960 and 1963, and more use of boarding homes from 1963 to 1971.

*Work and income source.* A significantly greater percentage of Vermont subjects were employed full-time between 1960 and 1975 (30.9% v. 12.7%). In contrast, more Maine subjects were unemployed from 1974 to 1975, and 1977 through 1979 (60.2% v. 41.3%). Naturally, the proportion of individuals described as unemployed would tend to increase over time as individuals age.

*Community resources.* On average, throughout most of the period from 1960 to 1978, Vermont subjects were not making use of community programs at the same level as Maine subjects (43.3% v. 12.9%). However, more Vermonters were enrolled in VR between 1960 and 1970. This can be contrasted to the higher percentage of Mainers enrolled in community mental health centre programs in 1962 and between 1964 and 1969.

### DISCUSSION

The longitudinal course comparisons demonstrate clearly that the Vermont program had a significant impact on the course for Vermont subjects compared to that of Maine subjects. Perhaps the most important aspect of the program was that it gave Vermont patients an earlier opportunity to adapt to life in the community. This opportunity, when combined with an array of residential, work, and social opportunities, resulted in a more diverse and favorable course compared to the Maine group across the domains studied.

Early differences in residential status can be attributed directly to the policy and program differences between the states. The Vermont rehabilitation program, which began in 1955, had both a rehabilitation goal and a depopulation goal. Therefore, alternative residences such as independent living, boarding homes, and halfway houses were needed and developed much earlier in Vermont. Depopulation was not pursued in Maine until 1971, and alternative residences were not available or used until this time. Therefore, Maine subjects spent more time in hospital between 1960 and 1975, while Vermont subjects spent more time in independent residences between 1960 and 1971, in boarding homes between 1963 and 1971, and in halfway houses between 1960 and 1963. Once Maine pursued a policy of depopulation, these differences in residential status disappear.

Over the entire period, the percentage of Vermonters engaged in some form of employment, either full-time or part-time paid work or volunteer work, ranged between 35 and 60%. For full-time work alone, the range was 25 to 30%. For Maine subjects, the range for some kind of employment was 12 to 30%, and for full-time work, 10 to 12%. While not directly comparable, employment rates from short-term cross-sectional studies have ranged from 20 to 30% for full-time employment 1 year post-discharge (Anthony et al., 1972). The Vermont rehabilitation program was an eclectic program that integrated the knowledge from social psychiatry, including principles of milieu therapy, therapeutic community, and interpersonal psychiatry, with the use of medicine and vocational rehabilitation (Chittick et al., 1961). The program created a comprehensive system of care prior to the development of community mental health centers and community support systems (Morrissey & Goldman, 1984; DeSisto et a., 1991).

The relationship with vocational rehabilitation was abandoned in 1970 when Vermont pursued a policy of regionalization which made mental health centers the primary referral and aftercare agents. This paradigm shift (Kuhn, 1962) from a rehabilitation program which emphasized work and self-sufficiency, to a treatment program which emphasized cure of illness through treatment by mental health centers, resulted in some loss of continuity and comprehensiveness.

The Vermont legacy is not to be found, as Bachrach (1989) has suggested, in the details of the program or the methods used. Instead, its legacy is the values and principles that guided it. Perhaps the most important value was that the program had a pervasive attitude of hope and optimism about human potential through the vision that, if given the opportunity, persons with mental illness could become self-sufficient. Anecdotal literature and personal accounts in both the medical and psychiatric fields support the notion that hope is an important factor in recovery (Deane & Brooks, 1963; Cousins, 1979; Lovejoy, 1984). With this hope and optimism, however, there were realistic expectations that not everyone would proceed at the same pace. There was the assumption that people were unique, and that the dignity and integrity of the person must be respected. This respect was honored by asking sufferers about what they wanted, how things were going, whether the program was meeting their needs, and by involving them in program planning. Thus, collaboration was the hallmark of the program. In addition, services had to be comprehensive, deal with all aspects of life, be flexible because needs and situations changed over time, and have long-term continuity. Finally, there was a concern about what happened to people over the long-term and a recognition of the need to keep in touch in order to find out.

Both the Maine and Vermont cohorts became ill during a period when law and society allowed long periods of hospitalization. They were hospitalized prior to the availability of modern pharmacological treatment and changes in family structure and demography that have occurred over the past 30 years. Nonetheless, the individual Life Charts and course trajectories for both groups confirm the heterogeneity of the long-term course of serious mental illness (Ciompi & Muller, 1976; Bleuler, 1978; Harding et al., 1987a, b; Harding, 1988; Harding et al., 1989). In addition, the accumulated domain-specific courses in this report have demonstrated that the natural history of individuals and policy and program events affect the course of specific outcome domains.

Acknowledgements

This work was supported by NIMH ROI-40032 to Drs. DeSisto and Harding, NIMH RO1-29575, and RO1-4067 to Dr Harding, and a Robert Wood Johnson Foundation Grant No. 190300 to Drs. Harding and DeSisto. The work was also supported by the State of Maine, Department of Mental Health and Mental Retardation, Robert Clover. PhD, Commissioner, and Medical Care Development, Inc., John A. LaCaase, EngScD, President. Portions were read before the annual meeting of the American Psychiatric Association, New York, May 1990. The authors would like to thank all those who contributed to various aspects of this work: Priscilla Ridgway, MA, for her work on the matching subjects protocol and original application; Margaret Fuller, MSW, and Millard Howard, MA, for abstracting Maine records and documenting Maine history; Alan McKelvy, MSW, and Christopher Salamone, MSW, for conducting the field interviews; Paul Landerl, MSW, from the Vermont team, trained Maine field workers; Janet Wakefield, PhD, from the Vermont team trained Maine record abstractors; Carmine Consalvo, PhD, from the Vermont team, provided consultation to Maine interviewers; Alan Gelenber, MD, trained Maine field workers to assess abnormal movement; Owen Buck, MD, and Victor Pentlarge, MD, conducted DSM-III rediagnosis of the Maine cohort; Walter Rohm, MD, and the late William Schumacher, MD, and Roy Ettlinger, MHA, provided Maine policy and program historical information; Dorothy Myer of the Vermont Department of Medical Biostatistics supervised the data entry and coding; Walter Lowell, EdD, provided Maine hospital data; John Pierce and Rodney Copeland, PhD, provided Vermont policy information; Vasilio Bellinin in Vermont and Ann DeWitt in Maine provided social security historical data; Lois Frost located Maine records; Kevin Concannon, MSW, supported the initiation of the project; Robert Clover, PhD, and John LaCasse, EngScD, supported its completion; and Linda Clark managed the project office and typed early drafts; and Eunice Reneyske, Micheline Morin Huggett, and Ellen Rector typed the manuscript revisions. Finally we would like to thank all the other people and patients who participated in the study.

## REFERENCES

American Psychiatric Association (1968). *Diagnostic and statistical manual of mental disorders (2nd ed.) (DSM-II)*. Washington, DC: APA.

Anthony, W. A., Buell, G. J., Sharratt, S., & Althoff, M. E. (1972). Efficacy of psychiatric rehabilitation. *Psychological Bulletin, 78*, 447–456.

Bachrach, L. L. (1989). The legacy of model programs. *Hospital and Community Psychiatry, 40*(3), 234-235.

Bleuler, M. (1978). *The schizophrenic disorders: Long-term patient and family studies*. Translated by S. M. Clemens. New Haven: Yale University Press.

Chittick, R.A., Brooks, G.W., Irons, F.S., et al. (1961). *The Vermont Story*. Burlington, VT: Queen City Press.

Ciompi, L., & Müller C. (1976). *Lebensweg und alter der schizophrenen: Eine katamnestische longzeitstudie bis ins senium*. Berlin: Springer-Verlag.

Cousins, N. (1979). *The anatomy of an illness as perceived by the patient.* New York: Norton.

Deane, W. N. & Brooks, G. W. (1963). Chronic schizophrenics view recovery. *Journal of Existential Psychiatry, 4.* 121–130.

DeSisto, M. J., Harding, C. M., Howard, M. A., et al. (1991). *Perspectives on rural mental health: A comparison of mental health system policy and program development in Maine and Vermont.* Augusta, ME: Kennebec Press.

Fleiss, J. (1973). *Statistical methods for rates and proportions.* New York: John Wiley & Sons.

Harding, C.M. (1988). Course types in schizophrenia: An analysis of European and American studies. *Schizophrenia Bulletin, 14,* 633–643.Harding, C.M. & Brooks, G.W. (1984). Life assessment of a cohort of chronic schizophrenics discharged twenty years ago. In S. Mednick, M. Harway, K. Finello (Eds.), *The handbook of longitudinal research, vol. II,* pp 375–393. New York: Praeger.

Harding, C. M. & Brooks, G. W. (1986). Speculations on the measurement of recovery from severe psychiatric disorder and the human condition. *Psychiatric Journal of the University of Ottawa, 11,* 199–204.

Harding, C.M., Brooks, G.W., Ashikaga, T., Strauss, J.S., and Breier, A. (1987a). The Vermont longitudinal study of persons with severe mental illness: I. Methodology, study sample, and overall status 32 years later. *American Journal of Psychiatry, 144,* 718–726.

Harding, C.M., Brooks, G.W., Ashikaga, T., Strauss, J.S., and Breier, A. (1987b). The Vermont longitudinal study of persons with severe mental illness: II. Long-term outcome of subjects who restrospectively met DSM-III criteria for schizophrenia. *American Journal of Psychiatry, 144,* 727–735.

Harding, C.M., Consalvo, C.M., Landerl, P.S., et al. (1981). *The Vermont Longitudinal Questionnaire.* Burlington, Vermont.

Leighton, A.K. & Leighton, D.C. (1949). *Gregorio, the hand-trembler: A psychobiological personality study of a Navaho Indian.* Peabody Museum Papers. Cambridge, MA: Harvard University Press.

Lovejoy, M. (1984). Recovery from schizophrenia: a personal odyssey. *Hospital and Community Psychiatry, 35,* 809–813.

McGlashan, T. H. (1986). The prediction of outcome in chronic schizophrenia: IV. The Chestnut Lodge follow-up study. *Archives of General Psychiatry, 43,* 167-176.

McGlashan, T. H. (1991). A selective review of recent North American longterm follow-up studies of schizophrenia. In *Psychiatric treatment: Advances in outcome research* (Eds S. Martin, J. Goset & S. Grob), pp. 61–105. Washington, DC: APA.

Meyer, A. (1951) The life chart and the obligation of specifying positive data in psychopathological diagnosis. Reprinted in *The collected papers of Adolf Meyer* (ed. E. E. Winters), pp. 52–56. Baltimore: Johns Hopkins University Press.

Morrissey, J. P. & Goldman, H. H. (1984). Cycles of reform in care of the chronically mentally ill. *Hospital and Community Psychiatry, 35,* 785–793.

# The Natural History of Schizophrenia in the Long Term

*Luc Ciompi*

At the time of original publication, Luc Ciompi was Specialist FMH for Psychiatry and Psychotherapy, Director of the Sociopsychiatric University Clinic, Berne, Switzerland.

This article originally appeared in the *British Journal of Psychiatry,* 1980, 413–420, and is reprinted with permission. The paper was presented at the Tenth Annual Meeting of the International Society for Psychotherapy Research, European Conference, Oxford, England, 1–5, July 1979.

It is well known that in some small European countries there exist especially favorable conditions for certain types of research which elsewhere meet enormous difficulties. This is exemplified in Denmark and other Scandinavian countries by the famous studies on the influence of genetic and environmental factors in schizophrenia, which were made possible by the exceptional availability of well organized national registers on twins, adoptees, and psychotics.

Some time ago we realized that similar favorable conditions exist in Switzerland for long-term follow-up research. It possesses the advantages of being a small and well ordered country without wars and major troubles during the last 100 years, leading to intact and meticulously well kept records of population movements, combined with an exceedingly low social mobility within a very limited geographic area. These features made it possible to trace and find within a short period over 96% of all former patients, even after many changes of address through several decades. Another advantage is the division of the country into 23 political districts or "cantons," each one with its own hospitals and health care organizations, which have provided for many decades clearly delimited catchment areas, forming an ideal basis for epidemiological research.

These favorable conditions led at the beginning of the sixties to the mounting in one of these districts of the so-called *Enquête de Lausanne,* an extended follow-up research program on the long-term evolution of mental illnesses of all kinds. The program was initiated by C. Müller and carried out by L. Ciompi and collaborators over more than 10 years. About 50 papers dealing with the long-term evolution of various psychiatric conditions have been published within the framework of this project; a final synthesis is currently in elaboration. The findings concerning schizophrenia have been published in the form of a monograph (Ciompi & Müller, 1976). In the following, some of the most important findings of this study are briefly summarized, with particular reference to the problems of treatment.

## THE GENERAL FRAMEWORK OF THE SCHIZOPHRENIA STUDY

The 5,661 former patients of the Psychiatric University Hospital of Lausanne, included in the Enquête de Lausanne, represent all the psychiatric patients born between 1873 and 1897, hospitalized from the beginning of the century until 1962 in a catchment area with about 500,000 inhabitants today. Age criteria were chosen in order to obtain from all the survivors virtually life-long follow-ups until at least the age of 65 years. Systematic additional cause-of-death and mortality studies provided precise information about the most important selection factors operating in the samples that were finally examined, since attrition was mainly due to death.

One thousand, six hundred and forty-two patients (29%) were diagnosed as schizophrenic at first admission, according to strict Bleulerian criteria, which do not include a bad outcome as obligatory. Heavy mortality during the follow-up period and some other minor factors, probably introducing a slightly favorable bias in the course of the illness, reduced the initial sample to 289 patients. These were personally re-examined by an experienced psychiatrist in their homes, using a semistructured interview of about 2 hours duration. Additional information was systematically collected from hospital files, family members, authorities etc.

The average duration of follow-up from first admission to re-examination was 36.9 years. The longest catamnesis was 65 years and about 50% of the cases had a catamnesis of more than 40 years (Fig 1). To our knowledge, based on a synopsis of papers published in 1970 by Stephens and augmented by ourselves, these are the longest known follow-ups of such a large number of schizophrenics in world literature. The follow-up observations were classified under 6 main headings (which could be viewed, according to a concept recently introduced by Strauss and Carpenter (1977), as "linked-open systems") namely:

- the end-states at follow-up

- the development of schizophrenic symptoms and syndromes

- the development of additional, not specifically schizophrenic, symptoms (for instance depression, anxiety, etc.)

- the development of organic brain syndromes

- the development of social adaptation

- the overall course (combined measure of the preceeding evolving aspects).

In order to identify some of the main factors influencing the long-term course, every aspect of outcome was statistically related to a set of more than 20 general, anamnestic, psychopathological and situational variables.

**OVERALL OUTCOME**

From the many aspects of outcome studied, we will briefly report here the following four: admission to hospital, types of course, global outcome of schizophrenia, social outcome.

Regarding *admission to hospital,* it is interesting to note that the total duration was less than 1 year for about half of the probands. On the other hand, about one quarter spent more than 20 years in hospitals (Figure 2). A very similar picture is obtained when the duration of admission to hospital is related to the total follow-up period. Most patients spent less than 10% of the whole follow-up period in hospital, but about one quarter of the probands remained there nearly all of the time.

By combining the type of onset, the form of development and the end-state reached (in the sense of M. Bleuler), a great variety of *types of course* were observed, which can be summarized schematically in the eight types of Figure 3. The first four types are commonest and result from combinations of a phasic or continuous course with a favorable or unfavorable outcome; the following four less frequent types are alternative combinations. It is noteworthy that an acute onset combined with a phasic course and a favorable outcome was

**Figure 1. Duration of Follow-up**

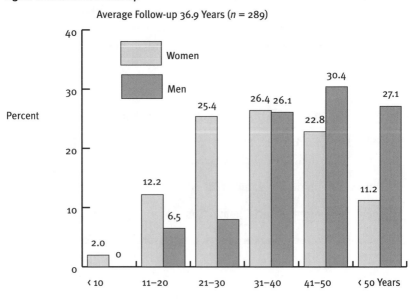

Average Follow-up 36.9 Years (*n* = 289)

The Natural History of Schizophrenia in the Long Term

Figure 2. Total Time of In-Patient Hospital Care

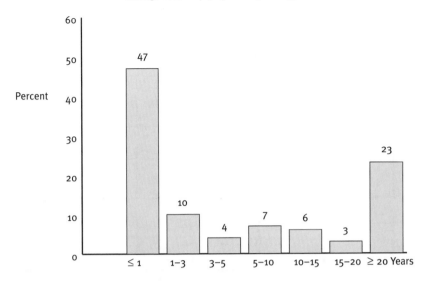

Average Follow-up 36.9 Years (*n* = 289)

exhibited by 25% of the sample and was the most frequent and also the most favorable type. The most unfavorable one (Bleuler's so-called "catastrophic schizophrenia"), beginning with an acute onset and leading directly to a severe endstate, affected 6% of the sample and was sixth in order of frequency.

The *global outcome* of schizophrenia, as measured by the end-states reached was favorable in 49% of the cases, 27% complete remissions and 22% minor residuals, compared to 42% with unfavorable outcomes of intermediate or severe degree (Figure 4). In comparison with the situation at first admission, mental health was completely or partially improved in about two thirds of the cases (Figure 5).

Concerning *social outcome* at follow-up, we found about two fifths of the patients living with their family or by themselves, one fifth in community institutions, and the rest in hospitals (Figure 6). Although the mean age of our probands was 74 years at follow-up, more than half (51%) were still working; about two thirds of them in part-time and one-third in a full-time occupation. The final social adaptation was assessed from a combination of social dependency and from quality and quantity of social contacts. Combined in a global score, the overall social adaptation appeared as good or fair in only about one third of the cases, whereas it was intermediate or bad in two thirds. This showed that the main residuals or consequences of the illness were not in the field of persisting schizophrenic psychopathology, but of impaired social functioning.

## Figure 3. Long-Term Evolution of Schizophrenia

(Dotted lines represent variations of the same type of course.)
Average Follow-up 36.9 Years (*n* = 228)

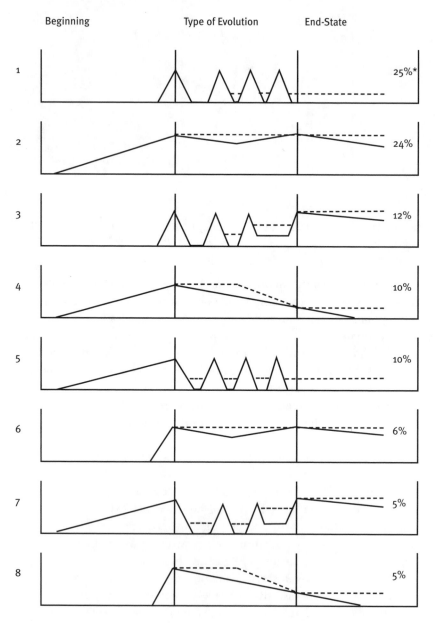

*Only one single attack in 10% of all cases

The Natural History of Schizophrenia in the Long Term

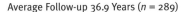

**Figure 4. End States for >5 Years in Schizophrenia**

Average Follow-up 36.9 Years ($n$ = 289)

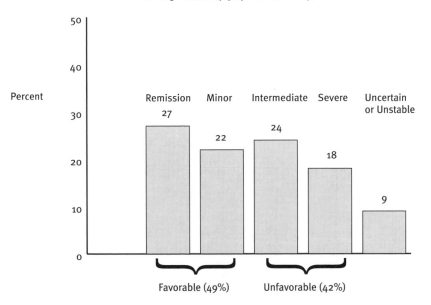

### RELATIONS BETWEEN OUTCOME, TREATMENT AND OTHER VARIABLES

Concerning the relations of outcome with treatment, as well as with some other important variables, the study provides the probably unique opportunity to compare the course and outcome of first admissions from the beginning of the century until the 1960s. In order to examine the possible influence of the introduction of new treatment methods, we divided our sample into 6 decades according to first admission, and also into three main groups: first the patients admitted before the beginning of the active shock treatment era in 1933 (61%), second the patients first admitted between 1933 and the introduction of neuroleptics in 1953 (35%), and third the patients first admitted after 1953. The last group with only 4% was, however, too small for valid statistical comparisons. The surprising and disappointing finding was that no statistically significant difference could be found between the outcomes of first admissions during this whole, very extended period of observation. In other words, the schizophrenic patients first admitted in the 1940s or 1950s had no better long-term course than those first admitted at the beginning and during the three first decades of the century!

This seems to show that the apparent improvements in treatment methods, hospital conditions, psychological understanding, etc., from the beginning of the century until at least the 1950s, with the possible exclusion of the neuroleptics because the last subgroup was too small, made no difference at

**Figure 5. Overall Evolution of Schizophrenia**

Average Follow-up 36.9 Years (*n* = 289)

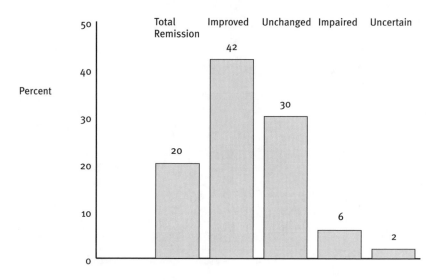

**Figure 6. Housing Situation at Follow-up**

Average Follow-up 36.9 Years (*n* = 289)

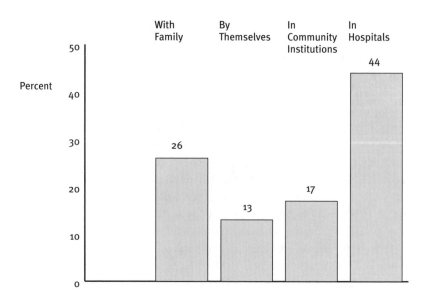

The Natural History of Schizophrenia in the Long Term

all to the course of the illness. Closer examination reveals, however, several selective sampling factors, partly related to mortality. Among them an increasing proportion of prognostically more unfavorable schizophrenics with late onset during the later decades could conceal more favorable courses in recent years. But such possibly hidden improvements were not overwhelming enough to counterbalance the sampling effects mentioned.

A second important finding, which points in the same direction, is the relationship between the outcome on one hand and various methods of treatment on the other, such as electroshock (given to 6.5% of patients), insulin (12.5%), pre-neuroleptic drugs (31%), or complete lack of any particular therapy (50%). Here also, no significant differences of outcome could be found between all these different approaches.

Again these results should be interpreted with great care. Various treatments could have been effective for a short time without, however, improving the final outcome. Furthermore, there is no guarantee that the different groups of patients and treatments are really comparable. It might well be, for instance, that only the most unfavorable cases received electroshock and insulin, which in contrast were given very seldom or not at all to the most favorable cases. The only thing that once more can be safely said is that any possible favorable effects of the treatments mentioned were certainly not overwhelming enough to counterbalance the likely biases.

Continuing in the same line, some other negative findings may be of particular interest. Contrary to common beliefs and information in the literature, no specific relations at all were found between the different aspects of outcome and sex, constitution, heredity (schizophrenia or other mental illnesses), intelligence, school education, and age of onset.

By contrast, the following variables, weighted by the sum of their correlation coefficients with the different aspects of outcome (without organic brain syndrome), were most closely related to the outcome of the illness:

1. Current housing situation
2. Total duration of hospital admission
3. Type of course
4. Duration of first period of hospital care
5. Current employment situation
6. Premorbid social adaptation
7. Premorbid occupational adaptation
8. Premorbid personality
9. Type of onset
10. Current physical health
11. Severity of initial symptomatology
12. Age at first admission

13. Current age
14. Civil status
15. Occupational training
16. Occupation

Except for the obviously circular relations between outcome and several aspects of the current situation such as housing, employment and perhaps physical health, it seemed that three general factors emerged, which were determinants for the overall outcome, namely

1.   A *personality factor:* the better adapted and the more harmonious the premorbid personality was, the more probable statistically was a favorable course of illness.

2.   An *illness-Gestalt-factor* (which is perhaps related to or even identical with the personality factor): the more florid and transient certain main characteristics of the illness were (such as type of onset, productivity and acuteness of the initial symptomatology, developing form), the more probable statistically was a favorable course of illness.

3.   An *age factor:* it was found that the latter half of life often exerts a leveling, smoothing and calming influence on schizophrenia. The further the person advanced into old age, the more probable statistically was a favorable course of illness.

### DISCUSSION AND CONCLUSIONS

During recent years, not only our own, but also two other major long-term studies on schizophrenia have been published in German, providing together a view of the course of about 1,000 cases over several decades. In 1972, also from Switzerland, came Manfred Bleuler's book, which has just been translated into English, on a very careful 22-year follow-up investigation of 208 schizophrenics in Zurich, and in 1979 appeared the important study by Gerd Huber and co-workers from Bonn on 502 schizophrenics followed-up after an average of 21.4 years. These three studies, closely comparable in their methodology and framework, in spite of a quite different theoretical approach by Huber, were undertaken completely independently of each other. The concordance of the results in general, as well as in many details, is striking.

Thus, favorable end-states were found in 53% of cases by Bleuler, 49% by us in an identical evaluation, and 57% by Huber and collaborators. In all three studies, a great variety of developing types was found by combining various aspects (Huber for instance identified initially 72 types of development which he condensed to 12, as compared to the eight types reported, with very similar frequencies, by Bleuler and ourselves).

Many findings are very similar concerning the variables related to favorable or unfavorable outcome, such as for instance the premorbid personality and social adaptation, the type of onset, the form of development, and to some extent also the initial symptomatology. A common finding, with some minor variations, was also the lack of correlation between course and outcome on one hand and genetic factors on the other (as assessed by schizophrenia or other mental illnesses among family members).

Concerning the influence of treatment, however, the findings are somewhat different. Bleuler avoided statistical calculations because of the enormous inherent methodological uncertainties. Huber on the other hand, whose cases were examined between 1945 and 1959, identified some possible, but questionable, indications of a positive long-term effect of neuroleptics as well as of electroshock treatment, especially when they were given shortly after the onset of the illness. This points to a possible bias, as the cases with chronic onset have a worse prognosis.

Our own stand is, as mentioned, intermediate. We would certainly fully agree with Bleuler's (1972) very thoughtful general reflections on the effective factors in the treatment of schizophrenia. He considers that three principles are vitally important in every one of the many old and new therapeutic approaches. The first consists in therapists relating constantly and actively to the healthy aspects of the psychotic patient. The second concerns the therapeutic effect of sudden and surprising changes in general, social and somatic conditions, often leading to a mobilization of hidden resources. The third consists in calming actions and influences which can be introduced in many ways, the best of them being talking and togetherness, and another being neuroleptic drugs. Bleuler is, however, against a regular, heavy and prolonged use of such drugs, giving many convincing arguments on the basis of his long-term observations. It is striking, and emphasized by Bleuler himself, how these three general therapeutic principles can be seen at work in nearly all treatment methods in schizophrenia, as in many other mental conditions and even in normal growth and creativity. Bleuler is convinced that a "specific treatment of schizophrenia" does not exist.

On the same lines is the following general conclusion we can draw from our own recent long-term investigations and those of the authors mentioned. For everyone who does not link the concept of schizophrenia itself to an obligatory bad outcome, the enormous variety of possible evolutions shows that *there is no such thing as a specific course of schizophrenia*. Doubtless, the potential for improvement of schizophrenia has for a long time been grossly under-estimated. In the light of long-term investigations, what is called "the course of schizophrenia" more closely resembles a life process open to a great variety of influences of all kinds than an illness with a given course. Just as in normal life processes, here what we call illness may represent the complex and variable reaction to an equally complex global situation of a given person, with his particular sensibilities and idiosyncrasies, personality structure, behavior and communication patterns, and past and present experiences. Several important environmental influences on the course have already clearly been identified, among them family attitudes and stressful life-events according to investigations by Brown et al (1968, 1972) and Vaughn and Leff (1976), as well as the expectations of the patient himself, his family and surrounding persons which, according to our own recent research, seem often to act strongly as self fulfilling prophecies (Ciompi et al., 1979).

Such a conclusion may be both bewildering and encouraging at the same time. Practically none of the old and seemingly secure dogmas about this illness hold when we look at them closely and long enough. But also no approach that takes the person into account more than the illness, and is hence "psychotherapeutic" in a wider or narrower sense, has to be *a priori* discarded. Viewing schizophrenia as closer to a life process than to an illness might not be a less useful concept for therapeutic purposes than any other. Anyhow it inspires hope as well as modesty in dealing and communicating with our fellow men hidden by the fascinating and as yet unsolved enigma of psychotic alienation.

## REFERENCES

Bleuler, M. (1978). Die Schizophrenen Geistesstorungen im Lichte langjdhriger Kranken- und Familien-geschichten. Thierne, Stuttgart 1972. *The schizophrenic disorders: Long-term patient and family studies,* translated by S. M. Clemens. Yale University Press, New Haven and London.

Brown, G. W., & Birley, J. L. T. (1968). Crises and life changes and the onset of schizophrenia. *Journal of Health and Social Behaviour, 9,* 203–214.

Brown, G. W., Birley, J. L. T., & Wing, J. K. (1972). The influence of family life on the course of schizophrenic disorders: a replication. *British Journal of Psychiatry, 121,* 241–258.

Ciompi, L., Dauwalder, H. P. & Ague, C. (1979). *Ein Forschungsprogram zur Rehabilitation psychisch Kranker: III. Langsschnittuntersuchung zum Rehabilitationserfolg und zur Prognostik.* Nervenarzt, 50, 366–378.

Ciompi, L., & Müller, C. H. (1976). *Lebensweg und Alter der Schizophrenen. Eine katamnestische Langzeitstudie bis ins Senium.* Springer, Berlin-Heidelberg-New York.

Huber, G., Gross, G., & Scheuttler, R. (1979). *Schizophrenie. Eine verlaufs-und sozial-psychiatrische Langzeitstudie.* Springer, Berlin-Heidelberg-New York.

Stephens, J. H. (1970). Long-term courses and prognosis in schizophrenia. *Seminars in Psychiatry, 2,* 464–485.

Strauss, J. S., & Carpenter, W. T., JR. (1977). The prediction of outcome in schizo-phrenia. III. Five-year outcome and its predictors. *Archives of General Psychiatry, 34,* 159–163.

Vaughn, C., & Leff, J. (1976) The measurement of expressed emotion in the fami-lies of psychiatric patients. *British Journal of Social and Clinical Psychology, 15,*157–165.

# The Varied Outcomes of Schizophrenia

*Larry Davidson and Thomas H. McGlashan*

At the time of original publication, Larry Davidson, PhD, was Assistant Professor of Psychiatry, Yale University School of Medicine; Director, Psychosis Program, Connecticut Mental Health Center, New Haven, Connecticut; and Thomas McGlashan, MD, was Professor of Psychiatry, Yale University School of Medicine; Executive Director, Yale Psychiatric Institute, New Haven, Connecticut.

This article originally appeared in the *Canadian Journal of Psychiatry, 1997;* 42, 34–43 and is reprinted with permission.

**Abstract:** *Objective.* To review variations in outcomes in schizophrenia across individual, historical, and cross-cultural boundaries, as well as within specific domains of functioning. *Method.* Research literature on the outcomes of schizophrenia appearing within the last 8 years was reviewed. *Results.* First, a review of follow-up studies published in the developed world suggests that, heterogeneity in outcome across individuals with schizophrenia remains the rule, with affective symptoms, later and acute onset, and responsiveness to biological treatments predictive of good outcome. Negative symptoms are associated with poor outcome, cognitive impairments, and incapacity in social and work domains. Deterioration appears to occur within the first few months of onset if not already in the prodrome, with recent early-course studies finding longer duration of untreated psychosis associated with insidious onset, negative symptoms, social and work incapacity, and poor outcome. Second, a review of recent cross-cultural and historical studies provides evidence that outcome varies across time and place, schizophrenia having a more favorable outcome in the developing world and becoming a more benign disorder over the course of this century. Third, a review of studies of the domains of functioning within individuals identifies 4 relatively independent dimensions of depression and negative, psychotic, and disorganized symptoms. Cognitive deficits, which are associated with negative symptoms, also constitute a relatively stable dimension over time, showing neither marked deterioration nor improvement once established early in the course of disorder. *Conclusions.* The early appearance and stability over time of negative symptoms and cognitive impairments call for assertive intervention efforts early in the course of disorder to prevent chronicity and prolonged disability.

This paper will review the varied outcomes of schizophrenia in three senses. First, there is the variation in outcomes seen *across individuals* with the disorder, what has come to be called the "heterogeneity of the long-term course of schizophrenia" (Carpenter & Kirkpatrick, 1988). Second, there appears to be a variation in outcomes between groups of individuals when one considers both sociocultural and historical context, with outcome varying in part as a result of time and place (Basic Behavioral Science Task Force of the National Advisory Mental Health Council, 1996; Lin & Kleinman, 1988). Third, there is a variation in outcomes *within any given individual* when one considers in finer detail the relatively independent domains of functioning that constitute global measures of outcome (Harding, Brooks, Ashikaga, Strauss & Landerl, 1987; Strauss & Carpenter, 1974; Strauss & Carpenter , 1977). These domains include positive, disorganized, and negative symptomatology and neurocognitive functioning, among others. In this review, we summarize the recent literature in each of these 3 areas, beginning with 1) overall course and outcome, moving through 2) cross-cultural and historical influences on outcome, and closing with 3) outcome in specific domains of functioning. Following this review, we conclude with a brief consideration of future directions for research.

### VARIATIONS IN COURSE AND OUTCOMES AS OF 1988

We take as our point of departure for this section the reviews of international long-term follow-up studies of schizophrenia collected into a 1988 special issue of the *Schizophrenia Bulletin* (McGlashan & Carpenter, 1988). This issue provides a comprehensive picture of the accumulated knowledge of the course and outcome of schizophrenia as of the late 1980s and offers a convenient benchmark for the identification of recent advances made in understanding the longitudinal aspects of the disorder.

Several conclusions were drawn from these reviews of long-term follow-up studies in Europe, North America, and non-Western developing countries, the most consistent of which is that there was a *heterogeneity* in long-term outcome for individuals with schizophrenia within each study sample, regardless of setting (Lin & Kleinman, 1988; Angst, 1988; McGlashan, 1988). Each study found a range in long-term outcome from fully recovered to severe and continuous incapacity, with substantial numbers of patients in each of the various categories. Differences in the percentages of patients achieving favorable outcomes across studies were attributed at least in part to differing sample characteristics and diagnostic systems (McGlashan & Carpenter, 1988; Angst, 1988), with the one exception of mounting evidence for a more favorable outcome for individuals in the developing world (Lin & Kleinman, 1988).

With Kraepelinian negative prognosis and progressive, deteriorating course refuted, the remainder of this issue focused on ways to reduce heterogeneity by identifying dimensions of chronicity, prognostic factors, and course patterns. McGlashan (1988) suggested 4 dimensions of chronicity: length of mental illness, institutionalization, resistance to biological treatments, and age of onset. In addition, he considered gender, the paranoidnonparanoid distinction, and a range of other nondiagnostic predictors such as family history of schizophrenia and level of premorbid functioning as useful determinants of outcome. Building upon the earlier work of Ciompi (1980), Harding (1988) described 8 course patterns based on combinations of acute versus chronic onset, simple versus undulating course, and end states ranging from recovery to severe incapacity. As a first step toward reducing the heterogeneity of course and outcome, Carpenter and Kirkpatrick (1988) suggested the delineation of 3 epochs in the course of schizophrenia for use in future long-term studies: the onset epoch, the middle-course epoch, and the late-course epoch. In looking toward the next generation of research, several investigators suggested that a focus on the onset epoch or the early course might be particularly useful in future prospective studies, as existing studies may have underestimated recovery rates because of the failure to include, or early attrition of, healthier subjects who would have met initial diagnostic criteria for schizophrenia.

### STUDIES OF VARIATIONS IN COURSE AND OUTCOME APPEARING SINCE 1988

The most concentrated research efforts examining outcome since the late 1980s have had just such a focus on the onset epoch and early course of disorder through prospective studies of first-episode patients. In addition to this focus, new findings from several follow-up studies have appeared within the last 8 years, largely confirming the findings of earlier studies, particularly in relation to cross-cultural differences. Two prognostic factors have been the focus of considerable attention. With few exceptions (Turner & Tsuang, 1990; Maninez-Arevalo & Caicedo-Ordonez & Varo-Prieto, 1994)), the most recent studies and reviews continue to provide evidence that substance abuse, most often alcohol and cannabis and most frequently in young men, has a detrimental effect on course and outcome (Linszen, Dingemans & Lenior, 1994; Duke, Pantelis & Barnes, 1994; DeQuardo, Carpenter & Tandon, 1994); Kozarie-Kovacic, Folnegovic-Smaic, Folnegovic & Marusic, 1995; Chouljian, Shumway, Balancio, Dwyer, Surber & Jacobs, 1995; Smith & Hucker, 1994; Drake & Wallach, 1989; Test, Wallisch, Allness & Ripp, 1989; Mueser, Yamold, Levinson, Singh, Bellack, Kee et al.,1990; Dixon, Haas, Weiden, Sweeney & Frances, 1991; Zisook, Heaton, Moranville, Kuck, Jernigan & Braff, 1992). Literature on gender differences has been more mixed, with a comprehensive review of 102 studies pointing out that only half of the studies provided evidence for superior outcome in women, the remaining half showing no differences (Angermeyer, Kuhn, & Goldstein, 1990). Consistent with this mixed picture, some recent studies continue to provide support for later onset, greater responsiveness to treatment, and better outcomes for women (Szymanski, Lieberman, Alvir, Mayerhoff, Loebel,

Geisler et al., 1995; Bardenstein & McGlashan, 1990; McGlashan & Bardenstein, 1990; Childers & Harding, 1990), while other studies show either no differences (Kendler & Walsh, 1995) or superior outcome in men (Ohaeri, 1993).

In the remainder of this section, we first review the recent long-term follow-up studies completed in developed countries before turning to consider new studies focusing on the onset epoch and early course of disorder. In the next section, we review the cross-cultural findings produced from studies in the developing world, in addition to considering evidence of historical changes in the severity of schizophrenia over the course of this century.

### Long-Term Follow-up Studies

We were able to locate 9 follow-up studies that have been completed within the last 8 years in the developed world (Carpenter & Strauss , 1991; Mason, Harrison, Glazebrook, Medley, Dalkin & Croudace, 1995; Shepard, Watt, Falloon & Smeeton, 1989; Carone, Harrow & Westermeyer, 1991; Breier, Schreiber, Dyer & Pickar, 1991; DeSisto, Harding, McCormick, Ashikaga & Brooks, 1995a, 1995b; Marneros, Deister, Rohde, Steinmeyer, & Junemann, 1989; Steinmeyer, Manneros, Deister, Rohde, Junemarin, 1989; Mameros & Deister, 1990; Helgason, 1990; Geddes & Kendell, 1995). While primarily confirming the findings of earlier long-term studies regarding the heterogeneity of course and outcome in schizophrenia, several of these studies provide important indications about course and outcome that we describe below.

In the most recent report to come out of their landmark study of the International Pilot Study of Schizophrenia (IPSS) Washington cohort, Carpenter and Strauss (1991) provided 11-year follow-up data on 40 of the original 131 patients evaluated between 1968 and 1969 who met DSM-II criteria for schizophrenia. These data were consistent with the findings at both 2- and 5-year follow-up that suggested that symptom severity, duration of hospitalization, and work and social functioning constituted "loosely linked" domains of functioning, with level of functioning in each domain at or prior to index admission being most predictive of outcome in that domain. In addition, a global measure of outcome at 11 years remained consistent with outcome assessed at 2 and 5 years, providing evidence of neither marked deterioration nor improvement over the 6- to 9-year period. The investigators suggested that these findings of a lack of deterioration and consistency in outcome indicate that psychopathology tends to plateau early in the course of illness following an initial deterioration, with later-course improvement more likely than progressive deterioration.

Two additional studies provide evidence for this pattern of initial deterioration followed by a plateau in functioning early in the course of disorder and followed by later-course improvements. Mason and others (1995) reported on the 13-year outcome of an epidemiologically defined cohort of 67 patients with an ICD-9 diagnosis of schizophrenia having their first contact with psychiatric services in Nottingham, England, between 1978 to 1980. Of the 58 patients available for follow-up after 13 years, 52% were without psychotic symptoms, 52% were without negative symptoms, and 55% demonstrated good to fair social functioning. While only 22% of the sample had been employed during the last 2 years of follow-up, 97% were living independently in the community, and 44% achieved a mild to recovered global outcome. Carone and others (1991) followed a group of 79 young patients with DSM-III schizophrenia 2.5 and 5 years after hospitalization and found an improvement between first and second follow-up, with 10% achieving a good outcome after 2.5 years to 17% after 5 years. There was more consistency among the 58% of the sample achieving a poor outcome, most of whom already had demonstrated the worst outcome at 2 years. This study also found a decrease in rates of hospitalization over the follow-up period, despite persisting symptoms and dysfunction in a majority of the sample.

Breier and others (1991) examined the outcome of 58 patients with Research Diagnostic Criteria (RDC) schizophrenia hospitalized between 1976 and 1984 at the National Institutes of Health in Bethesda, Maryland. Patients tended to be relatively young and referred from community-based settings, but also had been only partially responsive to conventional treatments and had continued to experience residual positive and negative symptoms an average of 7 years into their illness. On a composite overall outcome measure an average of 6 years later, 42% of the sample had a poor outcome, 38% had a moderate outcome, and 21% had a good outcome. Seventy-four percent of the sample had moderate to high levels of positive symptoms, 84% had moderate to high levels of negative symptoms, and 50% had either no or only superficial social contacts. Patients with a longer duration of illness had significantly more negative symptoms. Of note is that 24% of the sample experienced at least one episode of major depression during the follow-up period, and that these patients spent less time in the hospital during this period than those who did not experience depression. Levels of both positive and negative symptoms were related to functional incapacity in social, work, and independent living domains. Frontal lobe dysfunction was associated both with negative symptoms and with social functioning but not with positive symptoms. Lastly, while index symptom levels measured drug-free were not related to outcome, both positive and negative symptom levels during optimal medication predicted both outcome symptoms and functioning, suggesting that responsiveness to biological treatments and Postmedication symptom severity may be strongly predictive of outcome.

Another study to emphasize the role of treatment as a factor influencing outcome was conducted by DeSisto and others (1995a, 1995b) in Maine. Using a retrospective, group matching design, the investigators compared the long-term outcome of 269 patients with DSM-III schizophrenia admitted to Maine hospitals between 1956 and 1961 with that of the cohort of 269 patients reevaluated 32 years after discharge from the Vermont State Hospital in the earlier Vermont Longitudinal Study (Harding, Brooks, Ashikaga, Strauss & Breier, 1987a, 1987b). Comparisons between the 119 Maine subjects who were available for follow-up interviews 36 years after their index admission with the 180 subjects interviewed for the Vermont study showed that Vermont subjects were more productive and had fewer symptoms and better community adjustment and global functioning than Maine subjects. The investigators suggest that the more favorable outcome in Vermont may be attributable to the model rehabilitation program and focus on a return to community living developed there in the 1950s, when no similar programs or assistance were available in Maine, suggesting that assertive rehabilitation can exert a beneficial effect on the outcome of the disorder.

Two studies have looked at outcome for patients with schizophrenia as compared with other psychotic disorders. Johnstone and others (1992) followed up 326 patients with psychotic disorders over a 2.5-year period and compared those with schizophrenia (DSM-III and Present State Examination [PSE]) with those with affective disorders. They found outcome to be worse for those with schizophrenia on all dimensions, and those with schizoaffective disorders to be in the midrange between schizophrenia and affective disorders. The presence of cognitive impairments, however, was found to be equal across all diagnoses and to be strongly associated with the presence of negative symptoms, regardless of diagnosis. As part of the Cologne long-term study, Marneros and others (1989, 1989, 1990) followed up, over a mean duration of 25 years, 148 patients with narrowly defined DSM-III schizophrenia, categorizing 101 patients with affective symptomatology as schizoaffective. Patients with schizophrenia had consistently poorer outcome as compared with patients with either schizoaffective or affective disorders, with only 19% achieving no to slight disturbances and 70% having severe to very severe disturbances. Good to excellent adjustment was achieved by only 36% of those with schizophrenia, as compared with 90% of those with schizoaffective disorders. Given the relatively favorable outcome of schizoaffective and affective disorder patients, the investigators suggest that the more narrow the diagnostic criteria for schizophrenia, the less favorable the outcome will be.

Lastly, two studies provide information regarding patients who avoid admission to inpatient care, thereby constituting a subpopulation who may not have been included in prior outcome studies conducted in clinical sites. Helgason (1990) reported on a 20-year follow-up of 107 patients with ICD-9 schizophrenia first presenting for treatment in Iceland between 1966 and 1967. By the end of the 20-year period, 20% had yet to be admitted to the hospital. Overall outcome was good for 33% of the total sample, and extremely poor for 21%, with the remainder in the moderate range. There was a mean delay between symptom onset and first psychiatric contact of 6 to 7 years, with those patients who sought treatment earlier in the course of illness having a more favorable outcome. In addition, a comparison of the number of patients presenting for treatment with the number expected to manifest the disorder suggests that only 60% of people with schizophrenia in Iceland seek psychiatric care at all, possibly comprising a biased sample of those with more severe forms of the disorder.

Geddes and Kendell (1995) identified 66 people diagnosed with schizophrenia in the United Kingdom between 1978 and 1989 who had no history of hospitalization prior to 1991. This sample constituted 6.7% of the estimated annual rate of first diagnosis. When compared with a control group of patients admitted to the hospital within 3 months of diagnosis, these patients were generally less disturbed, had lower levels of violent behavior, less evidence of neglect or hallucinations, a longer duration of illness prior to diagnosis, and were more often unemployed. Outcome for 43 patients who could be traced and who met RDC criteria was heterogeneous, however, with the majority demonstrating residual impairments and subsequent exacerbations. The investigators found no significant differences in outcome between this group and the control group of hospitalized patients, suggesting that the exclusion of patients who are not hospitalized should have little influence on future outcome studies. It should be noted, however, that this study compared outcome only among individuals receiving outpatient care, as opposed to those hospitalized, and did not include those individuals who remained outside of the treatment system altogether.

In summary, recent follow-up studies continue to find a broad heterogeneity in long-term outcome in schizophrenia, with 21% to 57% of subjects achieving a good outcome ranging from mild impairment to recovery. These studies provide further evidence that deterioration occurs within the first few months of onset, followed by a plateau in functioning which then may or may not be followed by gradual improvements later in the course of disorder. Affective symptoms and depressive episodes appear to be predictive of a more favorable outcome, with the result that the more narrow the diagnostic criteria for schizophrenia, the less favorable the outcome. Negative symptoms appear to be associated with poor outcome, cognitive impairments, and functional incapacity in social and work domains. Assertive rehabilitation efforts appear to improve long-term outcome, while responsiveness to biological treatments early in the course of illness may be strongly predictive of long-term outcome. Lastly, early results are inconclusive in relation to the importance for outcome studies of identifying and following individuals who do not seek care. While a longer duration of untreated illness may be predictive of poor outcome, those who do not seek care may also constitute a less, or at least more quietly, disabled population. With increasing attention shifting to the examination of negative symptoms (Davidson & McGlashan, 1995), a more adequate characterization of this population may become an important area for future research.

### Early-Course Studies

Following a workshop on first-episode psychosis organized by the National Institute of Mental Health in 1991 (Kirch, Keith & Matthews, 1992), 3 special issues of the *Schizophrenia Bulletin* have been devoted to early-course, first-episode, and early-detection and intervention studies (Kirch, Keith & Matthews, 1992; Lieberman, Matthews & Kirch, 1992; McGlashan, 1996), breaking what may be considered to be new ground in schizophrenia research. A comprehensive review of the existing studies of first-episode patients in North America and Europe as of 1992 (Ram, Bromet, Eaton, Pato & Schwartz, 1992) found that approximately one third of first-admission patients were relapse-free for the 2 years following discharge, with a larger proportion of first-episode patients achieving a good outcome when compared with previous follow-up samples of consecutive admissions. Better premorbid social and work functioning, acute onset, shorter duration of untreated illness, rapid treatment response, and shorter duration of first hospitalization were all predictive of good outcome. These findings have since been replicated and expanded in more recent early course studies, which we review below.

In a series of reports examining hospitalization rates, Eaton and others (1992a, 1992b) used case registers to track 20 years of hospitalizations for individuals discharged from their first ever hospitalization in Victoria, Australia; Maryland, United States; Salford, England; and Denmark. The percentage of patients eventually rehospitalized following their first admission varied from 50% to 80% in the 4 areas, but consistently showed a significant decrease in hospitalizations 2 to 3 years following discharge. Early age of onset predicted higher risk for rehospitalization. The clustering of most hospitalizations within the first 2 years after first admission, as well as the decrease in hospitalizations over time, suggested a course of progressive amelioration of the disorder rather than progressive deterioration.

Drawing from an ongoing, prospective study of first episode patients, Lieberman and others (1992) reported on the first 70 subjects to complete at least 8 weeks of the study, including both biological and clinical measures and a standardized treatment protocol. Median time to recovery was 11 weeks, 74% of the sample achieved a full remission of symptoms, and outcome assessed 6 months after remission revealed 38% of the sample to be in the excellent to good range, with 45% fair, and 17% poor. Treatment response and remission of symptoms were associated with the presence of akathisia and dystonia. Longer time to remission and poor outcome were associated with elevated GH levels, abnormal brain morphology, longer duration of untreated psychosis, higher levels of negative symptoms, and the presence of the "deficit syndrome." In addition, significant abnormalities were found in eye movement function as well as a psychotogenic response to dopamine agonists. Thus, although the treatment response of these first-episode patients was encouraging, the preliminary study results suggest that significant psychobiological dysfunction may already be present at the time of the first episode of psychosis and that the presence of such abnormalities may be predictive of treatment response and outcome.

In a related study, Bilder and others (1992) compared evidence of the premorbid intellectual and social functioning and cognitive deterioration of 51 first-episode patients with those of 50 chronic patients with schizophrenia and 22 healthy controls. Evidence of early developmental social and cognitive impairments was found in both first-episode and chronic groups. These groups did not differ on estimates of premorbid intellectual ability. First-episode patients were found to have substantial deficits in current intellectual functioning when compared with the controls, but these deficits were less severe than those found in the chronic sample, suggesting that cognitive deterioration occurs both prior to and following the onset of psychosis. These findings were supported by evidence of enduring neurocognitive deficits in first-episode patients in a study of psychobiological vulnerability indicators in schizophrenia by Nuechterlein and others (1992).

A number of studies have found a heterogeneity among first-episode patients in terms of premorbid functioning, clinical presentation, and treatment response that parallels the longer-term follow-up studies reviewed previously. Shtasel and others (1992), for example, compared the symptom profiles of 37 first-episode patients with those of 70 more chronically affected patients and found no significant differences in symptom profile or severity. Negative symptoms, in particular, were no less severe in first-episode patients. Consistent with long-term findings, they also were associated with poor premorbid and current functioning. In a related study, Szymanski and others (1996) also found no differences in response to neuroleptic treatment between first-episode patients and chronic patients experiencing an acute exacerbation, suggesting that maximum symptomatic improvement occurs within the first 6 months of treatment regardless of the timing of the episode in the course of the disorder.

Looking back retrospectively from onset, Haas and Sweeney (1992) characterized the premorbid adjustment and clinical history of 71 first-episode patients meeting DSM-III-R criteria for schizophrenia, schizoaffective disorder, or schizophreniform disorder. They found that 39.4% of the sample had a history of good premorbid adjustment, another 39.4% had a history of chronically poor functioning from childhood through onset of symptoms, and the remaining 21.2% had a pattern of progressive decline from childhood through onset, with a higher percentage of males in this last category. The good premorbid group had a later age of onset and first treatment, while the group showing an insidious decline in functioning had a longer history of psychotic symptoms before hospitalization and more negative symptoms on admission.

In a pair of articles also examining the link between premorbid adjustment and onset, Larsen and others (Larsen & McGlashan, 1996; Larsen, McGlashan &, Johannessen, 1996) characterized the premorbid and early-course parameters of a sample of 43 first-episode patients with nonaffective psychoses in Norway. They found that longer duration of untreated psychosis was associated with poor work, social, and global functioning in the year before admission, a more insidious onset, and more negative symptoms at admission. Males were found to be more likely to be single, have a lower educational status, an earlier age of onset, and lower global functioning in the year before admission, show a rapid deterioration in functioning prior to onset of psychosis, and have a duration of untreated psychosis almost 4 times that of women. Strong support for the prognostic significance of duration of untreated psychosis was also found in a study by Loebel and others (1992), which involved 70 first-episode patients meeting RDC criteria for schizophrenia or schizoaffective disorder. They found that a longer duration of untreated psychosis was associated both with longer time to remission of symptoms and with lower level of remission and that later age of onset and higher premorbid functioning were associated with better levels of remission.

Mounting evidence for the presence of an active disease and deterioration process early in the course of illness, if not predating onset, and for the deleterious impact of untreated psychosis on outcome have most recently moved investigators to focus on early detection and intervention during or prior to the first episode (McGlashan & Johannessen, 1996; Falloon, 1992; Falloon, Kydd, Coverdale & Laidlaw, 1996; Yung, McGorry, McFarlane, Jackson, Patton & Ralckar, 1996; McGorry, Edwards, Milialopoulos, Harrigan & Jackson, 1996). Although quite preliminary and exploratory, early results from these studies suggest that it is feasible to identify a group of young people who are at high risk for developing psychosis and at least to reduce the duration of untreated psychosis and delay onset, if not prevent psychosis altogether (McGlashan & Johannessen, 1996; Falloon, 1992; Falloon, Kydd, Coverdale & Laidlaw, 1996; Yung, McGorry, McFarlane, Jackson, Patton & Ralckar, 1996). Studies of early intervention with first-episode patients (McGorry, Edwards, Milialopoulos, Harrigan & Jackson, 1996) have been more complicated to interpret thus far, but they have generated considerable interest and optimism that chronicity may be prevented in some patients through targeted and intensive efforts to ameliorate symptoms and restore functioning prior to the development of secondary deficits and disability. We anticipate that these 2 areas will attract increasing attention in the near future, as research continues to explore and attempt to address the active disease and deterioration processes that are now evident in the earliest phases of illness.

## CROSS-CULTURAL AND HISTORICAL INFLUENCES ON COURSE AND OUTCOME

### Cross-Cultural Studies

One of the most striking and unexpected findings of the World Health Organization (WHO) IPSS conducted in the 1960s and 1970s was the more favorable outcome for patients in the developing world. This finding, while controversial, has received additional confirmation over the last 8 years with the completion of 5 longer-term studies that were outgrowths of the IPSS (Ohaeri, 1993; Leff, Satorius, Jablensky, Konen & Emberg, 1992; Leon, 1989; Verghese, John, Rajkumar, Richard, Sethi & Trivedi, 1989; Thara, Henrietta, Joseph, Rajkumar & Eaton, 1991). We review these studies here.

The first study is actually the report of the 5-year outcome of the original IPSS cross-cultural cohort of 1202 patients with a PSE diagnosis of schizophrenia drawn from Colombia, Czechoslovakia, Denmark, India, Nigeria, China, the United Kingdom, the United States, and the Union of Soviet Socialist Republics (Leff, Satorius, Jablensky, Konen & Emberg, 1992). At 5-year follow-up, information was obtained on 807 patients, representing 76% of the original cohort. Results largely confirm the 2-year findings of broad heterogeneity and a more favorable outcome for developing countries, specifically finding better clinical and social outcomes for patients in India and Nigeria (up to 67% were asymptomatic) and better social outcome in Colombia. Being female, having an acute or recent onset, and having negative life experiences before onset predicted better outcome, while having a premorbid personality disorder predicted poor outcome.

In one of the studies to build on the IPSS, Leon (1989) reported on the 10-year follow-up of the cohort of 101 patients first identified in Cali, Colombia, as part of that study who were later rediagnosed as having schizophrenia by ICD-8 and ICD-9 criteria. This rediagnosis eliminated 8 cases (of the 84 located) as not fitting the more rigid criteria, leaving 76 patients for 10-year follow-up. Complete recovery was found in 43.4% of the sample, with an additional 8% achieving partial recovery. A number of these patients married, completed secondary education, and experienced upward vocational mobility during the follow-up period. Only one patient had committed suicide. Positive prognostic indicators included being female, having less education, and having a "normal" childhood. Outcome at 10 years was consistent with that at 2 and 5 years, suggesting a more favorable outcome for people in Colombia than for those in Europe and North America.

A series of studies have been completed in India that also continued the work of the IPSS. First, a multicentre study (Verghese A, John, Rajkumar, Richard, Sethi & Trivedi, 1989) in Lucknow, Vellore, and Madras of 323 early-course patients meeting modified Feighner's criteria for schizophrenia found a 66% remission rate at 2-year follow-up. As in Colombia, there was only a 2% suicide rate, and 40% of patients were employed at 2 years. Positive prognostic factors included short duration of illness, compliance with medications, rural background, and being agitated at intake. Poor prognosis was associated with economic difficulties, decrease in religious activity, perceived dangerousness, and premorbid schizoid personality. In a second study, Thara and others (1991) then followed up the Madras cohort after 10 years and located 76 of the original 90 cases meeting ICD-9 criteria. Both positive and negative symptoms showed a significant decline at the end of 10 years, with 67% of the sample showing a good pattern of course leading to partial or complete recovery. Sixty percent of the subjects were employed at 10 years, while only 4 people had committed suicide. Being female and having an earlier age of onset predicted good outcome, while insidious onset and longer duration of illness predicted poor outcome.

In the last study to be stimulated by the IPSS, Ohaeri (1993) conducted a retrospective follow-up of 142 patients meeting RDC criteria for schizophrenia that spanned a range of 7 to 26 years. Outcome was consistent over the 7 years of follow-up, with a good outcome achieved by 50.7% and a moderate outcome achieved by 23.9%. The most typical course was acute onset followed by an episodic course with rapid remission in response to treatment. Negative symptoms were rarely noted. Women had an older age of onset and, in a rare finding, a poorer outcome than men. The author noted that many men, even those in moderate- to poor-outcome categories, were able to complete education and/or work in order to become self-sustaining.

As they continue to demonstrate a better outcome for patients in the developing world, with a range from 52% to 67% achieving a good outcome, these studies raise intriguing and important questions about the possible role of sociocultural factors in shaping the course and outcome of schizophrenia. The poorer prognosis of women in Nigeria and the prognostic significance of decreased religious activity in India draw attention to specific examples of ways in which cultural norms and practices may influence outcome and provide valuable directions for future research.

### Schizophrenia in Historical Perspective

In addition to considering variations in outcome for schizophrenia across cultures, people continue to speculate about the possibility of schizophrenia disappearing, or at least becoming a more benign disorder, over the course of this century (Harrison & Mason, 1993; Der, Gupta & Murray, 1990; Harrison, Cooper & Gancaryczyrk, 1991). Whether due to the natural evolution of the illness itself, changes in diagnostic criteria, improved treatments, or the shift to community care, clinical accounts are suggestive of less severe forms of the disorder, with catatonia, for example, apparently disappearing from the developed world (Kendel, Malcolm & Adams, 1993; Abrahamson, 1993; Wyatt, 1991; Hegarty, Balclessarini, Totten, Watemaux & Oepen, 1994). One important study conducted recently provides some empirical support for this contention and has stimulated interest in this possibility.

Hegarty and others (1994) conducted a meta analysis of outcome studies for the years 1895 to 1991, limiting the comparative analysis to 320 studies (of 51,800 subjects) that assessed outcome under 10 years to detect trends by decade. The analysis revealed an increase in the proportion of patients showing improvement over an average of 6 years of follow-up after mid-century, with 35.4% showing improvement between 1895 and 1955 versus 49.5% between 1956 and 1985. This rate has declined again over the last decade to 36.4%, however, possibly reflecting a narrower conception of the disorder. The study clearly demonstrated that outcome is influenced by choice of diagnostic criteria, with broader criteria producing a better outcome (46.5% improvement with broad criteria versus 27.3% with narrow criteria). What remains to be determined is whether the improvement in outcome seen at mid-century is due entirely to diagnostic criteria or if other as yet unknown factors brought about changes in disease severity.

### OUTCOMES IN SPECIFIC DOMAINS OF FUNCTIONING

As noted at the beginning of this paper, earlier studies have established heterogeneity of levels of symptoms and functioning *within* individuals with schizophrenia as well as across individuals (Harding, Brooks, Ashikaga, Strauss & Breier, 1987b). This section reviews recent advances made in differentiating these domains, exploring their relationships over time, and investigating their links to neurocognitive functioning and outcome.

Building on the earlier work of Strauss and Carpenter pointing out the "loosely linked" nature of the relationships between symptoms and functioning (1974, 1977) and resurrecting the positive and negative symptom dichotomy (1974), many researchers have been devoted in recent years to identifying these relatively independent domains both cross-sectionally and over time, with a particular emphasis on negative symptoms and the "deficit syndrome" (Davidson & McGlashan, 1995; Carpenter, 1994; Carpenter, Heinrichs & Wagman, 1988). These latter components, while considered essential to schizophrenia since Kraepelin and Bleuler, were deemphasized in *DSM-III* because of concerns that they could not be rated as reliably as positive symptoms and that their inclusion as diagnostic criteria would generate an overly broad conception of schizophrenia (Andreasen & Carpenter, 1993; Kane JM, Dauphinais, Barnes, Adler & Rifkin, 1993; Tsuang, 1993; Kibel, Lafficint, Liddle, 1993). Research conducted over the last 8 years has demonstrated, however, that negative symptoms can be identified, distinguished from affective symptoms, and rated in an objective and reliable fashion (Kibel, Lafficint, Liddle, 1993; Dollfus, Petit & Menard, 1993; McGlashan & Fenton, 1994). Field trials for *DSM-IV* also showed that including negative symptoms did not lead to a significant inflation in the rate of diagnosis (Andreasen & Carpenter, 1993). While there do not appear to be 2 distinct types of schizophrenia, a "purely positive" and a "purely negative" type, these categories do seem to represent independent symptom clusters both cross-sectionally and longitudinally (Marneros, Rohde & Deister, 1995; Eaton, Thara, Federman, Melton & Liang, 1995). The negative symptom cluster, once established, is more stable over time and is more likely to be associated with neurocognitive impairments (Brier, Schreiber, Dyer & Pickar, 1989; Johnstone, Frith, Crow, Owens, Done et al., 1992; van der does, Dingemans, Linszen, Nugter et al., 1993), brain abnormalities (Breier, Schreiber, Dyer & Pickar, 1991; Lieberman, et al., 1992; Tsuang, 1993), genetic inheritance (Tsuang, 1993), and work and social incapacity (Breier et al., 1991; McGlashan & Fenton, 1994; Hwu, Tan, Chen & Yeh, 1995). In conjunction with these findings, the concept of the "deficit syndrome," first introduced by Carpenter and colleagues (1994, 1998), constitutes a relatively stable dimension that is associated with poor premorbid social functioning; lower intelligence, educational level, and work capacity; insidious onset; a continuous course which appears unresponsive to life events; and a high risk of poor outcome with long-term disability (Fenton & McGlashan, 1994).

Within the positive symptom cluster, a finer distinction has been drawn between the 2 relatively independent dimensions of "psychotic" symptoms (hallucination and delusions) and the "disorganized" symptoms of disorganized speech, disorganized behavior, and inappropriate affect (Arndt,

Andreasen, Flaum, Miller & Nopoulos, 1995). This 3-factor model first proposed by Liddle (1987) (including negative symptoms as the third factor) has since been confirmed through several factor analytic studies (Eaton, Thara, Federman, Melton & Liang, 1995; van der Does, Dingemans, Linszen, Nugter & Scholte, 1993; Arndt, Andreasen, Flaum, Miller & Nopoulos, 1995; Malla, Norman, Williamson, Cortese & Diaz, 1993; Miller, Arndt & Andreasen, 1993; Lenzenweger, Dworkin & Wethinglon, 1991) but has also been potentially broadened to include depression as a fourth dimension (van der Does, Linszen, Dingemans, Nugter & Scholte, 1993; van der Does, Dingemans, Linszen, Nugter & Scholte, 1995). Because these symptom dimensions are found consistently to show independent patterns of evolution over the course of the disorder (Eaton et al., 1995, Arndt et al., 1995), evidence accumulates for a dimensional as opposed to categorical approach to symptomatology in schizophrenia. Future research will need to determine if such an approach can replace the conventional subtypes of paranoid, undifferentiated, and hebephrenic or if the coexistence of these symptom clusters within a given individual presents a more complicated picture.

The last domain of functioning to attract increasing attention in recent literature has been the area of neurocognitive functioning. While there continues to be a wide heterogeneity in cognitive functioning in individuals with schizophrenia, a number of recent studies (Goldberg, Hyde, Kleinman & Weinberger, 1993; Harvey, White, Parrella, Putnam, Kincaid, Powchik et al., 1995; Harvey, Lombard, Kincaid, Parrella, White, Powchik et al, 1995) have suggested that cognitive deficits, once established, are relatively stable over time. As mentioned previously, first-episode studies have shown that cognitive impairments can be established early in the course of the disorder, if not already present in the premorbid phase. Studies of cognitive functioning have suggested that these impairments remain consistent over the course of the disorder, showing neither marked improvement nor deterioration (Goldberg, Hyde, Kleinman & Weinberger, 1993; Harvey, White, Parrella, Putnam, Kincaid, Powchik et al., 1995; Harvey, Lombard, Kincaid, Parrella, White, Powchik et al, 1995). In addition to being linked to negative symptoms (Breier et al., 1991; Johnstone et al., 1992; van der Does et al., 1993), cognitive deficits have been associated with work incapacity (Lysaker, Bell & Bioty, 1995; Lysaker, Bell, Zito & Bioty, 1995). Attempts to remediate these deficits (Green, Satz, Ganzell &Vaclav, 1992; Spring & Ravin, 1992; Liberman & Green, 1992; Jaeger & Douglas, 1992; Green, 1993; Benedict & Harris, 1989; Delahunty, Morice & Frost, 1993; Bellack, 1992), although still in the early stages of development, show some promise of being able to help patients regain abilities or compensate for more enduring deficits. More work will be required, however, to assist patients in generalizing the gains they are able to make in controlled laboratory conditions to their day-to-day lives in the community.

## CONCLUSION

Several discussions of methodological issues for long term follow-up, early-course, first-episode, and early detection and intervention studies (McGlashan, Carpenter & Bartko, 1988; Keshavan & Schooler, 1992; Flaum, Andreasen & Arndt, 1992; McGlashan, 1996) have identified a range of short-comings in existing studies, including those reviewed in this paper. These issues include, most predominantly: concerns about the lack of clear and broadly accepted criteria for diagnosis and definitions for such key concepts as the prodrome, onset, and recovery; the sample bias introduced through the underidentification and exclusion of healthier subjects for follow-up studies; the lack of control and comparison groups because of ethical consid-erations and resource constraints; the complicated interplay of disease processes' treatment effects, and social and cultural contexts; and the practi-cal and logistic complexities of gaining access to and closely tracking large-scale populations for epidemiologic and prevention studies.

Despite these considerable challenges to improving the rigor and valid-ity of future studies, we have gained a few important insights about the course and outcome of schizophrenia over the last few years. First, it appears that the broad prognostic heterogeneity that was initially discovered through long-term follow-up studies may already be present at the time of the first episode. It also appears that the most significant amount of deterioration in functioning that will occur for many individuals with schizophrenia has already occurred by the time of the first episode, if not by the prodromal phase. Negative symptoms and the deficit syndrome continue to represent an important component of the phenomenology and outcome of the disorder, being relatively stable over time and associated with cognitive impairments and incapacity in social and work domains. In addition to there being varia-tions within individuals with respect to symptom dimensions and levels of functioning, as well as variations across individuals with respect to global outcome, there also appear to be variations in clinical presentation and out-come across sociocultural and historical boundaries. Challenges for future research and clinical practice include developing a better understanding of the sources of cross-cultural, historical, and individual differences in outcome and applying these findings to the improvement of current clinical and reha-bilitative efforts (Sullivan, 1994; Rund, 1990). A new but related and equally important challenge will be to focus intensively on the prodromal and early phases of the course of disorder in a concerted effort to prevent disability and chronicity. Progressing from recognition of heterogeneity in outcome to efforts to prevent the worst outcomes from occurring represents a logical next step in the evolution of schizophrenia research and treatment. This is a new conceptualization of a disorder once assumed to have a progressive course leading inevitably to premature dementia. It remains for future research to determine how successful this new approach will be.

### Clinical Implications

With considerable evidence suggesting that the active disease and deterioration process is established by onset of psychosis, efforts need to be directed at early detection and intervention to prevent secondary deficits and disability for those individuals experiencing the more severe forms of the disorder.

### Limitations

Limitations identified in the studies reviewed include the lack of clear and broadly accepted criteria for diagnosis and definitions of such key concepts as the prodrome, onset, and recovery; the sample bias introduced through exclusion of healthier subjects for follow-up studies; and the lack of control and comparison groups.

### REFERENCES

Abrahamson D. (1993). Institutionalization and the long-term course of schizophrenia. *British Journal of Psychiatry, 162,* 533–538.

Andreasen, N.C., & Carpenter, W.T., Jr. (1993). Diagnosis and classification of schizophrenia. *Schizophrenia Bulletin, 19,* 199–214.

Angermeyer, M.C., Kuhn, L., & Goldstein, J. M. (1990). Gender and the course of schizophrenia: Differences in treated outcomes. *Schizophrenia Bulletin, 16,* 293–307.

Angst, J. (1988). European long-term follow-up studies of schizophrenia. *Schizophrenia Bulletin, 14,* 501–513.

Arndt, S., Andreasen, N.C., Flaum, M., Miller, D., & Nopoulos P. (1995). A longitudinal study of symptom dimensions in schizophrenia. *Archives of General Psychiatry, 52,* 352–360.

Bardenstein, K.K., & McGlashan, T.H. (1990). Gender differences in affective, schizoaffective, and schizophrenic disorders: a review. *Schizophrenia Research, 3,* 159–172.

Basic Behavioral Science Task Force of the National Advisory Mental Health Council. (1996). Basic behavioral science research for mental health: Sociocultural and environmental processes. *The American Psychologist, 51,* 722–731.

Bellack, A.S. (1992). Cognitive rehabilitation for schizophrenia: Is it possible? Is it necessary? *Schizophrenia Bulletin, 18,* 43–50.

Benedict, R.H., & Harris A. (1989). Remediation of attention deficits in chronic schizophrenic patients: a preliminary study. *British Journal of Clinical Psychology, 28,* 187–188.

Bilder, R.M., Lipschultz-Broch, L., Reiter, G., Geisler, S.H., Mayerholff, D.I., & Lieberman, J.A. (1992). Intellectual deficits in first-episode schizophrenia: Avidence for progressive deterioration. *Schizophrenia Bulletin, 18,* 437–448.

Breier, A., Schreiber, J.L., Dyer, J., & Pickar, D. (1991). National Institute of Mental Health longitudinal study of chronic schizophrenia: Prognosis and predictors of outcome. *Archives of General Psychiatry, 48,* 239–246.

Carone, B.J., Harrow, M., & Westermeyer, J.F. (1991). Posthospital course and outcome in schizophrenia. *Archives of General Psychiatry, 48,* 247–453.

Carpenter W.T., Jr. & Kirkpatrick, B. (1988). The heterogeneity of the long-term course of schizophrenia. *Schizophrenia Bulletin, 14,* 645–652.

Carpenter W.T., Jr. & Strauss, J.S. (1991). (1991). The prediction of outcome in schizophrenia, IV: Eleven-year follow-up of the Washington IPSS cohort. *Journal of Nervous and Mental Disease, 179,* 517–525.

Carpenter, W.T. Jr. (1994). The deficit svndrome. *American Journal of Psychiatry, 151,* 327–329.

Carpenter, W.T. Jr., Heinrichs, D. W., & Wagman, A. M. (1988). Deficit and nondeficit forms of schizophrenia: The concept. *American Journal of Psychiatry, 145,* 578–583.

Childers, S.E., & Harding, C.M. (1990). Gender, premorbid social functioning, and long-term outcome in DSM-III schizophrenia. *Schizophrenia Bulletin, 18,* 309–318.

Chouljian, T.L, Shumway, M., Balancio, E., Dwyer, E.V., Surber, R., & Jacobs, M. (1995). Substance use among schizophrenic outpatients: Prevalence, course, and relation to functional status. *Annals of Clinical Psychiatry, 7,* 19–24.

Ciompi, L. (1980). Catamnestic long-term study on the course of life and aging of schizophrenics. *Schizophrenia Bulletin 6,* 606–618.

Davidson, L., & McGlashan, T.H. (1995). Schizophrenia: Diagnosis and phenomenology. *Current Opinion in Psychiatry, 8,* 21–24.

Delahunty, A., Morice, R., Frost, B. (1993). Specific cognitive flexibility rehabilitation in schizophrenia. *Psychological Medicine, 23,* 221–227.

DeQuardo, J.R., Carpenter, C.F., & Tandon, R. (1994). Patterns of substance abuse in schizophrenia: Nature and significance. *Journal of Psychiatric Research, 28,* 267–275.

Der, G., Gupta, S., & Murray, R. (1990). Is schizophrenia disappearing? *Lancet, 335,* 513–516.

DeSisto, M., Harding, C. M., McCormick, Ashikaga, T., & Brooks, G. (1995a). The Maine and Vermont three-decade studies of serious mental illness I. Matched comparison of cross-sectional outcome. *British Journal of Psychiatry, 167,* 331–338.

DeSisto, M., Harding, C. M., McCormick, Ashikaga, T., & Brooks, G. (1995b). The Maine and Vermont three-decade studies of serious mental illness II. Longitudinal course comparisons. *British Journal of Psychiatry, 167,* 338–342.

Dixon, L., Haas, G., Weiden, P.J., Sweeney, J., & Frances, A. (1991). Drug abuse in schizophrenic patients: Clinical correlations and reasons for use. *American Journal of Psychiatry, 148,* 224–230.

Dollfus, S., Petit, M., & Menard, J.F. (1993). Relationship between depressive and positive symptoms in schizophrenia. *Journal of Affective Disorders, 28,* 61–69.

Drake, R.E., & Wallach, M.A. (1989). Substance abuse among the chronically mentally ill. *Hospital and Community Psychiatry, 40,* 1041–1046.

Duke, P.J., Pantelis, C., & Barnes, T.R.E. (1994). South Westminster Schizophrenia Survey: Alcohol use and its relationship to symptoms, tardive dyskinesia, and illness onset. *British Journal of Psychiatry, 164,* 630–636.

Eaton, W.E., Thara, R., Federman, B., Melton, B., & Liang, K. (1995). Structure and course of positive and negative symptoms in schizophrenia. *Archives of General Psychiatry, 52,* 127–134.

Eaton, W.W., Bilker, W., Haro, J.M., Herrman, H., Mortensen, P.B., Freeman, H., et al. (1992). Long-term course of hospitalization for schizophrenia, part U: change with passage of time. *Schizophrenia Bulletin, 18,* 229–241.

Eaton, W.W., Mortensen, P.B., Herrman, H., Freeman, H., Bilker, W., Burgess, P., et al. (1992). Long-term course of hospitalization for schizophrenia, part 1: risk for hospitalization. *Schizophrenia Bulletin, 18,* 217–228.

Falloon, I.R.H. (1992). Early intervention for first episodes of schizophrenia: A preliminary exploration. Psychiatry, 55, 4–15.

Falloon, I.R.H., Kydd, R.R., Coverdale, J.H., &Laidlaw, T.M. (1996). Early detection and intervention for initial episodes of schizophrenia. *Schizophrenia Bulletin, 22,* 271–282.

Fenton, W.S., & McGlashan, T.H. (1994). Antecedents, symptom progression, and long-term outcome of the deficit syndrome in schizophrenia. *American Journal of Psychiatry, 151,* 351–356.

Flaum, M.A., Andreasen, N.C., & Amdt, S. (1992). The Iowa prospective longitudinal study of recent-onset psychoses. *Schizophrenia Bulletin, 18,* 481–490.

Geddes, J.R., & Kendell, R.E. (1995). Schizophrenic subjects with no history of admission to hospital. *Psychological Medicine, 25,* 859–868.

Goldberg, T.E., Hyde, T.M., Kleinman, J.E., & Weinberger, D.R. (1993). Course of schizophrenia: neuropsychological evidence for a static encephalopathy. *Schizophrenia Bulletin, 19,* 797–804.

Green, M.F. (1993). Cognitive remediation in schizophrenia: is it time yet? *American Journal of Psychiatry, 150,* 178–187.

Green, M.F., Satz, P., Ganzell, S., & Vaclav, F.J. (1992). Wisconsin Card Sorting Test perform-ance in schizophrenia: remediation of a stubborn deficit. *American Journal of Psychiatry, 149,* 62–67.

Haas, G.L., & Sweeney, J.A. (1992). Premorbid and onset features of first-episode schizophrenia. *Schizophrenia Bulletin, 18,* 373–386.

Harding, C.M. (1988). Course types in schizophrenia: An analysis of European and American studies. *Schizophrenia Bulletin, 14,* 633–643.

Harding, C.M., Brooks, G.W., Ashikaga, T., Strauss, J.S., & Landerl, P.D. (1987). Aging and social functioning in once-chronic schizophrenic patients 22–62 years after first admission: The Vermont story. In N.E. Miller & G.D. Cohen (Eds.). *Schizophrenia, paranoia and schizophreniform disorders in later life.* New York: Guilford Press, pp 74–83.

Harding, C.M., Brooks, G.W., Ashikaga, T., Strauss, J.S., and Breier, A. (1987a). The Vermont longitudinal study of persons with severe mental illness: I. Methodology, study sample, and overall status 32 years later. *American Journal of Psychiatry, 144,* 718–726.

Harding, C.M., Brooks, G.W., Ashikaga, T., Strauss, J.S., and Breier, A. (1987b). The Vermont longitudinal study of persons with severe mental illness: II. Long-term outcome of subjects who restrospectively met DSM-III criteria for schizophrenia. *American Journal of Psychiatry, 144,* 727–735.

Harrison G, & Mason P. (1993). Schizophrenia: Failing incidence and better outcome? *British Journal of Psychiatry, 163,* 535–541,

Harrison, G., Cooper, J.E., & Gancaryczyrk, R. (1991). Changes in the administrative incidence of schizophrenia. *British Journal of Psychiatry, 159,* 811–816.

Harvey, P.D., Lombard, J., Kincaid, M.M., Parrella, M., White, L., Powchik, P., et al. (1995). Cognitive functioning in chronically hospitalized schizophrenic patients: age-related changes and age disorientation as a predictor of impairment. *Schizophrenia Research, 17,* 15–24.

Harvey, P.D., White, L., Parrella, M., Putnam, K.M., Kincaid, M.M., Powchik, P., et al. (1995). The longitudinal stability of cognitive impairment in schizophrenia: Mini mental state scores at one- and two-year follow-ups in geriatric inpatients. *British Journal of Psychiatry, 166,* 630–633.

Hegarty, J.D., Balclessarini, R.J., Totten, M., Watemaux, C., & Oepen, G. (1994). One hundred years of schizophrenia: a meta-analysis of the outcome literature. *American Journal of Psychiatry, 151,* 1409–1416.

Helgason L. (1990). Twenty years' follow-up of first psychiatric presentation for schizophrenia: What could have been prevented? *Acta Psychiatrica Scandinavica, 81,* 231–335.

Hwu, H.G., Tan, H., Chen, C.C., & Yeh, L.L. (1995). Negative symptoms at discharge and outcome in schizophrenia. *British Journal of Psychiatry,166,* 61–67.

Jaeger J., Douglas, E. (1992). Neuropsychiatric rehabilitation for persistent mental illness. *Psychiatric Quarterly, 63,* 71–94.

Johnstone, E.C., Frith, C.D., Crow, T.J., Owens, D.G.C., Done, D.J., Baldwin, E.J., et al. (1992). The Northwick Park "Functional" Psychosis Study: Diagnosis and outcome. *Psychological Medicine, 22,* 331–346.

Kane, J.M., Dauphinais, D., Barnes, T.R.E., Adler L.A., & Rifkin A. (1993). Assessing negative symptoms and extrapyramidal symptoms in schizophrenia: workshop report. *Psychopharmacology Bulletin, 29,* 45–49,

Kendell, R.E., Malcolm, D.E., & Adams, W. (1993). The problem of detecting changes in the incidence of schizophrenia. *British Journal of Psychiatry, 162,* 212–218.

Kendler, K.S., & Walsh, D. (1995). Gendre and schizophrenia: Results of an epi-demiologically-based family study. *British Journal of Psychiatry, 167,* 184–192.

Keshavan, M.S., & Schooler, N.R. (1992). First-episode studies in schizophrenia: Criteria and characterization. *Schizophrenia Bulletin, 18,* 491–513.

Kibel, D.A., Laffont I., & Liddle, P.F. (1993). The composition of the negative syn-drome of chronic schizophrenia. *British Journal of Psychiatry, 162,* 744–750.

Kirch, D.G., Keith, S.J., & Matthews, S.M. (1992). Research on first-episode psy-chosis: Report on a National Institute of Mental Health workshop. *Schizophrenia Bulletin, 18,* 171–183.

Kozarie-Kovacic, D., Folnegovic-Smaic, V., Folnegovic, Z., & Marusic A. (1995). Influence of alcoholism on the prognosis of schizophrenic patients. *Journal of Studies on Alcohol, 56,* 622–627.

Larsen, T.K, McGlashan, T.H., & Moe, L.C. (1996). First-episode schizophrenia, I: Early course parameters. *Schizophrenia Bulletin, 22,* 241–256.

Larsen, T.K., McGlashan, T.H., Johannessen, J.O., & Vibe-Hansen, L. (1996). First-episode schizophrenia, II: Premorbid patterns by gender. *Schizophrenia Bulletin, 22,* 257–269.

Leff, J., Satorius, N., Jablensky, A., Konen, A., & Emberg, G. (1992). The International Pilot Study of Schizophrenia: Five-year follow-up findings. *Psychological Medicine, 22,* 131–145.

Lenzenweger, M.F., Dworkin, R.H., & Wethinglon, E. (1991). Examining the under-lying structure of schizophrenic phenomenology: Evidence for a three-process model. *Schizophrenia Bulletin, 17,* 515–524.

Leon, C.A. (1989). Clinical course and outcome of schizophrenia in Cali, Columbia: A10-year follow-up study. *Journal of Nervous and Mental Disease, 177,* 593–606.

Liberman, R.P., & Green, M.F. (1992).Wither cognitive behavioral therapy for schiz-ophrenia? *Schizophrenia Bulletin, 18,* 27–35.

Liddle, P.F. (1987). The symptoms of chronic schizophrenia: A re-examination of the positive-negative dichotomy. British Journal of Psychiatry, 151, 145–151.

Lieberman, J.A., Alvir, J.M.J., Woemer, M., Degreef, G., Bilder, R.M., Ashtari, M., et al. (1992). Prospective study of psychobiology in first-episode schizophrenia at Hillside Hospital. *Schizophrenia Bulletin, 18,* 351–371.

Lieberman, J.A., Matthews, S.M., & Kirch, D.G. (1992). First-episode psychosis, part II: Editors' introduction. *Schizophrenia Bulletin, 18,* 349–350.

Lin, K. M., & Kleinman, A.M. (1988). Psychopathology and clinical course of schiz-ophrenia: A cross-cultural perspective. *Schizophrenia Bulletin, 14,* 555–567.

Linszen, D. H., Dingemans, P. M., & Lenior, M. E. (1994). Cannabis abuse and the course of recent-onset schizophrenic disorders. *Archives of General Psychiatry, 51,* 273–279.

Loebel, A.D., Lieberman, J.A., Alvir, J.M.J., Mayerhoff, D.I., Geisfer, S.H., & Szymanski, S.R. (1992). Duration of psychosis and outcome in first-episode schizophrenia. *American Journal of Psychiatry 1992,* 1183–1188.

Lysaker, P.H., Bell, M., & Bioty, S.M. (1995a). Cognitive deficits in schizophrenia: Prediction of symptom change for participators in work rehabilitation. *Journal of Nervous and Mental Disease, 183,* 332–556.

Lysaker, P.H., Bell, M., & Bioty, S.M. (1995b). Social skills at work: Deficits and predictors of improvement in schizophrenia. *Journal of Nervous and Mental Disease, 183,* 688–692.

Malla, A.K., Norman, R.M.G., & Williamson, P., Cortese, L., & Diaz F. (1993). Three syndrome concept of schizophrenia: A factor analytic study. *Schizophrenia Research, 10,* 143–150,

Mameros, A., Deister, A., & Rohde, A. (1990). Psychopathological and social status of patients with affective, schizophrenic, and schizoaffective disorders after long-term course. *Acta Psychiatrica Scandinavica, 82,* 352–358.

Maninez-Arevalo, M.J., Caicedo-Ordonez, A., & Varo-Prieto, J.R. (1994).Cannabis consumption as a prognostic factor in schizophrenia. *British Journal of Psychiatry, 164,* 679–681.

Marneros, A., Deister, A., Rohde, A., Steinmeyer, E.M., & Junemann, H. (1989). Long-term outcome of schizoaffective and schizophrenic disorders, a comparative study, I: Definitions, methods, psychopathological and social outcome. *European Archives of Psychiatry and Neurological Sciences, 238,* 118–125.

Marneros, A., Rohde, A., & Deister, A. (1995). Validity of the negative/positive dichotomy of schizophrenic disorders under, long-term conditions. *Psychopathology, 28,* 32–37.

Mason, P., Harrison, G., Glazebrook, C., Medley, I., Dalkin, T., & Croudace, T. (1995). Characteristics of outcome in schizophrenia at 13 years. *British Journal of Psychiatry, 167,* 596–603.

McGlashan, T.H. (1988). A selective review of recent North American long-term follow-up studies of schizophrenia. Schizophrenia Bulletin, 14, 515–542. McGlashan, T.H., & Bardenstein, K.K. (1990). Gender differences in affective, schizoaffective, and schizophrenic disorders. *Schizophrenia Bulletin, 16,* 319–329.

McGlashan, T.H. (1996). Early detection and intervention in schizophrenia: Research. *Schizophrenia Bulletin, 22,* 327–545.

McGlashan, T.H., & Carpenter, W.T., Jr. (1988). Long-term follow-up studies of schizophrenia: Editors' introduction. *Schizophrenia Bulletin, 14,* 497–500.

McGlashan, T.H., & Fenton, W.S. (1994). The positive-negative distinction in schizophrenia: Review of natural history validators. In T.A. Widiger, A.J. Frances, H.A. Pincus, M.B. First, R. Ross R, W. Davis, (eds.), *Volume 1, DSM-IV sourcebook.* Washington, DC: American Psychiatric Association, p 381–392.

McGlashan, T.H., & Johannessen, J.O. (1996). Early detection and intervention with schizophrenia: Rationale. *Schizophrenia Bulletin 22,* 201–222.

McGlashan, T.H., Carpenter ,W.T., Jr, & Bartko, J.J. (1988). Issues of design and methodology in long-term follow-up studies. *Schizophrenia Bulletin, 14,* 569–674.

McGorry, P.D., Edwards, J., Milialopoulos, C., Harrigan, S.M., & Jackson, H.J. (1996). EPPIC: An evolving system of early detection and optimal management. *Schizophrenia Bulletin, 22,* 305–326.

Miller, D.D., Arndt, S., & Andreasen, N.C. (1993). Alogia, attentional impairment, and inappropriate affect; their status in the dimensions of schizophrenia. *Comprehensive Psychiatry, 34,* 221–226.

Mueser, K.T., Yamold, P.R., Levinson, D.F., Singh, H., Bellack, A.S., Kee. K., et al. (1990). Prevalence of substance abuse in schizophrenia: Demographic and clinical correlates. *Schizophrenia Bulletin, 16,* 31–56.

Nuechterlein, K.H., Dawson, M.E., Gitlin, M., Ventura, J., Goldstein, M.J., Snyder, K.S., et al. (1992). Developmental processes in schizophrenic disorders: Longitudinal studies of vulnerability and stress. *Schizophrenia Bulletin, 18,* 387–425.

Ohaeri, J.U. (1993). Long-term outcome of treated schizophrenia in a Nigerian cohort: Retrospective analysis of 7-year follow-ups. *Journal of Nervous and Mental Disease, 181,* 514–516.

Ram, R., Bromet, E.J., Eaton, W.W., Pato, C. & Schwartz, J.E. (1992). The natural course of schizophrenia: a review of first-admission studies. *Schizophrenia Bulletin, 18,* 185–207.

Rund, B.R. (1990). Fully recovered schizophrenics: a retrospective study of some premorbid and treatment factors. *Psychiatry, 53,* 127–139.

Shepard, M., Watt, D., Falloon, I., & Smeeton N. (1989). *The natural history of schizophrenia: A five-year follow-up study of outcome and prediction in a representative sample of schizophrenics.* Cambridge: Cambridge University Press.

Shtasel, D.L., Gur, R.E., Gallacher, F., Heimberg, C., Cannon, T., & Gur, R.C. (1992). Phenomenology and functioning in first-episode schizophrenia. *Schizophrenia Bulletin, 18,* 449–462.

Smith J, & Hucker S. (1994). Schizophrenia and substance abuse. *British Journal of Psychiatry, 165,* 13–21.

Spring, B.J., & Ravin, L. (1992). Cognitive remediation in schizophrenia: Should we attempt it? *Schizophrenia Bulletin, 18,* 15–20.

Steinmeyer, E.M., Manneros, A., Deister, A., Rohde, A., & Junemarin, H. (1989). Long-term outcome of schizoaffective and schizophrenic disorders: A comparative study, II: Causal-analytical investigations. *European Archives of Psychiatry and Neurological Sciences, 238,* 126–134.

Strauss, J.S., & Carpenter, W.T. (1974). Prediction of outcome in schizophrenia, II: relationships between predictor and outcome variables. *Archives of General Psychiatry, 31,* 37–42.

Strauss, J.S., & Carpenter, W.T. (1977). The prediction of outcome in schizophrenia. III. Five-year outcome and its predictors: A report from the International Pilot Study of Schizophrenia. *Archives of General Psychiatry, 34,* 159–163.

Strauss, J.S., Carpenter, W.T. Jr., & Bartko, J.J. (1974). The diagnosis and understanding of schizophrenia, part III: Speculations on the processes that underlie schizophrenic symptoms and signs. *Schizophrenia Bulletin, 11,* 61–79.

Sullivan P. (1994). Recovery from schizophrenia: What we can learn from the developing nations. *Innovations & Research, 3,* 7–15.

Szymanski, S., Lieberman, J.A., Alvir, J.M., Mayerhoff, D., Loebel, A., Geisler, S., et al. (1995). Gender differences in onset of illness, treatment response, course, and biologic indexes in first-episode schizophrenic patients. *American Journal of Psychiatry, 152,* 698–703.

Szymanski, S.R., Cannon, .TD., Gallacher, F., Erwin, R.J., Got, R.E. (1996). Course of treatment response in first-episode and chronic schizophrenia. *American Journal of Psychiatry, 153,* 519–525.

Test, M. A., Wallish, L., Allness, D. J., & Burke, S. S. (1989). Substance use in young adults with schizophrenic disorders. *Schizophrenia Bulletin, 15,* 465–476.

Thara, R., Henrietta, M., Joseph, A., Rajkumar, S., & Eaton, W.W. (1991). Ten-year course schizophrenia: The Madras longitudinal study. *Acta Psychiatrica Scandinavica, 90,* 329–336.

Tsuang, M.T. (1993). Genotypes, phenotypes, and the brain: A search for connections ill schizophrenia. *British Journal of Psychiatry, 163,* 299–307.

Turner, W.M., & Tsuang, M.T. (1990). Impact of substance abuse on the course and outcome of schizophrenia. *Schizophrenia Bulletin, 16,* 87–95.

van der Does, A.J.W., Dingemans, P.M., Linszen, D.H,. Nugter, M.A., & Scholte, W.F. (1993a). A dimensional and categorical approach to the symptomatology of recent-onset schizophrenia. *Journal of Nervous and Mental Disease, 181,* 744–749.

van der Does, A.J.W., Dingemans, P.M., Linszen, D.H,. Nugter, M.A., & Scholte, W.F. (1993b). Symptom dimensions and cognitive and social functioning in recent-onset schizophrenia. *Psychological Medicine, 23,* 745–753.

van der Does, A.J.W., Dingemans, P.M., Linszen, D.H,. Nugter, M.A., & Scholte, W.F. (1995). Symptom Dimensions and subtypes of recent-onset schizophrenia: a longitudinal analysis. *Journal of Nervous and Mental Disease, 183,* 681–687.

Verghese, A., John, J.K., Rajkumar, S., Richard, J., Sethi, B.B., & Trivedi, J.K. (1989). Facts associated with the course and outcome of schizophrenia in India: Results of a two-year multicentre follow-up study. *British Journal of Psychiatry, 154,* 499–503.

Wyatt, R.J. (1991). Neuroleptics and the natural course of schizophrenia. *Schizophrenia Bulletin, 17,* 325–351.

Yung, A.R., McGorry, P.D., McFarlane, C.A., Jackson, H.J., Patton, G.C., & Ralckar A. (1996). Monitoring and care of young people at incipient risk of psychosis. *Schizophrenia Bulletin, 22,* 283–393.

Zisook, S., Heaton, R., Moranville, J., Kuck, J., Jernigan, T., & Braff, D. (1992). Past substance abuse and clinical course of schizophrenia. *American Journal of Psychiatry, 149,* 552–553.

# Operational Criteria and Factors Related to Recovery from Schizophrenia

*Robert Paul Liberman, Alex Kopelowicz, Joseph Ventura, and Daniel Gutkind*

At the time of original publication. the authors were affiliated with UCLA Department of Psychiatry and Biobehavioral Sciences, Los Angeles, CA.

This article originally appeared in the *International Review of Psychiatry,* 2002, 14, 256–272 and is reprinted with permission. The *International Review of Psychiatry* is published by Taylor & Francis Ltd (http://www.tandf.co.uk/journals).

**Abstract:** Schizophrenia is often conceptualized by clinicians and researchers alike as a chronic illness with persisting, relapsing or deteriorating symptoms, and no hope for sustained remission and recovery of functioning. Countering this perspective, retrospective and prospective studies with both chronic and recent onset patients suggest that schizophrenia has a heterogeneous course, which can be favorably influenced by comprehensive and continuous treatment as well as personal factors such as family support and good neurocognitive functioning. The factors influencing recovery are mostly malleable through treatment and may often lead to a sustained remission of symptoms and normal or near-normal levels of functioning. To facilitate future research in this area, an operational definition of recovery from schizophrenia is proposed that includes symptom remission; full- or part-time involvement in work or school; independent living without supervision by family or surrogate caregivers; not fully dependent on financial support from disability insurance; and having friends with whom activities are shared on a regular basis. To satisfy the definition of recovery from the long-term illness of schizophrenia, each of the above criteria should be sustained for at least 2 consecutive years. For validation, these criteria were submitted to focus groups comprising clients, family members, practitioners, and researchers. Using this operational definition, a pilot study was conducted to identify the self-attributions, clinical characteristics and neurocognitive correlates of 23 individuals who have recovered from schizophrenia. The focus groups endorsed most of the criteria as being relevant to the construct of recovery, although there were differences between research investigators and others. The pilot study generated hypotheses for future testing, suggesting that quality of sustained treatment, near-normal neurocognition, and absence of the deficit syndrome were key factors associated with recovery. With operational definitions and variables identified as possible facilitators of recovery, both hypothesis-generating and testing research can proceed with the aim to identify factors that are malleable and can become targets for therapeutic, intervention. There are many extant, evidence-based biobehavioral treatments, as well as mental health service systems for their delivery, that could form the basis for rapid progress in promoting recovery. However, obstacles would have to be overcome to the dissemination, re-invention and utilization of empirically validated treatments, while rigorous, controlled research on determinants of recovery are simultaneously begun.

## INTRODUCTION

At the turn of the twentieth century, schizophrenia was conceptualized as a chronic, inexorably deteriorating disorder with little chance for symptomatic or functional recovery. Kraepelin (1919) described the course of schizophrenia, which he called *dementia praecox,* as leading to mental deterioration, lack of volition, and social incompetence. Even though the heterogeneity of outcomes in schizophrenia has been recognized (Bleuler, 1950; Bellak, 1958), Kraepelin's pessimistic view of schizophrenia has persisted into modern diagnostic systems. For example, in DSM-III schizophrenia was delineated as a disorder such that "a complete return to premorbid levels of functioning in individuals diagnosed with schizophrenia is so rare as to cast doubt upon the accuracy of the diagnosis" (American Psychiatric Association, 1980, pp 191). Similarly, the authors of *DSM-IV* cautioned about "the unlikeliness of afflicted individuals making a complete return to full functioning" (American Psychiatric Association, 1994, pp 282).

With such nihilism entrenched in the nosology of schizophrenia, it is not surprising that many clinicians, patients, and families so readily resign themselves to the notion that individuals diagnosed with schizophrenia are doomed to a life of disability with little expectation for productive involvement in society. This fatalistic view of schizophrenia has practical consequences as well; because the disorder is severely stigmatized, patients often deny their illness and avoid effective biobehavioral treatments. Furthermore, practitioners tend to limit their time and professional skills, with the result that patients with schizophrenia often receive the lowest common denominator of treatment, a 5- or 15-minute medication management session once a month.

But, the truth about schizophrenia lies elsewhere. There is a growing body of empirically-based research showing that recovery from schizophrenia can occur under two conditions: a) when the disorder is treated early in its course with assertive case management and judicious use of antipsychotic medication; and b) when more chronic or relapsing forms of the disorder are treated for lengthy periods of time with comprehensive, well-coordinated, and continuous services. We will review the literature associated with these two pathways to recovery and outline the factors that may promote recovery in early and later stages of the disorder. Subsequently, we will propose an operational definition of recovery from schizophrenia to facilitate hypothesis generation for fostering much-needed research.

## SYMPTOMATIC RECOVERY AFTER EARLY TREATMENT

Reports have emanated from several clinical research centers demonstrating a high rate of symptomatic remission in recent onset cases, when treatment is provided in an assertive and targeted manner. For example, researchers at Hillside Hospital-Long Island Jewish Medical Center enrolled patients experiencing their first schizophrenic episode into an open, standardized treatment algorithm that involved titration of neuroleptic medication to optimal doses and changing medications, if necessary to achieve symptom control. Using a stringent definition of remission (ratings of three or lower on the SADS-C and Psychosis and Disorganization Scale psychosis items, a CGI severity item rating of "mild" or lower, and a rating of at least "much improved" on the CGI improvement item, all for at least eight consecutive weeks), 74% of the patients were considered to be fully remitted within 1 year (Loebel et al., 1992). In a subsequent paper from the same research group (Lieberman et al., 1993), the authors concluded that "most patients recover from their first episode of schizophrenia and achieve full symptom remission" (pp 375).

At the Early Psychosis Prevention & Intervention Center in Melbourne, Australia, 91% of young people with the recent onset of psychosis were in relatively complete remission of their positive and negative symptoms after one year of assertive case management, antipsychotic drugs, and cognitive-behavior therapy (Edwards et al., 1998; McGorry et al., 1996). Additional studies lend support to these findings. At the UCLA Aftercare Clinic (Gitlin et al., 2001), 80% of individuals with recent onset schizophrenia achieved a clinical remission of positive and negative symptoms during their first year of treatment. In Nova Scotia, 89% of individuals experiencing their first episode of schizophrenia survived the first year without rehospitalization and, of these, more than half were involved in full or part-time work or education (Kopala et al., 1996; Whitehorn et al., 1998). Most importantly, subsequent re-diagnosis of the individuals from these studies revealed that over 95% continued to meet lifetime DSM-IV criteria for schizophrenia or schizoaffective disorder, thus contradicting the view that remitted individuals had been misdiagnosed originally (Hegarty et al., 1994).

## SOCIAL RECOVERY AMONG PERSONS WITH CHRONIC SCHIZOPHRENIA

At the other end of the acute-chronic spectrum of schizophrenia, investigators from Europe, USA, and Asia have reported long-term follow-up studies that have documented the malleability of chronic schizophrenia to comprehensive and well-orchestrated intervention and rehabilitation programs (Bleuler, 1968; Ciompi, 1980; Harding et al., 1987a; 1987b; Huber et al., 1975; Ogawa et al., 1987). Each of these international studies followed cohorts of persons with schizophrenia for at least 20 years and found rates of social restoration of at least 50% (Harding et al., 1992). In the most rigorous of these studies, the Vermont Longitudinal Research Project (Harding et al., 1987a; 1987b), the highest social recovery rate (68%) was found in a sample that contained the greatest proportion of chronic, "back-ward" patients among the long-term studies. Over two thirds of this sample had no psychotic symptoms when carefully interviewed 20 to 30 years after their periods of prolonged hospitalization.

It should be pointed out that a key element in these favorable long-term outcomes was access to continuous and reasonably comprehensive mental health services. That the social and symptomatic recovery of patients is not a consequence of some aging or "burning out" process has been shown by studies of older persons with schizophrenia (Palmer et al., 1999) as well as by controlled studies that have shown the necessity of well-coordinated treatment to achieve salutary outcomes (Paul & Lentz, 1977; DeSisto et al., 1995a; 1995b).

## TOWARDS A COMPREHENSIVE DEFINITION OF RECOVERY

If treated properly, it appears that many persons with schizophrenia are capable of achieving symptomatic remission and high levels of social functioning. Why, then, has it been so difficult to disseminate this information throughout the research and clinical world? One contributing factor relates to the wide variety of definitions of improvement and recovery used in research studies. For example, outcome measures most frequently used in clinical studies of schizophrenia have included levels of positive symptoms; the presence of all or any psychiatric symptoms, including depression, anxiety, and/or negative symptoms; changes in the type and amount of medication; social and/or occupational functioning; and utilization of psychiatric services (e.g., rehospitalization). Inconsistency in the conceptualization and definition of successful outcome make research findings difficult to interpret and preclude comparisons across studies.

Most often, outcome is determined solely by the presence or absence of positive psychotic symptoms. As suggested by the term "survival analysis," those patients who complete a follow-up period without experiencing a return of psychotic symptoms are considered to have "survived" and thus, have a good outcome; those who experience a return of positive symptoms are defined as having a "poor outcome." Operationalizing outcome as the presence or absence of positive symptoms, rather than as the attainment of an improved level of functioning in a wide range of psychosocial domains, does not provide a complete representation of a person's outcome because positive symptoms experienced during a given follow-up period may be brief, lasting days or weeks, and may have a minimal impact on social or occupational functioning.

Conversely, failing to recognize the debilitating effects of symptoms such as depression, anxiety, and/or negative symptoms, may underestimate the level of disability experienced by an individual with schizophrenia. Both Strauss and Carpenter (1974) and Harding et al., (1987a; 1987b) demonstrated the partial independence of symptomatology, social functioning, and occupational or educational functioning. In fact, Harding and her colleagues described many subjects functioning adequately in society despite the presence of persisting symptoms. Many of these subjects were noted to have developed coping mechanisms that offset their persisting symptoms, thereby causing little or no impairment in functioning.

Another important consideration when formulating a concept of recovery from schizophrenia relates to the differences that researchers, clinicians, and consumers of mental health services may have in defining the term "recovery." Researchers often define recovery as an extended period of remission from psychotic symptoms. Clinicians may define recovery as an improvement in global functioning. Consumers often define recovery as "the ability to rejoin the mainstream and function again" in the absence of psychotropic medication. Continuing maintenance medication, however, is almost always a necessity for sustaining high functioning among persons diagnosed with schizophrenia and thus distinguishes recovery from "cure." Therefore, it will be important to modify consumers' perceptions of recovery to include the continued use of medication. There is precedence for this in the medical literature. For example, cardiac patients are often classified as *recovered* after a heart attack, despite adhering to medication, dietary and exercise regimens. By placing emphasis on *functioning*, rather than *symptomatology*, the concepts of recovery and maintenance medication should be more compatible. As has been noted for depression, the use of maintenance medication should not be seen as an obstacle to recovery (Frank et al., 1991).

A comprehensive, operational definition of recovery will therefore include normative levels of social and occupational functioning; independent living; and remission or non-intrusive levels of psychiatric symptoms. A spectrum of operational definitions of recovery are desirable because varied definitions with their own operational criteria could compete with each other for utility, feasibility, reasonableness and confirmation in research that includes concurrent, construct, discriminative and social validation. While the criterion-based definition developed in this article is categorical in its approach, we certainly would welcome classifications based on continua within domains or other alternative definitions with quantifiable criteria. It is hoped that articulating operational definitions of recovery may encourage research that will broaden our current conceptualization and treatment of schizophrenia.

We suggest an operational definition of recovery, delineated in Table 1 that is a multi-modal, socially normative inventory of personal assets and freedom from psychotic symptoms. This definition requires assessment of outcomes in dimensions of symptomatology, vocational functioning, independent living, and social relationships. These domains were selected because they represent the areas for the diagnosis of schizophrenia, are consistent with the World Health Organization's International Classification of Impairment, Disability, and Handicap (World Health Organization, 1980), are often cited by consumers as personal goals for themselves, and have considerable social and economic importance (Sturm et al., 2000).

**Table 1: Operational definition of recovery from schizophrenia**

| | |
|---|---|
| Symptom remission: | Score of "4" or less (Moderate) on each of the positive and negative symptom items of the Brief Psychiatric Ratings Scale for 2 consecutive years |
| Vocational functioning: | At least half time of successful employment in a job in the competitive sector or successful attendance in a school for at least half time for two consecutive years. If in the retirement age (e.g., over 60 years of age), participating actively in recreational, family, or volunteer activities |
| Independent living: | Living on one's own without day-to-day supervision for money management, shopping, food preparation, laundry, personal hygiene or need for structured recreational or avocational activities. Able to initiate own activities and schedule one's time without reminders from family or other caregivers. While most individuals will be living on their own or with a roommate, intimate, or friend, some individuals could meet this criterion if they are living at home with family if that is considered culturally and age-appropriate. The individual may be receiving disability benefits as long as he/she is participating constructively in instrumental activities for half time or more. In the context of the individual's cultural background and given constraints of geographical distance and socio-economic factors, the individual has cordial relations with his/her family. This may be limited to phone calls, correspondence, or occasional visits (e.g., on holidays and family events) |
| Peer relationships: | At least once per week, having a meeting, social event, meal, recreational activity, phone conversation or other joint interaction with a peer outside of the family |

The criteria we developed pertain to the past 2 years of an individual's life and involve: a) sustained remission of psychotic symptoms as measured by the Brief Psychiatric Rating Scale (Ventura et al., 1993) defined as a score of "4" (i.e., "moderate") or less on key psychotic symptoms of grandiosity, suspiciousness, unusual thought content, hallucinations, conceptual disorganization, bizarre behavior, self-neglect, blunted affect and emotional withdrawal; b) full or part-time engagement in an instrumental role activity (i.e., worker, student, volunteer) that is constructive and appropriate for culture and age; c) living independently of supervision by family or other caregivers such that responsibility for day-to-day needs (e.g., self-administration of medication, money management) falls to the individual; and d) participating in an active friendship and/or peer social relations or otherwise involved in recreational activities that are age-appropriate and independent of professional supervision.

The specific choice of dimensions for the above operational definition of recovery, as well as the quantitative thresholds selected, are arbitrary. One might argue, as is done in other articles in this series comprising the special issue of the *International Review of Psychiatry*, that there are other domains of human functioning and subjective experience that are also deserving of being included in an operational definition of recovery. For example, subjectively described quality of life might be an important variable to include. In her studies of long-term outcome of schizophrenia, Harding and her colleagues (1987b) found a high proportion of their subjects who endorsed satisfaction with their current lives. On the other hand, one might argue that there are many so-called normal individuals without psychopathology who are unhappy with their lives and report poor quality of life. The cut-off points that we selected for rating remission of psychotic symptoms was also arbitrary but based on generally agreed upon definitions of "clinical significance." Clinical significance has emerged as an important moderator of symptoms in defining "caseness" in epidemiological studies of psychiatric disorders (Narrow et al., 2002).

## FOCUS GROUPS AND VALIDATION OF CRITERION-BASED DEFINITION OF RECOVERY

Focus groups were convened from among clinical researchers, mental health professionals and paraprofessionals, and consumers being treated for schizophrenia. The 55 members of the focus groups were affiliated with a schizophrenia clinic sponsored by an academic Department of Psychiatry and a public community mental health center. Each group was administered a structured interview which queried the respondents on each of the dimensions of our operational definition; for example, respondents were asked to agree or disagree with-statements such as "Recovery is at least half-time employment or schooling for 2 consecutive years," and "Recovery is having a meeting or some social event at least once per week with a peer outside of the family."

Three fourths of the respondents overall endorsed the criterion related to living independently of supervision for money and medication management; more than two thirds endorsed the criteria related to work or school, social relations; and half endorsed the criteria related to symptom severity. However, only a small minority agreed that cordial relations with family members should be a criterion in the definition of recovery. Over 90% affirmed that recovery from schizophrenia was possible, using the term, recovery, without any qualifiers. Most of the respondents also believed that some residual or intermittent psychotic symptoms and occasional returns to hospital were not incompatible with recovery, as long as individuals could rapidly return to functional and satisfying lives.

A higher proportion of researchers than consumers and practitioners endorsed our operational and multi-modal approach to defining criteria for recovery, while a higher proportion of consumers and practitioners viewed recovery as better defined by an indefinite coping and striving process rather than attaining a particular endpoint or goal. It is reassuring to note the consensus across respondent populations on the criteria chosen by us for an operational definition of recovery; the differing views toward process vs. outcome definitions of recovery are congruent with the differential value of evidence-based practices by consumers and researchers (Frese et al., 2001).

### CASE VIGNETTE ILLUSTRATING RECOVERY CRITERIA
The following case vignette will highlight our operational definition of recovery.

Mr. S. is a 29-year-old, single Caucasian male who lives by himself and works fulltime as a paralegal. He moved to Los Angeles only a few months ago, but claims he is fitting in well, enjoys his job, and has made a number of male and female friends. Overall, he says, "things are going very well." Prior to his first psychotic episode, Mr. S. was a very successful young man. He excelled in his studies, graduating from high school with a 3.7 grade point average. He was also on the high school tennis team, played trumpet in the school band, and led a full and active social life. These qualities, along with an excellent score on college preparatory exams, led to his acceptance at a prestigious university near his home.

Several months into his freshman year, Mr. S. experienced his first psychotic episode. This episode came on suddenly, with a prodromal period of only 2 weeks in which he displayed social withdrawal, moodiness, and inattention to hygiene. During the acute psychotic phase, Mr. S. experienced misperception, delusions of persecution and reference, thought insertion, and auditory hallucinations. Specifically, he thought that his college professor was communicating with him telepathically and sending him messages by way of the television. Within a month from the onset of psychotic symptoms, Mr. S. was hospitalized after he destroyed his television set in response to a command hallucination.

Consistent with his claim never to have used alcohol or drugs, no evidence of either was found upon his admission to the psychiatric hospital. His clinical response to haloperidol was rapid, with almost complete remission of positive symptoms within a month. Subsequently, he was able to return to his premorbid level of functioning and continue his studies. He graduated from college with some adjustments, delays, and accommodations to reduce stress. Rather than apply to law school, as he had planned, he obtained training as a paralegal and has maintained consistent employment ever since.

During the first few years of his illness, Mr. S. had the good fortune of being treated by a psychiatrist who believed in the value of patient education. Using the Medication Management and Symptom Management modules of the UCLA Social and Independent Living Skills program (Liberman et al., 1993), the psychiatrist spent 45 minutes weekly for 6 months teaching Mr. S. how to 1) correctly self-administer and evaluate the effects of antipsychotic medication, 2) identify the side effects of medications, 3) identify the warning signs of relapse, and 4) intervene early to prevent relapse once these signs appear. At many of the sessions, the psychiatrist and Mr. S. invited his parents to attend so that they would be able to reinforce and support his self-management and use of medication. The family also participated in a family psycho-educational program and became active members of the local chapter of the Alliance for the Mentally Ill. Over the years, his parents have remained a key supportive element in Mr. S.'s treatment program.

Until last year, Mr. S. had been on haloperidol and benztropine continuously for 10 years, with the exception of four episodes when he discontinued his medication. Each time he stopped taking haloperidol his paranoid delusions returned, preceded by ideas of reference and social withdrawal. He has not attempted to discontinue his medications since 1991, which is the last time he experienced psychotic symptoms. One year ago, he began to manifest early signs of tardive dyskinesia. He and his psychiatrist agreed to try switching from haloperidol to risperidone. The crossover was uneventful, and soon thereafter, he was able to discontinue the use of benztropine. Since switching to risperidone, Mr. S. has noticed that he is sharper cognitively, including better concentration, attention, and memory. Supporting his own observations, his last few evaluations from work supervisors have commented on his improved job performance.

Although Mr. S. has been psychosis-free for nearly 8 years, he has had occasional concerns as to whether his co-workers really like him. Before he moved to Los Angeles, he was living in a house with several roommates. He sometimes felt uncomfortable around these roommates and wondered if they too might have disliked him. However, these thoughts were mostly fleeting, and he can put these doubts out of his mind when they arise using challenging self-statements and recognizing they might be indicators of stress.

Within weeks of moving to Los Angeles, Mr. S. made a number of friends he sees at work and on weekends. In addition, he enjoys running and hiking, and maintains a healthy, active lifestyle. He still does not drink or use street drugs. Although Mr. S. is not currently involved in any romantic relations, he states that he would like a girlfriend at some point, but is relatively content for the time being concentrating on work and spending time with his friends. He is happy with the direction his life has taken and pleased with his decision to move to Los Angeles.

Next year, he plans to start night school with the long-term goal of obtaining a law degree. He realizes that this may be stressful and is prepared to increase the frequency of his communication and support from his psychiatrist after entering law school. He also plans to obtain a few booster sessions in recognizing and monitoring his warning signs of relapse, as he understands that exacerbation of his illness is possible even with the ongoing protection afforded by medication.

### FACTORS ASSOCIATED WITH SYMPTOMATIC SOCIAL RECOVERY
The preceding case vignette highlighted several factors that may have facilitated Mr. S.'s recovery, including good premorbid functioning, a supportive social network, a brief duration of untreated psychosis, responsiveness to antipsychotic medication, good neurocognition, and the availability of continuous, coordinated and comprehensive psychiatric care. With the goal of promoting the systematic study of factors related to recovery from schizophrenia, we entered the words "recovery," "remission" and "schizophrenia" in a Medline search of the psychiatric literature from the past decade and identified 10 factors associated with symptomatic, social, and educational or occupational recovery. These factors are listed in Table 2.

As a first step to generating hypotheses that could be tested in more rigorously controlled research, we examined data obtained from structured interviews and neurocognitive tests from a sample of 23 individuals who met our operational criteria for recovery from schizophrenia to determine which factors, identified in the literature review, received preliminary support. The subjects were recruited from our clinical practices, research databases and through word-of-mouth referrals and included 16 males and seven females with a mean age of 37.7 years ($SD$ = 11.4) and mean education of 15.4 years ($SD$ = 1.8). The ethnic distribution of the sample was 82.6% Caucasian, 4.3% African-American, 4.3% Latino, and 8.7% Asian. Their marital status was as follows: 65.2% were single, 17.4% were married and 17.4% were divorced. All subjects met DSM-IV criteria for either schizophrenia ($n$ = 17; 74%) or schizoaffective disorder ($n$ = 6; 26%), and had durations of illness ranging from 12 to 23 years. Compared to most studies of schizophrenia, our highly selected sample was better educated and more often married at least once. Each of the 10 factors associated with recovery is discussed below with information obtained from our surveyed subjects.

**Table 2: Factors Associated with Recovery as Identified by Literature Review**

1. Family or residential factors: supportive family or other caregivers who encourage and positively reinforce incremental progress of the individual with realistic expectations for social, emotional, and instrumental role performance (i.e., low expressed emotion family or residential environment)
2. Absence of substance abuse
3. Shorter duration of untreated psychosis
4. Good initial response to neuroleptics
5. Adherence to treatment
6. Supportive therapy with a collaborative therapeutic alliance
7. Good neurocognitive functioning
8. Absence of the deficit syndrome
9. Good premorbid history
10. Access to comprehensive, coordinated, and continuous treatment

### Family Factors

Although there are no studies directly testing the hypothesis that having a supportive family is important for attaining a successful long-term outcome, two lines of research indirectly support this presumption. First, many international studies have replicated the findings that family stress—as reflected in high expressed emotion, attitudes of criticism and emotional over-involvement toward the mentally ill relative—is a powerful predictor of relapse in schizophrenia and mood disorders (Bebbington & Kuipers, 1994; Butzlaff & Hooley, 1998). Since frequency of relapse is a well-documented poor prognostic indicator, it would be predicted that schizophrenic individuals who had supportive families that expressed acceptance, warmth, understanding, and encouragement would be more likely to recover.

Second, the relationship between family stress and relapse has led to the development of several modes of family intervention which have been designed and empirically validated for their ability to equip relatives with communication, problem-solving and other coping skills, improve the emotional climate of the family and reduce the incidence of relapses and rehospitalizations. Over two dozen well-controlled studies in the past decade from several countries have demonstrated that family psycho-education and training in coping and problem-solving skills decreased the rate of relapse and subsequent hospitalization for patients who participated in that type of treatment (Barrowclough & Tarrier, 1998). Moreover, patients who participated in these types of family interventions also gained significantly more in social adjustment while requiring less overall antipsychotic medication. Together, these findings suggest that having a supportive family with realistic expectations for improvement and abundant reinforcement for incremental progress may be a critical factor in the long-term outcome of people with schizophrenia (Falloon et al., 1999).

Although our interviews with the recovered subjects did not include formal assessments of their families, 16 subjects (70%) reported good or very good current relationships with their families of origin. Moreover, of the subjects who had been ($n$ = 4) or currently were married ($n$ = 4), 6 (75%) stated that their spouse had played a key role in their recovery. Because cordial family ties are one of our criteria for recovery, it will be necessary to conduct prospective, longitudinal and intervention studies with persons having schizophrenia to demonstrate that treatments that improve the family emotional climate increase the rate of recovery. Using such designs would enable investigators to avoid the tautological relationship between family process and outcome in recovery from schizophrenia.

### Substance Abuse

An NIMH epidemiological study estimated the prevalence of lifetime drug abuse among schizophrenia patients at 47%, well above the rate for the general population (Reiger et al., 1990). The serious, clinical consequences that drug-using schizophrenia patients face warrant special attention. Patients who use drugs or alcohol have been found to be more symptomatic while hospitalized, relapse more frequently, have poorer psychosocial functioning, and to have poorer prognoses for recovery (Cleghorn et al., 1991; Bowers et al., 1990; Tsuang et al., 1982; Swofford et al., 1996). They have higher rates of violence and suicide, are less likely to have their basic needs of housing and nutrition met, and are less likely to comply with treatment (Lyons & McGovern, 1989; Swanson et al., 1990; Cuffel, 1994). These findings should be qualified by occasional reports in the research literature that limited amounts of alcohol and marijuana, when used in controlled and social contexts, may be relatively innocuous for persons with schizophrenia (Warner et al., 1994).

A number of factors may contribute to the deleterious interaction of most illicit drug use and schizophrenia psychopathology. Patients may stop taking their medication for fear of negative interactions between street drugs and neuroleptics, or because alcohol and drugs of abuse interfere with memory. Some may fail to appear for scheduled appointments in their treatment programs if they are "high," especially since active drug use or abuse may jeopardize the benefits they obtain from treatment. Drug abusing schizophrenia patients may have fewer resources than non drug-abusing patients (e.g., a home, a car) and may therefore have more difficulty adhering to their treatment program even if they are motivated to participate in services. Using cocaine may be particularly damaging to schizophrenia patients because of the severe financial and social consequences as well as the fact that cocaine, like other stimulants, operates on the dopaminergic system, which has been linked to the pathophysiology of schizophrenia psychosis and relapses (Shaner et al., 1998) .

Corroborating the association of substance abuse with a poor prognosis for recovery, only four (17.4%) of our recovered subjects reported using illicit substances or abusing alcohol after the onset of their psychotic disorder, despite lifetime histories of substance use in three quarters of the sample. Additionally, none of the subjects reported current use of drugs and only two had had an alcoholic beverage in the past year.

### Duration of Untreated Psychosis

Longer duration of untreated psychosis (DUP), usually defined as the number of weeks from the onset of psychotic symptoms until first hospitalization or initial neuroleptic treatment, has been shown to be a predictor of poorer outcomes (Loebel et al., 1992; Lo & Lo, 1977; Crow et al., 1986; Fenton & McGlashan, 1987; Helgason, 1990). For example, a longer duration of psychotic symptoms before treatment was significantly associated with greater time to remission as well as a lesser degree of remission (Loebel et al., 1992). Longer duration of illness that included prodromal symptoms was also associated with longer time to remission. A review of the literature concluded that among a list of pre-treatment history variables, duration of untreated psychosis was found to be the best predictor of symptomatic and functional recovery in the studies of recent-onset schizophrenia (Wyatt, 1991).

However, it may be difficult to prove a causal relationship between longer DUP and poorer outcome or, conversely, shorter DUP and better outcome (Lieberman & Fenton, 2000). The methodological obstacles in making inferences from DUP as this factor may relate to recovery comes from the many other factors that may be confounding this relationship. For example, those who seek treatment soon after the onset of psychosis might have more firmly established social support networks that encourage early treatment (McGlashan, 1996). Similarly, shorter DUP might be related to higher levels of premorbid functioning, higher socioeconomic status, higher intelligence, better neurocognitive functioning, or greater access to health service resources. Nevertheless, because psychosis may be associated with deleterious changes in the brain (Lieberman et al., 1993; Wyatt, 1991), early intervention in treating psychosis may be especially important for a favorable prognosis.

Evidence from prospective studies of young adults treated for their first episode of psychosis, some of whom had been followed closely during prior periods of prodromal symptoms, substantiate the value of rapid intervention in reducing the duration of untreated psychosis and aborting psychotic symptoms in achieving recovery. Several investigators from these studies have reported that both positive and negative psychotic symptoms quickly clear within 6 months of initiating antipsychotic drug treatment and adjunctive psychosocial services. Moreover, the psychosocial functioning of these young adults actually show improvement subsequent to treatment to levels higher than exhibited prior to the psychotic episode (McGlashan, 1996). The neurocognitive functioning of these individuals also improves, often reaching the normal range. These findings suggest that rapid involvement in evidence-based treatment may actually contain the seeds of protection against the neurodevelopmental aberrations often found in persons with schizophrenia.

Because we did not interview the family members of our recovered subjects and did not have access to their medical records at the time of first treatment, we were unable to accurately determine the duration of untreated psychosis. However, 15 subjects (65%) reported a sudden onset of psychotic symptoms proceeded by a short (if any) prodromal phase and followed rapidly by a psychiatric hospitalization. Only 3 subjects (13%) reported a delay of more than a year between the onset of psychotic symptoms and treatment with antipsychotic medications.

### Good Initial Response to Neuroleptics

A number of studies have found that improvement of symptoms or lack of a dysphoric effect within several days after receiving neuroleptics significantly predicts outcome after several weeks or months (May et al., 1980; Awad & Hogan, 1985). It has been suggested that the short-term (i.e., 1 month) gains seen in patients who responded positively to haloperidol within 3 days was not due to any specific drug effects, but rather may represent a premorbid prognostic indicator related to the neurodevelopmental severity of the disorder (Klimke et al., 1993). More rapid clinical response to antipsychotic drugs may be mediated by lack of side effects and thus more reliable adherence to longer-term medication regimens (Ayers et al., 1984). The advent of the novel, atypical antipsychotic medications—with fewer subjectively aversive side effects—may promote more reliable, maintenance use of medication and higher rates of recovery.

More confirmatory, empirical evidence must be amassed before it can be concluded that a favorable response to initial neuroleptic treatment has any long-term prognostic benefit. In the clinical vignette above, Mr. S. experienced a positive initial response to his neuroleptic, which presaged his long-term improvement and recovery. Moreover, he reported even greater cognitive and social benefits subsequent to shifting from haloperidol to risperidone. It is worth noting that 20 of the recovered subjects (87%) in our pilot sample reported that the first antipsychotic medication they were given was effective in controlling their psychotic symptoms.

### Adherence to Treatment

The evidence for the efficacy of antipsychotic medication in the treatment of schizophrenia has been recognized for many years (Davis, 1975), yet failure to comply with medication regimens remains a significant problem for many individuals with the disorder (Hoge et al., 1990). Clearly, failure to take antipsychotic medication as prescribed hampers both short-term and long-term stabilization in areas such as psychopathology, rehospitalization, interpersonal relationships, illicit drug and alcohol use, frequency of violent and otherwise criminal activities, as well as overall quality of life (Weiden et al., 1997). Conversely, the consistent administration of antipsychotic medications—titrated judiciously to doses designed to maximize efficacy while minimizing side effects—is a necessary prerequisite to achieving optimal social and community functioning (Loebel et al., 1992).

A variety of obstacles to regular use of medication must be overcome if the benefits of treatment are to emerge. These obstacles can be found in the patient, the treatment, the therapeutic relationship, and the mental health service delivery system (Corrigan et al., 1990). Although the data regarding the efficacy of psychosocial interventions are not as robust as the psychopharmacology literature, the evidence in favor of treatments such as family psycho-education, social skills training and vocational rehabilitation suggests that greater utilization of these modalities by practitioners and their clientele would have similar salutary effects on the long-term outcome of individuals with schizophrenia (Lehman et al., 1998; Scott & Dixon, 1995; Mueser & Bond, 2000).

Overall, recovered subjects from our sample had very positive attitudes toward psychiatric treatment in general and antipsychotic medication in particular. Supporting the importance of adherence to treatment, all of the

recovered subjects were under the care of a psychiatrist and taking antipsychotic medications (35% conventional antipsychotics and 65% atypical
antipsychotics) at the time of their interviews. Moreover, 13 subjects (57%)
believed that the use of antipsychotic medications represented their most
effective strategy for coping with their illness, a conclusion that appeared to
be related to the education on medication they received from their psychiatrists. Of course, these positive attitudes toward treatment were predictable,
given the highly selected manner by which the sample was chosen.
Hypothesis testing research would have to involve much larger numbers of
unselected individuals with schizophrenia and follow them over several years
to nail down relationships between treatment adherence and recovery.

### Supportive Therapy with a Collaborative Therapeutic Alliance

Studies that have examined the role of psychotherapy in the lives of
persons with schizophrenia have found the relationship with their psychiatrists, therapists and treatment teams to be essential to improvement
(Gunderson, 1978; Lamb, 1988; Dingman & McGlashan, 1989). Supportive
therapy is considered a necessary foundation for delivering all types of treatments and for therapeutic changes (Frank & Gunderson, 1990; Kopelowicz et
al., 1996). Supportive therapy is not, however, "non-specific" or based solely
on office-based discussions. Instead, its efficacy appears to be mediated by a
spectrum of effortful and personal involvement by the psychiatrist or therapist who are capable of developing a positive, therapeutic alliance and relationship with client and family members, often in the face of considerable
passivity, lack of insight and non-cooperation.

Effective psychosocial therapies in schizophrenia require competencies
by the psychiatrist or therapist in active outreach to the client and family;
solving problems in everyday life including in-vivo, assertive treatments; a
directive yet empathic and compassionate approach by the therapist who,
when appropriate, uses his own life experiences and self-disclosure as a role
model for the patient; and, encouragement and education of the patient and
family for proper use of antipsychotic medication and psychosocial treatment (Liberman et al., 2001). The importance of supportive therapy to the
recovery process has been corroborated by a few randomized, long-term,
well-controlled studies that have demonstrated lower relapse rates and
improved social functioning (Hogarty et al., 1974; Gunderson et al., 1984).
Additional evidence comes from several first-person accounts by individuals
who have recovered from schizophrenia, attributing part of their success to
the relationship with their therapist (Spaniol & Koehler, 1994).

Consistent with the literature on the benefits of supportive therapy for
schizophrenia, 21 subjects (91%) in our sample were receiving some form of
psychotherapy at the time of the interviews. Eighteen subjects (78%) report-

ed that accessible and supportive psychiatrists and therapists in providing professional help when needed was a contributing factor to their recovery. Most subjects believed that their therapist was highly skilled and a good listener who was courteous and responsive to their concerns and needs. These descriptions by our subjects were accompanied by their impression that the treatment they received was driven by their own personal goals in life, and focused on maintaining and enhancing their level of functioning and subjective quality of life.

### Neurocognitive Factors in the Prediction of Recovery

Neurocognitive functioning has been found to be a correlate and predictor of social learning and instrumental role outcome in schizophrenia. For example, measures of working memory, vigilance and early perceptual processing were among the best predictors of work functioning after one year of outpatient treatment for young, recent-onset persons with schizophrenia (Nuechterlein et al., 1999). Reviews of the literature have found that specific neurocognitive factors were associated with functional outcome in three areas: community outcome, social problem solving, and acquisition of social skills (Green, 1996). Secondary verbal memory and executive functions, such as concept formation and cognitive flexibility, emerged as the specific neurocognitive predictors of community functioning. Secondary verbal memory and vigilance were found to predict social problem solving. Immediate and secondary verbal memory and vigilance were consistently associated with acquiring social skills. Similarly, schizophrenic patients with good vocational performance did better than those with poor vocational performance on the Wisconsin Card Sorting Task, a test of executive functioning, and several measures of secondary verbal memory, but not on a variety of other neurocognitive measures (Gold et al., 1997). As research accumulates in this area, it is expected that more specific linkages will emerge between selected neurocognitive factors and focal areas of psychosocial functioning.

One of the promising avenues for increasing prospects for recovery from schizophrenia come from atypical antipsychotic medications which, because of their salutary effects on neurocognition and their reduced neurotoxicity, enable individuals with schizophrenia to adhere better to their medication regimens and participate more actively in psychiatric rehabilitation (Kopelowicz & Liberman, 1999). Another new direction of research in this area is cognitive remediation, from which numerous studies have documented the malleability of cognitive impairments in schizophrenia to training (Liberman, 2002). An alternative strategy has been to compensate for cognitive impairments through highly structured and systematic social skills training, supported employment and social learning programs which appear to be able to surmount the obstacles posed by neurocognitive deficits in determining treatment outcome (Liberman et al., in press; Bond et al., 2001).

As a first pass at identifying neurocognitive correlates of recovery from schizophrenia, we administered a battery of neurocognitive tests to our sample of recovered subjects. The domains evaluated included verbal learning, executive functioning, verbal fluency, verbal working memory, vigilance and visuo-perceptual skills. Scores of the recovered subjects were compared to normative data from similarly aged and educated community samples. Our recovered subjects demonstrated normal or near normal functioning on tests of executive functioning (Wisconsin Card Sort Test), verbal working memory (Auditory Consonant Trigrams) and visuo-perceptual skills (Rey-Osterreith Complex Figure Test). Conversely, our recovered subjects performed as much as one standard deviation below normative levels on verbal learning (California Verbal Learning Test), verbal fluency (Controlled Oral Word Fluency) and early visual processing (Span of Apprehension).

These findings suggest that our recovered subjects may have acquired the knowledge and skills required for successful community adjustment by pacing their learning in school and job situations, thereby compensating for their slower than normal verbal learning and fluency and visual processing. One subject who was functioning well as an elementary school teacher, for example, told of how he took copious notes and even made audiotapes of lectures in college, which he later reviewed and studied repeatedly to master the material. Another individual described his job doing computer entry in a finance company as relying on procedural learning and memory—repetitive tasks that can be done with a burden on volitional, verbal learning and attentional capacities.

Thus, despite the limitations of our methodology, our findings were consistent with previous findings demonstrating a linkage between verbal memory and executive functioning on the one hand and community functioning on the other in individuals with schizophrenia. While our small sample precluded statistically partializing out the relationships between specific neurocognitive functions and specific instrumental skills, anecdotally several of our subjects who were using high levels of social skills in their work and friendship circles did score well on tests of vigilance as well as immediate and secondary verbal memory.

### Presence of Negative Symptoms in the Prediction of Recovery

A consistent conclusion of review articles has been that negative symptoms or the presence of the deficit syndrome were associated with poor outcome, cognitive impairments, and functional incapacity in social and work domains (Pogue-Geile & Harrow, 1987; Buchanan & Gold, 1996; Davidson & McGlashan, 1997; Glynn, 1998). For example, long-term outcome in the domains of hospitalization, employment, social functioning and global out-come was significantly poorer among patients with the deficit syndrome than among patients with non-deficit schizophrenia in the Chestnut Lodge Follow-Up Study (Fenton & McGlashan, 1994). Several cross-sectional studies have found an association between negative symptoms and pronounced frontal lobe dysfunctions (Liddle & Morris, 1991; Strauss, 1993; Hammer et al., 1995). Moreover, a 5-year longitudinal study in individuals with recent-onset schizophrenia found that improvements in negative symptoms corre-lated with improvements in neuro-psychological test performance (Gold et al., 1999) suggesting that these domains overlap as predictors of recovery.

Social and vocational adjustment may be especially susceptible to the influence of negative symptoms, in part because negative symptoms are defined as deficits in interpersonal behavior relative to social expectations. Empirically, levels of negative symptoms have been correlated with the degree of disability in social and vocational role functioning in recent-onset schizophrenia (Johnstone et al., 1990; van der Does et al., 1993) and chron-ic schizophrenia (Morrison et al., 1990; Lysaker & Bell, 1995). While inten-sive social skills training can have durable and substantial effects on second-ary negative symptoms (Kopelowicz et al., 1997), no medication or psychoso-cial treatments have been yet documented as effective in overcoming the deficit syndrome.

Consistent with the incompatibility of primary negative symptoms and successful community functioning, none of the recovered subjects in our sample met criteria for the deficit syndrome. Moreover, none of the subjects scored above a "2" (Very Mild) on the negative symptom item of the Brief Psychiatric Rating Scale (Ventura et al., 1993), which reflected both primary (deficit syndrome) and secondary negative symptoms. The low level of sec-ondary negative symptoms in our pilot sample may be attributed to their sat-isfaction with life, nil depression, active participation in daily routines, and low levels of extrapyramidal side effects, in part because the majority were receiving atypical antipsychotics.

### Premorbid History in the Prediction of Recovery

Extensive evidence from long-term follow-up research supports the notion that deterioration in schizophrenia occurs within the first few months and years of onset, followed by a plateau in functioning which then may or may not be followed by gradual improvement later in the course of the disorder (Davidson & McGlashan, 1997; McGlashan, 1988; Robinson et al., 1999). It is difficult to say what proportion of clients will make a recov-ery because it appears that wide heterogeneity of outcome predominates and because good outcome, defined as mild impairment to recovery, can range from 21% to 68% (Davidson & McGlashan, 1997). There is a consensus from a number of reviews of long-term follow-up studies of schizophrenia that have implicated specific premorbid variables as predictors of outcome (Davidson & McGlashan, 1997; McGlashan, 1988; Bland, 1982). Premorbid factors that are predictors of poor outcome include: male gender (vs. female), early age of onset, insidious onset, poor prior work history, low level of prior social adjustment, and long length of prodrome. It is not known how much treatment and rehabilitation, provided continuously and comprehensively as well as keyed to the phase of each person's disorder, can compensate for these premorbid characteristics of the patient. However, social skills training provided twice a week for a minimum of 6 months has been shown to significantly improve social competence as measured in simulated situations and social adjustment in the community (Heinssen et al., 2000).

One of the important vulnerability factors, most likely linked to the biologically based, genetic and neurodevelopmental abnormalities that are present in persons with schizophrenia, is premorbid social functioning. The prognosis for recovery among persons who later develop schizophrenia is much brighter when their premorbid adjustment has been higher in school, work, and peer relationships. This source of vulnerability or resilience (Wolkow & Ferguson, 2001) can be influenced by systematic training of individuals in social and independent living skills which has been shown to raise the level of social competence and coping ability in individuals with schizophrenia after the onset of their illness (Liberman et al., 1993; Wallace &Liberman, 1985; Marder et al., 1996; Glynn et al., 2002). Buttressing clients' social competence through structured and prescriptive training programs thus leads to greater protection against the disability and maladjustment that otherwise would diminish social activity and quality of life.

Although ratings of the premorbid functioning of the recovered subjects in our sample was not undertaken, their level of education may serve as a proxy measure for this variable. Sixteen subjects (70%) had graduated from college before becoming ill. Another 13% ($n = 3$) had completed 2 years of college prior to the onset of their illness. Three of the remaining 4 subjects were employed full-time when they first experienced psychotic symptoms. Taken together, it appears that almost all of the recovered subjects were functioning at near normal levels prior to the onset of their psychotic disorder, thus substantiating the importance of good premorbid functioning in predicting recovery.

### Access to Comprehensive, Coordinated, and Continuous Treatment

The contribution of continuous, comprehensive, consumer-oriented and coordinated treatment to good outcome in chronic schizophrenia was shown in a long-term follow-up study comparing a sample of well-diagnosed clients with schizophrenia from Vermont to a similar cohort in Maine

(DeSisto et al., 1995a; 1995b). While the state of Vermont established a well-crafted system of accessible treatment that was flexibly linked to the needs of its clients with schizophrenia early in the 1960s, Maine did not. Cohorts of chronic schizophrenic clients from these two states were carefully matched for age, education, sociodemographic factors, and duration and severity of illness during their early periods of treatment. Recovery, as defined by remission of psychotic symptoms and a score of 70 or above on the Global Assessment Scale, occurred twice as frequently in Vermont as in Maine.

Complementing the findings from the Vermont and Maine samples, reviews of psychosocial treatments in combination with antipsychotic drugs for schizophrenia have identified other studies with zero relapses and better rates of social functioning when comprehensive, continuous and well-coordinated services were accessible and utilized by patients with carefully diagnosed schizophrenia (Liberman et al., 1995; Penn & Mueser, 1996; Goldstein, 1999). One such study, conducted by Hogarty and colleagues (Hogarty et al., 1986; 1991), randomly assigned individuals with schizophrenia to one of four groups: a) adequate antipsychotic medication; b) medication plus social skills training; c) medication and family psycho-education; or d) medication, social skills training and family psycho-education. Relapse rates in the first year for the first three groups were 40%, 21%, and 19%, respectively. Interestingly, not one subject in the group that received all three treatments experienced a relapse during the first year of treatment (Hogarty et al., 1986). Not surprisingly, as the psychosocial treatments were faded and then discontinued during the second year, relapse rates began to approximate the rates achieved by subjects in the medication only treatment condition (Hogarty et al., 1991).

Some publicly funded mental health agencies have shifted to a capitation approach to psychiatric treatment and rehabilitation for persons with schizophrenia. In addition to crisis intervention, supportive community-based services, medication and other psychiatric treatments, some of these programs now utilize transitional and supported employment, supported housing, social skills training, family education, and a major emphasis on self-help, consumer-run social and work activities. These new developments—including Assertive Community Treatment (Stein & Santos, 1998), use of evidence-based services by teams with requisite professional competencies (Liberman et al., 2001), Colorado Health Networks (Forquer & Knight, 2001) and Integrated Service Agencies sponsored by the Los Angeles County Department of Mental Health (Chandler et al., 1997)—augur well for an increased rate of recovery for participants with schizophrenia.

Although systematic confirmation of the degree to which our pilot study subjects received high quality, biobehavioral treatment was not undertaken, subjects' responses provided some indication that they had received continuous and comprehensive treatment. For example, 21 (91%) subjects reported having been in psychiatric treatment continuously since illness onset. Only 2 (8.7%) subjects stated that they had ever gone as long as 2 months without antipsychotic medications. Of note is the fact that these 2 subjects were the only ones in the sample who had had more than two psychiatric hospitalizations over the course of their illnesses.

As noted in an earlier section, 21 (91%) subjects were receiving psychopharmacological and psycho-therapeutic treatment at the time of their study interview. Eleven (47.8%) subjects had received social skills training, 13 (56.5%) reported that their families had either participated in psycho-education or belonged to the National Alliance for the Mentally Ill, 6 (26%) had been engaged in vocational rehabilitation, and 14 (61%) had benefited from one or more self-help groups. Overall, subjects reported that the treatments they received were very good or excellent.

### DISCUSSION AND CONCLUSION

Since the time of Kraepelin, recovery from schizophrenia has been considered rare or even impossible (Warner, 1985). However, recent studies have documented symptomatic and social recovery from schizophrenia for individuals experiencing their first episode of psychosis and for others after many years of illness. The eight articles in this special issue of *International Review of Psychiatry* lend further support to recovery as an achievable outcome of schizophrenia. Moreover, personal reports of recovery, albeit anecdotal, have regularly appeared in journals such as the *Schizophrenia Bulletin, Psychiatric Services, Psychiatric Rehabilitation Journal* and *Psychiatric Rehabilitation Skills*. These converging sources of information suggest that schizophrenia has a heterogeneous course, which can lead to a sustained remission of symptoms and a return to premorbid levels of functioning, especially when comprehensive, evidence-based, continuous, coordinated, and consumer-oriented services are accessible.

One subject from our pilot study of recovery stated:

I just completed my 30th year working full time as an engineer and computer technician at the same company. I've gotten good personnel appraisals and enjoy what I do in my job. I've received continuous treatment for schizophrenia for over 24 years and have been able to find psychiatrists who will listen to me and help me find medications that are not toxic. My marriage has been very happy, although we don't have any children. I just completed training to serve on an NIMH Initial Review Committee to evaluate research grants and have gotten satisfaction doing advocacy for research on Capitol Hill with researchers, family advocates and recovered patients. I guess anything is possible.

Recognition of the existence of recovery from schizophrenia is the first step towards studying the phenomenon in an empirical fashion. While frameworks for conceptualizing recovery from schizophrenia have been proposed (Anthony, 1993; Davidson & Strauss, 1995), to date these have not generated hypothesis-driven studies because they have lacked clarity and specificity in their definition of recovery. To facilitate future research in this area, we have proposed an operational definition of recovery from schizophrenia that is within the normal range of functioning in the domains of symptomatology, work or school activity, independent living, and social relationships. We recognize that our criterion-referenced, categorical definition is not the only way to reliably measure recovery. In fact, alternative approaches to operationalizing recovery are to be encouraged, including those which view recovery as falling on continua and those that employ domains other than the ones we included.

In addition, we have delineated 10 factors linked to recovery and provided evidence for their role in the recovery process. In Figure 1, we display these factors with proposed linkages among them that may be heuristic in promoting hypothesis-testing research. It must be recognized, however, that most of the evidence for the role of these factors in recovery is correlational, not experimental. As such, the available evidence cannot prove the direction of causality. Only hypothesis-testing studies, especially prospective, long-term, randomized, controlled clinical trials that manipulate the variables within each factor can shed more light on the etiological significance of our 10 putative factors associated with recovery.

One of the most productive ways to advance research and knowledge on the factors related to recovery is to design randomized, controlled, intervention studies with "blind" assessors that attempt to modify one or more of the factors in the direction of promoting recovery. Such studies would permit investigators to determine whether or not hypothesis-driven interventions result in a larger number of individuals meeting recovery criteria than subjects in comparison or control conditions who did not receive that intervention. There are an abundance of interventions—both pharmacological and psychosocial—that are excellent candidates for use in these types of studies: social skills training; family psycho-education and training in communication, problem-solving and coping skills; supported employment; assertive community treatment; self-help programs such as psychosocial clubhouses; atypical antipsychotic drugs, including clozapine; and cognitive-behavioral therapy. Combinations of these interventions, when organized and delivered in a comprehensive program of services, will be more fruitful for research and

**Figure 1. Factors Linked to Recovery with Proposed Linkages to Relevant Aspects of Recovery**

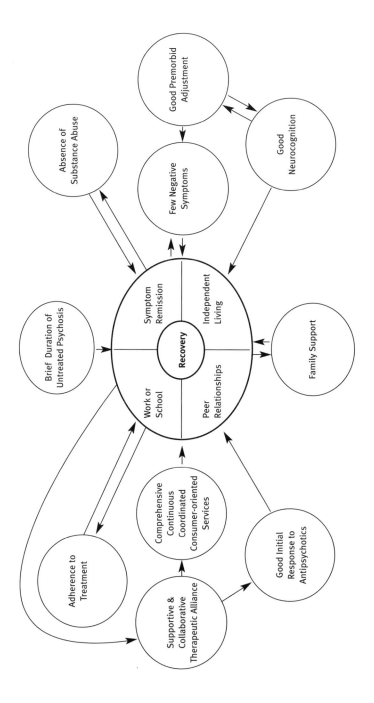

evaluation as they more closely reflect the priorities increasingly given by public agencies to the treatment and rehabilitation of persons with schizophrenia.

In the past few years, evidence-based treatments and modes of service delivery have been well documented for their favorable impact on persons with schizophrenia. Unfortunately, grant-supported research rarely permits the long-term intervention studies that will be needed to further our knowledge about what types of variables contribute to recovery from schizophrenia. Thus, one of the obstacles that must be removed for further advances is the reluctance of NIMH and other granting agencies to sponsor long-term, prospective treatment trials. At present, it requires Herculean efforts by charismatic scientist-practitioners to organize long-term studies of recovery, one example being the "Optimal Treatment Project" led by Ian Falloon in several countries of Europe and Oceania (Falloon, 1999). Once grants are available for this type of work, various interventions can be evaluated for their proximal impact on the factors thought to be important for improving rates of recovery and also for their more distal impact on recovery outcomes.

With the factors in Figure 1 inspiring this type of research, we can begin to consider the role of cognitive remediation in normalizing verbal memory, executive functioning, working memory, and vigilance (van der Gaag et al., 2002; Wexler et al., 1997; Wykes et al., 1999). For those whose key cognitive functions are successfully normalized, how many are then able to meet criteria for recovery?

Family support is certainly amenable to strengthening through psychoeducational family interventions; premorbid social functioning can be mitigated by social skills training; substance abuse has been shown to respond to comprehensive biobehavioral programs that integrate treatments for mental illness and substance abuse concurrently; secondary negative symptoms can be remediated by atypical antipsychotics and social skills training; and there are a variety of evidence based methods for improving adherence to treatment (Drake et al., 2001; Mellman et al., 2001; Dixon et al., 2001).

It is hoped that by promulgating operationalized criteria and definitions of recovery one can promote research that will foster our understanding of the nature of recovery, as well as the process by which recovery from schizophrenia occurs. Ultimately, what we learn from individuals who have recovered from schizophrenia should help us to develop interventions designed to enhance the likelihood of recovery, or even greater improvement short of recovery, for those individuals with schizophrenia who are still suffering from the ravages of this disorder. Increasing the rate of recovery from schizophrenia will also go far to de-stigmatize this disease, reduce the emotional burden on families, and lighten the financial weight of schizophrenia on communities, states and the nation.

**REFERENCES**

American Psychiatric Association (1980). *DSM-III: Diagnostic and statistical manual of mental disorders, 3rd edition*. Washington, DC: American Psychiatric Association.

American Psychiatric Association (1994). *DSM-IV: Diagnostic and statistical manual of mental disorders, 4th edition*. Washington, DC: American Psychiatric Association.

Anthony, W. (1993). Recovery from mental illness. *Psychosocial Rehabilitation Journal, 16*, 12–23.

Awad, A.G. & Hogan, T.P. (1985). Early treatment events and prediction of response to neuroleptics in schizophrenia. Progress in *Neuropsychopharmacology & Biological Psychiatry, 9*, 585–588.

Ayers, T., Liberman, R.P. & Wallace, C.J. (1984). Subjective response to antipsychotic drugs: Failure to replicate predictions of outcome. *Journal of Clinical Psychopharmacology, 4*, 89–93.

Barrowclough, C. & Tarrier, N. (1998). Social functioning and family interventions. In K.T. Mueser & N. Tarrier (Eds.), *Handbook of social functioning in schizophrenia* (pp. 327–341). Boston: Allyn & Bacon.

Bebbington, P. & Kuipers, L. (1994). The predictive utility of expressed emotion in schizophrenia: An aggregate analysis. *Psychological Medicine, 24*, 707–718.

Bellak, L. (Ed.) (1958). *Schizophrenia: A review of the syndrome*. New York: Logos.

Bland, R.C. (1982). Predicting the outcome in schizophrenia. *Canadian Journal of Psychiatry, 27*, 52–62.

Bleuler, E. (1950). *Dementia praecox or the group of schizophrenias*. Translated and edited by J. Zinkin. New York: International University Press.

Bleuler, M. (1968). A 23-year longitudinal study of 208 schizophrenics and impressions in regard to the nature of schizophrenia. In D. Rosenthal & S.S. Kety (Eds), *The transmission of schizophrenia*. Oxford: Pergamon.

Bond, G.R., Becker, D.R., Drake, R.E., Rapp, C.A., Meisler, N., Lehman, A.F., Bell, M.D. & Blyler, C.R. (2001). Implementing supported employment as an evidence-based practice. *Psychiatric Services, 52*, 313–322.

Bowers, M.B., Mazure, C.M., Nelson, J.C. & Jatlow, P.I. (1990). Psychotogenic drug use and neuroleptic response. *Schizophrenia Bulletin, 16*, 81–85.

Buchanan, R.W., & Gold, J.M. (1996). Negative symptoms: diagnosis, treatment and prognosis. *International Clinical Psychopharmacology, (Suppl 2)*, 3–11.

Butzlaff, R.L. & Hooley, J.M. (1998). Expressed emotion and psychiatric relapse. *Archives of General Psychiatry, 55*, 547–552.

Chandler, D., Meiser, J., Hu, T, Mcgowen, M. & Madison, K. (1997). A capitated model for a cross-section of severely mentally ill clients: employment outcomes. *Community Mental Health Journal, 33*, 501–516.

Ciompi, L. (1980). Catamnestic long-term study on the course of life and aging of schizophrenics. *Schizophrenia Bulletin, 6*, 606–618.

Cleghorn, J.M., Kaplan, R.D., Szechtman, B., Szechtman, H., Brown, G.M. & Franco, S. (1991). Substance abuse and schizophrenia: Effect on symptoms but not on neurocognitive function. *Journal of Clinical Psychiatry, 52*, 26–30.

Corrigan, P.W., Llberman, R.P. & Engel, J. (1990). From compliance to adherence in psychiatric treatment: strategies that facilitate collaboration between practitioners and patient. *Hospital and Community Psychiatry, 41,* 1203–1211.

Crow, T.J., Macmillan, J.F., Johnson, A.L. & Johnstone, E. (1986). The Northwick Park study of first episodes of schizophrenia: II. A randomized controlled trial of prophylactic neuroleptic treatment. *British Journal of Psychiatry, 148,* 120–127.

Cuffel, B.J. (1994). Violent and destructive behavior among the severely mentally ill in rural areas: Evidence from Arkansas' community mental health system. *Community Mental Health Journal, 30,* 495–504.

Davidson, L. & Mcglashan, T.H. (1997). The varied outcomes of schizophrenia. *Canadian Journal of Psychiatry, 42,* 34–43.

Davidson, L. & Strauss, J.S. (1995). Beyond the psychosocial model: Integrating disorder, health and recovery. *Psychiatry: Interpersonal and Biological Processes, 58,* 44–55.

Davis, J.M. (1975). Overview: Maintenance therapy in psychiatry: I. Schizophrenia. *American Journal of Psychiatry, 132,* 1237–1245.

Desisto, M.J., Harding, C.M., McCormick, R.V., Ashikaga, T. & Brooks, G.W. (1995a). The Maine and Vermont three-decade studies of serious mental illness. I. Matched comparison of cross-sectional outcome. *British Journal of Psychiatry, 167,* 331–338.

Desisto, M.J., Harding, C.M., McCormick, R.V., Ashikaga, T. & Brooks, G.W. (1995b).The Maine and Vermont three-decade studies of serious mental illness. II. Longitudinal course comparisons. *British Journal of Psychiatry, 167,* 338–342.

Dingman, C.W. & McGlashan, T.H. (1989). Psychotherapy. In A.S. Bellack (Ed.), *A clinical guide for the treatment of schizophrenia* (pp. 263–282). New York: Plenum Press.

Dixon, L., McFarlane, W.R., Lefley, H., Lucksted, A., Cohen, M., Falloon, I., Mueser, K., Miklowitz, D., Solomon, P. & Sondheimer, D. (2001). Evidence-based practices for services to families of people with psychiatric disabilities. *Psychiatric Services, 52,* 903–910.

Drake, R.E., Essock, S.M., Shaner, A., Carey, K.B., Minkoff, K., Kola, L., Lynde, D., Osher, E.C., Clark, R.E. & Rickards, L. (2001). Implementing dual diagnosis services for clients with severe mental illness. *Psychiatric Services, 52,* 469–476.

Edwards, J., Maude, D., McGorry, P.D., Harrigan, S.M., & Cocks, J.T. (1998). Prolonged recovery in first-episode psychosis. *British Journal of Psychiatry, 172* (Suppl 33), 107–116.

Falloon, I.R.H. (1999). Optimal treatment for psychosis in an international, multisite demonstration project. *Psychiatric Services, 50,* 615–618.

Falloon, I.R.H., Held, T, Cloverdale, J.H., Roncone, R. & Laidlaw, T.M. (1999). Family interventions for schizophrenia: a review of international studies of long-term benefits. *Psychiatric Rehabilitation Skills, 3,* 268–290.

Fenton, W.S. & McGlashan, T.H. (1987). Sustained remission in drug-free schizophrenic patients. *American Journal of Psychiatry, 144,* 1306–1309.

Fenton, W.S. & McGlashan, T.H. (1994). Antecedents, symptom progression, and long-term outcome of the deficit syndrome in schizophrenia. *American Journal of Psychiatry, 151,* 351–356.

Forquer, S., & Knight, E. (2001). Managed care: Recovery enhancer or inhibitor? *Psychiatric Services, 52,* 25–26.

Frank, A.F. & Gunderson, J.G. (1990). The role of the therapeutic alliance in the treatment of schizophrenia: Relationship to course and outcome. *Archives of General Psychiatry, 47,* 228–236.

Frank, E., Prien, R.F., Jarrett, R.B., Keller, M.B., Kupfer, D.J., Lavori, P.W., Rush A.J. & Weissman, M.M. (1991). Conceptualization and rationale for consensus definitions of terms in major depressive disorder: Remission, recovery, relapse, and recurrence. *Archives of General Psychiatry, 48,* 851–855.

Frese, F.J., Stanley, J., Kress, K. & Vogel-Scibilia, S. (2001). Integrating evidence-based practices and the recovery model. *Psychiatric Services, 52,* 1462–1468.

Gitlin, M.J., Nuechterlein, K.H., Subotnik, K.L., Ventura, J., Mintz, J., Fogelson, D.L., Bartzokis, G. & Aravagiri, M. (2001). Clinical outcome following neuroleptic discontinuation in remitted recent-onset schizophrenia patients. *American Journal of Psychiatry, 158,* 1835–1842.

Glynn, S.M. (1998). Psychopathology and social functioning in schizophrenia. In K.T. Mueser & N. Tarrier (Eds), *Psychosocial functioning in schizophrenia* (pp. 66–78). Boston: Allyn & Bacon.

Glynn, S.M., Marder, S.R., Liberman, R.P., Blair, K., Wirshing, W.C., Wirshing, D.A., Ross, D. & Mintz, J. (2002). Supplementing clinic-based skills training with manual-based community support sessions: Effects on social adjustment of patients with schizophrenia. *American Journal of Psychiatry, 159,* 829–837.

Gold, S., Arndt, S., Nopoulos, P., O'Leary, D.S. & Andreasen, N. (1999). Longitudinal study of cognitive function in first-episode and recent-onset schizophrenia. *American Journal of Psychiatry, 156,* 1342–1348.

Gold, J.M., Bryant, N.L., Vladar, K. & Buchanan, R.W. (1997). Successful vocational functioning in schizophrenia. *Schizophrenia Research, 24,* 222.

Goldstein, M.J. (1999). Psychosocial treatments for individuals with schizophrenia and related disorders. In N.E. miller & K.M. magruder (Eds), *Cost-effectiveness of psychotherapy: A guide for practitioners, researchers, and policymakers* (pp. 235–247). New York: Oxford University Press.

Green, M.F. (1996). What are the functional consequences of neurocognitive deficits in schizophrenia? *American Journal of Psychiatry, 153,* 321–330.

Gunderson, J.G. (1978). Patient/therapist matching: A research evaluation. *American Journal of Psychiatry, 135,* 1193–1197.

Gunderson, J.G., Frank, A.F., Katz, H.M., Vannicelli, M.L., Frosch, J.P., Knapp, P.H. (1984). Effects of psychotherapy in schizophrenia: II. Comparative outcome of two forms of treatment. *Schizophrenia Bulletin, 10,* 564–598.

Hammer, M.A., Katsanis, J. & Iacono, W.G. (1995). The relationship between negative symptoms and neuropsychological performance. *Biological Psychiatry, 37,* 828–830.

Harding, C.M., Brooks, G.W., Ashikaga, T., Strauss, J.S. & Breier, A. (1987a). The Vermont longitudinal study of persons with severe mental illness: I. Methodology, study sample, and overall status 32 years later. *American Journal of Psychiatry, 144,* 718–726.

Harding, C.M., Brooks, G.W., Ashikaga, T., Strauss, J.S. & Breier, A. (1987b). The Vermont longitudinal study of persons with severe mental illness: II. Long-term outcome of subjects who retrospectively met DSM-III criteria for schizophrenia. *American Journal of Psychiatry, 144,* 727–735.

Harding, C.M., Zubin, J. & Strauss, J.S. (1992). Chronicity in schizophrenia: revisited. *British Journal of Psychiatry, 161* (Suppl 18), 27–37.

Hegarty, J.D., Baldessarini, R.J., Token, M., Waternaux, C. & Oepen, G. (1994). One hundred years of schizophrenia: A meta-analysis of the outcome literature. *American Journal of Psychiatry, 151,* 1409–1416.

Heinssen, R.K., Liberman, R.P. & Kopelowicz, A. (2000). Psychosocial skills training for schizophrenia: Lessons from the laboratory. *Schizophrenia Bulletin, 26,* 21–46.

Helgason, L. (1990). Twenty years' follow-up of first psychiatric presentation for schizophrenia: what could have been prevented? *Acta Psychiatrica Scandinavica, 81,* 231–235.

Hogarty, G.E., Anderson, C.M., Reiss, D.J., Kornblith, S.J., Greenwald, D.P., Javna, C.D. & Madonia, MJ. (1986). Family psycho-education, social skills training and maintenance chemotherapy in aftercare treatment of schizophrenia. 1. One-year effects of a controlled-study on relapse and expressed emotion. *Archives of General Psychiatry, 43,* 633–642.

Hogarty, G.E., Anderson, C.M., Reiss, D.J., Kornbijth, S.J., Greenwald, D.P., Ulrich, R.F. & Carter, M. (1991). Family psycho-education, social skills training, and maintenance chemotherapy in the aftercare treatment of schizophrenia: II. Two-year effects of a controlled study on relapse and adjustment. *Archives of General Psychiatry, 48,* 340–347.

Hogarty, G.E., Goldberg, S.C. & Schooler, N. (1974). Drug and sociotherapy in the aftercare of schizophrenia patients. III. Adjustment of non-relapsed patients. *Archives of General Psychiatry, 31,* 609–618.

Hoge, S.K., Appelbaum, P.S., Lawlor, T., Beck, J.C., Litman, R., Greer, A., Gutheil, T.G., & Kaplan, E. (1990). A prospective, multicenter study of patients' refusal of antipsychotic medication. *Archives of General Psychiatry, 47,* 949–956.

Huber, G., Gross, G. & Schuttler, R. (1975). A long-term follow-up study of schizophrenia: psychiatric course of illness and prognosis. *Acta Psychiatrica Scandinavica, 52,* 49–57.

Johnstone, E.G., MacMilllan, J.F., Frith, C.D., Benn, D.K. & Crow, T.J. (1990). Further investigation of the predictors of outcome following first schizophrenic episodes. *British Journal of Psychiatry, 157,* 182–189.

Klimke, A., Klieser, E., Lehmann, E. & Miele, L. (1993). Initial improvement as a criterion for drug choice in acute schizophrenia. *Pharmacopsychiatry, 26,* 25-29.

Kopala, L.C., Fredrikson, D., Good, K.P. & Honer, W.G. (1996). Symptoms in neuroleptic-naive, first-episode schizophrenia: Response to risperidone. *Biological Psychiatry, 39,* 296–298.

Kopelowicz, A., Corrigan, P., Wallace, C. & Liberman, R.P. (1996). Biopsychosocial rehabilitation. In A. Tasman, J. Kay & J.A. Lieberman (Eds), *Psychiatry* (pp. 1513–1534). Philadelphia: W.B. Saunders Company.

Kopelowicz, A. & Liberman, R.P. (1999). Biobehavioral treatment and rehabilitation of persons with serious mental illness. In J.R. Scotti (Ed.), *New directions in behavioral interventions: Principles, models, and practices* (pp. 123–128). Baltimore: Brookes Publishing Company.

Kopelowicz, A., Liberman, R.P., Mintz, J. & Zarate, R. (1997). Efficacy of social skills training for deficit versus non-deficit negative symptoms in schizophrenia. *American Journal of Psychiatry, 154,* 424–425.

Kraepelin, E. (1919). *Dementia praecox and paraphrenia.* Translated and edited by R.B. Barclay. Edinburgh: ES Livingston.

Lamb, H.R. (1988). One-to-one relationships with the long-term mentally ill: Issues in training professionals. *Community Mental Health Journal, 24,* 328–337.

Lehman, A.F., Steinwachs, D.M., & PORT Co-Investigators. (1998). Translating research into practice: The schizophrenia Patient Outcomes Research Team (PORT) treatment recommendations. *Schizophrenia Bulletin, 24,* 1–10.

Liberman, R.P. (2002). Cognitive remediation in schizophrenia. In H. Kashima, I.R.H. Falloon, M. Mizuno & M. Asai (Eds), *Comprehensive treatment of schizophrenia* (pp. 254–278). Tokyo: Springer-Verlag.

Liberman, R.P., Gutkind, D., Mintz, J., Green, M., Marshall, B.D., Robertson, MJ. & Hayden, J. (2002). Impact of risperidone vs. haloperidol on activities of daily living in treatment refractory schizophrenia. *Comprehensive Psychiatry, 43*(6), 469–73.

Liberman, R.P., Hilty, D.M., Drake, R.E. & Tsang, H.W.H. (2001). Requirements for multidisciplinary teamwork in psychiatric rehabilitation. *Psychiatric Services, 52,* 1331–1342.

Liberman, R.P., Vaccaro, J.V. & Corrigan, P.W. (1995). Psychiatric rehabilitation. In H.I. Kaplan & B.J. Sadock (Eds.), *Comprehensive textbook of psychiatry.* Baltimore: Williams &Wilkins.

Liberman, R.P., Wallace, C.J., Blackwell, G., Eckman, T.A., Vaccaro, J.V. & Kuehnel, T.G. (1993). Innovations in skills training for the seriously mentally ill: The UCLA Social & Independent Living Skills modules. *Innovations and Research, 2,* 43–60.

Liddle, P.F. & Morris, D.L. (1991). Schizophrenic syndromes and frontal lobe performance. *British Journal of Psychiatry, 158,* 340–345.

Lieberman, J.A. & Fenton, W.S. (2000). Delayed detection of psychosis: causes, consequences and effect on public health. *American Journal of Psychiatry, 157,* 1727–1730.

Lieberman, J., Jody, D., Geisler, S., Alvir, J., Loebel, A., Szymanski, S., Woerner, M. & Borenstein, M. (1993). Time course and biological correlates of treatment response in first-episode schizophrenia. *Archives of General Psychiatry, 50,* 369–376.

Lo, W.H. & Lo, T. (1977). A 10-year follow-up study of Chinese schizophrenics in Hong Kong. *British Journal of Psychiatry, 131,* 63–66.

Loebel, A.D., Lieberman, J.A., Alvir, J.M.J., Mayerhoff, D.I., Geisler, S.H. & Szymanski, S.R. (1992). Duration of psychosis and outcome in first-episode schizophrenia. *American Journal of Psychiatry, 149,* 1183–1188.

Lyons, J.S. & McGovern, M.P. (1989). Use of mental health services by dually diagnosed patients. *Hospital and Community Psychiatry, 40,* 1067–1069.

Lysaker, P. & Bell, M. (1995). Negative symptoms and vocational impairment in schizophrenia: Repeated measurements of work performance over six months. *Acta Psychiatrica Scandinavica, 91,* 205–208.

Marder, S.R., Wirshing, W.C., Mintz, J. & Mckenzie, J. (1996). Two-year outcome of social skills training and group psychotherapy for outpatients with schizophrenia. *American Journal of Psychiatry, 153,* 1585–1592.

May, P.R., van Putten, T., & Yale, C. (1980). Predicting outcome of antipsychotic drug treatment from early response. *American Journal of Psychiatry, 137,* 1088–1089.

McGlashan, T.H. (1988). A selective review of recent North American long-term follow-up studies of schizophrenia. *Schizophrenia Bulletin, 14,* 515–542.

McGlashan, T.H. (1996). Early detection and intervention in schizophrenia: research. *Schizophrenia Bulletin, 22,* 327–345.

McGorry, P.D., Edwards, J., Mihalopoulos, C., Harrigan, S.M., & Jackson, H.J. (1996). EPPIC: An evolving system of early detection and optimal management. *Schizophrenia Bulletin, 22,* 305–326.

Mellman, T.A., Miller, A.L., Weissman, E.M., Crismon, M.L., Essock, S.M., & Marder, S.R. (2001). Evidence-based pharmacologic treatment for people with severe mental illness: A focus on guidelines and algorithms. *Psychiatric Services, 52,* 619–625.

Morrison, R.L., Bellack, A.S., Wdcted, J.T. & Mueser, K.T. (1990). Positive and negative symptoms in schizophrenia: a cluster-analytic approach. *Journal of Nervous and Mental Disease, 178,* 377–384.

Mueser, K.T. & Bond, G.R. (2000). Psychosocial treatment approaches for schizophrenia. *Current Opinion in Psychiatry, 13,* 27–35.

Narrow, W.E., Rae, D.S., Robins, L.N. & Regier, D.A. (2002). Revised prevalence estimates of mental disorders in the United States. *Archives of General Psychiatry, 59,*115–123.

Nuechterlein, K.H., Subotnik, K.L., Gitlin, M., Dawson, M.E., Ventura, J., Snyder, K.S., Fogelson, D.L., Shaw, S. & Mintz, J. (1999). Neurocognitive and environmental contributors to work recovery after initial onset of schizophrenia: Answers from path analyses. *Schizophrenia Research, 36,*179.

Ogawa, K., Miya, M., Watarai, A., Nakazawa, M., Yuasa, S. & Utena, H. (1987). A long-term follow-up study of schizophrenia in Japan with special reference to the course of social adjustment. *British Journal of Psychiatry, 151,* 758–765.

Palmer, B.W., Heaton, S.C. & Jeste, D.V. (1999). Older patients with schizophrenia: challenges in the coming decades. *Psychiatric Services, 50,* 1178–1183.

Paul, G.L. & Lentz, R.J. (1977). *Psychosocial treatment of chronic mental patients: milieu versus social-learning programs.* Cambridge, MA: Harvard University Press.

Penn, D.L. & Mueser, K.T. (1996). Research update on the psychosocial treatment of schizophrenia. *American Journal of Psychiatry, 153,* 607–617.

Pogue-Geile, M.F. & Harrow, M. (1987). The longitudinal study of negative symptoms in schizophrenia. In R.R. Grinker & M. Harrow (Eds), *Clinical research in schizophrenia: A multidimensional approach* (pp. 189–199). Springfield: Charles C. Thomas.

Regier, D.A., Farmer, M.E., Rae, D.S., Locke, B.Z., Keith, S.J., Judd, L.L. & Goodwin, F.K. (1990). Comorbidity of mental disorders with alcohol and other drug abuse: results from the Epidemiologic Catchment Area (EGA) study. *Journal of the American Medical Association, 264,* 2511–2518.

Robinson, D., Woerner, M.G., Alvir, J.M., Bilder, R, Goldman, R., Geisler, S., Koreen, A., Shettman, B., Chakos, M., Mayerhoff, D. & Lieberman, J.A. (1999). Predictors of relapse following response from a first episode of schizophrenia or schizoaffective disorder. *Archives of General Psychiatry, 56,* 241–247.

Scott, J.E. & Dixon, L.B. (1995). Psychological interventions for schizophrenia. *Schizophrenia Bulletin, 21,* 621–630.

Shaner, A., Roberts, L.J., Eckman, T.A., Racenstein, J.M., Tucker, D.E., Tsuang, J.W. & Mintz, J. (1998). Sources of diagnostic uncertainty for chronically psychotic cocaine abusers. *Psychiatric Services, 49,* 684–690.

Spaniol, L. & Koehler, M. (1994). *The experience of recovery.* Boston: Center for Psychiatric Rehabilitation, Boston University.

Stein, L.J. & Santos, L.B. (1998). *Assertive community treatment of persons with severe mental illness.* New York: Norton.

Strauss, M. (1993). Relations of symptoms to cognitive deficits in schizophrenia. *Schizophrenia Bulletin, 19,* 215–232.

Strauss, J.S. & Carpenter, W.T. (1974). The prediction of outcome in schizophrenia: II. Relationships between predictor and outcome variables: A report from the Who International Pilot Study of Schizophrenia. *Archives of General Psychiatry, 31,* 37–42.

Sturm, R., Gresenz, C., Pacula, R. & Wells, K. (2000). Labor force participation by persons with mental illness. *Psychiatric Services, 50,* 1407.

Swanson, J.W., Holzer, C.E., Ganju, V.K. & Jono, R.T. (1990). Violence and psychiatric disorder in the community: Evidence from the Epidemiologic Catchment Area surveys. *Hospital and Community Psychiatry, 41,* 761–770.

Swofford, C.D., Kasckow, J.W., Scheller-Gilkey, G. & Inderbitzin, L.B. (1996). Substance use: A powerful predictor of relapse in schizophrenia. *Schizophrenia Research, 20,* 145–151.

Tsuang, M.T., Simpson, J.C. & Kronfol, Z. (1982). Subtypes of drug abuse with psychosis: demographic characteristics, clinical features, and family history. *Archives of General Psychiatry, 39,* 141–147.

van der Does, A.J., Dingemans, P.M., Linszen, D.H., Nugter, M.A. & Scholte, W.F. (1993). Symptom dimensions and cognitive and social functioning in recent-onset schizophrenia. *Psychological Medicine, 23,* 745–753.

van der Gaag, M., Kern, R.S., van Den Bosch, R.J. & Liberman, R.P. (2002). A controlled trial of cognitive remediation in schizophrenia. *Schizophrenia Bulletin 28,*167–176.

Ventura, J., Green, M.F., Shaner, A. & Liberman, R.P. (1993).Training and quality assurance in the use of the Expanded Brief Psychiatric Rating Scale: The "drift busters." *International Journal of Methods in Psychiatric Research, 3,* 221–244.

Wallace, C.J. & Liberman, R.P. (1985). Social skills training for patients with schizophrenia: a controlled clinical trial. *Psychiatry Research, 15,* 239–247.

Warner, R. (1985), *Recovery from schizophrenia: Psychiatry and political economy.* London: Routledge & Kegan Paul.

Warner, R., Taylor, D., Wright, J., Sloat, A., Springett, G., Arnold, S. & Weinberg, H. (1994). Substance use among the mentally ill: Prevalence, reasons for use and effects on illness. *American Journal of Orthopsychiatry, 64,* 465–476.

Weiden, P., Olfson, M. & Essock, S. (1997). Medication noncompliance in schizophrenia: effects on mental health service policy. In B. Blackwell (Ed.), *Treatment compliance and the therapeutic alliance* (pp. 35–60). New York: Harwood Academic Publishers.

Wexler, B.E., Hawkins, K.A., Rounsavtlle, B., Anderson, M., Sernyak, MJ. & Green, M.F. (1997). Normal neurocognitive performance after extended practice in patients with schizophrenia. *Schizophrenia Research, 26,*173–180.

Whttehorn, D., Lazier, L. & Kopala, L. (1998). Psychosocial rehabilitation early after the onset of psychosis. *Psychiatric Services, 49,* 1135–1137.

Wolkow, K.E. & Ferguson, H. (2001). Community factors in the development of resiliency. *Community Mental Health Journal, 37,* 489–498.

World Health Organization (1980). *International classification of impairment, disabilities, and handicaps.* Geneva: World Health Organization.

Wyatt, R.J. (1991). Neuroleptics and the natural course of schizophrenia. *Schizophrenia Bulletin, 17,* 325–351.

Wykes, T., Reeder, C., Corner, J., Williams, C. & Everitt, B. (1999).The effects of neurocognitive remediation on executive processing in patients with schizophrenia. *Schizophrenia Bulletin, 25,* 291–307.

# Psychological and Social Aspects of Negative Symptoms

*John S. Strauss, Jaak Rakfeldt, Courtenay M. Harding, and Paul Lieberman*

At the time of original publication, John S. Strauss, MD; Jaak Rakfeldt, PhD; Courtenay M. Harding, PhD; Paul Lieberman, MD, were affiliated with Yale University School of Medicine, Department of Psychiatry, New Haven, CT.

This article is from the *British Journal of Psychiatry*, 1989, 155 (suppl. 7), 128–132, and is reprinted with permission.

Our reintroduction of the concept of negative symptoms in schizophrenia (Strauss et al., 1974) has been followed by much productive research on this topic. As in the work of Andreason, Crowe, and others, the focus of most of this research has been on improving descriptive assessments of these symptoms (Andreason, 1982) and exploring thier biological correlates (Crowe, 1981). This work has been extremely important, but psychological and social aspects of negative symptoms are also important (Barton, 1959; Wing & Brown, 1970; Gruenberg, 1967), and in these areas there as been little research. Nevertheless, it is crucial to explore possible psychological and social factors in negative symptoms more fully and to provide a basis for more adequate prevention and treatment. It is important to clarify psychological and social factors in these symptoms to provide a basis for more effective biological research, since the heterogeneity of negative symptoms at a psychological level could hide significant biological correlates.

In this paper we will explore the possible psychological and social aspects of negative symptoms utilizing information from our intensive longitudinal studies and from large sample studies, first-person accounts, and clinical experiences. Based on these sources, we will develop two hypotheses: a) Negative symptoms arise in many instances as responses to extremely difficult psychological and social situations. These symptoms may even serve to help the person with schizophrenia survive. In such instances, the term "negative symptoms," although descriptively useful, may be misleading, since these symptoms may reflect active coping on the part of the patient; b) Negative symptoms have a psychological and social impact on the further course of disorder. Negative symptoms may provide some psychological solutions for the problems patients encounter, but these symptoms may also generate a cyclical feedback process that removes patients from social functioning and in this way reduces the likelihood of improvement. This impact may contribute to the poor prognostic implications of negative symptoms.

Thus, in this paper we develop further our thesis that as part of understanding severe mental disorders and improving their treatment, one must use an interactive developmental model (Strauss & Carpenter, 1981). This approach requires viewing persons who have these disorders as complex evolving systems operating in biological and social contexts. Negative symptoms arising from psychological, biological, or social origins may then influence the further evolution of any or all of those domains.

To explore the many aspects of negative symptoms various approaches are necessary. In spite of the advances made in developing rating scales (Andreasen, 1982), such ratings may not tap underlying psychological processes adequately. More intensive and extensive exploration is also essential. For example, Bouricius (1989) reports an instance in which her son had been diagnosed as having schizophrenia and was viewed as having flat affect at a time when his appearance and behavior were dull and apathetic. At the same time, however, he was writing very emotionally charged poetry. Noting associations between negative symptoms and the psychological and social contexts in which they emerge can help prevent naive interpretations from brief descriptive reports and provide important clues to psychological processes that might contribute to the generation of the symptoms (Strauss & Hafez, 1981; Strauss et al., submitted for publication). Thus this exploration suggesting that negative symptoms are often responses to difficult psychological and social situations uses more detailed description of patients' reports and contexts than is found in traditional symptom ratings.

## POSSIBLE PSYCHOLOGICAL AND SOCIAL SOURCES OF NEGATIVE SYMPTOMS

Reports of patients from our own intensive studies (Strauss et al., 1985), reviews of first-person accounts (*Schizophrenia Bulletin,* 1987), and clinical experiences suggest several specific psychological and social contexts in which negative symptoms often arise. These sources suggest ten different kinds of situations that may contribute to these symptoms. The following is a list of these situations with illustrative examples.

### 1. The Pain of Relapse into Positive Symptoms

A schizophrenic patient considered by his psychiatrist to have an "anhedonic syndrome" described in an interview with one of the investigators (JS) a sequence of factors occurring in his illness. This young man had been a motorcycle racer. He then started developing schizophrenia with delusions of persecution and threatening auditory hallucinations. When he was engaged in motorcycle racing, especially if he were close to winning, these symptoms would become unbearably intense. The patient described this as such a horrible experience that he finally gave up motorcycle racing entirely, an activity that had been one of the few pleasures of his life.

### 2. The Loss of Hope and Self-esteem

One person seen in our intensive longitudinal study who had a history of 12 years of schizophrenic disorder had sunk drastically in quality of life during and between his psychotic episodes. Before the onset of his illness, he had been a highly skilled craftsman. He had been married with one child and was involved with his mother and siblings. Over the years however, he was repeatedly admitted to hospital. When he was able to work, it was as an unskilled laborer. He was divorced, out of touch with his child, and lost contact with other family members as well. He had no friends. How many people could maintain motivation and involvement under such a decline? But somehow, this patient had kept trying, although more and more feebly.

Most recently, he had been admitted to hospital with yet another psychotic episode. In the subsequent 3 months, although still slightly apathetic and withdrawn, he improved gradually and had started to become more autonomous. When noting in a research interview that he had improved, he added: "I'm almost afraid to think about it. How long will it be until the next time?" Given this attitude, it is perhaps not too surprising that when seen in a follow-up interview 1 month later the subject had withdrawn further. He had been spending most of his time in bed and had been advised finally by his clinician that he should apply for disability payments and would probably not be able to return to work.

### 3. The Possibility of Impulsive or Bizarre Behavior

Negative symptoms may arise when the patient has had problems acting impulsively or acting bizarrely. In some instances it appears as though massive apathy and withdrawal are mechanisms for avoiding such socially or personally destructive behaviors by damping down overall behavior, in psychotic states, when fine control of action and thinking is severely compromised, a massive withdrawal might be the only way in which display of bizarre behavior and thoughts, or actual destructiveness, can be avoided.

### 4. Problems in Finding a New Identity as Non-patient

Another situation in which negative symptoms may arise is when the patient confronts the difficulties of needing to find an identity that is not one of being sick. An example of the intensity of this problem was given by one subject in our intensive longitudinal study. This subject has improved considerably over the last several years and was now confronting this issue. She had not developed negative symptoms, but reflected how much she was tempted to give up and withdraw. This young woman wondered during a follow-up interview whether she was going "crazy" because as she had become better she was losing the structure of her life that had been provided by her illness. She was no longer in treatment other than receiving low-dose neuroleptic medication. She did not want to associate with other patients or former patients. On the other hand, people that she had known prior to her illness now had families and jobs. Having neither, the subject felt out of place with them. In addition, she was perplexed as to how she was going to function in the world as a "normal." With these concerns and the feelings they generated, she wondered whether she was going crazy again. Other subjects described being sick as an occupation in itself—a full-time career. One subject told us how difficult it was to give up being sick with its constant self-focus. This subject, like the other, also stated that being sick provided an entire framework for relating to others and receiving help from them.

### 5. The Feeling of Guilt for Past Dysfunction

One mother (DuVal, 1987), who had had repeated psychotic episodes, described poignantly her vague awareness during these episodes that they were harming her child who witnessed them. Often people with schizophrenia describe the guilt they feel at being unable to perform in the roles in which they have previously taken pride and also from the actual psychological or physical harm they might have done to their loved ones during the psychosis. During the process of improvement with its increasing awareness of environment, these realizations create for patients a further burden and a pressure to withdraw and give up.

### 6. The Potential Threat of Entering Complex Stressful Social Situations

For many patients, particular kinds of social and occupational situations may be extremely stressful, possibly even contributing to symptom recurrence. Interpersonal closeness, for example, is often extremely difficult for some persons with schizophrenia. Negative symptoms may arise from fears of such situations. The symptoms may be reinforced and maintained by also providing a mechanism for avoiding the threat or even the possibility of such a relationship.

### 7. Situations Where the Person Is Rendered Helpless from the Disorder, from Environmental Features, or Both

Persons with schizophrenia may find all their paths to improvement blocked. This may be especially true for people with repeated psychotic episodes who come from low socioeconomic classes, have few skills, and are isolated from family and friends. Here, too, there may be the possibility of secondary benefit from negative symptoms. As Schmale has pointed out in another context (Schmale, 1964), giving up under overwhelming conditions may not be as maladaptive as it seems. Giving up at least offers the possibility of recruiting help from others in the social context if such help is available at all.

## THREE ENVIRONMENTAL CONTRIBUTORS TO NEGATIVE SYMPTOMS

Beyond the negative symptoms possibly arising from the person's experience with the disorder itself as described above, these symptoms may also be associated with the following specific social-environmental characteristics.

### 8. Institutionalization

Behaviors reflective of negative symptoms associated with long-term institutionalization have been discussed in detail by other authors (e.g., Barton, 1959; Wing, 1962; Goffman, 1961).

### 9. The Social Benefit System

Although helpful for some, benefit systems sometimes punish patients who attempt to recover. As is so often true, one can see the situation facing a person about to improve by observing someone with schizophrenia who does not have negative symptoms and thus encounters the problems. One of our subjects, a 23-year-old woman with a 6-year history of psychotic symptoms, was able to work her way through college and part way through graduate school. She did this while at the same time working full time at a skilled job. She accomplished such feats in spite of recurring symptoms and the side effects from her psychotropic medications. However, because she then began to earn a modest salary, she was no longer eligible for welfare benefits. In addition, she had to pay for her own medications and treatment. As a result, she remained constantly in debt while only being able to support herself slightly above a poverty level. As she got better, she was thus far worse off materially and financially than she had been when she received disability benefits.

### 10. The Stigma of Schizophrenia

Stigma (Scheff, 1981) is a social situation that seems likely to contribute with particular power to the development of negative symptoms. Such an evolution is consistent with the concept of secondary deviance (Lemert, 1967), the reaction people often have to being viewed as defective, in this case as a mental patient. The reaction to being stigmatized often includes the acceptance of the role and loss of other strengths. This sequence may be influenced by many things including the intensity of the stigma, the severity or chronicity of the disorder, personality traits of the person, and pressures and supports of society.

Beyond these ten psychological and social situations, as further evidence for the hypothesis that psychological and social factors may be sources of negative symptoms, it is important also to note environmental situations that appear to reduce these symptoms. The helpful roles of modest increases in interpersonal contact or useful occupation have been discussed in many reports (Wing, 1962; Breier & Strauss, 1984). More striking changes in environmental situations may also have a salutory effect. There are many reports of withdrawn chronic schizophrenic patients who take leading roles in rescue operations during a flood or a fire, helping save other patients or even helping to organize the general rescue procedures. Only slightly less dramatic are the more systematic reports (Clark, 1988) describing how chronic schizophrenic patients participating in a challenging, engaging activity like a canoe trip begin to communicate, relate to each other, show pleasure, and take an increasingly active role in the venture. Characteristics of novelty, challenge, interpersonal support, trust, and free choice seem to be key factors in such situations.

### THE PSYCHOLOGICAL AND SOCIAL IMPACTS OF NEGATIVE SYMPTOMS ON COURSE OF DISORDER

One of the most striking aspects of negative symptoms has been their prognostic power. This has been shown in several large-sample short-term studies (Strauss et al., 1974). It has also been found to a lesser extent in at least one carefully conducted long-term follow-up (Warding et al., 1987a). What is the mechanism for this prognostic effect? One possibility is that negative symptoms contribute to poor prognosis by cutting the person off from potentially helpful environmental resources. Although negative symptoms may help patients avoid or cope with certain aspects of their life situation, these symptoms may also generate positive feedback mechanisms that maintain or exacerbate the disorder with its dysfunction (Strauss et al., 1985). There is evidence, for example, that in several mental disorders work and social relationships may prevent decompensation or help people improve (Brown & Harris, 1978; Henderson, 1981; Breier & Strauss, 1984; Strauss et al., 1981). Negative symptoms usually undermine functioning in these life contexts. Patients who are too withdrawn to work, who are too apathetic and without affect to form social ties, cut themselves off from the very sources that could provide motivation, structure, hope, material assistance, and advice. Furthermore, vocational rehabilitation programs often systematically exclude persons with low motivation. Even the treatment system may give up on the patient with negative symptoms, making fewer resources available.

### DISCUSSION

Why are negative symptoms so important in schizophrenia when there are so many other disorders that also engender despair, fear of recurrence, and similar problems? One possible answer is the severity of the stigma with which society, (including the patient) views schizophrenic disorders. The diagnosis of schizophrenia is almost unique among mental disorders in terms of the despair that it evokes. For example, a young woman in one study

(Rakfeldt, 1987) noted that because she was in hospital with an eating disorder her friends would accept her more than if she had been diagnosed as having schizophrenia. Another study subject (with the diagnosis of schizoaffective disorder) said almost desperately how important it was that he convince the hospital staff that he was depressed, not schizophrenic. He seemed driven to prove to himself and to others that he was not a "nut" or a "hopeless case."

The contributions of treatment interventions to apathy and withdrawal may also be particularly powerful in schizophrenia. Some of the most common treatment efforts may inadvertently create the opposite effect from the ones intended. Patients with schizophrenia are often told that they have a disease like diabetes. They are told that they will have the disease all their lives, that it involves major and permanent functional impairment, and that they will have a life-long need for medication (Harding et al., 1987b).

One person participating in a workshop on schizophrenia for professionals, consumers, and family members reported that after having received this message she gave up her teaching career. A few years later, a friend advised her instead: "Try to do a little something—little by little." She took the advice and started working part time. The patient, who was still psychotic, found that she was better able to control her psychosis while working. She then became more involved with the world, and began functioning more competently, finally returning to a teaching job. She had surmounted the withdrawal apparently fostered by the well-intended "therapeutic" intervention.

Finally, the accumulation of undermining experiences may be particularly powerful in schizophrenia. Stigma, discouraging "therapeutic" messages, social dysfunction, and the problems schizophrenia often generates in functioning cognitively may all interact over time to make remaining engaged, involved, and hopeful particularly difficult.

But could not experiences such as those described above be assumed to be adequately covered by some general term like "demoralization?" Perhaps, but such terms in psychological domains are often used as pseudo-explanations to note and de-emphasize the phenomenon in order to make way for detailed biological inquiry. This is similar to how the term "constitutional factors" was used as a biological pseudo-explanation not so long ago to "get that out of the way" so the "really important" psychological features could be explored in detail. Both tendencies are unfortunate. Just as the various possible biological contributions to negative symptoms need to be explored in detail, so too the various psychological and social sources need to be clarified. Only through such a combined approach will be it possible to achieve optimal understanding and treatment.

Acknowledgements

Preparation of this report was supported in part by NIMH Grants MH00340 and MH3436S and an award from the Scottish Rite Program.

## REFERENCES

Andreasen, N.C. (1982). Negative symptoms in schizophrenia: Definition and reliability. *Archives of General Psychiatry, 39,* 784–788.

Barton, R. (1959). *Institutional neuroses.* Bristol: Wright.

Bouricius, J.K. (1989). Negative symptoms and emotions in a schizophrenic. *Schizophrenia Bulletin, 15,* 201–208.

Breier, A. & Strauss, J.S. (1984). Social relationships in the recovery from psychotic disorder. *American Journal of Psychiatry, 141,* 949–955.

Brown, G.W. & Harris, T. (1978). *Social origins of depression.* New York: Free Press.

Clark, C. (1988). *Out of the hospital, into the wilderness: White-water canoeing for the long-term psychiatrically disabled.* Presented at the Canadian Occupational Therapy Association Annual Meeting.

Crowe, T.J. (1981). Positive and negative schizophrenia symptoms and the role of dopamine. British *Journal of Psychiatry, 139,* 251–254.

DuVal, M. (1987) Giving love—and schizophrenia. Reprinted in *Schizophrenia Bulletin,* Special issue: Schizophrenia: The Experiences of Patients and Families, pp. 8–13.

Goffman, E. (1961) *Asylums.* Garden City, NY: Doubleday.

Gruenberg, E.M. (1967). The social breakdown syndrome—some origins. *American Journal of Psychiatry, 123,* 1481–1489.

Harding, C.M., Brookes, G.W., Ashikaga, T., et al. (1987a). The Vermont longitudinal study: II. Long-term outcome of subjects who retrospectively met the DSM–III criteria for schizophrenia. *American Journal of Psychiatry, 144,* 727–735.

Harding, C. M., Zubin, J., Strauss, J.S. (1987b). Chronicity in schizophrenia: Fact, partial fact, or artifact? *Hospital and Community Psychiatry, 38,* 477–486.

Henderson, S. (1981) Social relationships, adversity, and neurosis: An analysis of prospective observations. *British Journal of Psychiatry, 138,* 391–398.

Lemert, E.M. (1967) *Human deviance, social problems, and social control.* Englewood Cliffs, NJ: Prentice Hall.

Rakfeldt, J. (1987). *The active role of patients in the course of their disorder: Labeling and metacognitive processes.* Presented at the 37th Annual Meeting of the Society for Study of Social Problems, Chicago, August 15, 1987.

Scheff, T. (1981). The labeling theory paradigm. In C. Eisdorfer, D. Cohen, A. Kleinman et al. (Eds.), *Models for clinical psychopathology,* pp. 27–41. New York: Spectrum.

*Schizophrenia Bulletin* (1989). Subjective experiences of schizophrenia. Issue edited by J.S. Strauss and S.E. Estroff, 15. (1987) Special issue: The Experiences of Patients and Families.

Schmale, A.H. (1964). A genetic view of affects with special reference to the genesis of helplessness and hopelessness. *The Psychoanalytic Study of the Child, 19,* 287–310.

Strauss, J.S. & Carpenter, W.T. Jr. (1981). *Schizophrenia.* New York: Plenum.

Strauss, J.S., & Hafez, H. (1981). Clinical questions and "real" research. *American Journal of Psychiatry, 138,* 1592–1597.

Strauss, J.M., Carpenter, W.T. Jr., & Bartko, J.J. (1974). Speculations on the processes that underlie schizophrenic symptoms. *Schizophrenia Bulletin. 11,* 61–70.

Strauss, J.M., Kokes, R.F., Klorman, R., et al. (1977). Premorbid adjustment in schizophrenia: Concepts, measures, and implications. *Schizophrenia Bulletin, 3,* 182–244.

Strauss, J.M., Loevsky, L., Glazer, W., et al. (1981). Organizing the complexities of schizophrenia. *Journal of Nervous and Mental Disease, 169,* 120–126.

Strauss, J.M., Hafez, H., Lieberman, P., et al. (1985). The course of psychiatric disorder: III. Longitudinal principles. *American Journal of Psychiatry, 142,* 289–296.

Strauss, J.M., Harding, C.M., et al. (submitted for publication) *Clinical questions and real research: II. Systematic exploratory research.*

Wing, J.K. (1962) Institutionalism in mental hospitals. *British Journal of Social and Clinical Psychology, 1,* 38–51.

Wing, J.K., & Brown, G. (1970). *Institutionalism and schizophrenia.* Cambridge: Cambridge University Press.

# What Is Recovery from Schizophrenia?

*Anne-Kari Torgalsbøen*

Anne-Kari Torgalsbøen, PhD, is with the Department of Psychology, University of Oslo, Norway.

## Introduction

Recovery challenges many traditional ideas about schizophrenia. While working on my doctoral thesis on full recovery in schizophrenia in the early 1990s, it was quite a challenge to attend and present on this topic at international conferences. The main attitude of colleagues was that recovery from schizophrenia was rare or impossible. Although heterogeneity with respect to outcome in schizophrenia has been recognized (Bleuler, 1950; Modestin et al., 2003), Kraepelin's view of schizophrenia has persisted into the modern diagnostic systems. For example, the authors of *DSM-IV* cautioned about "the unlikeliness of afflicted individuals making a complete return to full functioning" (APA, 1994, p. 282).

In the listing of course specifiers of schizophrenia in *DSM-IV,* there is only one specifyer termed "single episode in full remission "which indicates a positive course in schizophrenia. This specifyer applies when there has been a single episode in which criterion A for schizophrenia has been met and no clinically significant residual symptoms remain. In my opinion the difference between complete remission and full recovery is that full recovery includes sustained improvement in both symptoms and functioning and subjective experiences such as high quality of life and self-esteem. Complete remission can be a temporary improvement in symptoms. In *DSM-IV,* complete remission is defined as a return to full premorbid functioning and it is argued that this is probably not common in schizophrenia. By defining complete remission in this manner the authors are laying the ground for a self-fulfilling prophecy with regard to the pessimistic view of outcome in schizophrenia. Moreover, the DSM-IV definition of complete remission is not in accordance with the fact that many persons with schizophrenia have a sub-optimal functioning due to for instance cognitive deficits. Full recovery in schizophrenia is nonexistent in the "modern" diagnostic classification system.

However, there is now a growing body of empirically-based research showing that recovery from schizophrenia can occur. Follow-up studies examining outcome decades after an index episode have been the primary source of data on full recovery among patients with this disorder. These studies have shown that about half of patients eventually recover or have only mild impairment and as many as 20 to 25% will achieve full recovery (sustained improvement in both symptoms and social/vocational functioning) (Harding, 1994). Why, then has it been so difficult to disseminate this information throughout the research and clinical world? The aim of this paper is to give an answer to this question as well as give an overview of the different conceptualizations of the term *recovery* in schizophrenia and lastly, suggest a definition.

### Inconsistency in the Definition of Recovery

One contributing factor relates to the wide variety of definitions of improvement and recovery used in research. Inconsistency in the conceptualization and definition of successful outcome make research findings difficult to interpret and preclude comparisons across studies. As pointed out by Shapiro and Shader (1979), one of the complications in analyzing data across earlier studies is the fact that those studies often used the criteria "recovered" or "improved" without defining either concept. They also commonly used only a single measure of outcome, such as "hospitalized" or "discharged." Other measures that have been used to define outcome include relapse rate and rehospitalization.

In a meta-analysis undertaken by Hegarty and colleagues (1994), for the patients to be considered "improved" at follow-up it was required that they be described as "recovered, in remission, well without residual symptoms, minimally or mildly symptomatic, improved without significant deficit, socially recovered, or working or living independently"(p.1410). Bleuler on the other hand, restricted the definition of recovery to its purest form (i.e., not the slightest trace of disease symptoms present) and Mason (1995) defined complete recovery as "no symptoms, no disability and no treatment." Others, such as Harding and colleagues (1987 a, b) have included patients who were partially recovered (GAS score above 60) and on medication. However, these subjects were considered significantly improved and not fully recovered. In my own study (Torgalsbøen, 1999) full recovery was defined using the following criteria: a reliable diagnosis of schizophrenia at an earlier time but not at present, no psychiatric hospitalization for at least 5 years and present psychosocial functioning within the "normal" range (GAS scores above 65). An interesting question that arose was whether or not a patient could be considered to be fully recovered from an illness if he/she was still on medication. This also raised another issue: should being without medication be considered an absolute criterion for full recovery when all of the other inclusion criteria were fulfilled? In our study this dilemma was resolved by giving preference to those individuals who were not on medication, but including those who used less than a half "defined daily dose"(DDD) of neuroleptics.

The issue of whether it is necessary to continue medication in order to sustain a high level of functioning in patients with schizophrenia is controversial. However, many studies reveal the presence of a proportion of individuals, both early and late in their "careers" with schizophrenia, who appear to improve and even recover without the continuous, daily use of antipsychotic medication (Harding, 1987; Ciompi, 1992; Mosher & Bola, 2001). The toxic effect of untreated psychosis, proposed by some researchers, has also recently been questioned (Cannon, 1998, Rund et al, 2004). In our longitudinal study of fully recovered people with schizophrenia we found that 50% were not using antipsychotic medication and had been off medication for many years (Torgalsbøen, 2001, Torgalsbøen & Rund, 2002).

The term recovery as used in the literature has two connotations. The conventional use of the concept relates to an objective outcome, a point at which there is a lack of evidence of illness. The other, more recent connotation relates to a subjective attitude or orientation asserting that regardless of their state of illness or health, people can have hope, feel capable of expanding their personal abilities, and make their own choices (Resnick et al., 2004). The first definition is straightforward, and depicts the absence of or significant decrease in symptoms and full recovery of vocational or social functioning. This has been demonstrated in several large studies (Harding et al., 1987; Carpenter & Strauss, 1991; Hegarty et al., 1994; Harrow et al., 1997).

However, depending on how strictly this definition is adhered to the rates of fully recovered cases will differ from one study to another. It is unclear what distinguishes full recovery from recovery as these concepts are used inconsistently. As pointed out by Marengo (1994), standardized methods have not been devised for describing course patterns. Consequently, there has been prevailing uncertainty regarding the range and nature of long-term courses of schizophrenia. It is argued that future long-term studies should assess and depict, in standardized fashion, courses that reflect the syndromes onset, patterns change in syndrome, and outcome.

### Recovery as an Outcome Measure

Outcome in schizophrenia can be divided into two categories: clinical and functional. Clinical outcome include variables related to psychiatric symptoms, such as time to symptom remission, rehospitalization rates and clinical states. Functional outcome includes a variety of areas involved in the acquisition and retention of skills that are needed for community functioning (Green, 1998). A number of studies have shown that cognitive impairment, rather than symptoms, influence functional outcome (Mueser et al., 1991; Corrigan et al., 1994; Lysaker et al., 1995).

Nevertheless outcome is frequently determined solely by the presence of absence or positive psychotic symptoms. Failure to recognize the debilitating effects of symptoms such as depression, anxiety, cognitive and /or negative symptoms, may lead to an underestimation of the level of disability experienced by an individual with schizophrenia. Operationalizing outcome as the presence or absence of positive symptoms, rather than based on the individual level of functioning in a wide range of psychosocial domains, does not provide a complete representation of a person's outcome. Positive symptoms experienced during a given follow up period may be brief, lasting days or weeks, and may have a minimal impact on social and occupational functioning (Liberman et al., 2002). In prognostic studies of schizophrenia there is general agreement that outcome is manifold and should be measured in several areas. These include the assessment of clinical symptoms, working ability, degree of independence, social contacts, social competence, etc. (Jonsson & Nyman, 1991). Low or moderate correlations have usually been found between such areas, thus showing that it is possible to maintain a high level of functioning in the presence of severe symptoms (for instance, auditory hallucinations). Both Strauss and Carpenter (1974), Harding and colleagues (1987a, 1987b) and my own research (Torgalsbøen, 2001) have demonstrated the partial independence of symptomatology, social functioning and occupational or educational functioning. These findings illustrate the importance of keeping these dimensions separate when reporting schizophrenia outcomes.

Another important consideration when formulating a concept of recovery from schizophrenia relates to the differences that researchers, clinicians, and people with mental illnesses may have in defining the term "recovery." Researchers often define recovery as an extended period of remission from psychotic symptoms. Clinicians may define recovery as an improvement in global functioning. And lastly, for people with mental illnesses, recovery is a matter of retaining a meaningful life within the limitations of the disorder (Jacobson, 2004). For many this also means being without medication, while others see the controlled use of medication as fully compatible with recovery (Andresen et al., 2003). "Being in recovery means that I don't just take medications....Rather I use medications as part of my recovery process..." (Deegan, 1997, p. 21).

Although people with mental illnesses see recovery as an ongoing process, the description of the final stage of recovery in Andresen's (2004) model, called growth, suggests some measurable constructs. The person may not be free of symptoms completely, but knows how to manage the illness and to stay well. The person is resilient in the face of setbacks, has faith in his or her own ability to pull through and maintain a positive outlook. The person lives a full and meaningful life and looks forward to the future. This final stage of recovery closely mirrors the dimensions of psychological well being (PWB), defined as personal growth, self-acceptance, autonomy, positive relationships, environmental mastery, and purpose in life (Ryff & Keyes,

1995). Another quality of the growth stage is resilience or the ability to endure setbacks without giving up hope. Therefore constructs such as psychological well being and resilience warrant further investigation as outcome measures compatible with the experience of people with mental illnesses

According to Bonnano (2004), resilience is different from the process of recovery. Recovery connotes a trajectory in which normal functioning temporarily gives way to threshold or sub-threshold psychopathology, usually for a period of at least several months, and then gradually returns to pre-event levels. Full recovery may be relatively rapid or may take many years. By contrast, resilience reflects the ability to maintain a stable equilibrium. Recovering individuals often experience sub-threshold symptom levels. Resilient individuals, by contrast, may experience transient perturbations in normal functioning, but generally exhibit a stable trajectory of healthy functioning across time, as well as the capacity for generative experience and positive emotions (Bonnano, Papa & O'Neill, 2001).

### Recovery and Cure

When defining the concept of recovery in schizophrenia it is important to keep in mind that recovery is not synonymous with cure although these concepts are frequently used interchangeably. Some would claim that being on medication is one thing that distinguishes recovery from cure (Liberman et al., 2002). Bleuler (1908) defined cure as "restitio ad integrum" which means return to the state that existed prior to the onset of illness. Arieti (1974) has correctly maintained that this concept loses some of its significance in schizophrenia because the so-called premorbid state is clearly morbid and very much related to the subsequent condition. He argues that if we by cure simply mean loss of manifest schizophrenia symptomatology, it is possible to be cured from schizophrenia. It is also possible if we by cure mean "reestablishment of relatedness with other human beings, closeness with a few persons, love for spouse and children, a reorganization of the personality that includes a definite self-identity, a feeling of fulfilment or of purpose and hope" (Arieti, 1974, p.616).

However, cure is a medical concept and indicates a return to normal health, never experiencing relapses of psychotic symptoms. This rarely occurs in schizophrenia, but several lines of research, including my own, have shown that it is possible to be fully recovered from schizophrenia. By this I mean that it is possible to be free of symptoms, have a high level of functioning, be off medication, be employed and enjoy healthy social and romantic relationships. Jacobson (2001) argues that recovery is distinguished from cure both by its endpoint, which is not necessarily a return to "normal" health and functioning, and by its emphasis on the individual's active participation in self-help activities. Recently more emphasis is put on recovery as a subjective orientation or attitude suggesting that regardless of their state of illness or health, people can have hope and feel capable of expanding their personal abilities and making their own choices. These factors have to a lesser degree been implemented as outcome measures.

In a recent review, Liberman and colleagues (2002) identified several factors that have been hypothesized as being associated with a recovery orientation, including family support, treatment compliance, a strong working alliance with a treater and access to comprehensive services. As pointed out by Resnick and colleagues (2004), the relationship of client characteristics, clinical status and service use to a recovery orientation has not been empirically explored. Their results suggest that three factors were associated with several recovery domains, which suggests that reduced symptoms and side effects of medication and participation in family psychoeducation are especially important correlates of recovery orientation among persons with schizophrenia.

The book and movie "A Beautiful Mind" (1998), depicts the Nobel Prize winner John Nash's life story and gradual control and mastery over delusions and hallucinations, enabling him to regain a functional lifestyle. In the book he focuses on the problems represented by cure and recovery from his mental illness: "Suppose you have an artist. He's rational. But suppose he cannot paint. He can function normally. Is it really a cure? Is it really a salvation?....I feel I am not a good example of a person who recovered unless I can do some good work...although I am rather old..." (Nasar, 1998). (Prior to winning the Nobel prize, John Nash was nominated several times without receiving it. The reason for this was the Swedish academy's apprehension about his behavior during the ceremony. He is now back in business, writing scientific articles and teaching students, although he is still fighting with his delusions. John Nash is a good example that a person with schizophrenia can function and work on a high intellectual level although he is not fully recovered.

### Empirically-Based Concept of Recovery

Despite the growing interest in recovery as a possible outcome in severe mental illness, little empirical research has been undertaken on the concept. Giffort and colleagues (1999) have constructed a scale to measure recovery. The reliability and validity of this scale was examined in a study by Corrigan (1999). Thirty-five participants in a partial hospitalization program were administered the Recovery scale and measures of quality of life (Quality of Life Interview, Lehman, 1983), social support (Social Support Questionnaire, Sarason et al., 1983), self-esteem (Rosenberg Self-esteem Scale, Rosenberg, 1965), empowerment (The Empowerment Scale, Rogers et al., 1997) psychiatric symptoms (BPRS, Lukoff et al, 1986), needs and resources (NARA, Corrigan, 1995), global functioning (GAF, *DSM-IV*) and verbal intelligence (Vocabulary subtest, WAIS-R). Results showed the scale to have satisfactory test-retest reliability and internal consistency. Recovery was associated with three measures of successful living: self-esteem, self-orientation to empowerment, and quality of life. The results also showed that individuals who presented themselves as relatively more recovered showed good self-esteem, high self-orientation to empowerment, and good quality of life. Recovery was found to be correlated also with the size of the social support network: people with a greater number of support persons reported higher recovery scores. These results do not tell us anything about the direction of the relationship and it is unclear whether greater support leads to a sense of recovery or more recovery leads to the perception of having greater interpersonal support.

Recovery was also found to vary significantly with psychiatric symptoms. Individuals reporting greater symptoms on the BPRS experienced less recovery. This result suggests that people endorse the recovery process when they have gained some control of the symptoms of the disease (Mueser, 2002).The process of recovery may be more challenging for persons who have more severe symptoms, especially those with symptoms of depression (Resnick et al, 2004). Finally, recovery was found to be inversely related to age. Older people with history of mental illnesses were less likely to report themselves recovered. These findings seem to contradict implications of the longitudinal research on which recovery rests (Harding, 1988); namely, rather than perceiving one's disability as diminishing with age, older people are less likely to experience recovery than their younger counterparts. The relationship between age and recovery reflects similar findings with regard to quality of life: older people are likely to rate their life as less satisfactory (Skantze et al., 1992). Skantze and colleagues concluded from their results that older persons are less likely to deny the effects of their illness and hence better able to perceive the impact of their disabilities on the course of their life. However, Corrigan points out that the correlation between age and recovery did not meet the Bonferroni criterion for significance and may represent an artifact. Future research needs to replicate these findings with larger samples and to examine the paths between the different variables. Nevertheless, findings from this research suggest that there is a network of constructs that describe recovery as a psychosocial concept.

### A Conceptual Model of Recovery

Jacobson (2001) has developed a conceptual model of recovery from mental illness. In this model recovery refers to both internal and external conditions. Internal conditions refer to the attitudes, experiences and processes of change of individuals who are recovering, while external conditions refer to the circumstances, events, policies, and practices that may facilitate recovery. Together internal and external conditions produce the process of recovery. An analysis of numerous accounts by people with mental illnesses who describe themselves as "being in recovery" suggests that the key conditions in this process are hope, empowerment, healing, and connection.

In order to develop a model faithful to the experiences of people who have recovered, Andresen (2003) conducted a review of published experiential accounts of recovery by people with schizophrenia or other serious mental illness, self-report articles on the concept of recovery, and qualitative research. Meanings of recovery used by people with mental illnesses were sought to identify a definition of recovery. Common themes identified in this literature were used to construct a conceptual model reflecting the personal experiences of people with mental illnesses. A definition of psychological recovery was described in which hope and self-determination lead to a meaningful life and a positive sense of self, whether or not mental illness is still present. Andresen proposes a five-stage model compatible with psychological recovery, which offers a way forward for attaining recovery-orientated outcomes. The five stages of the model are: moratorium, awareness, preparation, rebuilding and growth.

### Recovery as a Process

Recovery has been conceptualized as a process, as an outcome and as both. What is critical about recovery is the personal meaning that each individual attaches to the concept. Common themes of recovery are the development of self-confidence, of self-concept beyond the illness, of enjoyment of the world and of a sense of well being, hope, and optimism (Corrigan, 1999, Torgalsbøen, 2001). These subjective indicators of the recovery process can be viewed as mediating the process leading to recovery, but they are also sensitive to treatment and the nature of the therapeutic relationship. For example, realistic hope for a better future and improvement in quality of life is generally responsive to the enthusiasm and collaborative alliance embedded in the therapeutic relationship. According to Anthony (1993) recovery involves the development of new meaning and purpose in one's life as one grows beyond the catastrophic effects of mental illness. Kindling and sustaining of hope and the opportunity to grieve over their disability, to let go of earlier dreams, and to pursue other sources of gratification and self-esteem, were all therapeutic elements mentioned by the fully recovered subjects in my study (Torgalsbøen, 2001).

The concept of recovery is according to Jacobson (2001) perhaps better captured by the notion of healing, a process that has two main components: defining a self apart from illness and control. People who have psychiatric disabilities often find that they lose their selves to mental illness. Recovery is in part the process of "recovering" the self by reconceptualizing illness as only a part of the self, not as a definition of the whole. The process of self-redefinition is central to recovery (Andresen et al, 2003). For the recovered patients in our study, the continuous work that had been done cultivated their hope of getting well and gave them perspective on the illness and some ability to separate a sense of self from the illness, i.e., they saw themselves as people with schizophrenia rather than schizophrenics (Torgalsbøen, 2001). When viewing themselves as people with schizophrenia their self-respect allows them to confront and overcome the stigma against individuals with mental illness that they may have internalized, thus allowing further connection with the self.

The second healing process is *control,* that is, finding ways to relieve the symptoms of the illness or reduce the social and psychological effects of stress. For some patient medication is a successful strategy for effecting control. Another strategy is learning to reduce the occurrence and severity of symptoms and the effects of stress through self-care practices such as adopting a healthy lifestyle or using symptom monitoring and response techniques. Improvement in coping with symptoms and the stresses of daily life is another common theme of recovery, because such improvement allows people to spend less time on their symptoms and more time pursuing their goals (Mueser, 2002). Thus illness management and recovery are closely related, with illness management primarily focusing on minimizing people's symptoms and relapses and recovery primarily focusing on helping people develop and pursue their personal goals.

The word *control* has a double meaning. In one sense it refers to the outcome of managing symptoms or stress. The second meaning refers to the locus of control, or who has control. In recovery, the person has taken control by becoming an active agent in his or her own life. Control is an important factor in *empowerment,* which in its simplest sense may be understood as a corrective for the lack of control, sense of helplessness and dependency that many people develop after long-term interactions with the mental health care system. In the recovery model the aim is to have people assume more and more responsibility for themselves. That includes developing goals, working with providers to make plans for reaching these goals, taking on decision-making tasks and engaging in self-care. Andresen (2003) has pointed out that this implies that professionals must embrace the concept of the dignity of risk, and the right to failure if they are to be supportive of people with mental illnesses.

Connection captures the aspect of recovery that has to do with rejoining the social world or what some have called "getting a life." To connect is to find roles to play in the world, for instance helping others. Finding meaning in life is integral to recovery, but the source of that meaning can vary greatly between individuals, and possibly over time (Andresen, 2003).

### Towards an Operational and Comprehensive Definition of Recovery

Recovery must be defined in ways that will promote replicable research on the subject with reliable outcome measures. It is also important to disentangle the positive subjective experiences that individuals with schizophrenia have as part of the process of recovering from schizophrenia from the criteria by which people with mental illnesses, families and practitioners may judge recovery as an outcome. Being engaged in the process of recovering is a motivation for the individual to strive towards the desired outcomes. These subjective variables are important additions to the more objective measures of outcome.

Liberman and colleagues (2002) have suggested an operational definition of recovery based on a multimodal, socially normative inventory of personal assets and freedom from psychotic symptoms. This definition requires assessment of outcomes in dimensions of symptomatology, vocational functioning, independent living, and social relationships. The criteria pertain to the past 2 years of an individual's life and involve: 1) sustained remission of psychotic symptoms as measured by the Brief Psychiatric Rating Scale (Ventura et al., 1993) defined as a score of 4 (i.e., moderate) or less on key psychotic symptoms of grandiosity, suspiciousness, unusual thought content, hallucinations, conceptual disorganization, bizarre behavior, self neglect, blunted affect and emotional withdrawal, 2) full- or part-time engagement in an instrumental role activity (i.e., worker, student, volunteer) that is constructive and appropriate for culture and age, 3) living independently of supervision by family or other caregivers so that day-to-day needs such as self-administration of medication and money management are the responsibility of the individual; and 4) participating in an active friendship and/or peer social relations or otherwise involved in recreational activities that are age-appropriate and independent of professional supervision.

Compared with the inclusion criteria for full recovery used in my study, these criteria reflect the heterogeneity of outcome in schizophrenia to a greater degree. The cut off points selected for rating remission of psychotic symptoms are based on generally agreed upon definitions of "clinical significance" rather than the absence of symptoms. The definition also takes into consideration the fact that outcome is manifold and should be measured in several areas and that it is possible to maintain a high level of functioning in the presence of moderate symptoms (for instance, auditory hallucinations). In my longitudinal study where the sample was dichotomized into fully recovered and non-recovered groups, the underlying heterogeneity within the non-recovered group was hidden. For example, some of the non-recovered subjects worked full time or part time and maintained good family relationships and friends, but still had delusions or hallucinations. Others were working, but were more socially isolated, while others had satisfactory social networks, but did not work.

In my opinion, an operational and comprehensive definition of recovery as an outcome measure is not complete without including those subjective experiences most frequently reported by persons who have recovered from schizophrenia. One of the criteria for a full and satisfactory recovery from schizophrenia is consensually seen as the experience of self-esteem (van Dongen, 1996, Giffort, 1999) and good quality of life (Giffort, 1999). Therefore measures of self-esteem and quality of life should be included as outcome measures.

### Concluding Remarks

Recovery in schizophrenia is an outcome measure, a process, and a definition. Full recovery in schizophrenia must be defined as a sustained improvement in both symptoms and social/vocational functioning with high self-esteem and quality of life. Being on a low dose of medication should, in my opinion, not be seen as an exclusion criterion for full recovery. In the medical literature cardiac patients are often classified as recovered after a heart attack, despite adhering to medication, dietary, and exercise regimens (Liberman et al., 2002). Why should we put stricter demands on the criteria for recovery in schizophrenia?

### References

American Psychiatric Association (1994). *Diagnostic and statistical manual of mental disorders, 4th ed, rev.* Washington: Author.

Andresen, R., Oades, L., & Caputi, P. (2003). The experience of recovery from schizophrenia: Towards an empirically validated stage model. *Australian and New Zealand Journal of Psychiatry, 37,* 586–594.

Anthony, W. A. (1993). Recovery from mental illness: the guiding vision of the mental health service system in the 1990s. *Psychosocial Rehabilitation Journal, 16,* 11–23.

Arieti, S. (1974). *Interpretation of schizophrenia.* New York: Basic Books Inc.

Bleuler, E. (1908). Die prognose der dementia praecox (schizophrenien gruppe). *Allgemeine Zeitschrift Psychiatrie, 65,* 436.

Bleuler, E. (1950). *Dementia praecox or the group of schizophrenias (translated by J. Zinkin).* New York: International University Press.

Bonnano, G. A., Papa, A. & O'Neill, K. (2001). Loss and human resilience. *Applied and Preventive Psychology, 10,* 193–206.

Bonnano, G.A: (2004): Loss, Trauma and Human resilience: Have we underestimated the human capacity to thrive after extremely aversive events? *American Psychologist, 59,* 20–28.

Carpenter, W. & Strauss, J. S. (1991). The prediction of outcome in schizophrenia. IV. Eleven-year follow-up of the Washington IPSS cohort. *Journal of Nervous and Mental Disease, 179,* 517–525.

Corrigan, P. W., Giffort, D., Rashid, F., Leary., M & Okeke, I. (1999). Recovery as a psychological construct. *Community Mental Health Journal, 35,* 231–239.

Corrigan, P. W., Green, M. F., & Toomey, R. (1994). Cognitive correlates to social cue perception in schizophrenia. *Psychiatric Research 53,* 141–151.

Deegan, P. (1997). Recovery and empowerment for people with psychiatric disabilities. *Social Work in Health Care, 25,* 11–24.

Giffort, D., Schmook, A., Woody, C., Vollendorf, C., & Gervain, M. (1999). Construction of a scale to measure consumer recovery. *Psychiatric Rehabilitation Skills.*

Green, M. F. (1998). *Schizophrenia from a neurocognitive perspective: Probing the impenetrable darkness.* Boston: Allyn and Bacon.

Harding, C. M., Brooks, G. W., Ashikaga, T., Strauss, J. S., & Breier, A. (1987a). The Vermont longitudinal study of persons with severe mental illness. I: Methodology, study sample and overall status 32 years later. *American Journal of Psychiatry, 144,* 718–726.

Harding, C. M., Brooks, G. W., Ashikaga, T., Strauss, J., & Breier, A. (1987b). The Vermont longitudinal study of persons with severe mental illness .II: Long-term outcome of subjects who retrospectively met DSM-III criteria for schizophrenia. *American Journal of Psychiatry, 144,* 727–735.

Harding, C. M. (1994). An examination of the complexities in the measurement of recovery in severe psychiatric disorders. In *Schizophrenia: Exploring the spectrum of psychosis.* Edited by R. Ancill. John Wiley & Sons Ltd.

Harrow, M., Sands, J. R., Silverstein, M. L., et al. (1997). Course and outcome for schizophrenia versus other psychotic patients: a longitudinal study. *Schizophrenia Bulletin, 23,* 287–303.

Hegarty, J. D., Baldessarini, R. J., Tohen, M., Waternaux, C., & Oepen, G. (1994). One hundred years of schizophrenia: A meta-analysis of the outcome literature. *American Journal of Psychiatry, 151,* 1409–1416.

Hoff, A. L., Sakuma, M., Razi, K., Heydenbrand, G., Csernansky, J. G., DeLisi, L. E. (2000). Lack of association between duration of untreated illness and severity of cognitive and structural brain deficits at the first episode of schizophrenia. *American Journal of Psychiatry, 157,* 1824–1828.

Jacobson, N., & Greenley, D. (2001). What is recovery? A conceptual model and explication. *Psychiatric Services, 52,* 482–485.

Jonsson, H., & Nyman, A. K. (1991). Predicting long-term outcome in schizophrenia. *Acta Psychiatrica Scandinavica, 83,* 342–346.

Lehman, A. F. (1983a). The well-being of chronic mental patients. *Archives of General Psychiatry, 40,* 369–373.

Liberman, R. P., Kopelowicz, A., Ventura, J., & Gutkind, D. (2002). Operational criteria and factors related to recovery from schizophrenia. *International Review of Psychiatry, 14,* 256–272.

Lukoff, D., Liberman, R. P., & Nuechterlein, K. H. (1986). Manual for the expanded Brief Psychiatric Rating Scale (BPRS). *Schizophrenia Bulletin, 12,* 594–602.

Lysaker, P. H., Bell, M. D., Zito, W. S., & Bioty, S. M. (1995). Social skills at work: Deficits and predictors of improvement in schizophrenia. *Journal of Nervous and Mental Disease, 183,* 688–692.

Marengo, J. ( 1994). Classifying the course of schizophrenia. *Schizophrenia Bulletin, 20,* 519–536.

Mason, P., Harrison, G., Glazerbrook, Medley, I., Dalkin, T., & Croudace, T. (1995). Characteristics of outcome in schizophrenia at 13 years. *British Journal of Psychiatry, 167,* 596–603.

Modestin, J., Huber, A., Satirli,E., Malti,T. & Hell, D. (2003). Long- term course of schizophrenic illness: Bleuler´s study reconsidered. *American Journal of Psychiatry, 160,* 2202–2208.

Mosher, L R,, & Bola, J. R. (2002). The Soteria Project: 25 years of swimming upriver. In T. Scrimali & L. Grimaldi (Eds.) *Cognitive psychotherapy: Toward a new millennium* (pp. 247-253). New York: Kluwer Academic/Plenum Publishers.

Mueser, K. T., Corrigan, P. W., Hilton, D. W, Tanzman, B., Schaub, A,, Gingerich, S., Essock, S. M., Tarrier, N., Morey, B., Vogel-Scibilia, S., & Herz, M. I. (2002). Illness management and recovery: a review of the research. *Psychiatric Service, 53,* 1272–1284.

Nasar..S. (1998). *A beautiful mind.* New York: Simon & Schuster.

Norman, R. M. G., Townsend, L., Malla, A. K (2001).Duration of untreated psychosis and cognitive functioning in first-episode patients. *British Journal of Psychiatry, 179,* 340–345.

Rosenberg, M. (1965). *Society and the adolescent self image.* Princeton, NJ: Princeton University Press.

Rogers, E. S., Chamberlin, J., Ellison, M. L., & Crean, T. (1997). A consumer- constructed scale to measure empowerment among users of mental health services. *Psychiatric Services, 48,* 1042–1047.

Resnick, S. G, Rosenheck, R. A., & Lehman, A. F. (2004). An exploratory analysis of correlates of recovery. *Psychiatric Services, 55,* 540–547.

Rund, B. R. (1990). Fully recovered schizophrenics: A retrospective study of some premorbid and treatment factors. *Psychiatry, 53,* 127–139.

Rund, B. R., Melle, I., Friis, S., Larsen, T. K., Midbøe, L. J., Opjordsmoen, S., Simonsen, E., Vaglum, P., & McGlashan, T. (2004). Neurocognitive dysfunction in first-episode psychosis: Correlates with symptoms, premorbid adjustment and duration of untreated psychosis. *American Journal of Psychiatry, 161,* 466–472.

Ryff, C. D., & Keyes, C. L. M. (1995). The structure of psychological well-being revisited. *Journal of Personality and Social Psychology, 69,* 719–727.

Sarason, I. G., Levine, H. M., Basham, R. B., & Sarason, B. R. (1983). Assessing social support: The Social Support Questionnaire. *Journal of Personality and Social Psychology, 44,* 127–139.

Shapiro, R., & Shader, R. (1979). Selective review of results of previous follow-up studies of schizophrenia and other psychoses. In *Schizophrenia: An international follow-up study.* World Health Organization. New York: John Wiley & Sons.

Skantze, K., Malm, U., Dencker, S. J., May, P. R., & Corrigan, P. W. (1992). Comparison of quality of life with standard of living in schizophrenic outpatients. *British Journal of Psychiatry, 161,* 797–801.

Strauss, J. S., & Carpenter, W. T. (1974). The prediction of outcome in schizophrenia: II. Relationships between predictor and outcome variables: A report from the Who International Pilot Study of Schizophrenia. *Archives of General Psychiatry, 31,* 37–42.

Torgalsbøen, A. K., & Rund, B. R. (1998). "Full recovery" in schizophrenia in the long term. A ten-year follow-up of eight former schizophrenic patients. *Psychiatry, 61,* 20–34.

Torgalsbøen, A. K. (1999). Full recovery from schizophrenia: the prognostic role of premorbid adjustment, symptoms at first admission, precipitating events and gender. *Psychiatry Research, 88,* 143–152.

Torgalsbøen, A. K. (2001). Consumer satisfaction and attributions of improvement among fully recovered schizophrenics. *Scandinavian Journal of Psychology, 42,* 33–40.

Torgalsbøen, A. K., & Rund, B. R. (2002): Lessons learned from three studies of recovery from schizophrenia. *International Review of Psychiatry, (14)*4, 312–317.

Ventura, J., Green, M. F., Shaner, A., & Liberman, R. P. (1993). Training and quality assurance in the use of the Expanded Brief psychiatric Rating Scale: the "drift busters." *Journal of Methods in Psychiatric Research, 3,* 221–244.

van Dongen, C. J. (1996). Quality of life and self-esteem in working and nonworking persons with mental illness. *Community Mental Health Journal, 32,* 535–548.

# The Low Turning Point: A Control Mechanism in the Course of Mental Disorder

*Jaak Rakfeldt and John S. Strauss*

At the time of original publication, Jaak Rakfeldt, PhD, and John S. Strauss, MD, were affiliated with Yale University School of Medicine, Department of Psychiatry, New Haven, CT.

This article was originally published in *The Journal of Nervous and Mental Disorders*, *1989*, 177(1), 32-37, and is published with permission.

**Abstract:** Recent research has suggested that persons with severe mental disorders may have psychological control mechanisms that influence the course of their disorders. One mechanism that appears to be particularly significant is the low turning point. Based on data obtained as part of an intensive follow-along study, the low turning point process is described in this report. It is identified as involving three phases: a) an initial rigid focus on one coping mechanism for dealing with stress; b) relinquishing of that focus and decompensation; and c) reorganizing one's life more broadly. The functioning that emerges from this experience often appears to be more adaptive than that existing before its onset. Conceptual implications of this process are discussed.

By understanding the course of severe mental disorders, we may learn much regarding the nature of these maladies and optimize treatment interventions. In a number of longitudinal studies, several investigators have suggested that one factor influencing the course of a disorder may be the patients' psychological control mechanisms that are used to influence their symptoms and their lives generally (Breier & Strauss, 1983; Cohen & Berk, 1985; Falloon & Talbot, 1981; Gunderson, 1987; McCandless-Glimcher et al., 1986; Strauss, 1986; Strauss et al., 1985).

Self-reports by former patients are consistent with theories stating that control mechanisms are important. For example, Marcia Lovejoy describes the emergence of an ability to control her illness as follows: "Attitude was the greatest struggle and, in the long run, I believe the most important....I wanted to have hope, and I wanted to believe I could live a life in control of my problems...that at this time my life is not out of control and I practice health" (Lovejoy, 1984). Likewise, a "recovering patient" describes his control mechanism: "I had a very strong observing ego, and I was fascinated and encouraged to think of my mind having that power to step away from the craziness, to look at it and understand it" (Anonymous, 1986). It is important to pursue an understanding of these control mechanisms further to clarify the role they may have in the course of mental disorder.

One important example of a control mechanism may be a process we call the low turning point, an experience often described by mental patients. It involves three phases: a) an initial rigid focus on one aspect of dealing with life, b) decompensation and relinquishing this focus that may have worked well in the past but, ironically, may have become a source of difficulty, and c) reorganizing one's life more broadly. As one subject diagnosed by DSM-III criteria as having schizoaffective disorder put it, "It's not that things have magically changed. Instead, I am much more mature about dealing and coping with everything. I was up against a brick wall. I had to change." She stressed that, during this process, after a downhill phase in her course, a major shift in her pattern of functioning occurred. She gave up her single-minded effort to succeed in her work. Previously, she said, "I had to have something of value to clutch; I couldn't think about anything else." She described how giving up this extremely focused direction—letting go of it and actually feeling worse before she began reorganizing her life—had helped her overcome her symptoms and attain new higher levels of functioning.

In this report, we will describe the study that suggested the existence of this process. We present material gathered from audiotaped interviews with two persons suffering from severe mental disorder who described the low turning point in detail. And finally, we suggest possible origins and implications of this mechanism.

**METHOD**

Data in this report were gathered in an intensive follow-along study of psychiatric patients (Strauss et al., 1985). The subjects ($N = 28$) were between the ages of 20 and 55 (mean = 29.8) who had been hospitalized for functional psychiatric disorders. Subject characteristics are shown in Table 1.

Interviews had been obtained during the hospitalization period in order to collect clinical, personal, and demographic data. Following discharge, the informants were interviewed bimonthly for 1 year and once again at 2 years. The focus of data collection was a wide variety of issues related to the patients' experiences, including symptoms, treatment, social relationships, employment, and their active roles, if any, in the course of their own disorders. Extensive ratings were made and narrative summaries of each interview were dictated and transcribed. This method of sequential interviews reduced problems inherent in single retrospective accounts covering longer periods, since subjects' unfolding experiences were reported shortly after they occurred (Strauss et al., 1985).

For this report, the written research data on the subjects and selected interview tapes were reviewed by (J. R.) to collect information relevant to the low turning point mechanism.

**Table 1: Subject Characteristics (N=28)**

| | |
|---|---|
| Sex | |
|     Female | 16 |
|     Male | 12 |
| Age | |
|     Mean | 29.8 |
|     Range | 20–55 |
| Marital Status | |
|     Married | 4 |
|     Divorced | 4 |
|     Separated | 2 |
|     Single | 18 |
| Diagnosis | |
|     Schizoaffective | 7 |
|     Major depression | 6 |
|     Bipolar disorder | 8 |
|     Schizophrenia | 5 |
|     Dysthymic disorder | 1 |
|     Atypical depression | 1 |
| Hollingshead-Redlich | |
|     Scale of Social Class | |
|     Mean | 3.5 (III) |
|     Range | I–V |

**RESULTS**

Several subjects described experiences with characteristics related to the low turning point phenomenon. Over the course of the various interviews, one patient in particular described the mechanism in its entirety.

**Case 1**

Karen M. (her name and other identifying information have been changed) is a 27-year-old, single woman who had worked in the fields of advertising and insurance. She had been diagnosed by DSM-III criteria as having bipolar disorder, mixed type, had been hospitalized for her illness on one previous occasion..

*Phase 1: Initial rigid focus on one way of dealing with life.* Karen M. began feeling depressed approximately 1 year before her hospital admission. She described the onset as follows:

> When I am depressed, I have trouble with memory. I only remember about half as much of the day-to-day things as I normally would. I also

have a lot of trouble remembering things that happened m the past. I have trouble conjuring up details or pictures of events or happenings, incidents that you might want to tell friends about. That frightens me because I'm afraid that I'm not going to be able to learn new things. And I don't have my past experience to draw upon, to talk to people about, and to share with people the interests that I have.

Work helps in the sense that it keeps you from thinking about problems. Before I became deeply depressed, there were things that were bothering me. But by going to work the next day, I was able to take my mind off the problems. I was forced to concentrate on something else. However, as I got worse, it was hard to pull my concentration away. When I had the advertising business and the insurance job, that was great because, if I had problems with the insurance, for example, I could go home and work on advertising and forget my problems at insurance, and vise versa. The only thing is that I became so involved in my work that I wasn't pursuing my interests in other things or cultivating friendships.

Beyond her increasing focus on work, Karen also became more focused and rigid cognitively. For example, she had attempted to come to terms with her disorder by attributing it solely to biological origins and denying any inherent problems in her ways of dealing with the world. Certainly, biological factors could have had a role in her difficulties. However, she apparently used her rigidly held conviction to prevent her from being open to solving life problems in alternative and more creative ways: "I think the whole disorder has something to do with my arousal system. I think that prior to my illness, my arousal system was diminished; perhaps the chemical balance in that section of my brain had changed." Thus, both in her work and in how she used her explanation of the disorder, Karen's solutions, like a Faustian "pact with the devil," became her problem. Although it protected her in some ways, the narrow, rigid focus actually prevented her from modifying her coping efforts. Thus, over the long run, it kept her from developing a wider range of coping strategies that might have helped her deal with or prevent the recurrence of her symptoms.

Although not found in all of our instances of the low turning point for Karen the narrowness and rigidity of focus in dealing with life seemed to have a long history. Closely related to her focus on work was her striving for perfection. This had always been an important issue for Karen, who had graduated at the top of her high school class. Her need for perfection seemed to be accompanied by fears about achieving success. She had experienced past successes as alienating her from others. In fact, she became more vulnerable to manic episodes and depression during periods of success or near success.

After the increasing narrowness and rigidity, the next step in the low turning point involves relinquishing this focus, often during a period of decompensation. Karen gave up her rigid way of dealing with life during this experience. Specifically, she relinquished her need to be perfect and her excessive focus on work, which was her monolithic explanation for her disorder and its course.

*Phase 2: Decompensation and relinquishing the rigid focus.* As Karen became depressed, she felt overcome by feelings of worthlessness and despair. In addition, she lost confidence and felt distanced from others at work. She became tearful and began spending more time in bed, ceasing to care for herself. Karen slept poorly, lost her appetite, and had recurring suicidal thoughts:

> I lost interest in things, even the things that I liked to do. As a result, I got to a point where there wasn't anything I wanted to do. And I was feeling bad about myself. I felt as if there were nothing to me—that I didn't have any interests—I didn't have anything to share. I felt that; I didn't really know anything well—that I didn't have anything to bring to situations. I didn't feel that there was much to me. And I began to feel depressed about that—that there was no substance to me.

Her demoralization reached the point that she stopped working. At the same time, she became discouraged with outpatient psychotherapy. Shortly after a suicide attempt, she was hospitalized. During this phase, Karen gave up her focus on work and her rigid cognitive orientation.

*Phase 3. Reorganizing one's life.* While in the depth of depression, several things began to happen to Karen. During the period of varying symptoms, she began to view herself in a more complex way. She recognized that she had problems she had to deal with, but also that she had strengths. She began to develop the ability to monitor her symptom cycles and to notice when she was about to enter one. This new awareness represented an important sense of control for her. She also emphasized that hope had been generated by the reaction that other people who had had similar problems were now quite successful. Karen now felt comfortable being more open about her disorder. This led to greater closeness with others. She also described the importance of relationships with others as a means of supplying feedback and of helping her maintain perspective.

As her depression lifted, Karen noted that friends had stood by her during her difficulties. They apparently realized that she was having emotional problems; she reported that in some instances people were even friendlier toward her now that she had problems. It appeared that they no longer perceived her as being as superior (due to her academic successes) as she had once been.

Interviewer: You mentioned before how, when you were in high school, people had a very high idea of what you were like; you were held up on a pedestal. What you are saying now is that you are cutting through this by sharing your idiosyncrasies and your less-than-perfect aspects with others. Is this important for you?

Karen: Yes. I've found people who are similar to me, with whom I really feel comfortable. I feel that I'm on the same plane as they are. In high school, there was a distance created because I did so well in school. And that created all sorts of problems, because my parents would say [to siblings and others],"Why don't you do well like Karen?" And then the others would say, "She's a goody-two-shoes. She always does well."

In the follow-up interview, Karen stated that now "things fit into place better" and that she felt more "on center" with her life. She now monitored her previously compulsive tendency to please others, which had left her "run down" and seemed to have contributed to her symptoms. Karen spontaneously described how each of her episodes of disorder had been followed by a "quantum leap" in her general maturity level. She noted that she now had a much more "three-dimensional view of the world" and a better understanding of herself. She added, "I wouldn't recommend mental illness," but stated that for her it had had a positive effect. In terms of a realignment of the pattern of her relationships, Karen reported that she now related better to others. This perception enhanced her self-esteem. The ability to relate well to others, coupled with her not needing to feel so superior, made her relationships more meaningful and more human. In addition, her situation with her family had improved considerably.

Before her low turning point experience, Karen often became symptomatic when faced with a new job or difficult relationships. After the experience, she developed the ability to express anger more openly and to manage the societal demands that her career and relationships placed on her.

### Case 2

The low turning point process, in spite of its rather characteristic pattern, transcends diagnostic categories. This is reflected in the second subject, Norman S. (pseudonym), a 19-year-old male with the diagnosis of schizophrenia, paranoid type. He too described experiencing the three phases of the low turning point. He suggested further that the increasingly rigid exaggerated focus may not be merely a difficulty, but a necessary part of the process of making a shift in how one deals with a life problem.

*Phase 1: Initial rigidly held focus on one way of dealing with life.* After several years of feeling very unsure of himself and being unclear regarding what was important to him, Norman graduated from high school and went to college.

When I went on to college, I studied with a rather brilliant man. When I talked with him I would go on and on about philosophy in a somewhat theoretical way. So it was easy for me to get lost in the clouds. I think that he helped me get further and further distracted from reality. At the same time there was nothing I could really do about it. I was wearing myself down to the bone—sort of trying to make something out of myself. But, I was doing it in a very artificial way. I thought that the only way to be a worthwhile person was by proving that I was some sort of a genius, or something. So I would do a lot of studying. And at the same time I had a lot of other interests. In high school I had been reading a lot of linguistics —psycholinguistics, semantics, and all that kind of stuff. So I had been mixing a lot of stuff together all at once. But one of the worse things that I ever did was to get into philosophy. I borrowed a lot from Kierkegaard. Existential philosophy is one of the easiest ways to get lost (laughs). It was like a fight for life. I just felt I had to do this. Much earlier in my life I had struggled with a strange feeling of being Christ-like or something. It's possible that I was intellectualizing everything to overcome this artificial, superficial type of thing that had been impressed upon me by my religion. It was like trying to prove to myself that I was a worthwhile person, beyond my faults. I knew I was getting into trouble with it; but I felt I had no other option. I wanted to consider myself a worthwhile person. I did this to compensate.

*Phase 2: Decompensation and relinquishing the rigid focus.* As he became more and more involved with philosophy, Norman felt increasingly unreal and unable to contact people around him. He became cognitively disorganized, experienced severe depersonalization, developed delusions of reference, and attempted suicide. This process also involved his giving up his narrow focus.

Norman described how his compensatory intellectualizing had led him to feel that he lived a "false life." He felt that periods of impulsiveness released the internal pressure generated by this inauthenticity.

The impulsiveness is a release from this pressure that I feel inside myself. The stress involves knowing that I'm basically living a false life. What happens is that I get totally absorbed and then I fall apart. Sooner or later I start taking my false premises to be true, because I have been living with them for so long. Unfortunately, the tragic thing in my life is that going to school was helpful because of how I hurt myself. It was a necessary evil in my life—that I had to live out this artificial thing to the point where I didn't want it anymore. That's a large part of my psychiatric problem. I had to get this out of the way before I could do anything else. I had to burn myself out until I had nothing left anymore. Essentially that's what I did to myself.

*Phase 3: Reorganizing one's life.* After Norman was hospitalized with psychotic symptoms for several months, he took a leave of absence from college. During the research interviews, toward the end of his hospitalization, he said:

I'm no longer living with a false self. I feel that I know a lot of things now, but they're all mixed together. It's difficult. It's probably an ego problem or something. Before, I couldn't believe in myself if I wasn't held up as being at the top. Now, I'm not sure if that's so important.

Norman's course reflected the low turning point process and left him more able to accept confusion and uncertainty.

### DISCUSSION

The above data describe a three-phase sequence that seems to reflect an important pattern in the course of disorder for many subjects. The pattern involves: a) an initial rigid focus on one way of dealing with life (e.g., working, obsession with philosophy). This is followed by b) relinquishing of the rigid focus and decompensation. This decompensation, paradoxically, leads c) to a reorganization and more diverse modes of dealing with life situations.

The sequence begins with increasingly maladaptive coping. The first phase involves a desperate effort to deal with stressors. This effort leads to increasing tension and frustration which contributes in turn to more rigidity, and also to sacrifice of alternatives which leads to more tension. This positive feedback system ends in decompensation. This involves dysfunction, symptoms, and disorganization, which among other things is accompanied by breaking the rigid focus. At the bottom of the decompensation, persons sometimes begin to reorganize their attitudes and approaches to life. This often includes developing a greater ability to observe themselves. This attitude, in other contexts termed metacognition (Brown, 1978; Flavell, 1979), involves the ability for self-reflection and also implies the ability to assume the roles of others, thus requiring a realignment of self-other relationships. In fact, a consistent theme of subjects in this study is that after the bottoming-out of their illness and during the hospitalization, they were able to develop more nurturing, reciprocal relationships with others. The subjects appear to become more available, and those around them, more caring.

The low turning point experience was the pattern by which these changes took place. Moreover, the improvement appeared to be relatively enduring. Both Karen and Norman were doing quite well at 2-year and l-year (the last completed so far) follow-up interviews respectively. However, other patterns following decompensation are also possible. For some patients, decompensation appears to be a prelude to further decline in functioning and to chronicity. Following decompensation, still other patients undergo periods in which not much change in either direction is evident. For such persons, it is not clear why the turning point improvement does not take place. In certain instances, it appears that for some reason the reorganization fails to occur. Clearly, this issue is crucial and requires further study.

The low turning point may be an example of a group of phenomena discussed elsewhere, termed control mechanisms, that regulate and modify the course of disorder (Lieberman and Strauss, 1986, Strauss, 1986). The low turning point is a pattern that we had not previously observed. As we learn more about this phenomenon, we will elaborate its relationship to the other patterns observed by our group (Strauss et al., 1985). With our limited sample, we cannot estimate the frequency of the low turning point phenomenon. It does not appear to be rare, however nor does it appear to be related to the patient's prior degree of chronicity. This control mechanism may be either conscious or unconscious. It may, depending upon the circumstances, be more or less under a patient's voluntary control.

One way of understanding such control mechanisms is described in the cybernetics literature (Bateson, 1972). Cybernetics is the process of regulating and controlling the self (and events) to adapt to the environment, both internal and external. This regulation can be aimed at maintaining certain states or at implementing change. Both Karen and Norman had allowed one aspect of their life situations to dominate the others. Through the low turning point, an unfreezing of attitude and behavior occurred in which they realigned the components of their lives in a more balanced fashion.

In addition to the processes of regulation that the low turning point reflects, it also provides a glimpse at the phenomenon of change in the course of disorder and recovery. The changes seen in the low turning point may perhaps be understood, at least metaphorically, in terms of principles from the field of biochemistry advanced by Prigogine and the Brussels School, dealing with self-organizing systems (Brent, 1978). Prigogine's notion involves negentropy within open-linked systems in which energy may spill in both directions across independent, yet linked systems. After their catastrophic plummeting, Karen and Norman experienced renewed vitality for change. It was as though the energy they had previously channeled into maintaining their rigidity was now released and available to them. This freed energy allowed them novel opportunities for an active, more adaptive, interchange and involvement with their environment.

Finally, beyond regulation and energy, the low turning point may also reflect a crucial choice point for the person that is similar to the notion of Kairos (or crisis) from Hippocratic medicine. Such a choice point is also noted in one interpretation of crisis in psychoanalytic theory (Menninger, 1963). Perhaps the low turning point involves a crisis in the sense that patients during this process experience emotionally charged moments that involve a delicate and tenuous balance of forces. They are then called upon to add their weight to this balance in order to determine the direction their lives will take. One way they may do this is to surrender their previously faulty control to the goals and needs of their broader range of interests and attachments.

## CONCLUSIONS

By understanding psychological control mechanisms used by patients during the course of their illness, some of the complexities of these disorders may be elucidated. More efficacious treatments may also be identified. We have described one such process in this report. During the low turning point, patients use (either consciously or unconsciously) this bottoming-out experience to realign important components of their lives. These changes often lead to more adaptive functioning. Since more effective coping and greater adaptation are vital concerns to patients, clinicians, and researchers, the study of such psychological control mechanisms is an essential area for further research.

Acknowledgments

This report has been supported by an NIMH Postdoctoral Fellowship (MH17122) for Dr. Rakfeldt. In addition, partial support has been provided by National Institute of Mental Health Grants MH00340 and MH3436B, as well as by an award from the Scottish Rite Program. The authors also appreciate the help of Francine Wynn; Drs. Paul Lieberman, Courtenay Harding, and Hisham Hafez.

### REFERENCES

Anonymous (1986). "Can we talk?" The schizophrenic patient in psychotherapy. *American Journal of Psychiatry, 143,* 68–70.

Bateson, G. (1972). *Steps to an ecology of mind.* New York: Ballantine.

Breier, A, & Strauss J. S. (1983). Self-control in psychotic disorders. *Archives of General Psychiatry, 40,* 1141–1146.

Brent, S. B. (1978). Prigogine's model for self-organization in non-equilibrium systems: Its relevance for developmental psychology. *Human Development, 21,* 374–387.

Brown, A. L. (1978). Knowing when, where; and how to remember: A problem of metacognition. In R. Glaser (Ed), *Advances in instructional psychology.* Hillsdale, NJ: Erlbaum.

Cohen, C. I., & Berk, L.A. (1985) Personal coping styles of schizophrenic outpatients. *Hospital and Community Psychiatry, 36,* 407–410.

Falloon, I. R., & Talbot, R. E. (1981). Persistent auditory hallucinations: Coping mechanisms and implications for management. *Psychological Medicine, 11*, 329–339.

Flavell, J. H. (1979). Metacognition and cognitive monitoring: A new area of cognitive-development inquiry. *American Psychologist, 36*, 906–911.

Gunderson, J. G. (1987). *Relation of change to intervention for borderlines.* Paper presented at APA annual meeting, Chicago.

Hafner, H., Gattaz, W. F., & Janzarik, W. (Eds). *In search of the causes of schizophrenia.* Berlin and Heidelberg: Springer Verlag.

Lieberman, P. B., & Strauss, J. S. (1986). Brief psychiatric hospitalization: What are its effects? *American Journal of Psychiatry, 143*, 1557–1562.

Lovejoy, M. (1984). Recovery from schizophrenia: A personal odyssey. *Hospital and Community Psychiatry, 35*, 809–812.

McCandless-Glimcher, L, McKnight, S., Hamera, E., et al. (1986). Use of symptoms by schizophrenics to monitor and regulate their illness. *Hospital and Community Psychiatry, 37*, 929–933.

Menninger, K. (1963). *The vital balance.* New York: Viking.

Strauss, J. S. (1986). Processes of healing and chronicity in schizophrenia. In *Search for the cause of schizophrenia: Proceedings of the symposium celebrating the 600th anniversary of the University of Heidelberg* (September 24–26).

Strauss, J. S., Hafez, H., Lieberman, P., & Harding, C. M. (1985). The course of psychiatric disorder: III. Longitudinal principles. *American Journal of Psychiatry, 142*, 289–296.

# It Is the Springtime of My Life

*Bonnie J. Twomey*

At the time of original publication, the following affiliation was cited for the author. Bonnie J. Twomey is a graduate of Northeastern University. She is active in the mental health field, and is currently writing her autobiography. She works for the Massachusetts Association for Mental Health, lobbying the legislature for consumer residential services.

This article originally appeared in the *Psychiatric Rehabilitation Journal,* 1999, 22(3), 305–306 and is reprinted with permission.

My first experience with the mental health system was discouraging to say the least. My psychiatrist gave me no hope for recovery. She blatantly told me I would "never feel good about myself, never have normal relationships and will never be able to return to work."

My family and I were not referred to any outside agencies, family groups, or advocacy agencies. We were basically left on our own. I received no constructive feedback on issues relating to schizophrenia or how to deal with my emotional struggles. I received no help on how to deal with my losses.

After years of unproductive therapy, I gained a new sense of learning how to use it to my benefit. I began to pinpoint stressors, which made my therapy sessions more productive. The first therapist I felt comfortable with gave me advice that will stay with me for a lifetime. She had told me to stop analyzing and that I needed to start to learn how to comfort myself. She gave me constructive feedback the way I needed and which felt comfortable. This was the beginning of receiving good therapy and being able to deal with issues constructively.

My current therapist is good. She seems to be sincere most of the time. She has shown excitement at some of my accomplishments, and has given me ideas on social activities relating to my interests. My recovery process has been faster and more painless when I have genuine support and caring. When I receive support from my therapist I feel in a "safe place."

It took many, many years to settle within myself that what I needed most of all was to find what makes me happy. My family is important, but I need to take care of myself. I overlook the desire to please others and turn to take care of myself.

I learned to accept my illness and began to learn how to accept living with it. The darkness I feel is incredible. The depression and levels of stress are difficult to manage. I have learned throughout the years to pinpoint what makes me depressed or stressed and to deal with whatever is bothering me head-on. If I do not have an answer, I take it easy, relax, try to have some fun, and deal with it in therapy. Some parts of my life will never be easy, but somehow I've settled with knowing I will always suffer at times. I know I will continue to fight, and love life again the way I feel comfortable with. This is the gift I gave to myself for all the years I had punished myself. I had no choice but to begin to love life again.

There are many ways I needed to rethink and redirect my energies in every stage of my life. With my disability, dealing with everyday ups and downs is extremely difficult. There are times I will go to the lake down the road and walk, reflect, make decisions, and sometimes sketch.

It took many years to find myself using and putting into practice good coping skills. I find exercising helps and I have a great feeling when I leave the gym. I can feel the tension lift off my shoulders when I have a good work-out. I learned that keeping busy often helps keep my mind off myself. My faith is my major source of strength. It is very personal for me, but it is so important I would not know what to do without my faith. I try to keep a positive outlook on life. I am generally positive, although I can distort reality and feel as though I have nothing. Most of the time I just do not know how I cope. Many of my skills are innate, and some are learned.

I first realized I deserved no blame for my illness in the fall of 1997. Through educating myself, I realized I was unfortunate to have a brain disorder, which could have occurred at any time in my life. I always thought I had played a role in causing my disability. The blame is indescribable. It is disabling in itself. The pain that was inside me was so ingrained that my body reeked of pain and sadness as I learned I was never to be blamed for this tragedy. It was fate. I would look to the past. What did I do wrong? Could I have changed my destiny? The answer is no.

I began to deal with the guilt. I learned how to take care of myself. I would take time in the morning to reflect on the day ahead, and to relax and enjoy life again to its fullest. My anger subsided and a new appreciation for my family and friends, even strangers, began to emerge. I realized not everyone is bad. I'm not bad. My family is not bad. We are dealt a heavy hand, and we are not alone.

My recovery took a long time to evolve. I learned who I am with and without the illness. I gained enough insight to tell others just enough to let them know I'm not all with it today. My expectations would be put in priority and whatever I accomplished, however small, would be enough. At the end of the day I would feel proud and still easy on myself.

When I lessened stressors in my life, I had a tendency to put more stressors on. Sound crazy? Learning that I can reduce stressors I put on myself is also learning I have some control in my life. I have learned when to stop.

Nobody will take better care of myself than me. It seems impossible at times because I want so much to live a normal life. Yet I expect myself to have normal, realistic goals.

"Living a normal life." That phrase sounds so profound to me. The hardest part of recovery is that we have learned not to know what to expect from ourselves due to a mental illness. Yeah, take a couple of aspirin and take a nap for the rest of your life. What is so sad is that your illness never goes away, yet you can learn to function with it. It hurts. The truth hurts.

I find that part time work seems to be just enough at this stage in my life. It is difficult for me to work full time and to live independently. I still wish to return to a job that will sustain independent living, and that will keep me happy.

Currently, I am working with a consumer advocacy agency. I have been blessed with great co-workers and a great supervisor. They are aware of my disability and are extremely supportive. After having experienced so many unthankful jobs, my position and the support I have received made me realize there are good people out there who care. It makes a world of difference. My outlook on life has changed over the years. I am more realistic. I still love my childish, positive side with a sense of humor. Although I feel hurt by life I still have a passion to help others, and to be around people. I need to be with people. I began to listen to my heart again.

# Introduction to Chapter 3

*Larry Davidson*

In this chapter we begin to explore the range of interventions that have been found to promote recovery in people with serious mental illnesses. Some readers may wonder why we have chosen to present articles on psychiatric rehabilitation and community integration first, to be followed in the next chapter (in Volume 2) by articles on treatment and case management. This order reverses what most would consider the usual order of these various components of care. Conventional practice assumes that active treatment is the first response to illness onset, to be followed, if needed, by assistance with basic needs and referrals to other services and supports through case management. Psychiatric rehabilitation and other interventions focused on community integration (i.e., those "other services") often are considered ancillary to these "core" clinical services, and may be reserved for people who have already benefited from treatment and shown considerable improvement in terms of their symptoms or other deficits. It unfortunately is not uncommon for clinicians or case managers to respond to clients' wishes to return to work or school, or to live in their own apartment, by indicating that they are not yet ready for such steps in their recovery and need to become more clinically stable first. We suggest, however, that this approach is based on a fundamental misunderstanding of the role of rehabilitation and community supports in the lives of people with serious mental illnesses. It is for this reason that we have placed this chapter first in the text.

What sense does it make, as Bill Anthony has often asked, to assert that someone is "too psychotic" to benefit from rehabilitation or supports? This would be on the same order as suggesting that someone was too blind to learn Braille or too deaf to learn sign language. For those people for whom a mental illness has become an enduring disability—in other words, for those who have not yet achieved recovery in the sense described in the previous two chapters—it is unreasonable, if not unethical, for us to ask them to wait until their psychiatric condition improves for them to pursue their interests and aspirations. In these cases, inclusion in community life through the provision of supports appears to provide a foundation for recovery rather than to be its reward. This shift in perspective is captured well in Marrone and Golowka's contribution to this chapter. Surveys of people with mental illnesses consistently have reported that 70% would like to work. In the past, however, many of them have been discouraged from seeking employment, both by mental health providers and by their families, due to the concern that work will be "stressful" and therefore will precipitate a relapse, lead to rehospitalization, or contribute in other ways to a deterioration in the person's condition. But as Marrone and Golowka pointedly ask: "If work makes people with mental illness sick, what do unemployment, poverty, and social isolation cause?"

In this chapter, we include several contributions that address this concern, demonstrating that vocational rehabilitation, supported employment, and work improve outcomes for people with mental illnesses. We begin first with an overview of psychiatric rehabilitation research by Anthony and colleagues to orient the reader to the overall field and offer a review of where the research support stands currently in relation not only to employment but also education, housing, and social functioning. We then turn to the contribution by Rog to review the evidence on the effectiveness, and costs, of supported housing in enabling people with psychiatric disabilities to live in the community settings of their choice. Next we turn to supported socialization and the various roles people in recovery can play in promoting the recovery of their peers in contributions by Davidson and colleagues, suggesting that friendship and peer support can serve as avenues to community integration for people who otherwise are isolated or disengaged. The papers of Marrone and Golowka and Russinova and colleagues then examine the evidence for vocational recovery in more detail, supporting the notion that employment can be at least as helpful in promoting recovery, if not more so, than unemployment, poverty, and social isolation. We end, again, with a first person account by Mahoney Holst that describes the crucial role that community supports and employment made in her recovery journey, turning a tragic sequence of events that resulted in alienation and loss into a homecoming of sorts. Her story, like thousands of others, demonstrates that life can indeed go on in the face of psychiatric disability, as long as the person perseveres and people and supports needed are available and effective.

# The Practice of Psychiatric Rehabilitation: Plans and Interventions

*William Anthony, Mikal Cohen, Marianne Farkas, and Cheryl Gagne*

At the time of original publication, William A. Anthony, PhD, Mikal Cohen, PhD, Marianne Farkas, ScD, and Cheryl Gagne, ScD, were with the Center for Psychiatric Rehabilitation at Boston University, Boston, MA.

This article originally appeared in *Psychiatric Rehabilitation, Second Edition*, 2002, 153–170, and is reprinted with permission.

*If to do were as easy as to know what were good to do, chapels had been churches and poor men's cottages prince's palaces.—William Shakespeare*

Diagnosis is difficult, but it is easier than intervening to address the diagnosis. In times past, mental health practitioners spent too much energy arriving at a psychiatric diagnosis and too little energy planning and intervening with the person based on the diagnosis. A psychiatric rehabilitation diagnosis is only the beginning of the psychiatric rehabilitation approach. If, based on what the practitioner and the individual know, little is done, then little is accomplished.

The psychiatric rehabilitation plan links the rehabilitation diagnosis to the rehabilitation interventions. Persons with psychiatric disabilities often have several skill and resource deficits. Interventions aim to eliminate these deficits. The rehabilitation plan essentially identifies who is responsible for doing *what*, by *when*, for *how long*, and *where*. The rehabilitation diagnosis provides the answer to the question, *why*.

Based on such criteria as urgency, motivation, and ease of achievement, the practitioner and the individual assign priorities to skill and resource objectives. The most urgent and easy-to-achieve objectives, for which motivation for achievement is high, are the focus of the interventions. The practitioner identifies a specific intervention for each skill or resource objective in the plan and a specific person responsible for providing each intervention. The client and practitioner sign the rehabilitation plan to indicate their agreement. Table 1 presents an example of how a rehabilitation plan might be recorded.

As illustrated by Table 1, several people are involved in providing rehabilitative interventions. The plan operationally defines the rehabilitation team approach. The problem in the past with the team approach has been an inability of the team members to understand the tasks for which the other members are specifically responsible, which frequently resulted in confusion and conflict between team members. Psychiatric rehabilitation cannot have a team approach without a plan that the entire team can understand.

The team must exemplify a team in more ways than just its title. Each member must have observable goals for his or her interventions. Obviously the complexity of the plan is related to the number and type of client skill and resource needs as well as to the number of rehabilitation environments under consideration. Many people require complex and detailed plans.

This article focuses on the major issues with respect to planning and implementing skill development and support interventions. First, some research relevant to each of these interventions is reviewed. Second, the issues and principles pertinent to these interventions are presented.

### RESEARCH REVIEW

Research relevant to the major interventions of psychiatric rehabilitation have been reported in a wide variety of professional journals. For example, research specific to the major interventions have come from decades of research in the fields of human resource development training (Carkhuff, 1969, 1971, 1974; Carkhuff & Berenson, 1976), social skills training (Hersen & Bellack, 1976; Dilk & Bond, 1996), social learning theory (Paul & Lentz, 1977), vocational rehabilitation (Anthony, Howell & Danley, 1984), and community support (Test, 1984). By drawing together the research from so many fields, support for these two major interventions becomes apparent. Four types of research are most relevant to these psychiatric rehabilitation interventions:

1. Research analyzing the ability of persons with psychiatric disabilities to learn skills.

2. Research examining the relationship between the skills of persons with psychiatric disabilities and their rehabilitation outcome.

3. Research investigating the relationship between skill development interventions and rehabilitation outcomes.

4. Research investigating the relationship between support interventions and rehabilitation outcome.

#### Persons with Psychiatric Disabilities Can Learn Skills

At first glance, research investigations as to whether persons with psychiatric disabilities can learn skills may seem superfluous. Common sense tells us they can learn skills. Yet, until the late 1960s and early 1970s, skill development interventions were far from the norm. During that period, a number of studies on skill training were published in a variety of professional journals.

**Table 1: Example: Rehabilitation Plan**

Overall Rehabilitation Goal: Mike intends to live in the Northwest apartments by January of next year.

| Priority Skill/Resource Development Objectives | Interventions | Person(s) Responsible | Starting Dates Projected/Actual | Completion Dates |
|---|---|---|---|---|
| Mike says what he thinks about a topic 4 times per week when conversing with residents during social interactions. | Direct skills teaching | Provider: House counselor Monitor: Mike and group home staff | April 14/April 20 | May 29 |
| Mike asks other residents for help 75% of the times per week when he is doing household chores. | Skills programming | Provider: Mike Monitor: Mike and group home staff | June 1/June 15 | July 31 |
| Welfare Department provides Mike with food stamps once per month | Resource coordination | Provider: Department of Social Services Monitor: Mike and house counselor | July 1/July 1 | July 31 |

I participated in developing this plan and the plan reflects my objectives.   Signature: _____

In 1974, Anthony and Margules reviewed these articles and concluded that persons with psychiatric disabilities, in fact, can learn useful skills (Anthony & Margules, 1974). Specifically, the studies reviewed at that time showed that persons with psychiatric disabilities could learn a variety of physical, emotional-interpersonal, and intellectual skills. For example, in the area of physical functions, skill-training programs have impacted skills in a variety of areas, including personal hygiene (Harrand, 1967; Retchless, 1967; Scoles & Fine, 1971; Weinman, Sanders, Kleiner & Wilson, 1970), cooking (Scoles & Fine, 1971; Weinman et al., 1970), use of public transportation (Harrand, 1967), use of recreational facilities (Harrand, 1967), use of particular job tools (Shean, 1973) and physical fitness (Dodson & Mullens, 1969). In the emotional-interpersonal area of functioning, skill-training programs have increased interpersonal skills (Ivey, 1973; Pierce & Drasgow, 1969; Vitalo, 1971) socialization skills (Bell, 1970; Weinman et al., 1970), self-control skills (Cheek & Mendelson, 1973; Rutner & Bugle, 1969), selective reward skills (Swanson & Woolson, 1972), and job interviewing skills (McClure, 1972; Prazak, 1969). Last, in the area of intellectual functioning, skill-training programs have increased money management skills, (Weinman et al., 1970), job-seeking skills (McClure, 1972) and job-applying skills (McClure, 1972; Safieri, 1970).

Many of these early studies trained persons with psychiatric disabilities who were long-term inpatients with a lengthy history of symptomatic behavior. It is now widely accepted that persons with psychiatric disabilities can learn skills, and that neither chronicity nor symptomatology prevents skill learning. The results of these early studies are thus seen as supportive of a psychiatric rehabilitation approach, with its emphasis on assessing and improving persons' skills. In the 1980s and 1990s, researchers in the area of social skills training, cognitive rehabilitation, and behavioral skills training demonstrated that people with psychiatric disabilities can learn a number of different skills. Comprehensive reviews of the skills training research found conclusively that people with psychiatric disabilities can learn a wide variety of interpersonal and cognitive skills (Benton & Schroeder, 1990; Dilk & Bond, 1996).

As can be seen from the studies cited, the concept of skills in psychiatric rehabilitation is much broader than daily living skills. Most problematic to assess and teach are intrapersonal and interpersonal skills. Yet these are the types of skills with which persons with psychiatric disabilities most often need help. Another type of skill area which is receiving increasing attention are cognitive skills (Green, 1996; Spaulding et al., 1999). It is often thought that basic neurocognitive deficits might inhibit the person's ability to learn more complex social skills. The hypothesis is that if basic attentional and perceptual skills can be learned first, then social skills learning would be more effective and efficient.

In a review of social problem-solving skills in schizophrenia, Bellack, Morrison, and Mueser (1989) concluded that persons diagnosed with schizophrenia are often critically deficient in their ability to communicate and make themselves understood. They report that "the evidence for this impairment is much stronger than the evidence for a deficit in problem-solving skill. It would appear that the communication impairment is more central to their interpersonal difficulties than deficits in problem-solving ability, and that the inability to make their desires and reasoning understood would seriously compromise the ability of persons with schizophrenia to use the strategies taught in problem solving training" (pp. 111–112). Hogarty (1999) argues that important skill deficits exist in the area of social cognition—the ability to act wisely in social interactions. The Center for Psychiatric Rehabilitation (1989) studied the efficacy of Direct Skills Teaching, a skill training technology, on the acquisition, application, and use of selected interpersonal skills. Using a single-subject experimental design, replicated across subjects, a number of unique interpersonal skills were assessed and taught. These skills included 1) Stating Personal Thoughts; 2) Refusing Requests; and 3) Sharing Negative Feelings. Analyses indicate that the technology of directly teaching skills positively and significantly affected the use of these interpersonal skills.

### Skills Relate to Rehabilitation Outcome

Other research studies central to the practice of psychiatric rehabilitation show a relationship between the skills of the person and measures of rehabilitation outcome. Arns & Linney (1995) found ratings of functional skills correlated positively with people's level of residential and vocational independence, and concluded that skill level is a better predictor of rehabilitation outcome than diagnostic variables. Many studies have investigated the positive relationship between work adjustment, interpersonal skills, and vocational outcome measures. Relatively fewer studies (Dellario, Goldfield, Farkas & Cohen, 1984; Schalock et al., 1995; Smith et al., 1996) have reported a significant relationship between ratings of skills and non-work outcomes, i.e., discharge from a psychiatric inpatient setting, hospital recidivism, and immediate post-discharge community adjustment.

The studies investigating the relationship between client skills and vocational outcome are remarkably consistent. Every study that assessed work adjustment skills found them to be significantly related to future work performance (Anthony, Rogers, Cohen & Davies, 1995; Bond & Friedmeyer, 1987; Bryson, Bell, Greig & Kaplan, 1999; Cheadle, Cushing, Drew & Morgan, 1967; Cheadle & Morgan, 1972; Distefano & Pryer, 1970; Ethridge,

1968; Fortune & Eldredge, 1982; Green, Miskimins & Keil, 1968; Griffiths, 1973; Miskimins, Wilson, Berry, Oetting & Cole, 1969; Watts, 1978; Wilson, Berry & Miskimins, 1969). When an overall measure of work adjustment skills was calculated, the total score was always predictive of future vocational performance (Bond & Friedmeyer, 1987; Cheadle et al., 1967; Cheadle & Morgan, 1972; Distefano & Pryer, 1970; Ethridge, 1968; Griffiths, 1973; Rogers, Anthony, Toole & Brown, 1991). The ratings of work adjustment skills in each of the studies were done by vocational counselors, occupational therapists, or work supervisors. The settings for these ratings were various sheltered or simulated work environments.

Ratings of interpersonal and/or social skills also have been found to predict vocational performance (Green et al., 1968; Griffiths, 1974; Gurel & Lorei, 1972; Miskimins et al., 1969; Mowbray, Bybee, Harris & McCrohan, 1995; Strauss & Carpenter, 1974; Sturm & Lipton, 1967). Again the data consistently suggested that knowledge of social functioning can be used to make inferences about people's future vocational performance.

The concept of social functioning is described differently in each study. For example, Green and associates (1968) rated the ability to initiate social contacts with other patients and staff. Miskimins and associates (1969) rated social skills, and Gurel and Lorei (1972) reported a significant relationship with the raters' estimate of restricted psychosocial functioning. Griffiths (1973) evaluated such items as getting along well with other people and communicating spontaneously, whereas estimates in the Strauss and Carpenter (1974) study were of personal-social relations, that is, meeting with friends or participating in activities with social groups. Thus, in spite of the wide range of items used to measure social functioning, the studies were remarkably similar in finding a relationship between social ability and future vocational performance.

Because skills, and not symptoms, are the focus of the psychiatric rehabilitation approach, it is interesting to contrast the preceding body of research with studies that have examined the relationship between symptoms and rehabilitation outcome. Many studies have illustrated the low correlations between a variety of assessments of psychiatric symptomatology and future work performance.

### Skill Development Interventions Impact Rehabilitation Outcome

Central to the psychiatric rehabilitation approach is the assumption that skill development interventions will increase the capacity to live, learn, socialize, and work more independently and effectively. In their early review of a number of databased studies, Anthony and Margules (1974, p. 104) indicated that the research suggested that "persons with psychiatric disabilities can learn skills; and that these skills, when properly integrated into a comprehensive rehabilitation program which provides reinforcement and support for the use of these skills in the community, can have an effect on the community functioning."

Although the majority of studies of skill development interventions are part of the behavioral psychology literature and are not focused on persons with severe psychiatric disabilities, a number of studies are relevant, with new studies appearing regularly (Liberman, Mueser & Wallace, 1986; Marder, Wirshing, Mintz & McKenzie, 1996; Wong et al., 1988). Anthony, Cohen, and Cohen (1984) identified studies undertaken with persons with severe psychiatric disabilities. Besides demonstrating that people with psychiatric disabilities can in fact learn skills, many studies have examined additional types of outcomes. For example, Vitalo (1979) compared a skill-training approach with a medication group for long-term outpatients and reported significant increases in the skill-training group in terms of the number of new friends and number of new activities in which the people were involved. Liberman et al. (1998) found independent living skills improvement at 2-year follow-up, and Smith et al. (1996) reported changes in initial community adjustment.

Some vocational outcome studies have examined the effects of training in job-seeking skills (Azrin & Philip, 1979; Eisenberg & Cole, 1986; McClure, 1972; Stude & Pauls, 1977; Ugland, 1977), decision-making skills (Kline & Hoisington, 1981), and occupational and work adjustment skills (Rubin & Roessler, 1978). Each study reported improved employment outcomes for the groups of persons with severe psychiatric disabilities who received skill training. For example, Eisenberg & Cole (1986) reported 61% of people trained in job-seeking skills obtained employment versus 12% for a matched control group.

A comment is in order. To achieve maximal outcome in practice, skill development interventions should be integrated within a process that considers both skills and support development interventions as complementary interventions—not mutually exclusive. Skills training researchers sometimes attempt to isolate the two types of interventions. In practice, this is usually neither possible nor desirable.

### Support Interventions Impact Rehabilitation Outcome

In addition to skill development interventions, the other major psychiatric rehabilitation intervention focuses on increasing the support in the person's environment. In essence, two types of research studies have manipulated the environment. The first type of study researched intervention strategies more exclusively focused on increasing the support in the environment in which the client functions with no deliberate attempt at skill training. The second type of study used both client skill development and support interventions in concert; thus, it is impossible to identify the unique contributions of either intervention to client outcome. The studies focusing more exclusively on support interventions are examined first.

Support interventions attempt to provide the individual with supportive persons, supportive places, supportive activities, and/or supportive things. A *supportive person* offers support through performing required behaviors or different roles (i.e., advocate, case manager, counselor, and/or advisor) (Dougherty et al., 1996; Salokangas, 1996). Improving the support provided by people, places, activities, or things focuses on accessing or modifying resources within the environment (i.e., sheltered or supported work and living settings, specific transportation, spending money, discharge programs). The purpose of distinguishing among supportive persons, supportive places, supportive activities, and supportive things is simply to highlight the different ways environmental modifications occur. In practice, these modifications often occur simultaneously.

The main identifying feature of support interventions, as distinguished from skill development interventions, is that they do not attempt to change the person's behavior. The early studies by Katkin, Ginsburg, Rifkin, and Scott (1971) and Katkin, Zimmerman, Rosenthal, and Ginsburg (1975) and later studies by Cannady (1982) and Schoenfeld, Halvey, Hemley van der Velden, and Ruhf (1986) have clearly demonstrated the positive impact on outcome for supportive persons. For example, Cannady (1982) employed citizens from the discharged patients' rural neighborhood to work as supportive case workers. Results indicate that over a 12-month period inpatient days were decreased by as much as 92%.

Witheridge, Dincin, and Appleby (1982) have reported on the use of a support team for persons with psychiatric disabilities at high risk for readmission. Working out of the individuals' homes and neighborhoods, this team intended to develop an individualized support system for each person. Of the original 50 participants, 41 remained in the program. One-year follow-up data indicated that days hospitalized decreased from 87.1 to 36.6 per individual.

A study by Stickney, Hall, and Gardner (1980) investigated the effects of introducing both a supportive person *and* a more supportive environment, separately and in combination, at the time of the person's hospital discharge. They studied the impact of four pre-discharge strategies that differed in the level of person and environmental support. The goals of the discharge plans were to increase the use of the community mental health center and decrease recidivism for 400 people discharged from a state psychiatric institution. The results of the study demonstrated the impact of increasing person and environmental support on both client cooperation with referral and 1-year hospital recidivism rates. With minimal environmental support, the referral cooperation and recidivism percentages were 22% and 68%; with increased person support, 36% and 39%; with increased person and environmental support, 75% and 28%. Thus, whenever an added element of support was introduced, the percentage of referral cooperation increased and the recidivism rate decreased.

Other studies (Valle, 1981; Weinman & Kleiner, 1978) have investigated the relationship between support persons and rehabilitation outcome. However, in each of these studies the effect of the support person could not be differentiated from the impact of skill training. Valle (1981) investigated the relationship between levels of interpersonal skills of the supportive counselor and rehabilitation outcome. He reported that the relapse rate of persons who were addicted to alcohol was significantly related to the level of interpersonal skills of their counselors. In other words, the best predictor of drinking behavior at the 6-, 12-, 18-, and 24-month follow-ups was the interpersonal skill level of the counselor.

Weinman and Kleiner (1978) did not measure the interpersonal skills of the support persons. Their study compared the effectiveness of community-based "enablers" with two hospital-based conditions: socioenvironmental therapy and traditional hospital treatment. The enablers' major roles were to teach skills and escort people to various community resources. Results of the project concluded that this combination of person support plus skill training was superior to one or the other of the hospital-based treatment approaches in terms of recidivism, self-esteem, and instrumental role performance.

Some case management studies have combined skill development and support interventions. In addition, studies of supported employment (Bond, Drake, Becker & Mueser, 1999), supported housing (Ogilvie, 1997), and supported education (Mowbray, Strauch-Brown, Furlong-Norman & Sullivan-Soydan, 2002) all show an effect on measures of role performance. While the emphasis of these interventions is on support and accommodations, many of these supportive programs and settings also have a skills component. It is virtually impossible at this time to separately analyze the contributions to outcome of the skill and support components of these types of interventions. Likewise, the studies of Assertive Community Treatment (ACT) are an excellent example of an intervention that effectively combines support and skill development interventions (Chinman, Allende, Bailey, Maust & Davidson, 1999).

Lastly, several inpatient studies have combined skill-training interventions with a variety of adjunctive services, including community support once the patient is discharged. These studies were undertaken when longer-term inpatient stays were still relatively common. Undoubtedly the most well known study is Gordon Paul's research (1984), which compared a traditional hospital unit to a milieu therapy approach and to a social learning approach. Among the many process and outcome measures used to evaluate these programs were community tenure figures that suggested the social learning approach was superior to milieu therapy, which in turn was superior to the traditional inpatient program. Other much less controlled and comprehensive evaluations have been performed on inpatient skills-oriented programs; each of these early studies reported favorable outcome on measures of community tenure and community functioning (Becker & Bayer, 1975; Heap, Boblitt, Moore & Hord, 1970; Jacobs & Trick, 1974; Waldeck, Emerson & Edelstein, 1979).

In summary, a variety of empirical studies conducted by researchers from different mental health and rehabilitation disciplines suggest that:

1. Persons with severe psychiatric disabilities can learn skills.

2. The skills of persons with psychiatric disabilities are positively related to measures of rehabilitation outcome.

3. Skill development interventions improve psychiatric rehabilitation outcome.

4. Support interventions improve psychiatric rehabilitation outcome.

### INTERVENTIONS ISSUES AND PRINCIPLES

As the research indicates, the acquisition of skills is not a major problem in rehabilitating persons with psychiatric disabilities. They can and do learn skills when effectively taught. However, the acquisition (learning) of skills is more easily demonstrated than the application (performance) of skills in the relevant environment. *Learning* relates to the question, Can the client acquire the skill? *Performance* asks the question, Will the client use the skill? (Goldstein, 1981).

Skill performance, application, or generalization is not a unique issue for skill development interventions. This has been a historical problem for psychotherapy in general. It has been estimated that the average generalization and maintenance rates for all psychotherapies combined is 14% (Goldstein & Kanfer, 1979). Nevertheless, this major issue must be directly confronted by skill development interventions.

Based on a review of the skill use literature, Cohen, Ridley, and Cohen (1985) summarized the 11 principles that should be incorporated into a skill development intervention to maximize the possibility of generalization:

1. Begin with skill goals and intervention strategies selected by the client.

2. Use the praise, encouragement, and the personal relationship between teacher and learner to reward learning in the training environment.

3. Provide support services to the client in the relevant environment.

4. Teach support persons to reinforce the use of the skill in the relevant environment using rewards previously selected by the individual.

5. Teach the person to identify intrinsic motivation as a replacement for extrinsic reward.

6. Increase the delay of reward gradually.

7. Teach skill performance in a variety of situations, preferably in vivo.

8. Teach variations of skill use in the same situations.

9. Teach self-evaluation and self-reward.

10. Teach the rules or principles that underlie the skill.

11. Use gradually more difficult homework assignments.

One skill teaching technology that incorporates these principles is Direct Skills Teaching (DST). DST is a systematic method of outlining the knowledge needed to learn any skill, developing a structured lesson plan to teach each component behavior, and involving the person in practicing each behavior individually and all the behaviors together (Cohen, Danley & Nemec, 1985). The difference between this skill teaching technology and many others is that DST involves the learner in an interactive, systematic skill development process of didactic understanding, experiential modeling, and practice or rehearsal for each component. Many other skill development technologies either teach the person the detailed knowledge needed to learn the skill and then expect the person to be able to apply that knowledge to perform the skill on his or her own, or use more sophisticated behavior modification techniques to shape the new behaviors through structured practice and reinforcement. Philosophically, the difference between DST and behavior modification techniques, for example, is that DST engages the person as a learner in an active partnership with the teacher. The active partnership promotes the learning of a particular skill that the person feels is relevant to their goal choice. In skill development interventions that use behavior modification as the primary technique, the role of the person is like that of a "subject," a somewhat passive recipient of reinforcers and information designed to help the person perform behaviors deemed important by the practitioner or significant others.

In addition to the development of practitioner-level technology, which teaches practitioners how to be more effective teachers, has been the development of client-level curriculum (Anthony, 1998). This type of technology can be designed to facilitate the person's participation and involvement in the diagnostic, planning, and/or implementation process using consumer-familiar language in specific areas—(e.g., social skills, job seeking, study skills). Client-level curriculum guides are usually available for practitioners to assist person to proceed through the curriculum. In order to implement the curriculum, practitioners do not have to be trained previously in psychiatric rehabilitation practitioner technology, although it is highly recommended.

Perhaps best known in the psychiatric rehabilitation field are client-level curricula emanating from behavioral rehabilitation (and social skills training in particular) and the ongoing technology development efforts of Boston University's Center for Psychiatric Rehabilitation. The Center's Choose-Get-Keep curriculum, with group curriculum currently available in the choosing (Danley, Hutchinson & Restrepo-Toro, 1998) and keeping areas (Hutchinson & Salafia, 1997), has been widely disseminated during its decades of development and piloting. Elements of this curriculum have been evaluated in supported education applications (Unger, Anthony, Sciarappa & Rogers, 1991), and supported living applications (Anthony, Brown, Rogers & Derringer, 1999).

Two new curriculum packages (a wellness curriculum and a recovery curriculum) recently have been developed by the Center and are undergoing further field testing. A study using an earlier version of the wellness curriculum found a significant positive impact of a wellness intervention upon the psychological and physical well-being of people with a serious mental illness and lent support of the role that wellness services have in the array of recovery-oriented services (Hutchinson, Skrinar & Cross, 1999; Skrinar & Hutchinson, 1994a; Skrinar & Hutchinson, 1994b; Skrinar, Unger, Hutchinson & Faigenbaum, 1992). This attention to the overall physical well being of people with psychiatric disabilities also has been promoted in other countries, such as China (Ng, 1992).

The recovery curriculum is designed to provide the information and skills needed to strengthen the recovery process, to cope more creatively, and to live life more fully. Included in the recovery curricula are a person's workbook (Spaniol, Koehler & Hutchinson, 1994a); a leader's guide (Spaniol, Koehler & Hutchinson, 1994b); and a book of readings (Spaniol & Koehler, 1994). The recovery curriculum has been used by thousands of people with disabilities across the United States, and is currently being evaluated for its usefulness in a managed care environment. The Center has translated the recovery curriculum into Spanish (Restrepo-Toro, 1999), and a version of the curriculum exists in Dutch.

Curricula have emerged in both treatment and rehabilitation as a useful tool in promoting the development of new behaviors and skills. Social skills trainers and researchers have been especially productive in designing and evaluating consumer curricula in a variety of modules. Some of the skill areas developed focus on the dysfunction (e.g., conversational skills), while others are useful as innovative treatment techniques for the regulation of the impairment (e.g., medication management and symptom management) (Liberman, Wallace, Blackwell, Eckman, Vaccaro & Khehnel, 1993; Liberman & Corrigan, 1993). Each skill module area consists of a trainer's manual, a participant's workbook, and a demonstration video. Numerous research studies have shown the efficacy of this curricula in promoting consumer skill use (Liberman, Vaccaro & Corrigan, 1995).

As mentioned previously, providing ongoing support for skill use is a major method for improving skill generalization. The two types of psychiatric rehabilitation interventions (skill development and support) are inextricably linked. Skill teachers support skill use (Cohen, Danley & Nemec, 1985). The use of skills by persons with psychiatric disabilities can be improved through simple social reinforcements as well as by elaborate token economies or reinforcement schedules (Armstrong, Rainwater & Smith, 1981). Social reinforcement is less expensive, more acceptable and normal, and can be effective in producing the desired skill use in the chosen environment.

Similarly, practitioners providing a support intervention can help people to learn to access natural supports rather than simply providing these supports. Along these lines, Mitchell (1982) has reported data suggesting that persons' skills are positively related to the size of the persons' support networks. Individuals can be taught to take an active role in the development of their own support network. Mitchell's (1982) data indicate that the level of independence and the level of peer support are positively related. The more support one feels, the more independently one can act. The principle is that if individuals are taught to get the support they want, they can act more independently.

Other studies have looked at the relationship between support and outcome (Greenblatt, Becerra & Serafetinides, 1982). Dozier, Harris, and Bergman (1986/1987) have found that moderate levels of network density, the extent to which network members know one another, was associated with fewer days in the hospital. In a study conducted in a Fountain House type clubhouse, Fraser, Fraser, and Delewski (1985) reported that reduced hospitalization was correlated with increases in the number of mental health professionals in the clubhouse members' networks. Sommers (1988) found that significant others' attitudes, that is, high demands for socially appropriate behavior, were correlated with instrumental performance. Baker, Kazarian, Helmes, Ruckman, and Tower (1987) found that readmitted patients rated their second most influential person higher on overprotection and criticism scales and lower on the care scale than did people who were not readmitted.

All types of support are critical but *the provision of personal support to persons with psychiatric disabilities is most critical.* To be supported by others is a natural human desire. This desire is especially significant for persons who are psychiatrically disabled because impairment may have caused them to withdraw from activities that provide a social outlet, that is, work, school, family activities (Harris, Bergman & Bachrach, 1987). The support networks of persons with psychiatric disabilities are characterized by small size, a lack of reciprocity, domination by family (Weinberg & Marlowe, 1983), and inflexibility and instability (Morin & Seidman, 1986).

Research into support interventions is plagued by conceptual and methodological shortcomings (Lieberman, 1986; Starker, 1986; Thoits, 1986). The concepts of support, support networks, and support systems do not have a clear definition. Uniform and reliable instruments are lacking. Despite these deficiencies, however, the idea of a support intervention as an effective rehabilitation intervention has taken hold.

One of the more useful and timeless definitions of support has been provided by Kahn and Quinn (1977), who describe support as an interpersonal transaction consisting of expression of positive affect, affirmation, and aid. *Positive affect* includes liking, admiration, respect, and other kinds of positive evaluation; *affirmation* includes endorsement of an individual's perceptions, beliefs, values, attitudes, or actions; aid includes such things as materials, information, time, and entitlements. Peers, practitioners, and family members provide varying levels and types of personal support. The principle is that if increased independent living is a goal, then some person or persons must be providing positive affect, affirmation, and aid.

Based on the research literature, possible interventions to improve supports have been suggested (Harris & Bergman, 1985; Marlowe & Weinberg, 1983). These interventions include:

1. Modification of the pre-existing network (family and friends) to increase their expressions of support.

2. Development of additional network members by using volunteers.

3. Development of additional network members by paying volunteers.

4. Strengthening involvement in natural networks (e.g., church, clubs) already in the community.

5. Development of a group of people who have similar problems into a support network.

6.    Strengthening the links between existing network members.

7.    Using larger networks for a crisis intervention function.

8.    Expanding the functions of the network.

A fundamental principle underlying any support intervention is that the person with the disability, not the practitioner, must perceive the intervention to be supportive. Like beauty, support also is in the eye of the beholder. Not all personal relationships are supportive and beneficial (George, Blazer, Hughes & Fowler, 1989). The affect, affirmation, or aid must be considered to be beneficial by the recipient of the support. Just as what stresses one person is different from what stresses another person, so it is with support.

Compared to skill development interventions, it has been only recently that support interventions have been correctly perceived as a fundamental psychiatric rehabilitation intervention, commensurate in importance to skill interventions, with both occurring in the context of a strong relationship between the helper and the person being helped. Perhaps because the initial technology of psychiatric rehabilitation focused on skill change (Anthony, Cohen & Pierce, 1980; Hersen & Bellack, 1976; Paul & Lentz, 1977), mental health professionals unfamiliar with psychiatric rehabilitation narrowly defined psychiatric rehabilitation as skills training. People always have understood the importance of supports to improved outcome, and the critical nature of supports in the context of a strong personal relationship, always has been conceptualized as part of the rehabilitation field (Anthony, 1979). Yet some practitioners still may discount the significance of support needs in contrast to skill needs. A recent study found that people with psychiatric disabilities reported that lack of environmental supports was a greater barrier to community integration than lack of skills (Mallik, Reeves & Dellario, 1998). In contrast, practitioners tended to view person and skill deficits as more of a barrier than did people with the disability (Mallik, Reeves & Dellario, 1998).

In essence, improvements in both skill and support are indications that the rehabilitation process has occurred, and that if the process was implemented effectively, then changes in outcome are apt to occur. It bears repeating that measures of both skill and support are process measures only. The outcome question is whether or not these skill and support changes have brought about improvements in role performance, i.e., whether persons are more successful and satisfied in their living, learning, and/or working environment of choice.

## CONCLUDING COMMENT

It should come as no surprise that even though the psychiatric rehabilitation process of diagnosis, planning, and intervening can be described relatively simply, it is not simple to provide. Expert personnel, effective programs, and well designed service systems must be in place in order to increase the chances of persons reaching their rehabilitation goals.

## REFERENCES

Anthony, W. A. (1979). *The principles of psychiatric rehabilitation.* Baltimore: University Park Press.

Anthony, W. A. (1998). Psychiatric rehabilitation technology: Operationalizing the "black box" of the psychiatric rehabilitation process. In P. W. Corrigan & F. Giffort (Eds.), Building teams for effective psychiatric rehabilitation (pp. 79–87, *New Directions for Mental Health Services, No. 79*). San Francisco: Jossey-Bass.

Anthony, W. A., Brown, M. A., Rogers, E. S., & Derringer, S. (1999). A supported living/supported employment program for reducing the number of people in institutions. *Psychiatric Rehabilitation Journal, 23*(1), 57–61.

Anthony, W. A., Cohen, M. R., & Cohen, B. F. (1984). Psychiatric rehabilitation. In A. Talbott (Ed.), *The chronic mental patient: Five years later* (pp. 137–157). Orlando: Grune & Stratton.

Anthony, W. A., Cohen, M. R., & Pierce, R. M. (1980). *Instructors' guide to the psychiatric rehabilitation practice series.* Baltimore: University Park Press.

Anthony, W. A., Howell, J., & Danley, K. S. (1984). Vocational rehabilitation of the psychiatric disabled. In M. Mirabi (Ed.), *The chronically mentally ill: Research and services* (pp. 215–237). Jamaica, NY: Spectrum Publications.

Anthony, W. A., & Margules, A. (1974). Toward improving the efficacy of psychiatric rehabilitation: A skills training approach. *Rehabilitation Psychology, 21,* 101–105.

Anthony, W. A., Rogers, E. S., Cohen, M., & Davies, R. R. (1995). Relationships between psychiatric symptomatology, work skills, and future vocational performance. *Psychiatric Services, 46*(4), 353–358.

Armstrong, H. E., Rainwater, G., & Smith, W. R. (1981). Student-like behavior as a function of contingent social interaction in a psychiatric day treatment program. *Psychological Reports, 48*(2), 495–500.

Arns, P. G., & Linney, J. A. (1995). Relating functional skills of severely mentally ill clients to subjective and societal benefits. *Psychiatric Services, 46*(3), 260–265.

Azrin, N., & Philip, R. (1979). The joy club method for the job handicapped: A comparative outcome study. *Rehabilitation Counseling Bulletin,* December, 144–156.

Baker, B., Kazarian, S. S., Helmes, E., Ruckman, M., & Tower, N. (1987). Perceived attitudes of schizophrenic inpatients in relation to rehospitalization. *Journal of Consulting and Clinical Psychology, 55*(5), 775–777.

Becker, P., & Bayer, C. (1975). Preparing chronic patients for community placement: A four-stage treatment program. *Hospital and Community Psychiatry, 26*(7), 448–450.

Bell, R. L. (1970). Practical applications of psychodrama: Systematic role playing teaches social skills. *Hospital and Community Psychiatry, 21,* 189–191.

Bellack, A. S., Morrison, R. L., & Mueser, K. T. (1989). Social problem solving in schizophrenia. *Schizophrenia Bulletin, 15,* 101–116.

Benton, M. K., & Schroeder, H. E. (1990). Social skills training with schizophrenics: A meta-analytic evaluation. *Journal of Consulting and Clinical Psychology, 58*(6), 741–747.

Bond, G. R., Drake, R. E., Becker, D. R., & Mueser, K. T. (1999). Effectiveness of psychiatric rehabilitation approaches for employment of people with severe mental illness. *Journal of Disability Policy Studies, 10*(1), 18–52.

Bond, G. R., & Friedmeyer, M. H. (1987). Predictive validity of situational assessment at a psychiatric rehabilitation center. *Rehabilitation Psychology, 32*(2), 99–112.

Bryson, G., Bell, M., Greig, T., & Kaplan, E. (1999). The work behavior inventory: Prediction of future work success of people with schizophrenia. *Psychiatric Rehabilitation Journal, 23*(2), 113–117.

Cannady, D. (1982). Chronics and cleaning ladies. *Psychosocial Rehabilitation Journal, 5*(1), 13–16.

Carkhuff, R. R. (1969). *Helping and human relations: A primer for lay and professional helpers: I.* Selection and training. NY: Holt, Rinehart and Winston.

Carkhuff, R. R. (1971). *The development of human resources: Education, psychology and social change.* NY: Holt, Rinehart and Winston.

Carkhuff, R. R. (1974). *The art of problem solving.* Amherst, MA: Human Resources Development Press.

Carkhuff, R. R., & Berenson, B. G. (1976). *Teaching as treatment: An instruction to counseling and psychotherapy.* Amherst, MA: Human Resource Development Press.

Center for Psychiatric Rehabilitation. (1989a). Refocusing on locus. *Hospital and Community Psychiatry, 40,* 418.

Center for Psychiatric Rehabilitation. (1989b). *Research and training center final report (1984–1989).* Boston: Boston University.

Cheadle, A. J., Cushing, D., Drew, C. D., & Morgan, R. (1967). The Measurement of the Work Performance of Psychiatric Patients. *British Journal of Psychiatry, 113*(501), 841–846.

Cheadle, A. J., & Morgan, R. (1972). The measurement of work performance of psychiatric patients: A reappraisal. *British Journal of Psychiatry, 120*(557), 437–441.

Cheek, F. E., & Mendelson, M. (1973). Developing behavior modification programs with an emphasis on self control. *Hospital and Community Psychiatry, 24,* 410–416.

Chinman, M., Allende, M., Bailey, P., Maust, J., & Davidson, L. (1999). Therapeutic agents of assertive community treatment. *Psychiatric Quarterly, 70*(2), 137–162.

Cohen, B. F., Ridley, D. E., & Cohen, M. R. (1985). Teaching skills to severely psychiatrically disabled persons. In H. A. Marlowe & R. B. Weinberg (Eds.), *Competence development: Theory and practice in special populations* (pp. 118–145). Springfield, IL: Charles C. Thomas.

Cohen, M. R., Danley, K. S., & Nemec, P. B. (1985). *Psychiatric rehabilitation training technology: Direct skills teaching* (Trainer package). Boston: Boston University, Center for Psychiatric Rehabilitation.

Danley, K., Hutchinson, D., & Restrepo-Toro, M. (1998). *Career planning curriculum for people with psychiatric disabilities.* Boston: Center for Psychiatric Rehabilitation, Boston University.

Dellario, D. J., Goldfield, E., Farkas, M. D., & Cohen, M. R. (1984). Functional assessment of psychiatrically disabled adults: Implications of research findings for functional skills training. In A. S. Halpern & M. J. Fuhrer (Eds.), *Functional assessment in rehabilitation* (pp. 239–525). Baltimore: Paul Brookes.

Dilk, M. N., & Bond, G. R. (1996). Meta-analytic evaluation of skills training research for individuals with severe mental illness. *Journal of Consulting and Clinical Psychology, 64*(6), 1337–1346.

Distefano, M. K., Jr., & Pryer, M. W. (1970). Vocational evaluation and successful placement of psychiatric clients in a vocational rehabilitation program. *American Journal of Occupational Therapy, 24*(3), 205–207.

Dodson, L. C., & Mullens, W. R. (1969). Some effects of jogging on psychiatric hospital patients. *American Corrective Therapy Journal, 23,* 130–134.

Dougherty, S. J., Campana, K. A., Kontos, R. A., Flores, M. K. D., & et al. (1996). Supported education: A qualitative study of the student experience. *Psychiatric Rehabilitation Journal, 19*(3), 59–70.

Dozier, M., Harris, M., & Bergman, H. (1987). Social network density and rehospitalization among young adult patients. *Hospital and Community Psychiatry, 38*(1), 61–65.

Eisenberg, M. G., & Cole, H. W. (1986). A behavioral approach to job seeking for psychiatrically impaired persons. *Journal of Rehabilitation,* April/May/June, 46–49.

Ethridge, D. A. (1968). Pre-Vocational Assessment of Rehabilitation Potential of Psychiatric Patients. *American Journal of Occupational Therapy, 22*(3), 161–167.

Fortune, J. R., & Eldredge, G. M. (1982). Predictive validation of the McCarron-Dial Evaluation System for psychiatrically disabled sheltered workshop workers. *Vocational Evaluation and Work Adjustment Bulletin, 15*(4), 136–141.

Fraser, M. W., Fraser, M. E., & Delewski, C. H. (1985). The community treatment of the chronically mentally ill: An exploratory social network analysis. *Psychosocial Rehabilitation Journal, 9*(2), 35–41.

George, L. K., Blazer, D. G., Hughes, D. C., & Fowler, N. (1989). Social support and the outcome of major depression. *British Journal of Psychiatry, 154,* 478–485.

Goldstein, A. P. (1981). *Psychological skill training*. New York: Pergamon Press.

Goldstein, A. P., & Kanfer, F. H. (Eds.). (1979). *Maximizing treatment gains: Transfer enhancement in psychotherapy*. New York: Academic Press.

Green, H. J., Miskimins, R. W., & Keil, E. C. (1968). Selection of psychiatric patients for vocational rehabilitation. *Rehabilitation Counseling Bulletin, 11*, 297–302.

Green, M. F. (1996). What are the functional consequences of neurocognitive deficits in schizophrenia? *American Journal of Psychiatry, 153*(3), 321–330.

Greenblatt, M., Becerra, R. M., & Serafetinides, E. A. (1982). Social networks and mental health: An overview. *American Journal of Psychiatry, 139*(8), 977–984.

Griffiths, R. (1974). Rehabilitation of chronic psychotic patients. *Psychological Medicine, 4*, 316–325.

Griffiths, R. D. (1973). A standardized assessment of the work behaviour of psychiatric patients. *British Journal of Psychiatry, 123*(575), 403–408.

Gurel, L., & Lorei, T. W. (1972). Hospital and community ratings of psychopathology as predictors of employment and readmission. *Journal of Consulting and Clinical Psychology, 39*(2), 286–291.

Harrand, G. (1967). Rehabilitation Programs for Chronic Patients: I. Testing the Potential for Independence. *Hospital and Community Psychiatry, 18*(12), 376–377.

Harris, M., & Bergman, H. C. (1985). Networking with young adult chronic patients. *Psychosocial Rehabilitation Journal, 8*(3), 28–35.

Harris, M., Bergman, H. C., & Bachrach, L. L. (1986/1987). Individualized network planning for chronic psychiatric patients. *Psychiatric Quarterly, 58*(1), 51–56.

Heap, R. F., Boblitt, W. E., Moore, C. H., & Hord, J. E. (1970). Behaviour-milieu therapy with chronic neuropsychiatric patients. *Journal of Abnormal Psychology, 76*(3, Pt. 1), 349–354.

Hersen, M., & Bellack, A. S. (1976). Social skills training for chronic psychiatric patients: Rationale, research findings, and future directions. *Comprehensive Psychiatry, 17*(4), 559–580.

Hogarty, G. E., & Flesher, S. (1999). Development theory for a cognative enhancement therapy of schizophrenia. *Schizophrenia Bulletin, 25*(4), 677–692.

Hutchinson, D., & Salafia, R. (1997). *Employment success and satisfaction: A seminar series (Version 1)*. Boston: Center for Psychiatric Rehabilitation, Boston University.

Hutchinson, D., Skrinar, G., & Cross, C. (1999). The role of improved physical fitness in rehabilitation recovery. *Psychiatric Rehabilitation Journal, 22*(4), 355–359.

Ivey, A. E. (1973). Media therapy: Educational change planning for psychiatric patients. *Journal of Counseling Psychology, 20*(4), 338–343.

Jacobs, M., & Trick, O. (1974). Successful psychiatric rehabilitation using an inpatient teaching laboratory: A one-year follow-up study. *American Journal of Psychiatry, 131*, 145–148.

Kahn, R. L., & Quinn, R. P. (1977). *Mental health, social adjustment, and metropolitan problems*. Research proposal, University of Michigan, Ann Arbor.

Katkin, S., Ginsburg, M., Rifkin, M. J., & Scott, J. T. (1971). Effectiveness of female volunteers in the treatment of outpatients. *Journal of Counseling Psychology, 18*(2), 97–100.

Katkin, S., Zimmerman, V., Rosenthal, J., & Ginsburg, M. (1975). Using volunteer therapists to reduce hospital readmissions. *Hospital and Community Psychiatry, 26*(3), 151–153.

Kline, M. N., & Hoisington, V. (1981). Placing the psychiatrically disabled: A look at work values. *Rehabilitation Counseling Bulletin, 24,* 366–369.

Liberman, R. P., & Corrigan, P. W. (1993). Designing new psychosocial treatments for schizophrenia. *Psychiatry: Interpersonal and Biological Processes, 56*(3), 238–249.

Liberman, R. P., Mueser, K. T., & Wallace, C. J. (1986). Social skills training for schizophrenic individuals at risk for relapse. *American Journal of Psychiatry, 143*(4), 523–526.

Liberman, R. P., Vaccaro, J. V., & Corrigan, P. W. (1995). Psychiatric rehabilitation. In H. Kaplan & B. Sadock (Eds.), *Completion textbook of psychiatry* (6th Ed.).

Liberman, R. P., Wallace, C. J., Blackwell, G., Kopelowicz, A., Vaccaro, J. V., & Mintz, J. (1998). Skills training versus psychosocial occupational therapy for persons with persistent schizophrenia. *American Journal of Psychiatry, 155*(8), 1087–1091.

Liberman, R. P., Wallace, C. J., Blackwell, G. A., Eckman, T. A., Vaccaro, J. V., & Kuehnel, T. G. (1993). Innovations in skills training for the seriously mentally ill. The UCLA Social and Independent Living Skills Modules. *Innovations & Research, 2,* 43–59.

Lieberman, M. A. (1986). Social supports: The consequences of psychologizing: A commentary. *Journal of Consulting and Clinical Psychology, 54*(4), 461–465.

Mallik, K., Reeves, R. J., & Dellario, D. J. (1998). Barriers to community integration for people with severe and persistent psychiatric disabilities. *Psychiatric Rehabilitation Journal, 22*(2), 175–180.

Marder, S. R., Wirshing, W. C., Mintz, J., & McKenzie, J. (1996). Two-year outcome of social skills training and group psychotherapy for outpatients with schizophrenia. *American Journal of Psychiatry, 153*(12), 1585–1592.

Marlowe, H. A., & Weinberg, R. (1983). *Proceedings of the 1982 CSP Region 4 Conference.* Tampa, FL: University of South Florida.

McClure, D. P. (1972). Placement through improvement of client's job-seeking skills. *Journal of Applied Rehabilitation Counseling, 3,* 188–196.

Miskimins, R. W., Wilson, Berry, Oetting & Cole. (1969). Person-placement congruence: A framework for vocational counselors. *Personnel and Guidance Journal, 47*(8), 789–793.

Mitchell, R. E. (1982). Social networks and psychiatric clients: The personal and environmental context. *American Journal of Community Psychology, 10*(4), 387–401.

Morin, R. C., & Seidman, E. (1986). A social network approach and the revolving door patient. *Schizophrenia Bulletin, 12*(2), 262–273.

Mowbray, C. T., Bybee, D., Harris, S. N., & McCrohan, N. (1995). Predictors of work status and future work orientation in people with a psychiatric disability. *Psychiatric Rehabilitation Journal, 19*(2), 17–28.

Mowbray, C. T., Strauch-Brown, K. S., Furlong-Norman, K & Sullivan-Soydan, A. (2002). *The supported education handbook: Models and methods.* Baltimore, MD: International Association of Psychosocial Rehabilitation Services.

Ng, M. L. (1992). Cultural factors in psychiatric rehabilitation in Hong Kong. *International Journal of Mental Health, 21*(4), 33–38.

Ogilvie, R. J. (1997). The state of supported housing for mental health consumers: A literature review. *Psychiatric Rehabilitation Journal, 21*(2), 122–131.

Paul, G. L. (1984). Residential treatment programs and aftercare for the chronically institutionalized. In M. Mirabi (Ed.), *The chronically mentally ill: Research and services* (pp. 239–269). Jamaica, NY: Spectrum Publications.

Paul, G. L., & Lentz, R. J. (1977). *Psychosocial treatment of chronic mental patients: Milieu versus social-learning programs.* Cambridge, MA: Harvard University Press.

Pierce, R. M., & Drasgow, J. (1969). Teaching facilitative interpersonal functioning to psychiatric inpatients. *Journal of Counseling Psychology, 16*(4), 295–298.

Prazak, J. A. (1969). Learning job seeking interview skills. In J. Krumboltz & C. Thoreson (Eds.), *Behavioral counseling* (pp. 414–428). New York: Rinehart & Winston.

Restrepo-Toro, M. E. (Ed.). (1999). *Recuperando la esperanza (The recovery workbook).* Boston: Boston University, Center for Psychiatric Rehabilitation.

Retchless, M. H. (1967). Rehabilitation programs for chronic patients: II. Stepping stones to the community. *Hospital and Community Psychiatry, 18*(12), 377–378.

Rogers, E. S., Anthony, W. A., Toole, J., & Brown, M. A. (1991). Vocational outcomes following psychosocial rehabilitation: A longitudinal study of three programs. *Journal of Vocational Rehabilitation, 1*(3), 21–29.

Rubin, S. E., & Roessler, R. T. (1978). Guidelines for successful vocational rehabilitation of the psychiatrically disabled. *Rehabilitation Literature, 39*(3), 70–74.

Rutner, I. T., & Bugle, C. (1969). An experimental procedure for the modification of psychotic behavior. *Journal of Consulting and Clinical Psychology, 33*(6), 651–653.

Safieri, D. (1970). Using an educational model in a sheltered workshop program. *Mental Hygiene, 54,* 140–143.

Salokangas, R. K. R. (1996). Living situation and social network in schizophrenia: A prospective 5-year follow-up study. *Journal of Psychiatry, 50*(1), 35–42.

Schalock, R. L., Touchstone, F., Nelson, G., Weber, L., & et al. (1995). A multivariate analysis of mental hospital recidivism. *Journal of Mental Health Administration, 22*(4), 358–367.

Schoenfeld, P., Halevy, J., Hemley Van der Velden, E., & Ruhf, L. (1986). Long-term outcome of network therapy. *Hospital and Community Psychiatry, 37*(4), 373–376.

Scoles, P., & Fine, E. W. (1971). Aftercare and rehabilitation in a community mental health center. *Social Work, 16*(3), 75–82.

Shean, G. (1973). An effective and self-supporting program of community living for chronic patients. *Hospital and Community Psychiatry, 24,* 97–99.

Skrinar, G., & Hutchinson, D. (1994a). Psychiatric disorders and exercise. In T. Fahey (Ed.), *Encyclopedia of sports medicine physiology.* New York: Garland Publishing.

Skrinar, G., & Hutchinson, D. (1994b). Exercise training and perceptual responses in adults with chronic mental illness. *Medicine and Science in Sports and Exercise, 26*(5).

Skrinar, G., Unger, K. V., Hutchinson, D., & Faigenbaum, A. D. (1992). Effects of exercise taraining in young adults with psychiatric disabilities. *Canadian Journal of Rehabilitation, 5*(3), 151–157.

Smith, T. E., Hull, J. W., MacKain, S. J., Wallace, C. J., Rattenni, L. A., Goodman, M., Anthony, D. T., & Kentros, M. K. (1996). Training hospitalized patients with schizophrenia in community reintegration skills. *Psychiatric Services, 47*(10), 1099–1103.

Sommers, L. (1988). The influence of environmental factors on the community adjustment of the mentally ill. *The Journal of Nervous and Mental Disease, 176,* 221–226.

Spaniol, L., & Koehler, M. (Eds.). (1994). *The experience of recovery.* Boston: Center for Psychiatric Rehabilitation, Boston University.

Spaniol, L., Koehler, M., & Hutchinson, D. (1994a). *Recovery workbook: Practical coping and empowerment strategies for people with psychiatric disability.* Boston: Center for Psychiatric Rehabilitation, Boston University.

Spaniol, L., Koehler, M., & Hutchinson, D. (1994b). *Leaders' guide: the recovery workbook.* Boston: Center for Psychiatric Rehabilitation, Boston University.

Spaulding, W. D., Fleming, S. K., Reed, D., Sullivan, M., Storzbach, D., & Lam, M. (1999). Cognitive functioning in schizophrenia: Implications for psychiatric rehabilitation. *Schizophrenia Bulletin, 25*(2), 275–289.

Starker, J. (1986). Methodological and conceptual issues in research on social support. *Hospital and Community Psychiatry, 37*(5), 485–490.

Stickney, S. K., Hall, R. L., & Gardner, E. R. (1980). The effect of referral procedures on aftercare compliance. *Hospital and Community Psychiatry, 31,* 567–569.

Strauss, J. S., & Carpenter, W. T. (1974). The prediction of outcome in schizophrenia: 11. Relationships between predictor and outcome variables. *Archives of General Psychiatry, 31,* 37–42.

Stude, E. W., & Pauls, T. (1977). The use of a job seeking skills group in developing placement readiness. *Journal of Applied Rehabilitation Counseling, 8*(2), 115–120.

Sturm, I. E., & Lipton, H. (1967). Some Social and Vocational Predictors of Psychiatric Hospitalization Outcome. *Journal of Clinical Psychology, 23*(3), 301–307.

Swanson, M. G., & Woolson, A. M. (1972). A new approach to the use of learning theory with psychiatric patients. *Perspectives in Psychiatric Care, 10,* 55–68.

Test, M. A. (1984). Community support programs. In A. S. Bellack (Ed.), *Schizophre-nia treatment, management, and rehabilitation* (pp. 347–373). Orlando, FL: Grune & Stratton.

Thoits, P. A. (1986). Social supports as coping assistance. *Journal of Consulting and Clinical Psychology, 54,* 416–423.

Ugland, R. P. (1977). Job seekers' aids: A systematic approach for organizing employer contacts. *Rehabilitation Counseling Bulletin, 22,* 107–115.

Unger, K. V., Anthony, W. A., Sciarappa, K., & Rogers, E. S. (1991). Development and evaluation of a supported education program for yound adults with long-term mental illness. *Hospital and Community Psychiatry, 42,* 838–842.

Valle, S. K. (1981). Interpersonal functioning of alcoholism counselors and treat-ment outcome. *Journal of Studies on Alcohol, 42,* 783–790.

Vitalo, R. L. (1971). Teaching improved interpersonal functioning as a preferred mode of treatment. *Journal of Clinical Psychology, 27*(2), 166–171.

Vitalo, R. L. (1979). An application in an aftercare setting. In W. A. Anthony (Ed.), *The principles of psychiatric rehabilitation* (pp. 193–202). Baltimore: University Park Press.

Waldeck, J. P., Emerson, S., & Edelstein, B. (1979). COPE: A systematic approach to moving chronic patients into the community. *Hospital and Community Psychi-atry, 30,* 551–554.

Watts, F. N. (1978). A study of work behaviour in a psychiatric rehabilitation unit. *British Journal of Social and Clinical Psychology, 17*(1), 85–92.

Weinberg, R. B., & Marlowe, H. A. (1983). Recognizing the social in psychosocial competence: The importance of social network interventions. *Psychosocial Rehabilitation Journal, 6*(4), 25–34.

Weinman, B., & Kleiner, R. J. (1978). The impact of community living and commu-nity member intervention on the adjustment of the chronic psychosis patient. In L. I. Stein & M. Test (Eds.), *Alternatives to mental hospital treatment.* New York: Plenum Press.

Weinman, B., Sanders, R., Kleiner, R., & Wilson, S. (1970). Community based treat-ment of the chronic psychotic. *Community Mental Health Journal, 6*(1), 13–21.

Wilson, L. T., Berry, K. L., & Miskimins, R. W. (1969). An assessment of characteris-tics related to vocational success among restored psychiatric patients. *The Vocational Guidance Quarterly, 18,* 110–114.

Witheridge, T. F., Dincin, J., & Appleby, L. (1982). Working with the most frequent recidivists: A total team approach to assertive resource management. *Psy-chosocial Rehabilitation Journal, 5*(1), 9–11.

Wong, S. E., Flanagan, S. G., Kuehnel, T. G., Liberman, R. P., & et al. (1988). Train-ing chronic mental patients to independently practice personal grooming skills. *Hospital and Community Psychiatry, 39*(8), 874–879.

# The Evidence on Supported Housing

*Debra J. Rog*

At the time of original publication, Debra J. Rog, PhD, was at the Vanderbilt Institute for Public Policy Studies, Center for Mental Health Policy, Washington, DC.

This article originally appeared in the *Psychiatric Rehabilitation Journal*, 2004, 27(4), 334–334, and is reprinted with permission.

## INTRODUCTION

Supported housing has increasingly become a preferred housing approach for persons living with serious mental illnesses (e.g., Tanzman, 1993). Supported housing is broadly defined as independent housing in the community that is coupled with the provision of community mental health and support services (Carling, 1992). It emerged in the 1980s as an alternative to the residential continuum (Ridgway & Zipple, 1990), a range of housing options with differentiating levels of staff intensity, from group living situations to progressively more independent housing through which individuals are expected to move as they transition into the community.

Critics of the residential continuum contend that it does not meet the varying and fluctuating needs that individuals with serious mental illnesses have over the course of their lives (Dickey et al., 1996); that the continuum as it was conceived is rarely available in a community (Randolph et al., 1989); and that the continuum does not honor an individual's preferences and choices (Ridgway, Simpson, Wittman & Wheeler, 1994). In addition, because individuals with serious mental illnesses comprise a significant percentage of homeless people (Tessler & Dennis, 1989; Federal Task Force on Homelessness and Mental Illness, 1992), there has been a greater emphasis on exploring a variety of permanent housing options for individuals with mental illnesses.

Supported housing offers an approach to housing for persons with serious mental illnesses that meets the criticisms of the residential continuum by having flexible, individualized voluntary services that come and go depending on the individuals' needs and choices (Carling, 1990, 1993; Ridgway & Zipple, 1990). It also can help alleviate the homelessness crisis by using existing housing stock. Those who believe in the continuum model or in a more integrated model of housing and services, however, believe that a number of individuals, especially those with more severe mental illnesses, cannot succeed in independent housing. They contend that congregate housing with on-site services provides the best setting for adequately meeting individuals' clinical needs (e.g., Bebout & Harris, 1992; Hatfield, 1993; Lamb & Lamb, 1990).

For the most part, the supported housing approach was adopted and promulgated in the 1990s without a great deal of evidence for the approach. Until the late 1990s, the research conducted on supported housing was largely descriptive (Rog, Holupka & Brito, 1996; Newman, 2000). Recent studies have provided more rigorous examination of housing and supports for persons with mental illnesses. These studies, reviewed in this article, have examined a broad range of independent housing with a range of supports. Some have been developed out of the mental health tradition of "housing as housing," most typically called "supported housing," and other models that have emerged from a movement focused on affordable housing as a means to decrease homelessness (Hopper & Barrow, 2003). Hopper and Barrow highlight the differences between these housing traditions, but also note some of the similarities in how they are implemented. Because both traditions are committed to increasing community housing options for persons with severe mental illnesses, studies on housing stemming from both traditions have been included in the evidence base for supported housing.

This article reviews the evidence base for supported housing that was initially prepared for the Texas Department of Mental Health and Mental Retardation's (TDMHMR) initiative "Blazing New Trails: Texas Consensus on Psychosocial Rehabilitation Services." In particular, the article describes the principles for guiding the implementation and delivery of supported housing that were accepted by TDMHMR. The article closes with cautionary notes about the evidence base on supported housing; the gaps in knowledge that remain; and the steps that can be taken to continue to add to the knowledge base.

## THE EVIDENCE BASE ON SUPPORTED HOUSING

### Overview of the Studies

As described in Cook, Toprac, and Shore (2003), as part of the TDMHMR meeting, five levels were used to characterize the evidence in support of a particular mental health practice. These levels are as follows:

*Level 1:* at least 5 published studies with scientifically rigorous designs (RCT, well-controlled quasi-experimental) using a variety of meaningful outcomes,

*Level 2:* less than five published scientifically rigorous studies and/or studies using less meaningful outcomes,

*Level 3:* published studies of less rigorous design (e.g., pre/post with no control group, study participant self-report of perceived changes following receipt of services/program participation),

*Level 4:* multiple organizational "case studies" with reported outcomes published in peer-reviewed journals,

*Level 5:* expert panel recommendations based on empirical research evidence but not including consensus (e.g. based on "surveys" of expert clinicians, surveys of consumer preferences, unpublished program evaluations).

Fifteen studies were included that have examined the outcomes of independent housing with supports for persons with serious mental illnesses. The levels were intended to aptly characterize any evidence that may be available, so that the quality and rigor of the evidence (as well as the number of studies providing this evidence) could also be considered in decision-making. Only studies fitting one of these levels were included in the evidence base. These studies include:

1.  Three studies on the New York/New York housing program, including a pioneering randomized experiment in the 1980s of New York housing compared to the status quo (Lipton, Nutt & Sabatini, 1988), a more recent longitudinal contrast of various intensities of New York/New York housing (Lipton, Siegel, Hannigan, Samuels & Baker, 2000); and a study of the comparative costs of supportive housing vs. the status quo (Culhane, Metraux & Hadley, 2001);

2.  Three projects supported under the McKinney Demonstration Program in the early 1990s. The Boston McKinney Demonstration (Goldfinger et al., 1999; Dickey et al., 1996; Dickey, Latimer, Powers, Gonzalez & Goldfinger, 1997) involved a randomized study of evolving consumer households (i.e., group homes with gradually reduced levels of staffing support over time) compared to supported housing. In the San Diego Demonstration (Hurlburt, Hough & Wood, 1996) individuals were randomly assigned to one of four conditions: supported housing with intensive case management, supported housing with traditional case management, comparison housing with intensive case management, and comparison housing with traditional case management. The New York Critical Time Intervention (Susser et al., 1997) randomly assigned men who were homeless and mentally ill and discharged from an on-site psychiatry program in a shelter who were entering a broad range of housing in New York City to receive the Critical Time Intervention (very intensive services from staff who had established relationships with the individuals during the critical time of transition to the housing), or services as usual (referrals as usual to the range of mental health services in the community);

3.  A longitudinal national study of veterans in a long-term supported housing program for homeless veterans (Kasprow, Rosenheck, Frisman & DiLella, 2000);

4. A study of the Pathways to Housing Program in New York (Tsemberis, 1999; Tsemberis & Eisenberg, 2000), a "housing first" approach funded and studied in part with federal funding;

5. The DC Homelessness Prevention Project (Bebout et al., 2001), funded as part of a multisite initiative by the Center for Mental Health Services that compared supported housing with continuum housing; and

6. A multisite initiative involving cross-site study and six individual studies (Connecticut; Massachusetts; Maricopa, County, Arizona; New York City; various counties in Oregon; and Upstate New York) designed to study a specific model of supported housing compared to a range of comparison housing approaches (group homes, supervised apartments, supportive communities) (CMHS Housing Initiative Steering Committee, 2002; Rog & Randolph, 2002).

Table 1 provides a summary of these studies, with randomized studies listed first, followed by quasi-experimental studies with comparison groups, and other types of quasi-experimental studies. Before reviewing the results of these studies, it is important to acknowledge several of their methodological features that affect interpretation of this review's findings. First, not all studies being reviewed meet the designation of "published." Preliminary findings for the cross-site study as well as individual studies recently supported as part of a federal multisite study funded by the Center for Mental Health Services have been presented at major academic conferences and final results are forthcoming (e.g., CMHS Housing Initiative Steering Committee, 2002). Similarly, Bebout and colleagues, having conducted another federal study of supported housing as part of a multisite initiative on prevention efforts, have a non-published report that is included in this review (Bebout et al., 2001). Because of the significance of these unpublished studies, their rigorous designs, and the fact that the database on supported housing is so nascent, they were included in the evidence base on supported housing.

Second, the studies are a mix of randomized and quasi-experimental studies, with most of the studies employing non-equivalent group quasi-experimental designs. Randomized studies are implemented less frequently in this area than in other service areas due to the ethical (perceived and real) and practical challenges that confront researchers (Rog & Randolph, 2002). As with other service areas, the unwillingness of some providers and others to follow a randomized placement process due to their perceptions of ethical problems can thwart implementation of an experimental study. In particular, providers are often reluctant to place

Table 1—Supported/Supportive Housing Outcome Studies Reviewed

| Study Author(s), Year | Design | Improvements Over Time | | | | Housing Condition Difference? |
|---|---|---|---|---|---|---|
| | | Tenure | Homeless | Hospital | Other | |
| Bebout et al. (2001) | RA/SH vs. Continuum Housing | Y | Y | Y | Y | Y – in favor of Continuum Housing vs. SH |
| Goldfinger et al. (1999) | Randomized SH vs. Staffed Group Homes (ECH) | Y | Y | Y | N | Y – in favor of Supported Housing vs. Range |
| Susser et al. (1997) | Randomized Broad spectrum of housing With or without CTI | Y | Y | — | — | Y – in favor of CTI |
| Hurlburt, Hough, and Wood (1996) | Randomized Four Section 8 and CM combinations | Y | — | — | — | Y – in favor of groups with access to Section 8, regardless of CM approach |
| Lipton et al. (1988) | Randomized NY/NY Housing vs. status quo | — | Y | Y | — | Y – in favor of Program Housing |
| CMHS Housing Initiative Steering Committee (2002) | Multi-site (6 sites) Cross-site Quasi-Experiments SH vs. Group homes, supervised apartments | Y | Y | Y | Y | N |
| Tsemberis and Eisenberg (2000) | QE/SH vs. SROs, community residences, other | Y | — | — | — | Y – in favor of Supported Housing vs. Range |
| Lipton et al. (2000) | Quasi-Experiment NY/NY Supportive Housing of various intensities (structure and independence) | Y | — | — | — | N |
| Culhane et al. (2002) | Quasi-Experiment SH vs. Matched controls (not in housing) | — | Y | Y | Y | Y – in favor of Supportive Housing vs. status quo |
| Kasprow et al. (2000) | Longitudinal | Y | — | — | Y | |

individuals discharged from hospitals directly into independent housing without having them first stay in one or more of the traditional settings. Supported housing, despite its intent to substitute for the approaches in the residential continuum, is often viewed as the last step in the continuum to which individuals must "graduate" or be "housing ready." Second, there are impracticalities of implementing randomization in studying housing. If a randomized process calls for withholding available housing at any time, ethical challenges are real and difficult to surmount. In addition, when housing is available, placement decisions are often made quickly and without the prior knowledge of the research team. Finally, contextual elements, such as funding of the housing, the role of managed care, and the dynamic nature of housing markets can make it difficult to put a randomization procedure in place.

A third important methodological feature of housing studies in this review is that they have examined a wide range of supported housing models. Several of the studies employ a strict definition of supported housing (independent permanent housing without services, choice, etc.) (e.g., Rog & Randolph, 2002), whereas other studies have employed a broader definition of "supportive" housing. Despite the variation, it does appear that the supported/supportive housing included in this review all have the general shared characteristics of being community-based, operating independently from the services, and providing choice in services.

The comparison approaches are even more wide-ranging than the supported housing programs studied. All but three of the studies compared supported housing to a specific alternative housing model or multiple comparison housing models. The three studies that did not use a comparison housing condition either used matched controls of individuals not in housing (Culhane, Metraux & Hadley, 2002), examined the same group over time (Kasprow et al., 2000), or included a group of individuals that represented the status quo—wherever anyone was living (Lipton et al., 1988).

A final methodological feature to consider in evaluating this evidence base is that many of the studies are hampered by low to moderate statistical power. Statistical power is the strength of a study's ability to detect outcome differences, if they exist, between the treatment and comparison conditions (Lipsey, 1990). The strength is based in part on the extent to which there is a large difference (or effect size) between the conditions and a sufficient sample size in each condition to adequately measure the difference. The effect size of a study is weakened when a study is not randomized, measurement is not reliable, and the treatment and comparison conditions are highly similar.

Some of the studies in our evidence base, as noted, are quasi-experiments and thus are not afforded the power of the randomized study. The relatively small effect sizes in most of the studies, however, are due to the small contrast between the supported housing and comparison housing alternatives; they are often similar on a number of features and thus affect the individual outcomes similarly. Not surprisingly, studies that compare alternative treatments also generally produce smaller effect sizes than studies that use no-treatment or status quo control groups. The studies that have status quo control groups (Culhane et al., 2002; Lipton et al., 1988) have the advantage of having significant contrasts between the treatment and control conditions, but continue to be challenged by population differences inherent in the design. Finally, because housing studies often limit the study participants to individuals entering housing, the lack of turnover of housing units results in sample sizes that are typically small and thus contribute to lower than desired statistical power.

In summary, the evidence base on supported housing is small, less than perfect (Newman, 2000), and nascent despite the length of time that the mental health service system has been debating the housing issues. There is enough quality evidence offered by the studies, however, to guide mental health providers in how best to meet the housing needs of their clients. However, there have been some liberties taken in how the levels to characterize the nature of evidence for supported housing have been used.

As already mentioned, several unpublished studies that are soon to be in the publication process are included in the evidence base though the initial guidelines refer only to published studies. Second, findings that are inconsistent among a set of five or more studies, even if the studies are rigorous, have been placed in Level 2 indicating the need for more consistent designs to clarify the outcomes. Finally, if fewer than five rigorous studies are available and the findings are inconsistent, the level of evidence has been characterized as Level 3.

### Evidence of Impact of Housing Overall on Resident Stability and Hospitalization—Level 1

As Table 1 illustrates, every study reviewed noted an impact of housing on residential outcomes overtime. Once in housing with supports, the majority of individuals with serious mental illnesses stay in housing, are less likely to become homeless, and are less likely to be hospitalized, regardless of the specific type of housing condition. Impact of housing on outcomes other than those related to residential stability and hospitalization have not been consistently studied and when they have, do not yield consistent improvements.

Level 1 characterizes the evidence in support of supported/supportive housing because all studies (and most importantly, those that have the most rigorous designs) examined one or more of these outcomes and the findings were unequivocal.

Some examples help to illustrate this finding. The Boston McKinney demonstration (Goldfinger et al., 1999; Dickey et al., 1997; Dickey et al., 1996) randomly assigned individuals who were homeless and had mental illnesses to evolving consumer households or supported housing, and found 76% of the clients in both groups still living in community housing at the end of 18 months. Eighty-four percent of homeless veterans with mental health and/or substance abuse problems who moved into supported housing were stably housed 1 year later (Kasprow et al., 2000). Similarly, examining the long-term effects of various supported housing approaches for individuals who are homeless and mentally ill, Lipton and colleagues (2000) found that 75% across the housing approaches had been housed after 1 year, and 50% after 5 years.

These findings suggest that housing with supports, regardless of the specific model, has a considerable impact on housing stability. In particular, several studies suggest that access to subsidized housing, especially rental subsidies, in turn provides access to safer, more decent housing (Newman, Reschovsky, Kaneda, et al., 1994), and improves stability (Hurlburt, Wood & Hough, 1996; Newman et al., 1994).

### Limited Evidence of Greater Impact of Supported Housing Over Alternatives— Level 2

The evidence for the greater impact of supported housing over other types of housing alternatives is characterized as Level 2 in that the studies have been inconsistent both in the comparisons that have been used and in their findings. When individuals in supported housing were compared to individuals not in any specific form of housing (Culhane et al., 2002; Hurlburt, Wood & Hough, 1996; Lipton et al., 1988), those living in supported housing had better outcomes. For example, individuals enrolled in supportive housing in New York City compared to those who remained in whatever situation they were in resulted in 69% vs. 30% living in permanent housing after 1 year (Lipton et al., 1988). Culhane and colleagues (2002) found that persons in supportive housing, compared to those individuals who were not in any specific housing, had significant reductions in shelter use, hospitalizations and length of stay in hospitals and jails/ prisons.

Having access to affordable housing appears to be the key in these studies. Hurlburt, Wood, and Hough (1996) conducted a study in which individuals were randomly assigned to one of four conditions: supported housing with intensive case management, supported housing with traditional case management, comparison housing with intensive case management, and comparison housing with traditional case management. The researchers found that individuals who received traditional case management were as likely to achieve stable housing as those who received intensive case management. However, individuals who had access to Section 8 certificates (i.e., subsidies for housing such that a household pays approximately 30% of its income toward rent and the federal government subsidizes the rest), regardless of the intensity of the services received, had a significantly greater probability of finding independent stable housing. Those who did not have access to Section 8, in contrast, were twice as likely to drop out of the program.

When supported housing was examined in comparison to an alternative type or types of housing, the results were more mixed. Several studies have found no difference among the various types of housing studied (Hurlburt, Wood & Hough, 1996; CMHS Housing Initiative Steering Committee, 2002). In the San Diego study, as noted, Hurlburt and colleagues found differences for access to Section 8 vs. no access, but did not find differences between housing that had intensive vs. traditional case management. The six quasi-experimental studies in the CMHS Housing Initiative, though still undergoing final analyses, also have not identified any major, consistent differences between the supported housing and the various forms of comparison housing (group homes, supervised apartment, supportive communities) that were studied, either as individual studies or in the multisite analyses.

Similarly, Goldfinger and colleagues (1999), in a randomized study comparing independent housing with group homes (or what was termed evolving consumer household), found no differences between the two groups in the extent to which individuals were residentially stable. The authors did find that individuals assigned to the independent apartments experienced a greater number of days homeless compared to those in group homes (mean of 78 days vs. mean of 43 days, respectively); however, the finding was specific to those residents who were members of minority groups (African American or Latino). The authors speculated that the difference could be due to differential treatment by landlords and/or different patterns of substance use for this subgroup.

The few studies that did find differences between housing types yielded somewhat inconsistent results. In a study of supported housing compared to continuum housing (i.e., housing that consists of housing in the residential continuum) (Bebout et al., 2001), participants in the continuum housing showed greater improvements in stable housing, homelessness, psychiatric symptoms, and quality of life than individuals in the supported housing. Fidelity information indicated, however, that neither the supported housing nor the continuum housing conditions held to consistent definitions. Some of the individuals randomly assigned to supported housing actually stayed in group homes for some period of time because permanent housing was scarce;

likewise, those who were randomly assigned to continuum housing at times went straight into supported housing. Thus, the housing was variable in each condition. The authors suspect that the continuum housing may have had a greater impact due to more intensive and consistent services from the service provider operating the continuum housing.

Tsemberis and Eisenberg (2000) found that, over a 5-year period, 88% of the individuals in the Pathways supported housing program who also received a modified Assertive Community Treatment (ACT) approach (e.g., Stein & Test, 1980; Teague, Bond & Drake, 1998) remained in housing, compared to 47% living in a range of housing in the linear residential continuum. Similarly, in the New York Critical Time Intervention (CTI) study, Susser and his colleagues (1997) found that the men who were randomly assigned to receive CTI in their housing had fewer days homeless (average of 30 days) after 18 months compared to those randomly assigned to receive services as usual (average of 91 days). The major impact of CTI was on extended homelessness (episodes of more than 54 days)—21% of the men receiving CTI experienced extended homelessness in this time period compared to 40% of the men in the comparison group.

It is possible that well-defined, potentially more consistent services in supported housing (e.g. services in the continuum housing; ACT; CTI), may help create an advantage in residential stability, especially for individuals with severe issues and problems. As noted earlier, however, the one study that did specifically examine differences in the intensity of case management (Hurlburt, Hough & Wood, 1996) did not find significant differences in client outcomes.

### Preliminary Evidence of Costs of Supported Housing—Level 3

Two studies (Culhane et al., 2002; Dickey et al., 1997) have published findings on the costs of supported/supportive housing. The studies differ in the specific form of supported/supportive housing studied, the comparison used, and the findings produced. The level of evidence is therefore characterized as Level 3. Dickey and colleagues (Dickey et al., 1997), in the Boston McKinney demonstration, studied the costs of supported housing and evolving consumer households, including costs of publicly funded treatment, case management, and housing itself. The mean annual total costs for evolving consumer households was $56,434, over $25,000 more than the $29,838 total annual costs per unit for supported housing. The difference was largely due to the high housing unit cost of the evolving consumer households.

Culhane and colleagues examined the costs of independent housing and supports in New York City and compared it to the costs incurred by homeless individuals who were not in housing. The results indicated that persons in supportive housing had significant reductions in shelter use, the number and length of hospitalizations, and length of stay in jails and/or prisons. The researchers estimated that placement in the housing reduced service use by $16,282 per year per unit, approximately $1,000 less than the estimated costs of a supported housing unit in NYC.

### Evidence on the Principles of Supported Housing—Level 3

Most of the studies had some operational definition of supported housing, but the definitions varied to some degree and were not always specifically described in operational terms. Recently, as part of the development of a Request for Proposals to examine the effectiveness of supported housing, CMHS conducted a set of interviews and surveys with key informants in the mental health field to hone the characteristics of the ideal model of supported housing for persons with serious mental illnesses (Center for Mental Health Services [CMHS], 1997). With this input, CMHS promulgated the following eight housing dimensions of supported housing (CMHS Housing Initiative Steering Committee, 2002):

1. the individual owns the housing or has a lease in his/her own name—the housing, therefore, is in the name of the individual and not linked to being in a specific program or with a specific agency. The housing is considered "permanent" in so much as any rental housing in the community is considered permanent;

2. housing and service agencies are legally and functionally separate;

3. housing is integrated into the community;

4. housing is affordable (i.e., no more than 40% of adjusted gross income);

5. services (including medication) offered are voluntary;

6. the individual has choice of the housing and services;

7. services are community-based; there are no live-in staff;

8. crisis services are available 24 hours a day, 7 days a week.

The CMHS Housing Initiative has examined the fidelity of the supported housing examined to each of these principles as well as the extent to which various alternatives incorporated these principles (CMHS Housing Initiative Steering Committee, 2002). The supported housing studied in this multisite initiative did incorporate these features and differed from the comparison housing, but many of the alternative housing programs incorporated some of the features as well (Rog & Randolph, 2002). When the relative presence or absence of the features was tested, however, there were no significant differential findings. This study, nor any previous study, therefore, has been able to distinguish the features of housing that are the active ingredients of housing that make the difference in resident outcomes.

Moreover, most other studies have not adhered to a strict definition of supported housing and have not specifically examined each principle. Consumer preference studies have focused on the principles and indicate that individuals consistently voice their preferences to live in housing that has flexible supports, is their own, and is affordable, permanent, and integrated into the community (Tanzman, 1993; Goldfinger & Schutt, 1996). Moreover, there are some data that support that living in independent housing rather than group housing is associated with greater satisfaction with housing and neighborhood (Newman et al., 1994). Additional correlational studies have found that achieving housing stability is related to choice and to matching individual needs and preferences with appropriate settings (Goering, Wasylenki, Lindsay, Lemire & Rhodes, 1997). In addition, affordability receives support on the basis of studies such as by Hulburt, Hough, and Wood, (1996) that found stability related only to access to Section 8 subsidies.

### Implications of the Evidence Base
The studies reviewed overwhelmingly find significant improvements in residential outcomes for individuals with mental illnesses who enter a range of housing with supports, but yield very little evidence in support of any specific form of supported housing. The predominance of a lack of difference in studies that compare different housing models may be due to several factors. First, the potency of housing itself on improving client outcomes is not a new finding (Rog & Holupka, 1999). Studies for persons who are homeless and mentally ill as well as other groups, such as homeless families (e.g., Rog & Gutman, 1997), have found that having any stable housing has a dramatic improvement on outcomes, especially those related to residential stability and use of institutional settings, such as hospitals, detox, and jails and prisons.

The ability to distinguish outcome differences between different housing models, however, is not hampered by the potency of housing alone. As noted, most studies include treatment and comparison housing approaches that are likely to affect outcomes. The comparison conditions in the models that are often volunteered for the studies, especially if random assignment is involved, are generally strong, often well-regarded alternatives. In addition, the principles of supported housing, although not empirically verified, have held consumer support for some time and have been appealing to others in the field. This acceptance of the supported housing principles has led to the adoption of some of these principles in other models typically not considered as supported housing (CMHS Housing Initiative Steering Committee, 2002).

Most of the studies also lack other design features that could increase their sensitivity to detect any small outcome differences that may exist (Lipsey, 1990). These features include large sample sizes, random assignment to the different housing models, and supported housing that has fidelity to a specific intervention model. In many of the existing studies, unfortunately, the sample sizes are small, limited by the housing that is available. In addition, as Bebout and colleagues (2001) illustrate, fidelity to a model is often difficult to sustain in the dynamic contexts in which we live. The resulting variation often does not produce the results that might emerge if the ideal models were in place.

## UNIQUE IMPLEMENTATION ISSUES

In addition to evidence of effectiveness, the TDMHMR asked each of the authors reviewing the research in a mental health practice area to place some focus on what can be learned about the implementation of the practice. For supported housing, among the key decisions involved include who to refer to the housing, and how best to structure the housing.

### Who Fares Relatively Better or Worse in Supported Housing?

The research evidence available on who fares better or worse in supported housing does not yield results that are distinct for supported housing, but rather pertain to housing with supports in general. Regardless of the specific housing approach, those who fare better in the housing are younger rather than older (Lipton et al., 2000; Tsemberis & Eisenberg, 2000; CMHS Housing Initiative Steering Committee, 2002); have mood disorders rather than schizophrenia (Tsemberis & Eisenberg, 2000); and are less likely to have co-occurring substance abuse problems (Tsemberis & Eisenberg, 2000; Lipton et al., 2000; Goldfinger et al., 1999; Hurlburt, Hough & Wood, 1996). The evidence is so consistent in these areas to warrant a Level 1 categorization.

In addition, in one study, homeless individuals referred from community and state psychiatric hospitals were more likely to have poor housing outcomes regardless of the type of housing they received. These individuals may have had relatively higher levels of functional impairment and higher rates of substance abuse and may have needed enhanced access to programs that focused on housing readiness (Lipton et al., 2000).

### When Is Supported Housing Not the Right Approach?

The evidence from the vast majority of studies reviewed suggests that people who enter supported housing stay stably housed at least 12 months. Those who appear to be least successful in housing drop out early—within the first 4 months (Lipton et al., 2000). The evidence indicates, therefore, that supported housing is not working when an individual cannot remain residentially stable in the housing. As noted above, individuals with dual diagnoses are the most likely to drop out of any housing approach (Tsemberis & Eisenberg, 2000; Lipton et al., 2000; Goldfinger et al., 1999; Hurlburt, Hough & Wood, 1996), including supported housing; therefore, greater attention is needed on the specific forms of housing and services that can help these individuals remain housed.

There may be some guidance also provided by what types of housing approaches consumers prefer as well as what clinicians recommend. In the Boston McKinney demonstration, Goldfinger and Schutt (1997) found that both consumer preferences and clinician recommendations predicted the number of days homeless. Individuals whose clinicians were strongly against their entering independent living experienced more days homeless regardless of the type of housing they entered. On the other hand, the stronger the consumer baseline preference for independent living, the greater number of days spent homeless. Both, therefore, may be important to consider in determining when supported housing is warranted.

### What Organizational Structure Works Best?

As with the other aspects of housing implementation, there is little research available to provide definitive guidance on what organizational approaches work best for delivering supported housing. Supported housing is intended to be offered in the broader community by private landlords who rent directly to the tenant. Services are intended to be provided through separately funded case managers who link residents to services in the community. The general model is of housing-services separation. It is not clear, however, if the housing and services necessarily need to be offered by different agencies (e.g., Bebout et al., 2001).

With respect to services, case management tends to be the most common service offered. Studies on case management have found that caseloads range, though the average is around 1:15 and the general advice is no greater than 1:20. Services offered through teams as well as individual case managers have been provided and both seem to be effective. What do seem to be important, especially with case managers who are para-professional workers, are the provision of supervision and the backup of psychiatrists and psychologists (Susser et al., 1997).

### THE BOTTOM LINE...SO FAR

Providers and policymakers are generally interested in knowing what housing approaches work best for individuals with severe mental illnesses. More pointedly, because supported housing has been a preferred approach by many consumers and providers over the last two decades, there has been interest in understanding the extent to which supported housing is the right approach for individuals with severe mental illnesses, and particularly identifying those clients for whom it works best and for whom it does not work.

Fifteen studies (including the six individual studies in the CMHS Housing Initiative) have provided data on the outcomes of supported housing. Although the number of studies is small and the results vary, the results indicate that housing with supports in any form is a powerful intervention that improves the housing stability of individuals with mental illnesses. Although the findings seem no more than common sense, they have political and practical value in clearly and dramatically demonstrating the effects of housing in maintaining residential stability, decreasing homelessness, and decreasing hospitalization. The results indicate that individuals with severe mental illnesses can, and do, live in the community with supports and that most can remain in the housing for long periods of time.

There is less known from the studies thus far as to what aspects of housing may affect individual outcomes or the extent to which supported housing is more effective than other forms of housing. We do know that housing with supports makes a difference over no housing, affordability is key, and there is some suggestion that housing with more well-defined services may be even more effective than other forms of housing with supports. Moreover, if one looks at the findings from the perspective of whether there is increased risk in placing individuals in supported housing, the data would suggest that the risk is no greater (at least for those groups studied).

However, there is a need for greater investigation into what aspects of the housing and supports make the most difference and for whom. In particular, there has been a call for research on the housing and service factors that influence an individual's integration into the community, a major goal of mental health policy and of housing in particular (Wong & Solomon, 2002). Unfortunately, the studies have been quite varied in the populations they have studied. Moreover, it is not clear how many of the studies have included individuals with a range of impairments and difficulties.

Similarly, we need to know more about the individuals who do not succeed in housing and the interventions needed to improve their chances. Despite the population differences that do exist among the studies, there is a great consistency in the characteristics associated with poorer outcomes. Those who do not fare as well tend to be younger with relatively more impairments, including co-occurring substance abuse. Research that can focus on the specific housing and support needs of individuals who are homeless and have mental illnesses, especially those who have dual diagnoses, would strengthen the evidence base, and most importantly, increase its usefulness to the providers who struggle in determining how best to meet the needs of these individuals.

The findings thus far also suggest that supportive housing has its greatest effects on residential outcomes. Again, upon reflection, this finding may not be totally unexpected; after all, housing in and of itself is not a treatment; in fact, supported housing is designed specifically to separate housing and treatment such that services and supports are accessed in the community where they are available to all individuals. In other housing approaches, although there may be staff on site, other mental health services are typically accessed through the community as well. Thus, one would not expect that there would be differences in the mental health functioning of individuals in the various housing approaches, especially if they are drawing from the same system of mental health services and supports.

Clearly, there is more we can learn about what features of supported and supportive housing are most cost-effective and desired by individuals, and about the specific approaches that may be needed by those who have not fared well in community housing. Yet, the evidence is overwhelming that individuals with severe mental illnesses can live successfully in a wide range of supportive housing approaches. The scarcity of housing, coupled with these findings, suggests that providers should look to maximize the housing stock available to them, regardless of some of the specific physical features of the housing. However, given that supported housing may be a less expensive alternative (at least when start-up costs are considered), and that the principles and values of supported housing are most consistent with the preferences of consumers, mental health authorities may do well in developing their housing portfolio in a manner that is aligned to the philosophy and spirit of supported housing.

### REFERENCES

Bebout, R. R., & Harris, M. (1992). In search of pumpkin shells: Residential programming for the homeless mentally ill. In H. R. Lamb, L. L. Bachrach, & F. I. Kass (Eds.), *Treating the homeless mentally ill: A task force report.* Washington, DC: American Psychiatric Association.

Bebout, R. R., McHugo, G. J., Cleghorn, J. S., Harris, M., Xie, H., & Drake, R. E. (2001). *The DC Homelessness Prevention Project: A study of housing and support models for mentally ill individuals at risk for homelessness: Final Report.* Rockville, MD: Substance Abuse and Mental Health Services Administration.

Carling, P. J. (1990). Major mental illness, housing, and supports: The promise of community integration. *American Psychologist, 45*(8), 969–975.

Carling, P. J. (1992). Housing, community support, and homelessness: Emerging policy in mental health systems. *New England Journal of Public Policy, 8,* 281–295.

Carling, P. J. (1993). Housing and supports for persons with mental illness: Emerging approaches to research and practice. *Hospital and Community Psychiatry, 44*(5), 439–449.

Center for Mental Health Services. (1997). *Cooperative agreements to evaluate housing approaches for persons with serious mental illness* (GFA No. SM 97-005). Washington, DC: U. S. Department of Health and Human Services.

CMHS Housing Initiative Steering Committee (2002, November). *Housing matters: Final results from the CMHS housing initiative.* Presentation by Debra Rog at the annual meeting of the American Public Health Association, Philadelphia, PA.

Cook, J., Toprac, M., & Shore, S. (2003). *Use of best practice and consensus-building to promote psychosocial rehabilitation in the Texas benefit redesign process.* Unpublished manuscript.

Culhane, D. P., Metraux, S., & Hadley, T. (2001). *The impact of supportive housing for homeless people with severe mental illness on the utilization of the public health, corrections, and emergency shelter systems: The New York-New York initiative.* Washington, DC: Fannie Mae Foundation.

Culhane, D. P., Metraux, S., & Hadley, T. (2002). Public service reductions associated with placement of homeless persons with severe mental illness in supportive housing. *Housing Policy Debate, 13*(1), 107–163.

Dickey, B., Gonzalez, O., Latimer, E., Powers, K., Schutt, R., & Goldfinger, S. M. (1996). Use of mental health services by formerly homeless adults residing in group and independent housing. *Psychiatric Services, 47*(2), 152–158.

Dickey, B., Latimer, E., Powers, K., Gonzalez, O., & Goldfinger, S. M. (1997). Housing costs for adults who are mentally ill and formerly homeless. *Journal of Mental Health Administration, 24*(3), 291–305.

Federal Task Force on Homelessness and Mental Illness. (1992). *Outcasts on Main Street: Report of the Federal Task Force on Homelessness and Severe Mental Illnesses.* Washington, DC: Interagency Council on the Homeless.

Goering, P., Wasylenki, D., Lindsay, S., Lemire, D., & Rhodes, A. (1997). Process and outcome in a hostel outreach program for homeless clients with severe mental illness. *American Journal of Orthopsychiatry, 67*(4), 607–617.

Goldfinger, S. M., & Schutt, R. K. (1996). Comparison of clinicians' housing recommendations and preferences of homeless mentally ill persons. *Psychiatric Services, 47*(4), 413–415.

Goldfinger, S. M., Schutt, R. K., Tolomiczenko, G. S., Seidman, L., Penk, W. E., Turner, W., & Caplan, B. (1999). Housing placement and subsequent days homeless among formerly homeless adults with mental illness. *Psychiatric Services, 50*(5), 674–679.

Hatfield, A. B. (1993). A family perspective on supported housing. *Housing and Community Psychiatry, 44,* 496–497.

Hopper, K., & Barrow, S. M. (2003). Two genealogies of supported housing and their implications for outcome assessment. *Psychiatric Services, 54*(1), 50–54.

Hurlburt, M. S., Hough, R. L., & Wood, P. A. (1996). Effects of substance abuse on housing stability of homeless mentally ill persons in supported housing. *Psychiatric Services, 47*(7), 731–736.

Hurlburt, M. S., Wood, P. A., & Hough, R. L. (1996). Providing independent housing for the homeless mentally ill: A novel approach to evaluating long-term longitudinal housing patterns. *Journal of Community Psychology, 24*(3), 291–310.

Kasprow, W. J., Rosenheck, R. A., Frisman, L., & DiLella, D. (2000). Referral and housing processes in a long-term supported housing program for homeless veterans. *Psychiatric Services, 51*(8), 1017–1023.

Lamb, H. R., & Lamb, D. M. (1990). Factors contributing to homelessness among the chronically and severely mentally ill. *Hospital and Community Psychiatry, 41*, 301–305.

Lipsey, M. W. (1990). *Design sensitivity: Statistical power for experimental research.* Newbury Park, CA: Sage.

Lipton, F. R., Nutt, S., & Sabatini, A. (1988). Housing the homeless mentally ill: A longitudinal study of a treatment approach. *Hospital and Community Psychiatry, 39*, 40–45.

Lipton, F. R., Siegel, C., Hannigan, A., Samuels, J., & Baker, S. (2000). Tenure in supportive housing for homeless persons with severe mental illness. *Psychiatric Services, 51*(4), 479–486.

Newman (2000). *Housing and mental illness: A critical review of the literature.* (Report). Baltimore, MD: Johns Hopkins University Institute for Policy Studies.

Newman, S. J., Reschovsky, J. D., Kaneda, K., et al. (1994). The effects of independent living on persons with chronic mental illness: An assessment of the Section 8 certificate program. *Milbank Quarterly, 72*(1), 171–198.

Randolph, F. L., Zipple, A. M., Rowan, C. A., Ridgway, P., Curtis, L. C., & Carling, P. J. (1989). A survey of selected community residential programs for people with psychiatric disabilities. *Monograph Series on Housing and Rehabilitation in Mental Health.*

Ridgway, P., Simpson, A., Wittman, R. D., & Wheeler, G. (1994). Home making and community building: Notes on empowerment and place. *The Journal of Mental Health Administration, 21*(4), 407–418.

Ridgway, P., & Zipple, A. M. (1990). The paradigm shift in residential services: From linear continuum to supported housing approaches. *Psychosocial Rehabilitation Journal, 13*(4), 11–32.

Rog, D. J., & Gutman, M. (1997). The homeless families program: A summary of key findings. In S. L. Isaacs & J. R. Knickman (Eds.), *To improve health and health care: The Robert Wood Johnson Foundation anthology.* San Francisco: Jossey-Bass Publishers, 209–231.

Rog, D. J., & Holupka, C. S. (1999). Reconnecting homeless individuals and families to the community. In L. B. Fosburg & D. L. Dennis (Eds.), *Practical lessons: The 1998 national symposium on homelessness research.*

Rog, D. J., Holupka, C. S., & Brito, M. C. (1996). The impact of housing on health: Examining supportive housing for individuals with mental illness. *Current Issues in Public Health, 2*, 153–160.

Rog, D. J., & Randolph, F. L. (2002). A multisite evaluation of supported housing: Lessons learned from cross-site collaboration. In J. M. Herrell & R. B. Straw (Eds.), *New directions for evaluation: No. 94. Conducting multiple site evaluations in real-world settings*. San Francisco: Jossey-Bass.

Stein, L. I., & Test, M. A. (1980). Alternative to mental hospital treatment: A conceptual model, treatment program, and clinical evaluation. *Archives of General Psychiatry, 37*, 392–397.

Susser, E., Valencia, E., Conover, S., Felix, A., Tsai, W., & Wyatt, R. J. (1997). Preventing recurrent homelessness among mentally ill men: A "critical time" intervention after discharge from a shelter. *American Public Health Association, 87*(2), 256–262.

Tanzman, B. (1993). An overview of surveys of mental health consumers' preferences for housing and support services. *Hospital and Community Psychiatry, 44*(5), 450–455.

Teague, G. B., Bond, G. R., & Drake, R. E. (1998). Program fidelity in assertive community treatment: Development and use of a measure. *American Journal of Orthopsychiatry, 68*(2), 216–232.

Tessler, R., & Dennis, D. (1989). *A synthesis of NIMH-funded research concerning persons who are homeless and mentally ill*. Washington, DC: U. S. Department of Health and Human Services.

Tsemberis, S. (1999). From streets to homes: An innovative approach to supported housing for homeless adults with psychiatric disabilities. *Journal of Community Psychology, 27*(2), 225–241.

Tsemberis, S., & Eisenberg, R. F. (2000). Pathways to housing: Supported housing for street-dwelling homeless individuals with psychiatric disabilities. *Psychiatric Services, 51*(4), 487–493.

Wong, Y. L. I., & Solomon, P. L. (2002). Community integration of persons with psychiatric disabilities in supportive independent housing: A conceptual model and methodological considerations. *Mental Health Services Research, 4*(1), 13–28.

# "It was just realizing...that life isn't one big horror": A Qualitative Study of Supported Socialization

*Larry Davidson, Karl E. Haglund, David A. Stayner, Jaak Rakfeldt, Matthew J. Chinman, and Jacob Kraemer Tebes*

At the time of original publication, author affiliations were cited as follows:

Larry Davidson, PhD, is an Associate Professor of Psychology in Psychiatry at the Yale University School of Medicine and Director of Clinical Services at the Connecticut Mental Health Center in New Haven, Connecticut.

Karl E. Haglund, MD, is currently a doctoral student at Yale University. At the time of this study, he was a James G. Hirsch, MD, Endowed Medical Student Research Fellow at the Yale University School of Medicine in New Haven.

David A. Stayner, PhD, is an Assistant Professor of Psychology in Psychiatry at the Yale University School of Medicine, and an Associate Director of Clinical Services at the Connecticut Mental Health Center in New Haven.

Jaak Rakfeldt, PhD, is an Associate Professor of Social Work at Southern Connecticut State University and Assistant Clinical Professor of Psychiatry at the Yale University School of Medicine, both in New Haven.

Matthew J. Chinman, PhD, is an Instructor in Psychiatry at the Yale University School of Medicine, and Director of Program Evaluation Services of The Consultation Center, both in New Haven.

Jacob Kraemer Tebes, PhD, is an Associate Professor of Psychology in Psychiatry and the Child Study Center, and Co-Director of the Division of Prevention and Community Research, both at the Yale University School of Medicine in New Haven.

This article originally appeared in the *Psychiatric Rehabilitation Journal,* 2001, 24(3), 275–292, and is reprinted with permission.

**Abstract:** This report describes the qualitative component of a large-scale study of supported socialization. Paralleling the recent advances made through supported housing, supported employment, and supported education, this approach seeks to increase the involvement of individuals with psychiatric disabilities in naturally occurring social and recreational activities in community settings of their choice. After a review of social relationships and psychiatric disability, we describe the Partnership Project and present findings from a series of qualitative interviews conducted with a subsample of participants. We then discuss the implications of these findings for the community integration of individuals with psychiatric disabilities.

*Like everyone else I feel the need of relations and friendship, of affection, of friendly intercourse, and I am not made of stone or iron, so I cannot miss these things without feeling, as does any other intelligent and honest man, a void and deep need...Do you know what frees one from this captivity? It is every deep serious affection. Being friends...love, these open the prison by supreme power, by some magic force. Where sympathy is renewed, life is restored.— Vincent Van Gogh (1878/1937, pp. 41, 48)*

Consumer satisfaction surveys, research interviews, and program evaluations consistently have shown that individuals with psychiatric disabilities prefer life in the community over extended stays in psychiatric hospitals (Bene-Kociemba, Cotton, & Fortgang, 1982; Davidson, Hoge, Godleski, Rakfeldt, & Griffith, 1996; Dickey, Gudeman, Hellman, Donatelle, & Grinspoon, 1981; Herman & Smith, 1989; Jones, Robinson, & Golightly, 1986; Lord, Schnarr, & Hutchison, 1987; MacGilp, 1991; Okin & Pearsall, 1993; Solomon, 1992). While these individuals identified a number of important advantages to community living—such as freedom, privacy, safety, and proximity to family and community of origin—they simultaneously identified a number of serious drawbacks to living outside of hospital settings (Davidson, Hoge, Merrill, Rakfeldt, & Griffith, 1995). These drawbacks, although not enough to tip the balance in favor of lengthy hospitalization, still pose significant obstacles to the community integration of individuals with psychiatric disabilities. Foremost among the drawbacks identified to leaving the hospital were lack of medical care and social isolation (Davidson et al., 1995). To move beyond the long standing hospital vs. community debate, innovative new approaches to meeting these needs for access to medical care and social support will have to be developed within community-based settings.

In this report, we present the findings of a qualitative study of one such approach to addressing the social needs of individuals with psychiatric disabilities living in the community. This approach, which we have referred to as "supported socialization," offers a promising parallel to the advances in the residential, educational, and vocational arenas made within the last decade under the rubrics of "supported housing," "supported education," and "supported employment." After a brief review of the literature on social relationships and psychiatric disability, we first describe our experience with the Partnership Project, one example of an application of a supported socialization approach to decreasing the loneliness, and increasing the community integration of individuals who are socially isolated. This project consisted of a randomized community trial of a 9-month social support program involving 260 participants and 180 volunteer partners. Following our description of the program and research design, we then present the findings from a series of qualitative interviews conducted with a subsample of the participants. In conclusion, we discuss the implications of these findings for approaches to enhancing the community integration of individuals with psychiatric disabilities.

## SOCIAL RELATIONSHIPS AND PSYCHIATRIC DISABILITY

In addition to the consumer-oriented studies of hospital vs. community living described above, there have been many clinical studies documenting restricted social networks among individuals with psychiatric disabilities living in the community (for a review, see Davidson, Stayner, & Haglund, 1998). Approximately 50% of two community samples of people diagnosed with schizophrenia, for example, reported that they had no friends or relationships outside of their families (Breier, Schreiber, Dyer, & Pickar, 1991; Hirschberg, 1985). Social network studies have, reported that people with psychiatric disabilities have fewer social contacts than others (Cohen & Sokolovsky, 1978), and that the number of people with whom they have regular contact, which is between six and 12, is significantly lower than the 30 to 40 people reported for the general population (Wallace, 1984). In addition, the few relationships that people with psychiatric disabilities do have have been described as "uni-directional," rather than reciprocal, in that they appear to receive more support than they are able to give (Cohen & Sokolovsky, 1978; Tolsdorf, 1976; Wallace, 1984). As a result, family members appear to represent the primary source of social support for many individuals, and they tend to report feeling overwhelmed by the needs of their disabled relatives (Tolsdorf, 1976). In turn, people with psychiatric disabilities tend to be characterized more as being taken care of by, rather than caring for, their relatives (Cohen & Kochanowicz, 1989; Cohen & Sokolovsky, 1978).

In the postinstitutional era, such a dismal picture can no longer be attributed to the chronicity and withdrawal thought to be brought about by processes of "institutionalization." Instead, clinical investigators have begun to attribute the social isolation of individuals with psychiatric disabilities to the nature of the disability itself, citing such factors as social skills deficits, affect dysregulation, and the so-called "negative symptoms" of asociality, anergia, anhedonia, and avolition as reasons for why it appears to be difficult for people to establish and maintain reciprocal, caring relationships (for reviews, see Davidson & McGlashan, 1997; Davidson, Stayner, & Haglund, 1998). This literature has gone so far as to characterize people with negative symptoms as "empty shells" who can no longer "think, feel, or act," having "lost the capacity both to suffer and to hope" (Andreasen, 1984, pp. 62–63). In this view, the lack of social support experienced by people with psychiatric disabilities is seen as having been brought about primarily by the ravages of the disorder itself, leaving the person isolated, apathetic, and no longer even desiring companionship or love (Davidson & Stayner, 1997).

A review of first-person accounts paints a very different picture, however. Like the opening quote from Van Gogh, these accounts are replete with poignant descriptions of loss, loneliness, and enduring but unfulfilled desires for love, warmth, and friendship (Davidson & Stayner, 1997; Davidson, Stayner, & Haglund, 1998). In addition to documenting clearly the strong needs and desires that people with psychiatric disabilities continue to have for social relationships—despite their outward appearance at times suggesting the contrary—these accounts also describe numerous obstacles that people face in attempting to reach out to others. Consistent with the clinical literature described above, people do report difficulties that are due to the nature of their disorders, including deficits in social skills and judgement; thought disorder and other attention, concentration, and communication difficulties; hypersensitivity to negative affect and interpersonal conflict; and loss of self and fears of engulfment (Davidson, Stayner, & Haglund, 1998). Without detracting from the extent of damage that psychiatric disorders may do to social relationships in these ways, it is important to note, however, that people also identified obstacles that do not have directly to do with the disorder itself, but with aspects of community living that have arisen outside of the institutional culture found in long-stay hospitals. These obstacles included the social stigma that continues to accrue to psychiatric disability in the popular culture; the demoralization and "internalized stigma" that results from repeated experiences of rejection and loss; poverty; unemployment; and a lack of opportunities for establishing meaningful, reciprocal relationships with peers outside of the formal mental health system (Davidson, Stayner, & Haglund, 1998).

This list of obstacles to forming relationships encountered within the community provides a possible point of departure for community-based program development efforts to address the social isolation of individuals with psychiatric disabilities. That is, acknowledging that there may continue to be some degree of social disability associated with psychiatric disorder, it may be possible, nonetheless, to overcome these other, less directly related, obstacles to social integration encountered by individuals with psychiatric disabilities living in the community. Particularly given the persistent yearning for love and companionship articulated in the first-person literature, it may be possible to increase social support directly, simply by increasing individuals' access to, and opportunities for, reciprocal, caring relationships with others.

Such an approach reverses the traditional order of priority within conventional strategies of psychiatric rehabilitation, shifting from a "train and place" skills development model to a "place and train" community integration model, consistent with recent innovations in the housing, educational, and vocational arenas. As a parallel to supported housing, supported education, and supported employment (e.g., Becker & Drake, 1994; Carling, 1990, 1993, 1995; Drake et al., 1994; Unger, 1998; Wehman, 1986; Wehman et al., 1991), a supported socialization approach focuses on expanding the access of individuals with psychiatric disabilities to the on-going social and recreational activities occurring within their community of origin, and then provides the in vivo supports needed for individuals to make successful use of these opportunities (Davidson et al., 1997; Stayner, Davidson, & Tebes, 1996). Rather than viewing socialization in community settings as an end goal to be achieved through various institutionally-based, rehabilitative means (e.g., social skills training), this approach assists individuals directly in establishing friendships and in participating in the ongoing social and recreational rhythms of communal life with people outside of the formal mental health system.

Although this development and evaluation is the preliminary phase, the application of this approach promises to offer similar advances in decreasing social isolation, as does the approach that gives individuals with psychiatric disabilities the opportunity to live in their own apartments, return to school, and maintain competitive jobs.

### PROGRAM DESCRIPTION

The Partnership Project that provides the context for the current report is one example of the application of a supported socialization approach to addressing the community needs of individuals with psychiatric disabilities. Based on the "Compeer" model first developed in Rochester, New York in the 1970's (Skirboll, 1994; Skirboll & Pavelsky, 1984), this program paired individuals with psychiatric disabilities living in the community, who were socially isolated and withdrawn, with volunteer partners with whom they were able to participate in social and recreational activities for a few hours per week over a 9-months period. The Partnership Project differed from the original Compeer Program by providing both participants and their volunteer partners with a stipend of $28 per month to defray the costs of these activities. In addition, participants were matched either with volunteers who had personal histories of psychiatric disability, but who now were far enough along in their own recovery to have established social networks ("consumer volunteers"), as well as with volunteers who had no personal history of psychiatric disability ("community volunteers"). All volunteers were provided with an initial training, and then with ongoing mutual support meetings with other volunteers facilitated by program staff. Funded by a research demonstration grant from the Center for Mental Health Services, this was the first randomized, controlled trial of this peer support model, investigating the impact of "supported friendships" on the social functioning, well being, quality of life, self-esteem, service use, and satisfaction of socially isolated individuals living in the community (Davidson, Stayner, Rakfeldt, Weingarten & Tebes, 1992).

Details of the experimental design, methods, and quantitative outcome evaluation for the overall study will be presented in future reports. For the present study, and embedded within the experimental design, we developed and conducted semistructured, qualitative interviews with a subsample of study participants to gain access to their first-hand experiences of the processes of meeting a partner, developing a friendship, and exploring community activities. The findings presented here illustrate both the complexity and breadth of these experiences, as well as the promise this type of intervention holds for increasing the social support of individuals with psychiatric disabilities living in the community.

## METHODS

### Participants
Participants for the qualitative interviews were drawn from the larger pool of 260 people who participated in the supported socialization study described above. To be eligible, participants had to have a DSM-III-R diagnosis of either a psychotic or major affective disorder and/or a debilitating character disorder, they also had to currently be receiving outpatient psychiatric treatment, be rated by their outpatient clinician as having moderate to severe impairment in social and occupational functioning, and be living in the community. All eligible individuals in public sector outpatient treatment in a total of 14 communities across the state of Connecticut (representing both urban and suburban settings) were invited by their clinicians to learn about the program from study staff. Before beginning the program, participants gave written, informed consent to being in a randomized trial, and then they were randomly put into one of three conditions in which they: 1) were matched with a volunteer from the community ("community volunteer" condition); 2) were matched with a volunteer who had a personal history of psychiatric disability and recovery ("consumer volunteer" condition); or 3) were not matched with a partner ("stipend-only" condition). In addition, all participants in each condition, and all volunteer partners, received a stipend each month over a 9-month period to defray the costs of their social and recreational activities. The first 27 participants to complete the program were invited to participate in the qualitative interviews. Of those invited, five declined, one was unable to complete the interview due to a physical illness,

and 21 completed the interview, resulting in a distribution that included seven participants from each of the three conditions. Demographic and diagnostic information on these 21 participants as compared to the overall sample are summarized in Table 1.

### Procedures

Following their completion of the 9-month program, participants were paid $20 to complete a two-part, semistructured interview administered by one of the investigators. Participants were encouraged to provide narrative responses to open-ended questions, and then were prompted to comment on specific areas or issues not mentioned spontaneously. Prompts were included based on the prominence of the themes they covered that emerged from open-ended interviews conducted with nine participants and from a series of focus groups conducted with 30 volunteers in an earlier pilot study. The first part of the interview explored the participant's experiences of the program, including the process of meeting and becoming friends with his or her partner; qualities of this relationship, and the extent of his or her participation in community activities during the program. The second part of the interview explored the participant's social relationships and extent of community integration before beginning the program, any important differences she or he had experienced since participating in the program, and his or her perceptions of the future. Interviews typically lasted between 45 and 90 minutes conducted over two sessions, and were audio-taped. Copies of the instruments used in interviewing participants in each of the three conditions are available from the authors.

Data analysis followed established qualitative data analytic procedures derived from the phenomenological perspective (e.g., Davidson, 1994; Davidson et al., 1995; Giorgi, 1970; Wertz, 1983). Audiotapes of the interviews were transcribed, and transcripts of all 21 interviews were given to each of four of the investigators. Three of these investigators were experienced qualitative researchers (LD, DAS, JR), while the fourth was a research fellow learning how to do qualitative research (KEH). These four investigators first independently analyzed each transcript to identify prominent themes that were contained in each participant's narrative responses. The research team then met to discuss each investigator's themes until a consensus was reached on each individual interview. Common themes were then identified across participants within each condition and then confirmed through a reexamination of the transcript material by all four investigators. Finally, the investigators' understanding of the prominent and common themes for participants in each condition were shared with a subsample of participants for their feedback and input (Tebes & Kraemer, 1991). The resulting themes are presented below, illustrated by representative quotes from individual participants.

**Table 1—Percentage of Selected Demographic and Diagnostic Characteristics of Participants Enrolled in the Partnership Project**

| Demographic and Diagnostic Characteristics | Accumulated Study Sample (*n* = 260) | Qualitative Study Sample (*n* = 21) |
|---|---|---|
| Gender | | |
| Female | 57 | 57 |
| Male | 43 | 43 |
| Race/Ethnicity | | |
| African-American | 11 | 10 |
| Hispanic/Latino | 2 | 0 |
| Caucasian | 82 | 90 |
| Asian/Pacific Islander | 1 | 0 |
| Marital Status | | |
| Unmarried/Never Married | 59 | 48 |
| Married/Living With Partner | 14 | 19 |
| Divorced/Separated/Widowed | 25 | 29 |
| Unknown | 0 | 5 |
| Education Level | | |
| Grade 6 or Less | 1 | 10 |
| Grade 7–12 (Not Graduating) | 21 | 10 |
| High School Graduate (Or Equivalent) | 38 | 14 |
| Partial College | 25 | 43 |
| Graduated 2-Year College | 2 | 5 |
| Graduated 4-Year College | 8 | 14 |
| Partial Graduate/Professional School | 2 | 0 |
| Graduate/Professional School | 1 | 5 |
| Age in Years, Mean (Std) | 42 (11) | 42 (11) |
| Axis I Diagnosis | | |
| Psychotic Disorder | 50 | 57 |
| Affective Disorder | 34 | 43 |
| Other Axis I Disorder | 16 | 0 |
| Co-Occurring Substance Use Disorder | 44 | 14 |
| Socio-Economic Status | | |
| Major Business And Professional | 0 | 0 |
| Medium Business/Minor Professional | 2 | 5 |
| Skilled Craftsmen/Clerical/Sales | 2 | 0 |
| Semi-Skilled Workers | 17 | 29 |
| Unskilled Employment/Minimally Employed | 75 | 52 |
| Unknown | 4 | 14 |

## FINDINGS

We present the findings in the following order: a) a description of participants' lives before the program; b) a description of the experiences of participants in the "stipend-only" condition; c) a description of the experiences of participants paired with volunteer partners; and d) a description of the differences between those with a community partner as compared to those with a consumer partner.

### Life Before the Program

*Loneliness, emptiness, and isolation.* Most participants described their day-to-day lives prior to beginning the program as boring, isolated, and lonely, spending much of their time in their apartments or rooms, either engaged in solitary activities or just "staring at the four walls." As one participant described: "I stayed glued to the radio or TV or read a book. That was my life." Most participants described this situation not as something they willingly chose, but rather as something that had happened to them, and over which they had little control. As one participant said:

> There were many lonely days just waiting…for someone to call me up…It was no fun. I found it a very lonely and isolated feeling…going to work and coming home and watching TV and that's it—not getting out.

Another participant who described a similar routine summed up his feeling about the emptiness of his situation by saying simply: "I was existing, but I wasn't living." If they tried to account for leading such a restricted life at all, participants typically attributed their isolation to their disability. As another participant explained:

> Usually you find a lot of isolation when you have a problem, an illness…And you spend a lot of time alone. And sometimes that's not good, because you start to dwell on things that are really not important. You worry about things that don't ever happen. You get yourself in a rut.

In addition to dwelling on their problems and being bored and lonely, participants described having only infrequent, strained contacts with family or a few friends, with the majority of their activities outside of their home revolving around their psychiatric treatment. As one participant described:

> I was depressed. I was sad. I didn't really want to do anything…I was sleeping late in the morning, and some days going to therapy, going to money management group, going to social club…sitting home doing

nothing, watching the boob tube or you know, sitting around the house. That's what I used to do.

As a result of their almost exclusive involvement in treatment and rehabilitative activities, the people dominating participants' social spheres were primarily mental health professionals and other mental health consumers. Although social clubs were a common source of activities and social interactions, many participants expressed their fatigue of being around people who they felt might display unpredictable behaviors or who would serve as a constant reminder of their own disability. Hence, they wanted more activities outside of social clubs, and relationships that were not based solely on shared experiences of disability and hospitalization or on being a recipient of services:

> My social life was kind of limited. I really didn't know too many people around here in town and so forth. And since I don't drive it was another limiting factor...I did have friends, the mental health organization that I'm working with, they were like my friends, although...it's basically a professional type of relationship, so it's not a real, you know, like confiding. I mean, you could confide in them, but it's not the same as having a close friend... So socially, I was sort of restricted.

*Demoralization and estrangement.* In addition to lacking transportation, participants identified a number of obstacles to overcoming these isolating circumstances. Some felt they had been devastated by the experience of being hospitalized, and had become passive and helpless as a result. Since most participants were unemployed, financial limitations also emerged in the foreground of the myriad of obstacles they mentioned. Although their income paid for basic necessities, there was rarely enough left over, for example, to pay one's own way when going out for coffee with peers after an AA meeting or to go out for dinner or splurge on oneself. When combined with the other alienating circumstances associated with psychiatric disability—such as fear and experiences of stigma—a fixed income appeared to contribute to a sense of estrangement from the rest of the community. As related by one participant:

> You don't really feel normal if you can't go anywhere, if you can't do anything except free things. And everybody's out going out to dinner and you know, going to the movies and all these things, and you are stuck home or stuck at the [social] club.

### Stipend-Only Condition
*Disappointment.* Although all participants reported that the additional money provided through their monthly stipend was a welcome resource, a major theme emerged from interviews with stipend-only participants that

involved disappointment over the loss of what they had hoped would be an opportunity to get out of their homes and do things with others. Compounding this disappointment was the fact that most participants had a clear vision of the benefits they were to reap from having a partner, such as having someone to be with, confide in, or receive encouragement from. As one woman said:

> Sometimes all you need is a little help and a little encouragement to get you through. Another person could do that, but when you're by yourself it's very hard to say "I'm an okay person"...It's easier to say "I'm no good, I'm not important, I'm evil, I'm bad, I don't deserve anything." And that's not good, because then that breaks down your self-esteem and all the good things inside you. People need each other...especially when you have an illness, you really need the support.

Said another:

> I guess maybe I was hoping I would be [given a partner] because then I'd maybe have somebody to pull me along and say "Okay, come on" because we were going to go and do something... maybe fearing, and rightfully so, initially, that I wouldn't do it myself. So initially I was a little bit disappointed, knowing I was going to be alone and I wasn't going to have...a boost from someone else.

Participants had such specific visions of what having a partner would be like, that many, in fact, voiced specific desires for partners with or without mental illness. They felt such partners might have been able either, in the case of consumer volunteers, to provide peer support and understanding in the struggle to live with a disability—"you really need the support of somebody who knows exactly what you're going through"—or, in the case of community volunteers, to give them a break from the "world of mental illness"— "like a friend that was thinking straight and... you know, had a job and was well."

*Doing something worthwhile.* Many participants, however, were able to buffer their initial hurt and disappointment about not being assigned a volunteer partner. They resigned themselves to be on what seemed to be the "unlucky" side of the program, with the hope that ultimately their participation in such a research project might help other people with mental illness, possibly—in the future—even themselves. Interviews abounded with statements like: "I was glad that I was able to participate in it to maybe help out more with mental illness" and "I felt like I was a participant in something pretty important, you know, as far as helping people like me maybe find something or maybe have a little more of an advantage." Adopting this point of view helped participants to feel that their personal sacrifice could be made into a grander contribution to others with psychiatric disabilities. Many gained a sense of pride by making a concerted effort to provide honest and carefully thought out answers to interview questions. A minority even came to value the interviews as helpful to them as a rare outlet, a source of feedback, and an accepting and supportive interpersonal milieu in which they could reflect on their experiences.

*To be or not to be social.* In terms of their day-to-day lives, however, many participants in this condition felt that participating in the project made no long-term difference for them. In this regard, two distinct patterns emerged among stipend-only participants. Many participants used their monthly stipends to offset their regular bills and expenses, feeling that, since they did not receive a partner, they continued to have few if any opportunities for socialization. These participants described very few positive experiences associated with the program, and did not experience any significant changes in their social lives as a result. That is, none of the participants felt that they had made any new friends since their participation in the project, and experiences of stigma and discrimination, strained family relations, and fears of the community at large continued to be prominent in their descriptions. As demonstrated by the number of references made to them, these issues seemed to continue to pose significant barriers separating participants from the rest of the community. Other participants, however, chose to use their monthly stipend to "treat" themselves to activities they otherwise would not have pursued, such as going out to restaurants or the movies, and found that their relationships with their few existing friends did deepen or expand as a result of their feeling that they now could "pull their own weight" and contribute to these activities. As one man described: "It wasn't much, but I didn't feel like I was on poverty row anymore...I didn't feel...like a user."

Certainly, in all of these instances, the stipend was seen as making such experiences possible. Given that other participants chose not to spend the money on themselves, but rather on their bills, however, highlights the choice that these participants made to commit themselves to engaging in social activities. In these instances, it appeared that participants were responding not only to the money itself, but also to their perception of having entered into a type of informal contract with study staff. Because program staff members advised participants to use the money for social or recreational activities in the community, some participants felt loosely bound to do so. Even though the additional facilitating factor of a partner was not in place for these participants, knowing that there was an expectation that they use the money in a particular way, and that, as a result, they had the permission to "splurge" on themselves, seemed to provide enough motivation in and of itself to encourage them to try new activities.

*Pleasure, diversion, and intimacy.* In this way, the most commonly mentioned benefit of this condition was being able to engage in enjoyable activities that were previously unaffordable, either alone or with others. Although the activity levels of participants ranged from doing only one or two things over 9 months to carefully planning new activities for each week, all those who made a foray into the community came to value the benefits of having some new things to do that were unrelated to their disability. For example, giving a friend money for gas to be able to take a meandering drive through the Vermont fall foliage, or going to the movies alone were seen as new avenues for unwinding, getting away from the daily stresses of life, and finding some diversion and pleasure. The importance of such activities was evident both as a contrast to the way participants had previously spent their days, as well as by how much they began to look forward to these activities from week to week.

Finally, these experiences also were described by participants as having the by-product of strengthening existing friendships. Even though most stipend-only participants made no new friends during the project and still found it difficult to meet people, having the money for activities with existing friends enhanced relationships that had been difficult to develop previously. For example, one participant expressed appreciation to the project for allowing him "to have a social life again." The extra money enabled him to join in activities with acquaintances that he previously had to miss, allowing him to spend time with them, and build up the trust that was necessary for true friendships to develop. In his words:

> I have a closer relationship with them. As I spent more time with them, I built up trust issues. And my friends are worth more to me today than say, they were a year ago...because I was able to go out with them and spend time.

*Jump start.* Regardless of the initial motivation to seek out activities, participants' enjoyment of these activities seemed to build by itself and lead to a renewed desire for more and more involvement. One participant described this as a kind of "jump start" for his social engine, leading him to pursue part-time employment after the project ended in order to be able to continue to afford the new interests and activities that he came to describe as the "best antidepressant" he could take:

> Initially it started out as having the ability to do it because of a couple of extra bucks every month. But that's what I kind of needed to get my engines started and it got to the point where, then, it wasn't necessarily the money, it was just the desire to get out of the house and do something...One day I said to myself "so, big deal, so you don't have a part-

ner, does that mean that you just have to take the money...put it away somewhere and not do anything with it. Why don't you go out and gain some enjoyment from it?"...it's almost like opening up a little hole in a piece of paper that you kind of poke and its gets bigger and bigger and bigger...To me, the project opened up, gave me that opening. Maybe I made it a little bit bigger, but I think without the project, it would have been tough for me to find another way to...see something other than that "I can't" mode...I said to myself one day "you've got a couple of extra bucks, so why don't you just try at least to do something that maybe you normally wouldn't do." So I went and I did something...I actually did something different and I enjoyed it! Then I found myself saying: "What can I do tomorrow?" And one [thing] led to another...If you could bottle it, it was the best antidepressant I could take...It's enabled me to go out looking for a job so now I can get some extra money. Getting used to having that $28 a month and learning to budget with it and learning the things I could do with that, enabled me to want to go out again, to go out and make more money, so I could spend more time with my friends.

### Community and Consumer Volunteer Conditions

The commonalties between the experiences of participants matched with consumer volunteers and those of participants matched with community volunteers far outweighed any differences between them. Therefore, the common themes across the experiences of all participants who received partners will be described in this section, to be followed in the next section by a description of the few differences that were found between the two conditions.

*Growing a friendship.* In interviews with participants who were matched with partners, there was an interesting parallel to the informal "contract" that some stipend-only participants felt they had made with study staff members to spend their stipends on social and recreational activities. In this case, however, the perception was more universal, and also was of a "contract" between the participants and their volunteer partners rather than with study staff members. This contract entailed a commitment that both participant and partner made to spend time together on a weekly basis over a 9-months period of time, and was described as a supportive structure through which they could, in the words of one participant, "grow a friendship." Such a contract appeared to be useful in several ways in facilitating the development of relationships in the lives of people who otherwise were socially isolated.

First, having a contract in place appeared to allow participants to overcome the usual anxiety, awkwardness, and insecurity that often had posed insurmountable obstacles to their cultivation of relationships in the past.

Based on these repeated difficulties, participants also appeared to need the perceived security of the contract to entice them out of a prolonged period of isolation that often dated back many years to their first episode of mental illness. As one participant described: "As time went by, going in and out of the hospital…I sort of lost…all hope and courage…to make friends." Having few, if any, friends and having become accustomed to keeping everything to themselves, participants described having serious doubts about their ability to relate to others, and worried that they wouldn't be able to hold up their end of the contract. "I tend to be isolated," described one man, "I didn't really have a lot of friends, so…I was a little nervous." Referring to keeping her weekly appointments with her partner, one woman said: "Before…I didn't think I could fulfill my duties about seeing her."

Final obstacles to the development of relationships that appeared to be overcome by the support and structure of the contract were the direct and indirect effects of participants' psychiatric disabilities. Direct effects included the lack of motivation and initiative associated both with depression and with the negative symptoms of schizophrenia, and cognitive deficits such as formal thought disorder and deficits in attention, concentration, and memory that made communication difficult. Indirect effects included internalized stigma and the resulting lack of self-esteem, lack of confidence, and passivity associated with feeling like an inept and unlovable person. Said one participant: "My partner helped me at the beginning to realize that I'm not just a mental patient and that I can form friends." Another participant described how, through the combination of these effects, he had become "locked inside [the] misery" of mental illness; an imprisonment that kept him from being available to relate to others in a satisfactory way:

> It's been an ongoing thing now… and it's something that I'm still struggling with. It's part of mental illness…I feel very isolated and alone and sort of go through this thing where I feel like nobody cares …and I get kind of out of it…It distracted me so much [that] even though I was with another person, I was still locked inside this misery… It's like being sick. It's like being nauseated or having a really bad headache and you're trying to relate, but there's something that's bothering you. It's a distraction… like if you have a headache or something, you can relate, but there's always the pain, so you're going to be thinking of that pain…I was trying to relate and yet…having to struggle to make conversation or to concentrate on something. My attention span was low and my concentration was low, and I think that's a very common problem with people who are mentally ill. Their attention span and their concentration seem to wax and wane and…they're not always there…People take for granted that you just do things. [But for] a person with…mental ill-

ness, it's sometimes hard...it's like you... can't get involved because you're not sort of all there.

There were two elements of the contract that appeared to be primarily responsible for facilitating participants' success in overcoming the variety of obstacles described above. These were a) participants' expectations of unconditional acceptance from their partners, and b) a consistency and regularity in contact with their partners that concretely embodied both this unconditional acceptance and the over-arching framework of a commitment to a 9-month partnership. For example, one woman reported that the most important thing allowing her to trust her partner was "having someone like you unconditionally... being in that position that...she knew she was being assigned to somebody." She described this sense of acceptance as being a palpable "welcome" from the very first meeting:

Just the first day meeting her [and her] saying right there before I said anything: "I think we'll make it and we'll be alright together"...It was a welcome at that time between her and I [to which the interviewer asked "a welcome?"]. Yeah, yeah. We had no reservation of "No, it's not going to work out" [because] that would be doubting the whole thing. And even if there are hard times, we'll give it a shot.

Building on this basic sense of acceptance, participants found it very helpful that their partners saw them on a regular and consistent basis; that their partners kept coming back to spend time with them again and again, even after interactions in which participants felt they were not up to the challenge of being an entertaining companion. For instance, an elderly man described what he liked best about his partner as: "She never let me go. . . [When] I couldn't see her, she came to me. She never let me go." When asked by the interviewer what that experience was like, he responded: "Oh, it was wonderful. I mean you don't have, well, maybe you do, but I have to say in my life, I certainly have not had that many friends that were that faithful." Another participant described being "fairly consistent," getting together with his partner "almost every week." When asked if that consistency was important, he replied:

Oh yeah. I thought it was good that that was consistent, considering my fluctuations in mood and things like that. And I, you know, was sort of proud of that, the fact that I was able to deal with something difficult and not cop out...He was always like there...[and] I felt good about that because, like when I get depressed—which I do at times, I get like very, I get lethargic and very sort of [with]drawn, I don't feel like doing, I don't feel like dealing with anything, I just want to kind of mope around by myself; and for me to like put myself in a position where we're gonna go out, we're gonna do such-and-such a thing, and see certain people and so forth, it was sort of difficult for me. But I mean, I was able to. I told [my partner] a couple of times I was really out of it and he was aware of it, but I was able, for most of the time I was able to, you know, not let it stop me from our getting together, so I felt good about that.

Especially at times like this, when participants felt that their disability posed an obstacle to relating or enjoying shared activities with their partners, they reported finding their partners' explicit acknowledgement and understanding of their "mental patient" status to be helpful in easing the pressure of the social demands made by the growing friendship. At other times, however, the explicit framework of the program and the implicit contract between participants and partners appeared to be experienced as artificial. This was especially true during the early days of the person's participation in the program when both people were just getting to know each other, and were still aware of the sense of having been "assigned" to each other. Considered by most participants to be the only drawback of the program, this sense of artificiality inevitably faded over time as participants and their partners came to care about each other genuinely, and in ways that transcended any initial trepidation based on the participant's disability. One participant described well the prevailing sentiment of those in the experimental condition when she said she felt that she had been "handed a friend on a silver platter." Described another:

I think there is sort of an artificial thing about this program...in the sense that you could get paired up with somebody you don't like, which wasn't...true in my case. In other words, if they pair you up with somebody you don't like...it becomes sort of like a drag or a hassle instead of a good time. Now [my partner] on the other hand was not like that, wasn't a drag or a hassle. So even though it was like an artificial type of set-up, it still worked out well, and we became friends.

Despite the fact that this participant, as well as most others, seemed to think that his own situation was fortunate or coincidental, most participants who were matched with partners reported that they came to feel that the relationship was a natural "fit." "Even though it is psychological research ultimately," said one participant, "it certainly didn't seem like [that] when we were together. When [my partner and I] are together it seems like just a friendship. We're buddies." Said another participant: "Yeah, we were like the perfect pair...on the same wave-length, the same level...The relationship me and [my partner] had as friends, I didn't look at that as being a project."

*The more you get out, the better you feel.* As their friendship with their partners started to grow, participants reported experiencing a number of benefits from the shared activities and relationship that they came to enjoy, value, and even cherish. Similar to those participants in the control condition who used their stipend to enjoy activities they otherwise could not have afforded, participants who were matched with partners appreciated being able to get away from their usual, limited surroundings and, perhaps more importantly, from their disability. They enjoyed being able to afford the simple—but for them, rare—pleasures of going out to dinner, a movie, or even just for coffee. As concisely put by one participant: "The more you get out, the better you feel." Getting out and joining their partners in "normal" activities in community settings served as a stark contrast to their prior experiences of being "locked inside the misery" of isolation and illness. As one woman poignantly described, these simple pleasures helped her to realize that life wasn't the "one big horror" to which she had grown accustomed:

> We always had a good time whenever we went out. We saw a movie, and it was fun, you know. Then I realized...hey, I can have more fun too. It just opened my eyes that there are other things to think about besides mental illness...It was just realizing that, you know, I could go places and have fun, that life isn't one big horror.

In this way, having fun, enjoyable experiences that had nothing to do with mental illness provided participants with relief and respite from their ongoing suffering, distracted them from their usual preoccupation with their difficulties, expanded their range of activities, and gave them something positive to look forward to as well. In the words of one participant:

> At least [now] I've got something to think about other than to think about the bad part, you know, the lonely part. At least I know I can think about: I'm going to go out with [my partner]. It's only lunch, but it'll be good.

Another participant described how looking forward to such activities helped "to break up the monotony." "It's been nice," she said, "knowing that I had something more interesting to have planned for the day, an outing or somewhere to go instead of sitting here at the house." Finally, another participant described how his partner's access to transportation broadened his usual horizons:

> [My partner] drives...so that created a certain amount of freedom as to where we could go and expanded the possibilities of things to do. . . . It was more exposure to things, like movies, we went to a few movies. We did a lot of hiking in parks and stuff...I love nature, I love the outdoors,

I love animals and things like that. And, you know, it's just beauti-ful...We went to a couple of hobby shops. [My partner] is interested in model trains and other things like that, so we went to that. That was sort of interesting to me, too, to see that kind of hobby shop, things like that. It just diversified my experiences. I wasn't so limited to just hang-ing around here or just going out to eat or something. I was able to expand my normal [range of activities].

*I wasn't by myself.* Like the stipend-only participants who used their stipend to explore the community, these participants credited the extra money as an important factor in allowing them to join in activities. But for most, the money and activities per se were not the most important aspects of the project. The experience of the program among participants in the exper-imental condition differed most significantly from those in the stipend-only condition by virtue of their appreciation of their new, growing friendship and of "being with" their volunteer partners as opposed to continuing to be alone. As one participant said: "It certainly wasn't the money that was the attraction, it was [my partner]." Said another:

It got me out of the house, and it got me to meet [my partner] and it got me to mingle with other people...And so it was good for me to be out, to be out just with a crowd...I wasn't by myself, I wasn't out there by myself.

As they found with their participation in community activities, partici-pants described a number of benefits to being with someone else in the con-text of a caring, reciprocal relationship. First, as alluded to in the previous quote, participants found that being "out there" with someone else was eas-ier than being "out there" alone. In other words, having a companion to go out and do things with helped to alleviate participants' initial trepidation, anxiety, and insecurities about venturing out into the community following many years of withdrawal from the social world. As one woman exclaimed after describing the limited life she had led during and following an extend-ed period of hospitalization: "It's the first time I've been able to go shopping in like 25 years!"

In addition to being easier, participants found sharing activities with others to be more enjoyable than taking part in them alone. Most partici-pants first and foremost enjoyed and valued being cared about by another person; being liked and appreciated as a worthwhile human being rather than as "a mental patient." As one participant described: "[Life before the program] was a lot lonelier. But then...she called me and stuff to see how I was doing because she genuinely cared about me and I cared about her, and that was a nice feeling." Even though most partnerships started out feeling awkward and artificial, most volunteers genuinely came to like their partners, to enjoy their company, and to care about them as friends. Participants were able to sense this, and enjoyed being the object of someone's positive attention and affection. As one participant described: "He just wanted to hang out with me, and I was kind of flattered by that." Another participant came to value his partner's early morning phone calls for the same reason: "We might talk for two minutes or a minute, but it's so good to hear from him because I know that he cares." After extolling the many virtues of his partner and describing her affection for him as providing a kind of antidote to his psychiatric disability, another participant quipped: "People talk about chemical imbalance. Well, [my partner] and I, [together we made] a chemical balance."

Participants also valued the opportunity to care about another person, again as a peer and in their own right, rather than because of what they do for the participant. For many participants, this felt like the first opportunity for them to form a "true" friendship since they had become disabled. In describing this experience and how it differed from other relationships since becoming disabled, participants often had to refer back to experiences in adolescence. When asked by the interviewer what the most important thing about the project was for him, one participant replied: "having a male friend who I was friends with in much the same ways I was friends with the kids I knew when I was growing up." Other men spoke in terms of the "male bonding" they experienced in the context of high school athletics, while women referred back to spending hours on the telephone engrossed in "girl talk." For another man, becoming friends with his partner also involved learning to care more deeply for someone than he had for his previous "acquaintances." His partner shared many of his own struggles with unremitting psychotic symptoms during their partnership; struggles that were difficult for the participant to absorb or to assist him with. Even though the participant, at times, found the stress of these experiences to exacerbate his own symptoms, he came to value the friendship with his partner all the more due to the fact that it taught him that he still had the capacity to care about someone else; a capacity he thought he had lost due to his own mental illness:

> It's nice to have somebody to care for...to be willing to hear his problems and to be able to give advice...I would rather have met him and gone through it than never to have met him at all and not known him or that experience...[Now] I'm more receptive and more caring. [Before] there was nothing there. I just didn't feel for the person one way or the other...And I have concluded from that that's maybe the price you pay for a friend, a good friend, is that, you know, you talk to them about their problems and you be there for them, whether it hurts or whether it doesn't.

Finally, participants emphasized the importance of these friendships to be reciprocal, mutual relationships between peers. This meant that participants had to take their partners' needs into account as well as their own, that negotiation and compromise were required to make sure that both partners had equal say in the decisions that shaped their time together. Concretely, this was manifest in decisions about when, where, how, and with whom they would spend their time together. Having to plan their activities together was a new experience for many participants, who had become accustomed either to following someone else's schedule (e.g., their clinician's) or being alone. Making plans that were mutually agreeable involved showing flexibility and responsiveness to another person's needs. As one participant described: "We were actually friends, and that meant a lot to me, you know. It was a learning experience. [I learned] something about life in general...[that] a relationship is a give and take thing."

Also essential to the reciprocity of the relationship was the participant's sense of having something to offer their partner in addition to their time, of being able to "hold up their end of the bargain" and contribute something worthwhile rather than being merely a "charity case." For many participants, this experience stood in stark contrast to their more typical experiences of being the recipient of care without feeling that they had much to offer in return. As an elderly woman who had spent over four decades in a state hospital prior to her participation in the pilot phase of the study explained: "I'm just so tired of taking, taking, taking, all the time" without ever being able to "give back." Having a partner gave her that chance to give back. In the words of another participant:

> It seems that I helped him, too. So I feel good about that. He just said that it helped him to have a friend—to have me for a friend. He gets lonely and bored. And I figure I added something to his life, and I'm really happy I could do that.

Adding something to their partners' lives, whether through advice, a sympathetic ear, or a favor, helped participants to feel that they had something of value to offer to another person, that they were as integral a part of the relationship as their partners were. Again, this stood in contrast to previous experiences of feeling inept and being treated by others as if they had nothing to offer. As one participant described:

> It's been actually quite rewarding...just having this friend who was like just a buddy and talked about sports with and to share my sorrows with was very good. And feeling that he liked me and that he esteemed me and respected my opinion on things was very good...I have a lot of mental health people in my life. But with [my partner] it was more like

fun. It was just having fun and being equals. He treated me as an equal. I respect him for that very much. He wasn't condescending at all.

*We were just at the same level.* As implied in this participant's words, the kind of mutual caring and reciprocity that participants experienced in these partnerships differed significantly from the other relationships they had with family and, in particular, with mental health providers. Whereas their partners treated them as equals and "on the same level," more often than not participants characterized their mental health providers as caring but condescending, as available to some degree, but also as patronizing or as "talking down" to them and treating them as inferior. Said one participant:

> I didn't consider [my partner] to be like a doctor or a, you know, nurse or social worker. He's just a friend, you know, he's in the same boat. The only difference is that he drives and I don't, and that he does certain things that I don't, but I do certain things that he doesn't. So, we were pretty evenly [matched]. It wasn't like he was, you know, talking down to me or being condescending or like that. We were just at the same level. And that was a good thing. Whereas sometimes the mental health professionals tend to be condescending...But [my partner] wasn't like that at all, so that was good.

In all cases, relationships with mental health providers also were seen as distant and as one-directional, as a relationship that was contained within certain defined parameters, in that there were clearly circumscribed roles that limited participants to receiving assistance from another person, without having a chance to give anything back. One participant captured this difference in a nutshell when she said of her partner: "I mean, she was a friend, the others are by appointment." In the words of another participant:

> I see a mental health worker as just a person who functions as a mental health worker. . . They're just doing their job, so, therefore, it's not up to them to like me or be my friend or anything like that. Not like with [my partner, where it is] natural, spontaneous, and intimate.

Given the fact that they were paid for their services, and that these services were provided from within the conventional, neutral framework of psychotherapy, participants did not find the care and concern of their mental health providers to reflect positively on them as people. That is, being cared for by a professional did not raise participants' self-esteem or self-efficacy, or help them to feel more like worthwhile and lovable human beings. If anything, such relationships perpetuated the sense of having nothing of value to offer and of having no expectations placed on them. As one man described:

You can get away with more with the mental health professionals because you kind of think they'll think it's all in a day's work. You don't think that consciously. I don't say, "Well now I'm going to go off on this person and I know I'll get away with it because they're obligated professionally." But you do have that feeling on a certain level that you can say stuff to them and pull stuff with them that you can't with other people or you might lose the friendship.

Participants' friendships with their partners differed importantly from these relationships by virtue of their being based precisely on the kind of mutual give and take, mutual respect and expectations, that are excluded from therapeutic relationships. Said one man:

I see a therapist on a weekly basis, and she's a lady, and I'm very, very fond of her. I've been seeing her for quite a while. The difference is, I could never be close to her, nor she to me, in the same way that [my partner] and I are close because she cannot—well, she does share little bits and pieces of her life—but she can't share her total life, nor should she. I'm talking about my therapist. So there's not the give and take that there is between [my partner] and I.

As implied in this passage, participants did not necessarily think their relationships with mental health providers should have been more reciprocal in this way. Although not appreciating the condescension they often reported experiencing in these relationships, some participants did appreciate the need for therapeutic relationships to be different from friendships or relations between peers. Since relationships with mental health providers predominated their otherwise isolated and lonely lives participants, however, found it problematic that these relationships were so one-directional, so nonreciprocal, and so denied them any opportunities to contribute to them in a positive way (i.e., other than by being a patient). Without having the opportunity to see themselves as having anything of value to offer others, participants remained trapped within the passive, recipient role of patient. Reciprocal relationships with their partners offered participants one avenue of escape from this trap, by providing them with a chance to learn concretely what it is they have to offer others.

*Expanding networks.* In addition to enjoying their time with their partners and coming to feel like worthwhile human beings, some participants described how their success in developing a new friendship with one person, led them to expanding their social networks more broadly, both through their partners, but then also on their own. A number of participants particularly cherished experiences of being included in their partners' family and friendship networks, such as being included in a fishing trip with a partner's three fishing buddies, or being invited over to a partner's home to trim the family Christmas tree. These experiences were distinguished from similar activities taking place at a consumer social club by virtue of their occurring in natural locations, within an existing community of people who cared for each other:

> I benefited from [the program] not only by doing things with [my partner], but [by] meeting other people. ...Associating with [my partner], his family, and his other friends...kind of expanded my awareness of other people [and] expanded my network of friends and so forth.

Participants who were not included to such a degree in their partners' own social networks described other ways their friendships enabled them to reach out and connect with additional people. For some this was through the encouragement and support of their partners, as for the woman who said: "[My partner] taught me not to be afraid to talk to other people and make friends." For others, it was reaching out through modeling and vicarious learning, as described by another participant:

> I could see the way my partner handled himself in a crowd of people, and I could learn from that. And it made me feel that I could handle myself better in a situation, in a social situation, than before the Partnership Project. I could learn from [my partner] from the way he does it. He talks to people and he's friendly, and it made me feel I could, you know, maybe I could do that too, if I put my mind to it.

Yet for still others, the difference was based on their sense of being accepted and cared about as a friend by another person, as expressed by one participant: "I made such good friends with [my partner], I could do it again with other people." The increased sense of confidence and self-esteem that resulted from feeling accepted then facilitated participants approaching others. One man described this process at length, both in terms of making it easier to meet strangers and also of deepening relationships with acquaintances in ways that otherwise would not have occurred:

> I learned to be less nervous around strangers. When I met [my partner] he was basically a stranger to me, and I learned how to be comfortable and relaxed with him, and that carries over into my life now. I think, when I meet a new person, a stranger who I don't know so much about, I'm not as nervous as I would have been had I not gone through the program. It was almost as if just the fact that we got together and we developed this thing, it taught me how to deal with other people as well. So that was one of the best things about it for me...being more comfortable and relaxed. . . I think meeting a stranger and learning to

be comfortable with that person, learning about that person to the point where you're more comfortable with that person, that does sort of affect your other relationships as well. You become a little bit more comfortable, and it's easier to deal with other people as well…with people who I don't know well, like acquaintances, on a more solid foundation, more comfortable, more relaxed, less nervous. I think that's one positive thing that came out of the Partnership Program, [like with] the relationships I already did have, people here from the Y[MCA] and people I see out of town and so forth, I think I'm a little more comfortable and relaxed with them as well, to the point where I can laugh and joke and have a good time…Like somebody I might see in the Y here, and say, "Come into my room, I want to show you this movie I'm watching" or something like that. Or "I want to show you some music, this interesting music I have" or a CD of something, and in that type of situation…I'll notice I'm a little less nervous…And I don't have any problems dealing with them as well. So I think that was a plus, a big benefit, of the program.

*Finding a place in the world.* Finding it easier to engage both new people and old acquaintances, appeared to lead participants to feel that they had found a place for themselves in the broader world rather than, or in addition to, their previous place within the stigmatized "world of mental illness." One man, for example, said the program had helped him to "feel like a more presentable person who can do things in the world." For another, this experience led to his feeling that he had become more of an active agent in his own life, and that his life was now more a part of others' lives as well. As he described:

[As a result of this experience] I think I am a little…less reticent to take on new responsibilities. I think there is something to that. I think there probably is a degree of a little more enthusiasm about things whereas before maybe I was, I'd tend to be a little withdrawn. [The program] might have contributed to my being a little more conscious of who I am, what I'm doing, what to do, what not to do, things like that—just a general awareness of how I fit in…where I fit in, and what I'm all about…People are gregarious basically by nature. I am too, I'm a person, so I am as well. It taught me that I need people, you know. And I think even when I get really cynical or really depressed or something like that, that it passes or I go out and see somebody. So, you know, I learned that, that I need people for fun and good times and stuff like that.

Feeling a sense of belonging and agency within the broader social world beyond their disability also appeared to bring about shifts in how participants viewed themselves, their capacities, and their possible future. For one participant who had battled severe depression and persistent suicidal ideation prior to his involvement in the program, this experience led him to feel that he had a future for the first time in many years. As he described:

> My life certainly was different [before the project]. I did not think that I was going to live to be 120. I did not think I was going to live very long; in fact, I wasn't sure that I wanted to. Now I feel totally different. I don't know how much or little my friendship with my partner has contributed...I can't quantify it...but certainly my life was enriched by my partner. And I think if one's life is enriched by whatever, then that is going to change your perspective on life and death.

For others, there were deeper, more internal changes as well. For example, one participant came to realize that before he met his partner: "I didn't feel like I deserved to have a halfway decent life." Another participant found his view of himself and his future to be "more focused," shifting from the sense of being "a nobody, a nothing" reminiscent of the clinical investigator's "empty shell" image to a sense of being able to "make it" in the world as a contributing citizen:

> I think my thought of so called "making it" in the world, being success-ful and such, is a little more focused...Just basically the experience of the project has just sort of opened up some doors for me in terms of dealing with people...and if you want to get somewhere in life, you have to deal with people. . . Like I could choose to be a nobody, a noth-ing, and just [say] "the hell with it, the hell with everything, I'm not going to deal with anything." And there are times when I feel like that. And yet, I'm part of the world, I'm a human being. And human beings usually kind of do things together to help each other out, that type of thing. And I want to be part of that...If you're not part of the world, it's a pretty miserable place, pretty lonely. So I think degree of involvement is important...involvement in some kind of activity. Hopefully an activ-ity which benefits somebody. I have something to offer, I can give you something that's going to make you healthier or make you happier or make you wiser...that's all I'm talking about. And I think the project maybe in a sense made it a little bit easier for me to think in those terms, to not be afraid to give things to people, and not be afraid to take things from people in return.

Such optimistic passages, while encouraging, should not be misread to represent a "cure" for mental illness. As one young woman somewhat sarcas-tically remarked: "[Having a partner] didn't make my mental illness go away or anything." While not representing a cure, however, addressing participants' unmet needs for acceptance and esteem (both from others as well as from one's self) appeared to provide a basic foundation for further efforts at recovery. The importance of having such a foundation in place was captured well by two female participants. One woman described how she had become resigned to feeling that she already had lost most of her mind to mental illness, and with that, any possibility for a brighter future. After befriending her partner, however, she felt that "it's nice for me to go out with somebody, and when you do something and you know that your mind isn't all gone. You know it's not always good, but you can still make it." For the other woman, there similarly was a basic sense of knowing that she now could "make it" in the broader community, based on her experiences with her partner; what remained for her was to figure out how. As she said: "I can develop a friend being mentally ill. I found that out. I don't know how yet, but I know I can." Reminiscent of the Chinese proverb that "a journey of a thousand miles begins with one step," participants appeared to have brighter views of their future based on their experiences of friendship and acceptance, feeling that they had gotten a "jump start" on what now might become a significantly longer journey.

### Consumer vs. Community Partner

Although we had planned near the end of the interviews to ask participants directly whether or not it was important to them that their partners either did or did not have their own personal history of psychiatric disability and recovery, many participants were quick to voice their perspectives on this issue before the interviewer had a chance to ask. One of the most interesting findings in this regard was that almost all participants came to feel that the particular condition (i.e., "consumer" vs. "community" volunteer) to which they were assigned represented the better of the two alternatives. In only one instance did a participant wish she had been assigned to the other condition. This was the instance of a young woman who was matched with a community volunteer whom she felt did not truly understand her difficulties, and who appeared to her not to want to learn about them. The participant found this to be a formidable gap to overcome, a gap she illustrated when she said of her partner: "She's going to get married in a couple of months and she's thinking about that, and I'm thinking about ways to get to [the grocery store] without freaking out." Even in this instance, however, the participant came to value her friendship with her partner, and to appreciate the chance this relationship, and their shared activities, gave her to get away from her disability. As she went on to describe:

I don't know if she really understands mental illness...She never had to deal with something like that...[But] in a way it was welcome. This way I could get a breather, away from mental illness. I could pretend I was normal. [The experience with my partner] made me see her side because I'm so used to being in my own head that when I went out with her I realized that that's not the way that everybody thought... So it widened my scope. Because I've been just with mentally ill people and that's all you think about.

All of the other participants who were matched with community volunteers expressed similar concerns related to their experience of the program, but to a lesser degree. For example, participants in this condition began their relationships with their partners aware of their differences in status and functioning, and worried that they would not be able to "rise up" to, or maintain themselves at their partner's "level." They worried about stereotypes of mental illness coloring their partner's expectations and perceptions of them, and feared rejection on this basis. In addition, interacting regularly for the first time in many years with a peer who does not have to cope daily with mental illness made some participants more acutely aware of their own pain and limitations—aspects of their lives to which they appeared to have become numbed. In all of these cases, however, the benefits of the relationship came to outweigh these concerns over time, leading all other participants to feel that they had landed in the better of the two conditions. In addition to being able to "get away from mental illness" and see how the "other side" (i.e., nondisabled people) lived, developing a friendship with a person who was not psychiatrically disabled, outside of mental health settings, offered participants a view of themselves beyond their mental illness as well. Although they initially worried about being stigmatized and rejected by their partners, participants reported that on the contrary their disability seemed to make no difference to their partners. This kind of unconditional acceptance, as well as their association with "normal" people doing "normal" activities, enabled participants to begin to view themselves as being on the same level as their nondisabled peers. One woman described this growth process in the following terms:

It's like being down here and they're being up there and kind of looking down at you down here, and eventually I did grow up to where she was. [It started out] with my low self-esteem and confidence, and brought up to kind of where she's at. It's made me stronger... And she would tell me, she would say whether or not it was okay, if I was doing the right thing. That kind of helped me to go on and think that I am somebody, and that I'm worthwhile.

For the most part, participants whose partners did have a history of psychiatric disability and recovery did not perceive such a vertical gap, such a difference in functioning and status, between themselves and their partners. Even though all consumer volunteers were further along in their recovery and had established social networks, participants appeared to minimize these differences on the one hand, but on the other hand they aspired to be like their partners. Participants started their relationships with their consumer partners more aware of being "in the same boat" due to their shared history of psychiatric disability, hospitalization, and medication, rather than focusing on differences in status. Rather than feeling uncomfortable about differences in functioning, participants described being relaxed with their partners from the start, due to this common ground of mental illness. Regardless of whether or not these experiences were spoken about explicitly, knowing that their partners had at least some of the same experiences seemed to quell participants' worries about negative stereotypes. Said one:

> If [my partner] hadn't been mentally ill himself, [he] would have had feelings about the mentally ill which would have come out and which would have made me uncomfortable. [But he] understands mental illness a little, so he's not really stigmatizing me for mental illness because he has it…He didn't stigmatize me…unconsciously or half consciously or whatever… because he is mentally ill…I think that the ideal situation is to get somebody who…has at least…some history of mental problems, rather than somebody who was very normal, you know, straight, normal.

In addition to stigma, participants in this condition felt that their experiences of hospitalization, estrangement, and disability would have been difficult to explain, had their partners not gone through them as well. Having such experiences in common provided an additional tacit bond and sense of mutual understanding. One man, for example, who previously had described the "male bonding" he and his partner had experienced based on their shared interests in sports, went on to speak of "mentally ill bonding," the "bonding of two mentally ill people," as well as: "We're both on medication. We've both been in hospitals. So there was that kind of bonding, too."

It was then on the basis of this common ground, within the context of this bonding, that participants went on to examine the differences that did exist between themselves and their partners. These differences were seen as less significant than the differences between participants and community volunteers, and often were seen as going in both directions as well. That is, participants saw their partners as being able to do some things they could not do, but also saw themselves as having strengths that their partners did not share. Said one participant: "[my partner] teaches me how to sail and I teach him how to fish." In a passage already quoted at length, another participant explained that the only difference between him and his partner is "that he drives and I don't, and that he does certain things that I don't, but I do certain things that he doesn't." Of particular importance to participants was one difference, however, and that was the perception that their consumer partners, despite their shared experiences of disability, had progressed further than they had in resuming a normal life in the community. Most participants were surprised at first to see another person with a psychiatric disability leading a relatively normal life. Over time, some participants then came to derive inspiration and hope from the example their partners set. "[My partner] is mentally ill," said one man, but "to an extent he's fairly, you know, with it." Similar to participants with community volunteers who felt that their partners had given them a taste of "the other side" (i.e., life without mental illness), participants with consumer volunteers came to feel that their partners had enabled them to imagine the possibility of a life beyond mental illness. It was to such a vision of recovery that they then came to aspire.

## DISCUSSION

The qualitative accounts presented in this report describe in detail participants' experiences of a supported socialization program. The most consistent finding across all of those interviewed was the degree to which participants desired, and responded to opportunities for, friendship. Even those in the stipend-only condition, who did not use their stipend to go out and participate in activities by themselves, expressed strong desires for human interaction and were disappointed by their "bad luck" in not receiving a partner. Given that social isolation and withdrawal were preconditions for inclusion in the study, this finding counters conventional perceptions of people with psychiatric disabilities either as apathetic about social relationships or as actively wishing to remain alone. To the contrary, friendship appeared in the lives of these people—just as it was when defined by Aristotle over 2000 years ago—to be "noble as well as necessary"; the necessity deriving from the fact, according to Aristotle, that human beings are by nature social animals (Aristotle, 384–322 BC/1962a, p. 215; Aristotle, 384–322 BC/1962b).

What may be particularly striking about the findings of this study is that Aristotle's insight about to the necessity of friendship appears just as relevant to those of us with psychiatric disabilities as to anyone else. As the eloquent voices coming through these accounts attest, mental illness—as debilitating as it may be—has not altered this fundamental aspect of human nature. Even people severely disabled by major mental illness remain essentially social animals. Such findings confirm the first-person accounts reviewed above which suggest that people with psychiatric disabilities are "not made of stone or iron" but miss and continue to desire human contact —no matter how withdrawn, apathetic, or empty they may appear. The other findings of the study, which speak to the benefits of reciprocal, caring relationships, also seem to concur with Van Gogh's view that friendship can "open the prison" and free participants from being "locked inside the misery" of their disability.

These findings also suggest that a little encouragement to participate in social activities, along with the infusion of a small amount of financial resources (e.g., $7 a week) for that purpose, may have a positive impact on the socialization of some individuals living in the community, as exemplified by some of the participants in the stipend-only condition. Across conditions, participants described valuing their experiences of being able to go out and do "normal" things and of regaining parts of themselves and their lives that they had lost since the onset of their illness. They felt good about getting away from their usual surroundings and from their absorption in mental illness and psychiatric treatment to relax, unwind, distract themselves from their on-going suffering, as well as broaden their horizons. They described cherishing moments of spontaneity and enjoyment of such seemingly trivial pleasures as sharing a relaxed lunch with their partners, going fishing, gardening, cooking, and sharing a Thanksgiving dinner with a partner's family. Essential to these experiences was the fact that they were occurring naturally, within the on-going rhythms and settings of "normal" communal life and with peers with whom they could develop reciprocal relationships, rather than within the institutional settings and hierarchical structures of the mental health system. Indeed, one of the more important dimensions of these experiences was the access they provided to a world beyond the parameters of the mental health system, the window they offered onto a life beyond disability. As one participant described, such experiences helped her to realize that "there are other things to think about besides mental illness," that "life isn't [just] one big horror."

On the surface, it may seem that the benefits of these "supported friendships" were limited to decreasing participants' isolation and loneliness, expanding their social networks, enhancing their self-esteem and confidence in social situations, and enriching their quality of life. Appreciating that otherwise life may, in fact, be "one big horror" for individuals with psychiatric disabilities, however, should help us to recognize that such benefits also should not be underestimated in their value in reopening long-closed doors back into the community. The benefits of opening such doors should encourage us to explore ways to remove the financial, cultural, attitudinal, instrumental, and emotional obstacles that continue to make the establishment and maintenance of caring, reciprocal relationships difficult for people with psychiatric disabilities in the context of community life.

The importance of such efforts is underscored particularly when one considers the earlier findings from surveys and interviews of institutional vs. community living described in the introduction to this report. What individuals with psychiatric disabilities valued about life within long-stay hospitals, and what they missed when they returned to the community, were the social structures that enabled them to participate in meaningful activities with their peers. Working in the hospital or on the grounds, "hanging out" with their friends in the canteen, attending religious services in the hospital chapel, all allowed them to feel part of a community, even if it was the mental health community. Living alone in an apartment and traveling to and from the mental health center for treatment appointments does not afford the same sense of community, and when given the choice, many individuals choose not to attend activities at social clubs due to a perception that attendence could affect their identity and sense of self.

What these findings argue for is not only this particular "compeer" approach to supported socialization, but also for the creation of additional "mediating structures" that enable participation in an array of naturally occurring activities that afford people an opportunity to give back to others (Bebout et al., 1995; Berger & Neuhaus, 1977). Without the structures and support offered by such an approach, mental illness will continue to pose a significant barrier in the social arena, as it did previously in the areas of housing, education, and employment. Once situated within a broader vision of "supported community life" (Ferguson, Hibb, Leiman, & Schaff, 1990), however, psychiatric disability potentially may be no more limiting or restrictive in a person's life than other disabilities, for which environmental accommodations have been developed and employed, such as cutting curbs in sidewalks and posting Braille signs in elevators.

This study has several obvious limitations. Being a qualitative study with a small sample size, it remains to be seen if these findings can be applied to the broader population of individuals with psychiatric disabilities. Also given that five participants declined the invitation to be interviewed, these findings may be positively skewed and not adequately represent some participants' negative experiences with the program. The fact that most of the themes described in this report were found to be common across participants in each of the three conditions, however, indicates their potential usefulness in understanding the nature of the experiences shared by individuals participating in a supported socialization program. The value of such understanding remains to be confirmed and/or amplified further when applied to the forth-coming interpretation of the quantitative outcome evaluation.

## REFERENCES

Andreasen, N. C. (1984). *The broken brain: The biological revolution in psychiatry.* New York: Harper & Row.

Aristotle (1962a). *Nicomachean ethics* (M. Ostwald, Trans.). Indianapolis, IN: Bobbs-Merrill Educational Publishing. (Original work published 384–322 B.C.)

Aristotle (1962b). *The politics* (Sinclair, T. A., Trans.). New York: Penguin Books. (Original work published 384–322 B.C.)

Bebout, R. R., Harris, M., Swayze, F. V., Beyer, L. L., Freeman, D. W., Jones, M., Landis, C. L., & Stowe, H. D. (1995). *The Community Connections social support network intervention model.* Washington, DC: Community Connections: New Hampshire-Dartmouth Psychiatric Research Center; Hanover, NH.

Becker, D. R., & Drake, R. E. (1994). Individual placement and support: A community mental health center approach to vocational rehabilitation. *Community Mental Health Journal, 30,* 193–206.

Bene-Kociemba, A., Cotton, P. G., & Fortgang, R. C. (1982). Assessing patient satisfaction with state hospital and aftercare services. *American Journal of Psychiatry, 139,* 660–662.

Berger, P. L., & Neuhaus, R. J. (1977). *To empower people: The role of mediating structures in public policy.* Washington, DC: American Enterprise Institute for Public Policy Research.

Breier, A., Schreiber, J. L., Dyer, J., & Pickar, D. (1991). National Institute of Mental Health longitudinal study of chronic schizophrenia. *Archives of General Psychiatry, 48,* 239–246.

Carling, P. (1990). Major mental illness, housing, and supports: The promise of community integration. *American Psychologist, 45,* 969–975.

Carling, P. (1993). Housing and supports for persons with mental illness: Emerging approaches to research and practice. *Hospital and Community Psychiatry, 44,* 439–449.

Carling, P. (1995). *Return to community: Building support systems for people with psychiatric disabilities.* New York: The Guilford Press.

Cohen, C. I., & Kochanowicz, N. (1989). Schizophrenia and social network patterns: A survey of black inner-city outpatients. *Community Mental Health Journal, 25,* 197–207.

Cohen, C. I., & Sokolovsky, J. (1978). Schizophrenia and social networks: Ex-patients in the inner city. *Schizophrenia Bulletin, 4,* 546–560.

Davidson, L. (1994). Phenomenological research in schizophrenia: From philosophical anthropology to empirical science. *Journal of Phenomenological Psychology, 25,* 104–130.

Davidson, L., Chinman, M. J., Kloos, B., Weingarten, R., Stayner, D. A., & Tebes, J.K. (1997). Mental illness as a psychiatric disability: Shifting the paradigm toward mutual support. *The Community Psychologist, 30,* 19–21.

Davidson, L., Hoge, M. A., Godleski, L., Rakfeldt, J., & Griffith, E. E. H. (1996). Hospital or community living? Examining consumer perspectives on deinstitutionalization. *Psychiatric Rehabilitation Journal, 19,* 49–58.

Davidson, L., Hoge, M. A., Merrill, M. E., Rakfeldt, J., & Griffith, E. E. H. (1995). The experiences of long-stay inpatients returning to the community. *Psychiatry, 58,* 122–132.

Davidson, L., & McGlashan, T. H. (1997). The varied outcomes of schizophrenia. *Canadian Journal of Psychiatry, 42,* 34–43.

Davidson, L., & Stayner, D. (1997). Loss, loneliness, and the desire for love: Perspectives on the social lives of people with schizophrenia. *Psychiatric Rehabilitation Journal, 20,* 3–12.

Davidson, L., Stayner, D. A., & Haglund, K. E. (1998). Phenomenological perspectives on the social functioning of people with schizophrenia. In K. T Mueser, & N. Tarrier (Eds.), *Handbook of social functioning in schizophrenia* (pp. 97–120). Boston: Allyn & Bacon.

Davidson, L., Stayner, D. A., Rakfeldt, J., Weingarten, R., & Tebes, J. K. (1992). Friendship and the restoration of community life: Supported socialization for people with psychiatric disabilities. In P. Stastny, & J. Campbell (Eds.), *Social supports and psychiatric rehabilitation.* New York: John Wiley.

Dickey, B., Gudeman, J. E., Hellman, S., Donatelle, A., & Grinspoon, L. (1981). A follow-up of deinstitutionalized chronic patients four years after discharge. *Hospital and Community Psychiatry, 32,* 326–330.

Drake, R. E., Becker, D. R., Biesanz, J. C., Torrey, W. C., McHugo, G. J., & Wyzik, P. F. (1994). Rehabilitative day treatment vs. supported employment: I. Vocational outcomes. *Community Mental Health Journal, 30,* 519–532.

Ferguson, P. M., Hibbard, M., Leinen, J., & Schaff, S. (1990). Supported community life: Disability policy and the renewal of mediating structures. *Journal of Disability Policy Studies, 1,* 9–35.

Giorgi, A. P. (1970). *Psychology as a human science: A phenomenologically based approach.* New York: Harper & Row.

Herman, N. J., & Smith, C. M. (1989). Mental hospital depopulation in Canada: Patient perspectives. *Canadian Journal of Psychiatry, 34,* 386–391.

Hirschberg, W. (1985). Social isolation among schizophrenic outpatients. *Social Psychiatry, 20,* 171–178.

Jones, K., Robinson, M., & Golightly, M. (1986). Long-term psychiatric patients in the community. *British Journal of Psychiatry, 149,* 537–540.

Lord, J., Schnarr, A. & Hutchison, P. (1987). The voice of the people: Qualitative research and the needs of consumers. *Canadian Journal of Community Mental Health, 6,* 25–36.

MacGilp, D. (1991). A quality of life study of discharged long-term psychiatric patients. *Journal of Advanced Nursing, 16,* 1206–1215.

Okin, R. L., & Pearsall, D. (1993). Patients' perceptions of their quality of life 11 years after discharge from a state hospital. *Hospital and Community Psychiatry, 44,* 236–240.

Skirboll, B. W. (1994). The Compeer model: Client rehabilitation and economic benefits. *Psychosocial Rehabilitation Journal, 18,* 89–94.

Skirboll, B. W., & Pavelsky, P. K. (1984). The Compeer program: Volunteers as friends of the mentally ill. *Hospital and Community Psychiatry, 9,* 938–939.

Solomon, P. (1992). The closing of a state hospital: What is the quality of patients' lives one year post-release? P*sychiatric Quarterly, 63,* 279–296.

Stayner, D. A., Davidson, L., & Tebes, J. K. (1996). Supported partnerships: A pathway into community life for persons with serious psychiatric disabilities. *The Community Psychologist, 29,* 14–17.

Tebes, J. K., & Kraemer, D. K. (1991). Quantitative and qualitative knowing in mutual support research: Some lessons from the recent history of scientific psychology. *American Journal of Community Psychology, 19,* 739–756.

Tolsdorf, C. C. (1976). Social networks, support, and coping: An exploratory study. *Family Process, 15,* 407–417.

Unger, K. V. (1998). *Handbook on supported education: Providing services for students with psychiatric disabilities.* Baltimore, MD: Paul H. Brookes.

Van Gogh, V. (1937). *Dear Theo: The autobiography of Vincent Van Gogh* (I. Stone, Ed.). New York: The New American Library. (original work published 1873-1890.)

Wallace, C. J. (1984). Community and interpersonal functioning in the course of schizophrenic disorders. *Schizophrenia Bulletin, 10,* 233–257.

Wehman, P. H. (1986). Supported competitive employment for persons with severe disabilities. *Journal of Applied Rehabilitation Counseling, 17,* 24–29.

Wehman, P. H., Revell, G., Kregel, J., Kreutzer, J. S., Callahan, M., & Banks, P. D. (1991). Supported employment: An alternative model for vocational rehabilitation of persons with severe neurologic, psychiatric, or physical disability. *Archives of Physical and Medical Rehabilitation, 72,* 101–105.

Wertz, F. J. (1983). From everyday to psychological description: Analyzing the moments of a qualitative data analysis. *Journal of Phenomenological Psychology, 14,* 197–241.

# Peer Support Among Individuals with Severe Mental Illness: A Review of the Evidence

*Larry Davidson, Matthew Chinman, Bret Kloos, Richard Weingarten, David Stayner, and Jacob Kraemer Tebes*

At the time of original publication, the authors were affiliated as follows: Larry Davidson, Matthew Chinman, Bret Kloos, Richard Weingarten, David Stayner, and Jacob Kraemer Tebes, Yale University School of Medicine, New Haven CT.

© 1999 American Psychological Association D12. This article originally appeared in *Clinical Psychology: Science and Practice*, 1991, 6, 165–187, 2002, 49–74, and is reprinted with permission. This is a revised version of an invited address presented to the Preconference Institute on Self-Help/Mutual Assistance of the 6th biennial conference on Community Research and Action, May 1997, Columbia, SC.

**Abstract:** This article reviews the history and potential effectiveness of peer support among persons with severe mental illness. Following a historical overview, we describe the three primary forms of peer support that have been developed to date by and for this population, and examine the existing empirical evidence of the feasibility, effectiveness, and utilization of each of these approaches in contributing to the recovery of individuals with psychiatric disabilities. These three forms are 1) naturally occurring mutual support groups, 2) consumer-run services, and 3) the employment of consumers as providers within clinical and rehabilitative settings. Existing studies of mutual support groups suggest that they may improve symptoms, promote larger social networks, and enhance quality of life. This research is largely from uncontrolled studies, however, and will need to be evaluated further using prospective, controlled designs. Consumer-run services and the use of consumers as providers promise to broaden the access of individuals with psychiatric disabilities to peer support, but research on these more recent developments is only preliminary and largely limited to demonstrations of their feasibility. We discuss issues entailed in participating in peer support for this population, and then close with a discussion of the implications for future policy, research, and practice.

*To me, mental illness meant Dr. Jekyll and Mr. Hyde, psychopathic serial killers, loony bins, morons, schizos, fruitcakes, nuts, straightjackets, and raving lunatics. They were all I knew about mental illness, and what terrified me was that professionals were saying I was one of them. It would have greatly helped to have had someone come and talk to me about surviving mental illness—as well as the possibility of recovering, of healing, and of building a new life for myself. It would have been good to have role models—people I could look up to who had experienced what I was going through—people who*

*had found a good job, or who were in love, or who had an apartment or a house on their own, or who were making a valuable contribution to society.*
—Deegan (1993)

This eloquent plea for peer role models was made by a woman who has spent the last 24 years of her life living with schizophrenia and who, most recently, has herself become such a role model for others with this disorder. During that time, she completed her doctoral training in clinical psychology and directed a community mental health center prior to becoming a national leader of the Mental Health Consumer Movement (MHCM) in the United States. Her argument—that people coping with severe mental illness could benefit from having peer role models who have been successful in managing their own disabilities—is both persuasive and challenging.

On the one hand, it certainly seems reasonable to suggest that people with schizophrenia and related disorders might benefit from being exposed to others who have recovered to some degree from the same disorder. Such experiences could act to counter stigma and prevailing cultural stereotypes about mental illness, and might offer the person hope and motivation to work for a better future. Beliefs such as these are integral to MHCM's conceptualization of "recovery," which—in contrast to the definition of an asymptomatic endstate offered in the American Psychiatric Association's DSM-IV (American Psychiatric Association, 1994) and practice guidelines for the treatment of schizophrenia (American Psychiatric Association, 1997)—refers to an ongoing process of learning to live with one's disability and gradually rebuilding a sense of purpose, agency, and meaning in life despite the limitations of the disorder (Davidson & Strauss, 1992; Deegan, 1992, 1993; Weingarten, 1994, 1997). From the perspective of MHCM, having visible examples of individuals with psychiatric disabilities who have resumed valued roles and reintegrated successfully into their communities could provide a useful impetus and concrete guidance for a shift in the focus of current treatment efforts beyond symptom reduction and stabilization precisely to such a notion of recovery (Carling, 1995; Frese & Davis, 1997; Reidy, 1994).

This core argument of the MHCM for the availability of peer role models seems all the more persuasive when one considers the important role of this resource in recovery from substance use disorders and other life circumstances. The substance abuse treatment community has long operated on the belief that there is value in mutual support groups and in hiring as counselors people who are in their own recovery from addictions due to their first-hand knowledge of the terrain and their credibility as role models. In addition, access to peers who have survived and/or recovered from similar circumstances is available through mutual support groups for individuals with a variety of other conditions. In Connecticut alone—a state with a census of approximately 3 million—in 1996 there were nearly 900 publicized mutual support groups in 108 different categories, covering every serious medical condition and life circumstance from anemia to bereavement to coping with handicapped children, divorce, and retirement (Connecticut Self-Help Network, 1996). The role of such groups in offering hope, facilitating coping, and enhancing quality of life for people facing adversities has become widely accepted in numerous arenas both inside and outside of the general medical community (Borkman, 1990; Jacobs & Goodman, 1989; Katz, 1981; Katz & Levin, 1980; Kurtz, 1990; Levin, Katz, & Hoist, 1976; Salem, Seidman, & Rappaport, 1988).

On the other hand, however, despite this well-established practice in the field of addictions treatment and the growing scholarly literature documenting the ubiquity and effectiveness of mutual support for a range of conditions and life circumstances (e.g., Borkman, 1991; Gartner & Riessman, 1984; Humphreys & Rappaport, 1994; Kyrouz & Humphreys, 1996), similar practices have attracted little attention to date in the treatment and rehabilitation of persons with mental illness. In the quote above, Deegan (1993) noted the lack of available role models in her own treatment and rehabilitation. In her oft-cited 1982 editorial calling for the promotion, and study, of mutual support among persons with serious mental illness, Estroff (1982) noted the lack of recognition of the legitimacy and utility of this resource within mental health. In the over 15 years since Estroff issued her challenge to the field, research has shown consistently that very few professionals refer their clients to mutual support groups, and that few individuals with serious mental illness make use of these options on their own (Chesler, 1990; Salzer, McFadden & Rappaport, 1994). Despite the persuasiveness of the argument for peer role models and mutual support for persons with serious mental illness, and their demonstrated benefit for individuals in other circumstances, most people with psychiatric disabilities continue either not to have access to, or to choose not to take advantage of, these potential resources.

This article reviews the history and evidence for the effectiveness of peer support among individuals with serious mental illness. Following a brief history, we describe the three forms of peer support that have been developed by and for this population to date, and examine existing empirical evidence of the feasibility, effectiveness, and utilization of each in contributing to the recovery of individuals with psychiatric disabilities. Due to its having been traditionally the primary vehicle for the provision of peer support—and to its having been, as a result, the object of considerable discussion—we begin with a conceptual definition and examination of 1) naturally occurring mutual support. Next, we examine two additional routes that have been developed more recently to expand the access of individuals with severe mental illness to peer support beyond mutual support groups: 2) consumer-run services and 3) mental health consumers as providers within clinical and rehabilitative settings. In the remainder of the article, we consider some of the issues entailed in participating in peer support for individuals with psychiatric disabilities, and conclude with a discussion of the implications for future mental health policy, research, and practice.

### HISTORICAL BACKGROUND

The first person to place an explicit value on the role of peer support in the treatment of mental disorders was Harry Stack Sullivan. While running an inpatient service for young men with schizophrenia at Sheppard and Enoch Pratt Hospital outside of Baltimore in the 1920s, Sullivan actively recruited young men who had recovered from their own psychiatric disorders to be aides on his unit. He felt that their own life experiences of psychosis and recovery would lend a particular sensitivity to their work, making them uniquely qualified to assist their peers in working through similar struggles in a humane and compassionate manner. Having had his own experience of psychosis, this also may have been true of Sullivan himself (Perry, 1982).

One can argue that the role Sullivan envisioned for his psychiatric aides was played in other clinical settings as well by people who had achieved some level of success in coping with their own psychiatric disabilities. In particular, the therapeutic communities developed in inpatient settings by Jones (1953), Edelson (1964, 1970a, 1970b), and others encouraged the use of peer support and mentoring, as well as confrontation, conflict, and collaborative problem-solving, as essential elements of the treatment milieu. Under the rubric of developing adaptive ego functions, it was considered mutually beneficial when one patient would offer his or her strengths to another in the roles of leader, role model, or friend. Sullivan's innovation was to extend the reach of the therapeutic milieu by offering a salary to bring back onto the unit successful patients who no longer needed the milieu for their own treatment.

It has been within the last 20 years that we have begun to revisit this strategy. Two unintended consequences of deinstitutionalization help to account for this. One has been the Mental Health Consumer Movement, mentioned above, which began as ex-patients banding together to protest the treatment they received while hospitalized (Chamberlin, 1978, 1984, 1990; Deegan, 1992; Frese & Davis, 1997; Zinman, 1986; Zinman, Harp, & Budd, 1987). Two of the core elements of this movement early in its evolution were mutual support groups and independent consumer-run services, both of which were designed initially to serve as alternatives to the formal mental health system. Having established its political identity as independent from the mental health system, this movement is now coming of age and seeking more of a collaborative relationship with providers (Emerick, 1989; Kaufmann, Freund, & Wilson, 1989). One important focus of this collaboration has been the training and hiring of consumers as staff in clinical and rehabilitative settings (Davidson, Weingarten, Steiner, Stayner, & Hoge, 1997; Mowbray, Moxley, Jasper, & Howell, 1997; Moxley & Mowbray, 1997; Stephens & Belisle, 1993). With the 1990 passage of the Americans with Disabilities Act, it became illegal in the United States to discriminate in the workplace on the basis of a history of psychiatric disability. This landmark legislation fueled the fires of consumer advocates, who now have legal backing to become a part of the system they wish to reform (Deegan, 1993; Moxley & Mowbray, 1997).

The other unintended consequence of deinstitutionalization has been a recognition that hospitals met a range of human as well as clinical needs, and that to be effective, community-based services need to move beyond reduction of psychopathology to focus on the restoration of community life (Carling, 1995). Along with this recognition has been an increasing awareness that clients being discharged into the community need more of a bridge into supportive social networks than that provided by formal mental health treatment alone (Gartner & Riessman, 1984; Godley, Sabin, McClure, Smerken, & Manion, 1988; Skirboll & Pavelsky, 1984). With the advent of the Community Support Movement (Parrish, 1989) in the 1970s, there has been a growing realization of the need to recreate a therapeutic milieu "without walls" in the community (Stein & Test, 1978). As Sullivan had explored within the hospital walls, mental health consumers, ex- or current patients who have achieved a level of mastery over their own disabilities, have been suggested as being able to play a useful role in establishing such a milieu in the community (Edmunson, Bedell, & Gordon, 1984; Moxley & Mowbray, 1997).

Although the mutual support group traditionally has been the primary vehicle for the creation of such a peer support milieu, we would suggest that some of the principles of mutual support may find additional expression both through consumer-run services and through the employment of consumer providers within mental health settings. As there has been more research on conventional mutual support groups, we summarize this literature by highlighting its major findings. Research on consumer-run services and consumer providers, which are more recent developments, is summarized by reviewing the studies conducted in each area to date.

## A CONCEPTUAL DEFINITION OF MUTUAL SUPPORT

In its most basic form, we define mutual support as a process by which persons voluntarily come together to help each other address common problems or shared concerns. Participation in such a process reflects an intentional effort to find a social niche in which there are resources and structures available to enhance an individual's ability to address such concerns. The resources and structures made available through mutual support derive from several of its characteristics.

First, sharing similar life experiences with others can increase a person's understanding of his or her situation and reduce social isolation. Involvement in mutual support may increase participants' social networks and may offer participants acceptance, support, understanding, empathy, and a sense of community, leading to an increase in hope and autonomy and an assumption of personal responsibility (Carpinello, Knight, & Janis, 1991; Levy, 2000; Salem, Seidman & Rappaport, 1988).

Second, a structured process of social interaction may allow people to adopt socially valued roles, in which they no longer are restricted to a passive role of "patient" relying on expert advice but now also may serve as role models for newer members, provide feedback and assistance to others, and receive feedback for their own efforts to address their problems (Levy, 2000; Maton, 1987; Roberts et al., 1991). Riessman (1965, 1990) identified this shift in role as the "helper therapy principle" and since has been joined by many researchers in documenting the impact this switch in perspective and activities can have in people's lives (Maton, 1987; Roberts & Thorsheim, 1991; Roberts et al., 1991).

Third, mutual support can be distinguished from naturally occurring social support in that it is an intentional process that includes standard procedures, routines, and prescriptions for addressing problems and issues of everyday life (Levine & Perkins, 1987; Levy, 2000). That is, mutual support creates a specific behavioral setting (cf. Barker, 1968; Levine & Perkins, 1987; Rappaport, 1977) that may offer new information, perspectives, training, and skills, and in which a supportive social climate may be fostered (cf. Moos, 1973). Mutual support in these settings often includes tasks of learning new information for how to address one's problem, such as coping strategies or alternative perspectives, and being exposed to successful role models, allowing for vicarious learning, modeling, and an enhancement of problem-solving skills (Gartner & Reissman, 1984; Kaufmann et al., 1989; Kurtz, 1990; Kurtz & Powell, 1987; Levy, 1976; Rootes & Aanes, 1992; Stewart, 1990).

Fourth, mutual support may offer worldviews and ideologies to assist persons in making sense of their experiences (Antze, 1976; Cain, 1991; Denzin, 1987; Humphreys, 1992; Kennedy & Humphreys, 1994). The exact forms in which mutual support is instantiated are greatly influenced by the particular ideology of those promoting it. The specific roles participants adopt, the skills they learn, and the nature of their social networks will be a function of the setting's ideology. Several writers have focused on the role of ideology in mutual support as a cognitive antidote to participants' problems (Antze, 1976; Kennedy & Humphreys, 1994; Levine & Perkins, 1987), assisting people in making cognitive changes in how they cope with difficulties, offering new worldviews and new ways to view themselves. With our definition, we finally see the development of mutual support, particularly in settings for persons with psychiatric disabilities, as possibly providing an environmental antidote as well (Kloos, 1998) to the realities of isolation and despair that many such persons encounter (Davidson, Hoge, Godleski, Rakfeldt, & Griffith, 1996). Through this combination of means, we contend that mutual support is an approach to structuring human relationships, ideology, and activity in ways that offer emotional and instrumental support for persons who are struggling with particular life difficulties.

### MUTUAL SUPPORT AMONG INDIVIDUALS WITH PSYCHIATRIC DISABILITIES

Despite the broad network of 12-step and abstinence-based groups for people with a variety of addictions noted above (e.g., Alcoholics Anonymous, Narcotics Anonymous, Cocaine Anonymous, Gamblers Anonymous), as well as groups for the spouses and children of people with addictions (Alanon, Alateen, Adult Children of Alcoholics), there are to date only a few groups that have been developed especially for people with serious mental illness. Organizations like GROW (Maton & Salem, 1995; Omark, 1979; Rappaport et al., 1985; Shannon & Morrison, 1990; Snowdon, 1980; Young & Williams, 1987, 1988), Recovery, Inc. (Kurtz & Chambon, 1987; Lee, 1971; Medvene, 1985; Raiff, 1982; Wechsler, 1960), Emotions Anonymous (Kurtz & Chambon, 1987), and Schizophrenics Anonymous (Joseph R. & Donald F., 1973; Ryback, 1971; Snowdon, 1980) have attempted to provide a supportive social network and concrete cognitive and behavioral guidelines for people being discharged from psychiatric hospitals. In the case of GROW, the support groups were formed and organized by former mental hospital patients, and in the case of Recovery, Inc., by psychiatrist Abraham Low. Both hoped to offer persons with histories of significant psychiatric difficulties guidance in negotiating their everyday lives, effective role models, and a belief that they can recover. Several authors have questioned whether these groups continue to be utilized by persons with psychotic disorders or if they have become more of a support for people with less severe disabilities (Emerick, 1989; Kurtz & Chambon, 1987; Shannon & Morrison, 1990; Young & Williams, 1988). As of the mid-1980s, however, 74% of GROW member study participants had been hospitalized before going to their first group (Kennedy,

1989). Currently, GROW continues to receive referrals and funding from state departments of mental health contingent upon their inclusion of people with serious mental illness, including diagnoses of schizophrenia (GROW in America, 1994; D. Maxwell and P. Voltarel, personal communication, February 29, 1996).

Although new groups continue to form as part of the Mental Health Consumer Movement (MHCM), most of the published, systematic research has focused on Recovery, Inc. and GROW (Borkman, 1991; Emerick, 1989, 1991; GROW, 1979; Kyrouz & Humphreys, 1996). We review empirical findings of who utilizes these mutual support groups and what benefits can be gained from them by persons with serious mental illness. The review focuses on studies that compare mutual support group participants to nonparticipants, include longitudinal data, or both. We have excluded from this review those studies that characterize themselves as "mutual support" but are actually psychotherapy or support groups led by professionals who do not share the condition addressed by the group. Although the body of work that we review is not large, it is helpful in documenting the limited use but potential value of mutual support for persons with histories of psychiatric disorders and in identifying directions for future research in this area.

### Who Uses Mutual Support?

Several studies report that approximately 60% of members of mutual support groups for persons with serious mental illness are women, most are currently single, and most (i.e., 55–74%) have been hospitalized for psychiatric difficulties (Kaufmann, Schulberg, & Schooler, 1994; Kennedy, 1989; Luke, Rappaport, & Seidman, 1991). Utilization of mutual support groups appears to be a matter of person-environment fit rather than a matter of universal appeal (Levine & Perkins, 1987; Luke, Roberts, & Rappaport, 1993). For example, Kaufmann et al. (1994) found in a controlled study of 90 participants that only 17% of persons who were invited to attend a mutual support group did so. Luke et al. (1993) conducted a 30-month study of 799 GROW members in 13 groups and found that approximately one third of persons who came to a GROW meeting did not continue after one or two meetings, another third came for 3 to 4 months, and the last third participated for periods exceeding 4 months. These findings of low rates of utilization underscore the fact that mutual support appears currently to be appealing to only a minority, perhaps up to one third, of individuals with severe mental illness.

Mutual support group members who do continue to participate appear to do so because they valued the mutual support meetings and the broader mutual support experience (Roberts, 1987), reported an instillation of hope, and developed greater self-understanding (Kennedy, 1995; Llewelyn & Haslett, 1986). In lieu of published data from controlled outcome research about those persons who do not continue, Markowitz et al. (1996) found that experiences of negativity from group members, as well as the illness itself, were major reasons why members of these groups dropped out. Clearly, more systematic studies are needed to learn why some persons with serious and persistent mental illness participate in mutual support groups while most others do not.

### Potential Benefits of Mutual Support

While conventional outcome research has focused primarily on symptom reduction, changing conceptions of what constitutes recovery dictate that other indices of functioning be included to understand the impact that mutual support can have on the lives of persons with psychiatric disorders. For example, a sole focus on symptoms misses the social consequences of mental illness, on which mutual support may have a stronger influence (Humphreys, 1997; Kaufmann, 1996). Furthermore, mutual support groups, as phenomena of interest, are understood as more than simply a treatment modality; they have also been described as normative communities, social support networks, and political action organizations (Humphreys & Rappaport, 1994; Maton & Salem, 1995; Salem et al., 1988). Here we review literature on the influence of mutual support on indicators of "treatment" efficacy, that is, a) symptom reduction and b) rates of hospitalization, as well as on c) the promotion of social integration.

Conclusions about the influence of mutual support on symptom reduction are limited by the nature of existing data (Humphreys & Rappaport, 1994; Levy, 2000). Kaufmann et al. (1994) found in their controlled study that members of mutual support groups did not differ in symptom expression from control group members in other treatment. Similarly, Raiff (1984) found that members of Recovery, Inc. did not have a change in symptoms while participating. However, Galanter's (1988) study of Recovery, Inc. found improved psychiatric symptomatology, increased coping skills, and increased life satisfaction for members. Both Galanter and Raiff found that Recovery, Inc. members who had participated in the groups for more than 2 years had the lowest level of symptomatology. Likewise, more committed GROW members changed in more positive directions than less committed members over 10 months of observation (Luke, 1989). Furthermore, a high level of group attendance was positively related to reports of lower rates of isolation and brooding when away from group, as well as increased support seeking (Reischl & Rappaport, 1988). Taken together, these findings appear to indicate that, in general, participants who select to continue in groups do not do worse, and those who are more committed to the group may be found to have significant gains.

This pattern of findings is perhaps more clear in several studies investigating how participation in mutual support groups is associated with rates of hospitalization. Studies of the Manic Depressive and Depression Association (MDDA) (Kurtz, 1988) and Recovery, Inc. (Galanter, 1988) report significantly lower rates of hospitalization after their members joined the respective groups compared to before they joined (MDDA: 82% before, 33% after; Recovery, Inc.: 52% before, 7% after). Galanter also reports that Recovery, Inc. members had increased utilization of outpatient services during this period. While these results are promising, interpretation of them is limited given their reliance on self-reports of hospitalizations, retrospective data, and lack of a comparison group. Additionally, the period of time prior to participation is longer than the period of participation, making comparisons extremely tenuous. However, this trend appears to continue in the only study that used hospital records to investigate similar questions in a prospective fashion (Kennedy, 1989; Rappaport, 1993). Using 12 demographic indices to best match GROW participants with people who had used services of the Illinois Department of Mental Health, researchers found that the two groups had no differences in rates of hospitalization and length of stay for the 32 months prior to GROW members joining a group. All participants had at least five recent hospitalizations during the baseline period. Similarly, the researchers found no differences in the rate of hospitalizations 32 months after members joined GROW; however, the length of stay in hospital was dramatically different. GROW members were hospitalized on average 179 days during the first 32-month period (i.e., pre-GROW) and 49 days for the second 32-month period (i.e., after joining GROW), while Department of Mental Health patients in the control group had 175- and 123-day stays for the same time periods. The data do not reveal why the length of stay is different, but from her observation, Kennedy (1989) suggests that the difference may be due to many GROW members using the mutual support group materials while in the hospital, supportive visits from other GROW members, and a tendency for hospital staff to release GROW members earlier because the staff knew that they were going back to situations in which members would have significant social support.

A second broad area of potential benefit of mutual support for persons with serious mental illness is in the area of social integration. Reidy (1992) defines social integration as "affording people with disabilities the opportunity to participate in all aspects of community life" (p. 3), which can be understood as having three essential elements—voluntary relationships, valued social roles, and life-enriching activities. We use this social integration conceptual framework to organize the remaining research findings about mutual support groups.

Many researchers have found that persons with serious psychiatric disabilities who come to mutual support groups have markedly reduced social networks when compared to persons who do not have mental illness (Kennedy, 1989; Ribisl & Luke, 1993). Many members tend to be unemployed (Kaufmann et al., 1994; Kennedy, 1989; Segal, Silverman, & Temkin; 1995) and have never been married (Kennedy, 1989; Kaufmann et al., 1994). Several different researchers have found in cross-sectional studies that longer participation in mutual support groups (e.g., 9 months) is positively correlated with having larger social networks when compared to persons who have shorter periods of participation (e.g., 3 months; Carpinello et al., 1991; Rappaport et al., 1985; van Uchelen, 1989). While cross-sectional data do not indicate direction of influence (whether people with larger networks participate longer or people who participate longer develop larger networks), it is interesting to note that in the study by Rappaport et al. (1985), longer term participants had larger social networks but did not differ in their history of psychiatric hospitalization, age, education, or marital status. Prospective studies of network supports are needed to understand better the benefits and mechanisms of increased relationships associated with mutual support experiences.

As argued by Reidy (1992), valued roles are essential for persons to view themselves as instrumental and valuable, and for positive self-esteem. A primary emphasis of mutual support is that one should not be restricted to the role of a "helpee" but also become a "helper" (Riessman, 1965). Through behavioral observation of 799 individuals in 13 GROW groups over 2.5 years, Roberts (1989) found that the frequency of helping others within group was positively related to increased social adjustment, although such helping was not associated with reductions in psychiatric symptomatology. Zimmerman et al. (1991) found that GROW intentionally creates roles for newer members as a means of expanding their groups. Similarly, over the course of 6 months of observation, Kloos (1998) found that a residential treatment facility operated by GROW had many more formal social roles (e.g., work team leader, activity organizer, representative to state boards, etc.) and more instrumental activities for members than a similar facility operated by a mental health center that emphasized staff roles (see also Carpinello et al., 1991).

Mutual support also appears to have promise in enhancing the quality of life for persons with persistent psychiatric disabilities. Several studies suggested that continued group membership is associated with increased perceptions of self-esteem, better decision-making skills, and improved social functioning (Carpinello et al., 1991; Galanter, 1988; Kaufmann et al., 1994; Markowitz et al., 1996). In fact, Markowitz et al. (1996) found modest positive effects for self-concept and interpersonal satisfaction, while "traditional services" had a small negative effect on study participants. Carpinello et al. (1991) found continued participation also was positively correlated with more members pursuing educational goals and finding employment.

Chamberlin (1978, 1996) and Deegan (1992) note that mutual support also can lead to collective action in the form of political advocacy, which might be considered an example of empowerment (Cornell University Empowerment Group, 1989).

The basis for these indications may be the many reports of positive experiences and personal growth from participating in mutual support. For example, data from the series of studies about GROW by Rappaport and colleagues suggest that GROW's practice of mutual support encourages helpful assistance among members and discourages negative interactions (Toro, Rappaport, & Seidman, 1987). Additionally, Roberts et al. (1991) conducted a rigorous, psychometrically sound behavioral analysis of the types of statements made in GROW groups and found that they were supportive seven times as often as they were negative. Furthermore, they found that highly personal and emotional self-disclosure was relatively infrequent (7% of comments) when compared to helping comments (25%). These results, while promising, are largely based on retrospective, self-report data, however, and do not provide a rigorous test of these hypotheses. Systematic and more rigorous research is needed to substantiate such claims and to identify the mechanisms of action taking place in mutual support groups in the areas of life satisfaction, security, education, work, social relationships, and spirituality (Galanter, 1988; Humphreys, 1997; Kennedy, 1995).

### Mutual Support Summary

These data suggest promising trends and are useful in beginning to suggest a theory about how mutual support might assist persons with severe mental illness. Conclusions about the effectiveness of mutual support will remain tentative, however, until there are more systematic, prospective studies completed with comparison groups. Our review includes only one controlled outcome study involving this population. Clearly, more rigorous research is needed to test these suggestions about the possible value of mutual support in promoting recovery. As we understand the existing evidence, we suggest that research focus on the potential for peer involvement both in efforts to address mental health concerns and in supporting mental health treatment. Given the evidence, mutual support should not be viewed as a panacea for addressing the range of needs of individuals with psychiatric disabilities, but as one potential resource that might contribute to social integration. In addition, the low rates of utilization and high attrition make it clear that mutual support groups alone, and in their current form, do not constitute a sufficient strategy to ensure opportunities for peer support and access to effective role models for persons with serious mental illness. Using the framework of "person-environment fit" (Kelly, 1966, 1971; Riger, 1984), other types of peer support may need to be offered to engage larger number of individuals in such activities, particularly in nongroup settings. Consumer-run services and the use of consumers as providers are two more recent developments that may offer broader access for individuals with psychiatric disabilities to the potential benefits of peer support.

### CONSUMER-RUN SERVICES

As noted above, a second important development within the MHCM has been the creation of independent consumer-run drop-in centers and residential, outreach, and vocational programs (Chamberlin, 1990). While such programs were originally developed as alternatives to the formal mental health system, they too are entering into a phase of partnership and collaboration (Kaufmann, Ward-Colasante, & Farmer, 1993). As with mutual support groups, use of consumer-run services involves a voluntary and intentional effort on the part of an individual to take advantage of the emotional and instrumental support available from his or her peers. In addition, the behavioral settings created by these services have the potential to incorporate the same kinds of expectations, routines, roles, information, and ideology found in mutual support groups.

Consumer-run services also may differ from mutual support groups, however, in two important ways. First, in contrast to mutual support groups, the peer support provided in consumer-run programs may not be entirely mutual. Although peers may be encouraged to support each other, the providers of service are paid employees of the program and may neither expect nor be allowed to receive support or other assistance from clients of the program. As such programs typically do not operate within conventional definitions of therapeutic or professional boundaries, however, it is an empirical question of the degree to which such peer relationships may in fact be mutual as opposed to the degree to which they may approximate conventional, one-directional, professional-client relationships (Armstrong, Korba, & Emard, 1995). Second, the presence of a more formalized infrastructure in a consumer-run program, and the necessity for more structured activities and interactions that it brings, may provide a particularly supportive setting for the cultivation of a consistency and regularity in peer support interactions that often is missing from more informally occurring mutual support groups.

#### Descriptive and Effectiveness Studies

In Table 1, we review studies of consumer-run services that were identified by key word searches on Medline and PsycInfo databases. Most studies (Kaufmann et al., 1993; Mowbray, Chamberlain, Jennings & Reed, 1988; Mowbray & Tan, 1993; Segal et al., 1995) have tended to be descriptive, characterizing who uses these services, who pays for them, who refers to them, and who runs them, and show that consumer-run services are feasible and

**Table 1. Consumer-Run Services**

| Study | Sample | Program Description | Method | Conclusions |
|---|---|---|---|---|
| Mowbray, Chamberlain, Jennings, & Reed (1988): projects funded by the Michigan Dept. of Mental Health (DMH) | 25 clients transitioning from the hospital to the community | Project Ease Out: 4 consumers visited clients while inpatients and provided support after discharge. | Feasibility study: surveyed program clients, calculated costs per client. | Five clients no longer required services; no client dropouts and one client readmission; high client satisfaction; one consumer was rehospitalized; cost $1.67/day/client. |
| | 10 psychiatric clients | Companions Program: consumers were paired with clients to practice social skills. | Feasibility study: assessed matches and productivity, calculated costs per client. | Most matches lasted beyond the 6-month target, few terminations of matches; cost = $2.25/match/week. |
| | Psychiatric clients at risk of hospitalization | Project Stay: ex-patient provide a support network and develop life skills, enhancing community tenure. | Feasibility study: assessed productivity, level of contact, and turnover rate; calculated costs per client. | Ex-patients maintained high amounts of contact and productivity despite high turnover, cost = $.21 /day/ client. |
| | Over 1,800 consumers, most with previous mental health experience, desiring mutual support | Daybreak Drop-in Centers: an unstructured setting that included recreational, cooking, housing assistance, and employment activities. | Feasibility study: surveyed program clients, tracked attendance, calculated costs per month. | Averaged over 150 persons a month for 12 months; high client satisfaction; cost = $470/month. |

*(continued)*

**Table 1. Consumer-Run Services** *(continued)*

| Study | Sample | Program Description | Method | Conclusions |
|---|---|---|---|---|
| Nikkel, Smith, & Edwards (1992): The Community Survival Program | 30 patients (mix of schizophrenia, schizoaffective, bipolar, & substance abuse) with long psychiatric histories | Consumer staff emphasize: 1) bond between providers and program participants, 2) use of coping skills found to be effective, 3) examining meaning of symptoms, 4.) living in the community, 5) peer support to address substance abuse, and 6) role modeling. | Outcome assessment: Tracked client hospitalizations | Preliminary data suggest this approach has potential impact on rate of hospitalization rates; authors concluded more objective outcome data are needed. |
| Mowbray & Tan (1993): Self-help group called the Justice in Mental Health Organization (JIMHO) received Michigan DMH funds | 120 clients (82% had used inpatient services) from the six centers | The centers were designed to provide a safe, supportive, normalizing, and accepting community environment; promote feelings of self-worth, dignity, and respect; and increase knowledge of the community by learning from each other | Feasibility study: conducted structured interviews using the Group Environment scale, the Community Oriented Program Environment scale, and the Client Satisfaction Questionnaire | Most clients believed they had input into center operations, felt supported, learned from one another, were encouraged to be independent and participated more in positive activities and less in negative activities; 80% reported being more confident in several life domains; 75% perceived the centers more positively than other mental health services in the area. |
| Kaufmann, Ward-Colasante, & Farmer (1993) | 478 consumers (psychiatric patients, excluding substance abusers, homeless) across nine centers during a 6-month period (average of 28/day for all centers) | Centers provide social support (through social gatherings and celebrations) and employment services. | Feasibility study: conducted interviews and focus groups with clients, tracked attendance | Clients liked the "relaxed atmosphere," being with similar people, having a place to go; clients wanted more equitable enforcement of rules, support, and expanded hours and activities; components of a successful center: participatory management, strong volunteers, relationships with other provider systems, resources, social activities, and special events; ongoing recruitment; cost = 243/consumer for 6-month period. |

**Table 1. Consumer-Run Services** *(continued)*

| Study | Sample | Program Description | Method | Conclusions |
|---|---|---|---|---|
| Kaufmann (1995) | 146 clients with serious mental illness | Self-Help Employment Center: Vocational services based on self-help principles; consumers collaborated with clients, allowing them to take much of the reponsibility. | Outcome assessment: clients were randomly assigned to the two groups and were assessed at baseline, 6, and 12 months on % working, % in new jobs, hours worked, time to present job, and time in present job. | Not many significant differences on employment variables; center clients were significantly more improved on an ordinal scale of vocational status created by the author at 12 months. |
| Segal, Silverman, & Temkin (1995) | 310 clients participated for at least 3 months (twice during the past week) | Four consumer-run self-help agencies. | Feasibility study: Goal was to characterize typical users: surveyed a randomly selected group of clients from the total population on service utilization, psychiatric history, functional status, symptoms, diagnosis, and health issues; interviewed the consumer staff and volunteers. | Typical center users were poor, African-American, and homeless and had a serious mental illness; centers first engaged clients informally with material services, then developed a counseling relationship and linked them to additional services later; a division of labor exists between self-help agencies that provide material (basic needs), psychosocial, and some counseling services, vs. community mental health centers that provide mostly medical and psychotherapeutic services. |

may be valuable. Some studies have also assessed client outcomes of these services (Kaufmann, 1995; Nikkel, Smith, & Edwards, 1992).

The studies reviewed in Table 1 suggest that consumer-run services can be viable organizations and can provide useful services. Several themes emerge from this review. First, despite the distrust that ethnic minorities often have of traditional mental health services, there has been strong minority representation in the population served in the studies that report this information (Kaufmann, 1995; Mowbray & Tan, 1993; Segal et al., 1995). This stands in contrast to mutual support groups, whose membership predominantly has been white. Perhaps since consumers share common experiences of discrimination with ethnic minorities, they are more sensitive to these issues and therefore design services that are more acceptable to these communities. Future research should assess this hypothesis further.

Second, regarding who refers to these services, referrals come mostly from informal sources (e.g., family, friends, word of mouth, self). Conversely, professional referrals ranged from one fifth to one third of the populations studied. Given that professionals seldom refer clients to mutual support groups (Black & Drackman, 1985; Katz, 1993), it is not surprising that the same would hold true for consumer-run services. Should consumer-run services prove to be effective for a broader range of clients, then professionals will need to be educated about their value (Black & Drackman, 1985; Chesler, 1990; Salzer, McFadden, & Rappaport, 1994).

Third, it is clear that consumer-run services need the support (especially financial) of local mental health systems. Almost all the services were funded by state mental health agencies, and Kaufmann et al. (1993) found that services that developed relationships early on with provider systems remained viable, while services that were not able to do so failed. Finally, although the degree to which consumer-run services embody the principles and contributions of mutual support has yet to be determined, they do provide persons with serious mental illness constructive roles beyond their status as mental patients and provide a viable route of access to peer role models for those not as far along in their own recovery.

### Methodological Limitations

Although some of the results from the studies examining consumer-run programs are promising, most of the studies reviewed here have not employed rigorous empirical methods. Among the six studies reviewed, only one used random assignment and assessed consumer outcomes (Kaufmann, 1995). The other studies collected either quality assurance data (e.g., finding that one consumer drop-in center averaged over 150 persons a month for 12 months and had high client satisfaction), descriptive data on drop-in center users, or attitudinal self-report data without a control group. The one study that was more rigorous (i.e., random assignment, sufficient sample) examined the differences between a consumer-run employment center and traditional vocational services and found few differences on several employment variables.

### CONSUMERS AS MENTAL HEALTH PROVIDERS

Despite their feasibility and potential usefulness, consumer-run programs remain largely dependent on the self-referrals of like-minded consumers, and continue to be a relatively limited resource for the general population of people with severe mental illness. The more recent development of hiring consumers for staff positions within conventional clinical and rehabilitative settings may provide a more expedient way to provide visible role models and peer support on a broader basis and for larger numbers of people recovering from serious mental illness (Bledsoe Boykin, 1997; Mowbray et al., 1997). To the degree that this initiative permeates the mental health system, it also may be more successful in bringing about reforms in the ways in which mental health services are designed and delivered (Bevilacqua, Gettys, & Cousins, 1997; Davidson et al., 1997).

As with consumer-run services, the use of consumer providers has the potential to offer many of the benefits of mutual support, involving individuals intentionally in voluntary relationships with their peers to gain exposure to hope, information, and coping and problem-solving skills in a supportive, accepting, and empathic milieu. As these services are provided within the context of conventional clinical and rehabilitative settings, however, the question of the mutuality of these relationships is most likely less ambiguous, and more likely to be guided by conventional definitions of therapeutic boundaries—although this issue has yet to be systematically explored. Perhaps more so than in the case of consumer-run services, consumers who are employed as providers within conventional clinical and rehabilitative settings also may be able to benefit directly from the provision of a structured and supportive milieu. A number of strategies have been devised to accommodate some of the needs such employees bring to the workplace and to maximize the unique contributions they have to offer based on their first-hand knowledge of the territory. We have referred to these strategies as "supported" peer support to indicate that these individuals have been provided with training, supervision, and environmental accommodations to facilitate their provision of peer support to others (Davidson, Stayner, Rakfeldt, & Tebes, 1995). In this section we discuss the feasibility and outcome studies conducted on this more recent approach to service delivery.

### Feasibility Studies

Initial credit for foreseeing potential value in employing consumers as providers goes to the Colorado Division of Mental Health, which in the spring of 1991 developed a program to train and employ individuals with psychiatric disabilities to provide case management services to their peers (Sherman & Porter, 1991). Similarly, Stoneking and Greenfield (1991), Mowbray et al. (1996), and Lyons, Karver, and Slagg (1996) addressed the issue of feasibility of this approach. As shown in Table 2, these studies suggest that although consumers may provide services differently from nonconsumers, they are able to perform their jobs adequately.

Other early reports of such efforts, based on anecdotal evidence from experiences with programs that have hired consumers as providers, have identified both the roles for which experience with serious mental illness would be an asset, and the potential benefits for hiring consumer providers (Besio & Mahler, 1993; Curtis, 1993; Davidson et al., 1997; Dixon, Krauss, & Lehman, 1994; Mowbray & Moxley, 1997a; Mowbray et al., 1997; Paulson, 1991; Shepard, 1992; van Tosh, 1993). Services for which consumer providers might be well suited include "advocacy and mediation; mentoring and role modeling; peer support, education and counseling; and assistance with meeting needs of daily living, such as housing and work" (Davidson et al., 1997, pp. 439–440). Additionally, these authors have suggested that consumer providers may be more able to empathize; to access social services; to appreciate clients' strengths; to be tolerant, flexible, patient, and persistent; and to be aware of and responsive to clients' desires (Davidson et al., 1997; Mowbray & Moxley, 1997b).

### Effectiveness Studies

Since the success of these programs, consumers have been hired across the country to work in a variety of clinical and rehabilitative roles, and a few empirical outcome assessments have been conducted. Studies that employed the use of consumers as service providers (not in consumer-run services) are reviewed in Table 2 and were identified by key word searches on the Medline and PsycInfo databases. Whereas Solomon and Draine (1993, 1994b, 1995b, 1995c, 1995d) found consumer treatment to result in essentially equivalent outcomes as compared to nonconsumer treatment, Felton et al. (1995) found that having consumers on a case management team yielded significantly better client outcomes compared to teams with no consumers.

### Methodological Limitations

As with consumer-run services, the studies examining consumer providers also were not rigorously conducted. Of the six studies reviewed here, only two used random assignment, and only one of those assessed out-

**Table 2. Consumer as Providers**

| Study | Sample | Program Description | Method | Conclusions |
|---|---|---|---|---|
| Sherman & Porter (1991) | 25 persons who met the Colorado Division of Mental Health criteria for chronic mental illness | Recruits received extensive classroom and supervised on-the-job training in basic clinical and case management skills. | Feasibility study: tracked training completion rates, employment rates, hospitalization rates of the ra managers, and conducted verbal surveys assessing productivity and satisfaction. | 18 completed the training and became gainfully employed; the case managers had a total of only two hospitalization days for the entire sample in over 2 years of employment; supervisors and case managers were highly satisfied; in general, case managers performed duties for which they were trained. |
| Stoneking & Greenfield (1991) | 8 Consumer Support Service Coordinators (SCs) (persons with a history of mental illness and hospitalizations) | 22 mental health consumers completed training to be consumer case managers (SCO. Eight were chosen to work in a Case Management Service agency, paired with nonconsumer case managers (CMs), and served about 80 clients; SCs used a self-help framework to help clients develop their social networks, use their strengths to live in the community, use community resources, obtain and maintain housing, use public transportation, and obtain benefits. | Feasibility study: SCs, of the SC-CM pairs, were compared to trainees not chosen (OT) on level of functioning (Ohio Level of Functioning scale) and symptornotology (Hopkins Symptom Checklist-40). | Few differences existed between the CMs and the OTs on functioning and symptornotology; the CIAs decreased their amount of social activities after 3 and 6 months of employment; CIAs had more social activities than OTs before and after training and after 3 and 6 months of employment. |
| Lyons, Cook, Ruth, Karver, & Slagg (1996) | 4 consumer providers (history of hospitalizations and medication use) | A Mobile Assessment Unit (MAU) in Chicago provides crisis intervention and referral services on a 16 hr/day basis. | Feasibility study: dyads formed naturally at the beginning of each shift; job performance of consumer dyads (either one or two consumers present) was compared to nonconsumer dyads. | Despite serving essentially the same clients, the consumer dyads did more mobile outreach and were less likely to be dispatched in an emergency; authors conclude consumers can be a valuable addibon to the MAU. |

*(continued)*

**Table 2. Consumer as Providers** *(continued)*

| Study | Sample | Program Description | Method | Conclusions |
|---|---|---|---|---|
| Mowbray, Moxley, Thrasher, Bybee, McCrohan, Harris, & Clover (1996) | 19 Peer Support Specialists (PSSs), who all had significant psychiatric histories | WINS (Work Incentives and Need Study), funded by the Center for Mental Health Services to increase vocational opportunities for clients already receiving services from case management teams. | Feasibility study: quantitative summaries from Service Activity Logs form; focus groups of the PSSs. | Authors concluded that PSSs performed the activities necessary for vocational services; sharing a common bond enhanced the relationship between the PSSs and their clients; PSSs demonstrated job sophistication and professional skills; and PSSs experienced significant role confusion (e.g., "Am I a friend or a clinician?") and did not feel adequately compensated for their work. |
| Felton, Stastny, Shern, Blanch, Donahue, Knight, & Brown (1995) | 104 clients with serious mental illness | Clients were served by one of three teams: 1) nonconsumer case managers only, 2) nonconsumer case managers plus nonprofessional paraprofessional assistants, and 3) nonconsumer case managers plus peer specialists, who performed case management services using a model similar to the model of Stein & Test (1978), including 24-hr availability, assertive outreach, advocacy, and a rehabilitation orientation. | Outcome assessment: compared the clients of these teams on self-image, quality of life, outlook, program engagement, and community tenure. | All clients improved over time on quality of life and on symptoms, but clients of team 3 were more satisfied with their living situations and finances and reported fewer life problems (assessed perceptions and objective indicators) compared to the two nonconsumer groups; client contact by team 3 remained steady over the 18 months but decreased for teams 1 and 2, perhaps because the consumer providers may have affected their nonconsumer teammates positively; there were no differences between teams 1 and 2, which led the authors to suggest the contributions by the consumer providers accounted for the differences in client outcomes. |

**Table 2. Consumer as Providers** *(continued)*

| Study | Sample | Program Description | Method | Conclusions |
|---|---|---|---|---|
| Solomon & Draine (1993, 1994a,1994b,1995a, 1995b, 1995c, 1995d, 1996) | 96 clients with a major mental disorder and histories of hospitalization | Two case management teams (one made of all consumers, the other made of nonconsumers) provided intensive case management services based on Stein & Test (1978), including 24-hr availability, assertive outreach, advocacy, and providing services in the clients' natural environments. | Outcome assessment: clients randomly assigned to each team and compared on a variety of standardized measures of functioning and symptoms over a 2-year period. | No differences generally were found between the two groups on nondisposable income, social network size, days hospitalized, symptoms, attitudes toward medication compliance, quality of life, interpersonal contact, social functioning, satisfaction with their treatment from their team, working alliance, and family member satisfaction; Solomon & Draine conclude that consumers can provide case management services as well as nonconsumers; some studies did not have adequate power, however. |

comes of the clients served by the consumers (the other examined the effect of employment on the consumer providers themselves). Again, the remaining studies either were descriptive, suffered from small samples and low power, were naturalistic studies (i.e., no random assignment), assessed quality assurance data from service activity logs, or used focus groups. One of the more rigorous studies of consumer providers (Solomon & Draine, 1995d) randomly assigned clients to a case management team either made of all consumers or made of all nonconsumers and found no differences on a variety of standardized measures of functioning and symptoms over a 2-year period.

Despite the lack of methodologically sound studies both of consumer-run services and of the employment of consumers as providers in clinical and rehabilitative settings, a consistent finding from all the studies has been that consumers can adequately provide services to others with serious mental illness, demonstrating their ability to occupy important roles beyond their status as mental patients. Beyond this conclusion, however, the effectiveness of using consumers to provide peer support to other consumers in these settings remains unclear. These types of peer support are still relatively new, and therefore more rigorous studies are needed to assess the potential demonstrated by this group of mostly descriptive research.

### PARTICIPATION IN PEER SUPPORT

The above discussion of the range of potential benefits to be derived from peer support suggests that it is a resource that might be welcome by most persons recovering from severe mental illness. Social support, positive social roles, coping and problem-solving skills, all typically are seen as lacking in people who are disabled by these disorders and who occupy largely stigmatized and isolated roles in a community to which they often do not feel they belong. Yet we have noted that these resources are used currently by only a minority of individuals with psychiatric disabilities. In addition, several studies of professionals' attitudes toward mutual support suggest that many professionals are reluctant to refer their clients to these groups, and that some professionals perceive these groups as potentially detrimental to their clients (Chesler, 1990; Salzer et al., 1994). Although, as Kyrouz and Humphreys (1996) have noted, low rates of utilization are not uncommon among other mutual support groups and voluntary organizations, there may be issues specific to persons with severe mental illnesses that impede their broader use of these options as well. Through our own attempts to foster the development of mutual support groups, consumer-run services, and the use of consumers as providers within our local service system, we have identified a series of issues confronted both by consumers and by providers that appear to limit access to, and utilization of, each of these three forms of peer support. We review each briefly below.

First, despite the fact that it has been over 20 years since Strauss, Harding, and their colleagues in the United States (Harding, Brooks, Ashikaga, Strauss, & Breier, 1987a, 1987b; Strauss & Carpenter, 1972, 1974, 1977) and Bleuler, Ciompi, and their colleagues in Europe (Bleuler, 1974, 1978; Ciompi, 1980) began to publish rigorous longitudinal studies that showed that many people with serious mental illness can in fact improve over time, the longstanding Kraepelinian view of a chronic and deteriorating course continues to predominate the field. Beliefs such as that "once you are a mental patient, you always will be a mental patient" (Harding & Zahniser, 1994) are common not only to the lay public and to mental health providers, but also to consumers themselves.

Such beliefs impede the development and use of peer support in a number of ways. Perhaps most important, the acceptance of such beliefs on the part of people with psychiatric disabilities—what has come to be called "internalized stigma" within the MHCM (Davidson, Stayner, & Haglund, 1998)—can contribute to an immobilizing sense of demoralization, apathy, despair, and helplessness experienced by many people with serious mental illness (Davidson, Stayner, Lambert, Smith, & Sledge, 1997). Feeling that there is little they can do to improve their own situation, many individuals with psychiatric disabilities find little appeal in mutual support groups or in programs run by their peers. Believing that there is little chance for recovery in others as well as in themselves, they are skeptical that their peers would have much to offer them and see little point in coming together with a group of individuals with similar problems to share their troubles. Similar beliefs on the part of providers make them skeptical of the value of mutual support groups or services provided by consumers, as the peer support leaders or providers continue to be perceived primarily within the role of mental patient. As a consequence, the rate of referral to these resources continues to be low, as does the level of formal support for such resources within most state mental health systems.

Second, in addition to beliefs about prognosis in serious mental illness, there is the devastation of the illness itself and its impact on functioning. There is increasing evidence from psychiatric rehabilitation that some disorders can be delimited to specific domains of functioning that leave other domains intact, allowing the person to achieve a sense of mastery over his or her condition (Anthony & Liberman, 1986; Bachrach, 1992). Depending on the severity of the disorder, however, many individuals with serious mental illness do experience significant impairments in multiple domains of functioning that can make participation in mutual support and in some consumer-run services extremely difficult, if not impossible—at least in the early, more active phases of illness (Davidson & McGlashan, 1997).

It may be useful in addressing the roadblocks posed by the disability itself to consider the role that the provision of supports and environmental modifications may play in assisting some individuals with psychiatric disabilities to participate in peer support. An example of the potential role of supports and accommodations in this area can be taken from the vocational area. Impairments in intellectual, emotional, or social spheres no longer need to pose as much of an obstacle to a person's chances at success on the job since the advent of "supported employment" and "supported education." With these advances in psychiatric rehabilitation, modifications can be made to the person's work or school environment, and supports can be provided "in vivo," to assist the person in compensating for his or her disabilities. Similar approaches have been explored in the context of consumer-run services and may be needed for those individuals who remain significantly disabled by their conditions if they are to participate in peer support. As mentioned above, we have referred to the range of strategies that might be employed to support individuals in participating in peer support activities under the rubric of "supported peer support." It remains for future research to evaluate the utility of these strategies, and to see if their implementation attracts more people to these activities.

Finally, despite cross-cultural studies in the developing world (Davidson & McGlashan, 1997; Lin & Kleinman, 1988) and studies of the effectiveness of paraprofessionals (Christensen & Jacobson, 1994; Durlak, 1979) showing that people can make significant improvements in the absence of professional intervention, the mental health system continues to be based on a belief that serious mental illness can be ameliorated only through the highly technical procedures of professionals. Whether through pharmacologic intervention, focused attention to developing a therapeutic relationship, or even highly specified modules of behavioral training in psychiatric rehabilitation, there continues to be a sense that improvement will come about only through intensive efforts on the part of the professionals involved. Such an exclusionary investment in professional role and identity allows little room for peer support in facilitating recovery from prolonged disorders (Chesler, 1990; Salzer et al., 1994). Even when conceptualized as playing only one part in the context of a comprehensive approach to the treatment of people with serious mental illness—alongside of medications, rehabilitation, and clinical case management—the potential value of peer support can be diminished significantly by the prevailing medical and clinical paradigms used in the settings in which most care is provided. This medical/clinical emphasis has been all the more heightened by the introduction of managed care into public sector mental health, with its foci on medical necessity for the authorization of services, credentialed providers, and utilization management. Even though consumer-run services are often less expensive than conventional services, and mutual support is most often free, proponents of peer support are increasingly concerned about the appeal of these services to managed care organizations, their chances for capturing reimbursement, and the impact of credentialing and liability issues that may need to be addressed if they are to survive.

In our own experience with our local mental health system, we have seen these last two issues played out on at least two different levels. On the programmatic level, we have seen consumer-run services undergo a process of "professionalization" in becoming integrated elements of the formal mental health system. This process involves what had been less formal services, based on such values as flexibility, autonomy, and consumer choice, becoming more structured and more driven by their needs to attract and justify funding. To the degree that such a service comes to resemble a more conventional provider agency, it also potentially begins to lose its unique character and role within a system of care.

On the more personal level, we have seen consumer providers undergo a similar process of "professionalization" in becoming staff within conventional clinical and rehabilitative programs (Davidson et al., 1997). In our training and supervision of consumer providers, we have been impressed by the power of the prevailing clinical culture and the "seduction" of higher status activities such as psychotherapy in constantly threatening to pull consumer providers away from their task of providing peer support. At least to an equal degree to the impact consumer providers have had on changing the systems of care that employ them, these same systems have "co-opted" consumer-run services and consumer providers to their own values and perspectives (Davidson et al., 1997). This not only has the effect of diminishing the value of peer support and leading consumer providers to want to become psychotherapists, but also has the effect of leading some individuals with psychiatric disabilities to reject the notion of peer support and to refuse to work with consumer providers because they are not credentialed clinicians. As one consumer advocate expressed it, "I don't want other mental patients taking care of me when I get sick. What could they know—they're not doctors." A healthy tension between the clinical and consumer perspectives, while perhaps optimal, appears hard to achieve and maintain when the clinical paradigm is so well established.

## IMPLICATIONS FOR MENTAL HEALTH POLICY, RESEARCH, AND PRACTICE

The disabling nature of serious mental illness, beliefs about a chronic and deteriorating course, and investments in the role of professional interventions pose formidable challenges to the development of peer support among people with severe psychiatric disorders (Estroff, 1982). For these and perhaps other reasons as well, peer support is neither well known nor well accepted by providers and consumers alike. The empirical evidence that exists to date, although preliminary and limited, suggests that both consumer-run services and the employment of consumer providers within conventional mental health settings have become additional routes to offering opportunities for peer support among individuals with serious mental illness. In addition, there are increasing numbers of people like Pat Deegan (1992, 1993), Dan Fisher (1994, 1996), Fred Frese (1993), Con Keogh (1979), and Kay Jamison (1995) who have recovered to a significant extent from their own disabilities and are becoming visible sources of inspiration, hope, and support to their peers, offering precisely the kind of role models Deegan would have valued in her own recovery. It is unclear at this time, however, to what degree any of these developments are having an impact either on the awareness or acceptance of peer support among individuals with serious mental illness or their clinicians.

With few exceptions, the empirical literature reviewed in this area consists mostly of quasi-experimental studies, qualitative reports, and anecdotal accounts of innovative programs, as opposed to randomized trials. This may in part be due to the difficulty in studying peer support using random invitation designs and high levels of experimental control, a process that may be so antithetical to the values of this approach that the phenomenon under investigation may no longer be indicative of peer support (Humphreys & Rappaport, 1994; Tebes & Kraemer, 1991). For the use of mutual support, consumer-run services, and consumer providers not to be merely the latest fad in community mental health, however, larger and better controlled studies will be needed that document their effectiveness and cost-effectiveness in facilitating recovery. Such studies will be important in securing for peer support a valued and enduring role in the comprehensive mental health systems of the future (Leff, Campbell, Cagne, & Woocher, 1997).

In addition to needing more information about the effectiveness of these approaches in promoting recovery, several questions remain about the differences between these three routes to peer support. First, there is the question of the degree of reciprocity between staff and clients both in consumer-run programs and in settings that employ consumer providers. Would the absence of reciprocity, should it not be present in these settings, also negate the operation of the "helper-therapy principle" (Riessman, 1990)? Second, consumer providers often experience confusions about their role, as they are torn between being a friend and the expectation of their setting that they "act like professionals" (Dixon et al., 1994; Manning & Suire, 1996; Mowbray et al., 1996; Solomon & Draine, 1996; Stoneking & Greenfield, 1991). Questions remain regarding how much room can be created within the conventionally boundaried practice of such settings for an appreciation of the common humanness, and shared experiences and concerns, between peers that is at the core of mutual support (Davidson et al., 1997).

Third, compared to clients receiving services from conventional mental health programs, participants in both mutual support groups and consumer-run services may play a more active role in creating their own environments, an aspect of these settings that in and of itself is thought to promote recovery (Kaufmann et al., 1993; Mowbray & Tan, 1993). While there is some evidence that consumer providers have been able to affect changes within the mental health settings in which they work (Bevilacqua et al., 1997; Davidson et al., 1997; Felton et al., 1995), their influence on these settings is most likely less than that of their counterparts in consumer-run services and mutual support groups. It remains to be determined whether or not clients in the conventional mental health settings that employ consumer providers have been able to move beyond the passive role of "mental patient" to other, more socially valued and positive roles (Corrigan & Garman, 1997).

Finally, consumer providers in conventional mental health settings have the potential to engage more individuals into receiving services, and to have access to more individuals, than would ordinarily seek out mutual support groups or consumer-run programs, especially given the limited professional utilization of such resources (Black & Drackman, 1985; Katz, 1993; Salzer et al., 1994). This fact alone suggests the value and merit of integrating access to peer role models into clinical and rehabilitative settings. A remaining question in this area, however, is the degree to which the programs studied, and ones to be developed in the future, incorporate an explicit recognition of the consumer staff member's personal history of disability and recovery into his or her work (Davidson et al., 1997). Although such programs may have shifted successfully from viewing a person's experience with severe mental illness as a detriment to viewing it as a valuable job qualification, little attention has been paid thus far to the ways in which these experiences are integrated into the consumer's role and direct work with clients. It may represent progress for consumers to be hired into conventional clinical roles, for in doing so they may already function as successful role models for their clients. But does Fred Frese, for example, function primarily as a peer or as a psychologist, and Dan Fisher primarily as a peer or as a psychiatrist—under what circumstances, and for whom? What remains to be explored is whether or not hiring consumers to be providers is an effective way to combine the strengths both of mental health services and of peer support. To what extent do mental health services provided by consumers, and programs that employ them, come to embody the characteristics of mutual support described above? This direction may provide a promising area for future research.

This review of the feasibility and usefulness of peer support among individuals with serious mental illness suggests that people with serious mental illness may constitute a promising but little utilized resource in the recovery of their peers. Such studies of the relative effectiveness of this approach, while clearly important, nonetheless tap only one dimension of the issue of the role of peer support in recovery from serious mental illness. Other dimensions of this issue—which were implicit in our discussion of the possible roadblocks to participation in peer support—are evident in the far-reaching repercussions of increasing the public visibility of, and access to, those role models for whom Pat Deegan had been searching. Infusing the mental health workforce with people who are coping successfully with their own psychiatric disabilities may not only provide direct effects on the level of individual client outcomes, but may also affect the lingering stigma surrounding people with mental illness that continues to permeate the mental health system and the broader culture (Bevilacqua et al., 1997; Davidson et al., 1997; Reidy, 1994). There may perhaps be no more powerful or direct way to bring about such changes in beliefs about mental illness than to have as colleagues people who have been personally effective in busting apart old stereotypes, and who in so doing provide positive role models both for our clients as well as for ourselves.

### Acknowledgments

Work on this article was supported by U.S. Public Health Service Grants MH47644 and SM51916 from the Substance Abuse and Mental Health Services Administration. We acknowledge the helpful comments of two anonymous reviewers on previous drafts of the manuscript.

### REFERENCES

American Psychiatric Association. (1994). *Diagnostic and statistical manual of mental disorders (4th ed.).* Washington, DC: Author.

American Psychiatric Association. (1997). Practice guidelines for the treatment of patients with schizophrenia. *American Journal of Psychiatry, 154*(4)(Suppl).

Anthony, W. A., & Liberman, R. P (1986). The practice of psychiatric rehabilitation: Historical, conceptual, and research base. *Schizophrenia Bulletin, 12,* 542–559.

Antze, P. (1976). The role of ideologies in peer psychotherapy organizations: Some theoretical considerations and three case studies. *Journal of Applied Behavioral Science, 12,* 323–346.

Armstrong, M. L., Korba, A. M., & Emard, R. (1995). Of mutual benefit: The recip-rocal relationship between consumer volunteers and the clients they serve. *Psychiatric Rehabilitation Journal, 19,* 45–49.

Bachrach, L. L. (1992). Psychosocial rehabilitation and psychiatry in the care of long-term patients. *American Journal of Psychiatry, 149,* 1455–1463.

Barker, R. G. (1968). *Ecological psychology: Concepts and methods for studying the envi-ronment of human behavior.* Stanford, CA: Stanford University Press.

Besio, S. W, & Mahler, J. (1993). Benefits and challenges of using consumer staff in supported housing services. *Hospital and Community Psychiatry, 44,* 490–491.

Bevilacqua, J. L., Gettys, D., & Cousins, V. (1997). Mental health systems develop-ment: Benefits created by consumer engagement. In C. T. Mowbray, D. P. Moxley, C. A. Jasper, & L. L. Howell (Eds.), *Consumers as providers in psychi-atric rehabilitation* (pp. 460–470). Columbia, MD: International Association of Psychosocial Rehabilitation Services.

Black, R., & Drackman, D. (1985). Hospital social workers and self-help groups. *Health and Social Work, 10,* 95–103.

Bledsoe Boykin, C. D. (1997). The consumer provider as role model. In C. T. Mowbray, D. P. Moxley, C. A. Jasper, & L. L. Howell (Eds.), *Consumers as providers in psychiatric rehabilitation* (pp. 374–386). Columbia, MD: International Association of Psychosocial Rehabilitation Services.

Bleuler, M. (1974). The long-term course of the schizophrenic psychoses. *Psychological Medicine, 4,* 244–254.

Bleuler, M. (1978). *The schizophrenic disorders: Long-term patient and family studies* (S. M. Clemens, Trans.). New Haven, CT: Yale University Press.

Borkman, T. (1990). Self-help groups at the turning point: Emerging egalitarian alliances with the formal health care system? American Journal of Community Psychology, 18, 321–332.

Borkman, T. S. (Ed.). (1991). Self-help groups [Special issue]. *American Journal of Community Psychology, 19*(5).

Cain, C. (1991). Personal stories: Identity acquisitions and self-understanding in alcoholics anonymous. *Ethos, 19,* 210–235.

Carling, P. (1995). *Return to community: Building support systems for people with psy-chiatric disabilities.* New York: Guilford Press.

Carpinello, S. E., Knight, E. L., & Janis, L. (1991). *A qualitative study of the percep-tions of the meaning of self-help, self-help group processes and outcomes by self-help group leaders, members, and significant others.* Unpublished manuscript.

Chamberlin, J. (1978). *On our own: Patient controlled alternatives to the mental health system.* New York: McGraw-Hill.

Chamberlin, J. (1984). Speaking for ourselves: An overview of the Ex-Psychiatric Inmates' Movement. *Psychosocial Rehabilitation Journal, 2,* 56–63.

Chamberlin, J. (1990). The Ex-Patients' Movement: Where we've been and where we're going. *Journal of Mind and Behavior, 11,* 323–336.

Chamberlin, J. (1996). Self-help: Living it, promoting it, and learning from it. *The Community Psychologist, 29,* 10–11.

Chesler, M. A. (1990). The "dangers" of self-help groups: Understanding and challenging professionals' views. In T. Powell (Ed.). *Working with self-help* (pp. 301–324). Silver Spring, MD: National Association of Social Workers Press.

Christensen, A., & Jacobson, N. S. (1994). Who (or what) can do psychotherapy: The status and challenge of nonprofessional therapies. *Psychological Science, 5,* 8–14.

Ciompi, L. (1980). Is chronic schizophrenia an artifact? Arguments and counterarguments. *Fortschrifte der Neurologie und Psychiatrie, 48,* 237–248.

Connecticut Self-Help Network. (1996). *The self-help directory: A guide to Connecticut and National groups.* New Haven: Author.

Cornell University Empowerment Group. (1989). Empowerment through family support. *Networking Bulletin, 1,* 2–12.

Corrigan, P. W., & Garman, A. N. (1997). Considerations for research on consumer empowerment and psychosocial interventions. *Psychiatric Services, 48,* 347–352.

Curtis, L. (1993). Consumers as colleagues: Partnership in the workforce. *In Practice, 1,* 4–5.

Davidson, L., Hoge, M. A., Godleski, L., Rakfeldt, J., & Griffith, E. E. H. (1996). Hospital or community living? Examining consumer perspectives on deinstitutionalization. *Psychiatric Rehabilitation Journal, 19,* 49–58.

Davidson, L., & McGlashan, T. H. (1997). The varied outcomes of schizophrenia. *Canadian Journal of Psychiatry, 42,* 34–43.

Davidson, L., Stayner, D. A., & Haglund, K. E. (1998). Phenomenological perspectives on the social functioning of people with schizophrenia. In K. T. Mueser & N. Tarrier (Eds.), *Handbook of social functioning in schizophrenia* (pp. 97–120). Needham Heights, MA: Allyn & Bacon.

Davidson, L., Stayner, D. A., Lambert, S., Smith, P., & Sledge, W. H. (1997). Phenomenological and participatory research on schizophrenia: Recovering the person in theory and practice. *Journal of Social Issues, 53,* 767–784.

Davidson, L., Stayner, D. A., Rakfeldt, J., & Tebes, J. K. (1995). *Supporting peer supporters: Strategies for the training, supervision, and accommodation of mental health consumers.* A symposium conducted at the 6th biennial conference of the Society for Community Research and Action, Chicago.

Davidson, L., & Strauss, J. S. (1992). Sense of self in recovery from severe mental illness. *British Journal of Medical Psychology, 65,* 131–145.

Davidson, L., Weingarten, R., Steiner, J., Stayner, D. A., & Hoge, M. A. (1997). Integrating prosumers into clinical settings. In C. T. Mowbray, D. P Moxley, C. A. Jasper, & L. L. Howell (Eds.), *Consumers as providers in psychiatric rehabilitation* (pp. 437–455). Columbia, MD: International Association of Psychosocial Rehabilitation Services.

Deegan, P. E. (1992). The Independent Living Movement and people with psychiatric disabilities: Taking back control over our own lives. *Psychosocial Rehabilitation Journal, 15,* 3–19.

Deegan, P. E. (1993). Recovering our sense of value after being labeled mentally ill. *Journal of Psychosocial Nursing, 31,* 7–11.

Denzin, N. (1987). *The alcoholic self.* Newbury Park, CA: Sage.

Dixon, L., Krauss, N., & Lehman, A. (1994). Consumers as service providers: The promise and challenge. *Community Mental Health Journal, 30,* 615–625.

Durlak, J. (1979). Comparative effectiveness of paraprofessional and professional helpers. *Psychological Bulletin, 86,* 80–92.

Edelson, M. (1964). *Ego psychology, group dynamics, and the therapeutic community.* New York: Grune & Stratton.

Edelson, M. (1970a). *Sociotherapy and psychotherapy.* Chicago: University of Chicago Press.

Edelson, M. (1970b). *The practice of sociotherapy: A case study.* New Haven, CT: Yale University Press.

Edmunson, E. D., Bedell, J. R., & Gordon, R. E. (1984). The Community Network Development Project: Bridging the gap between professional aftercare and self-help. In A. Gartner & F. Riessman (Eds.), *The self-help revolution* (pp. 184–195). New York: Human Sciences Press.

Emerick, R. E. (1989). Group demographics in the mental patient movement: Group location, age, and size as structural factors. *Community Mental Health Journal, 25,* 277–300.

Estroff, S. E. (1982). The next step: Self-help. *Hospital and Community Psychiatry, 33,* 609.

Felton, C. J., Stastny, P., Shern, D., Blanch, A., Donahue, S. A., Knight, E., & Brown, C. (1995). Consumers as peer specialists on intensive case management teams: Impact on client outcomes. *Psychiatric Services, 46,* 1037–1044.

Fisher, D. B. (1994). Health care reform based on an empowerment model of recovery by people with psychiatric disabilities. *Hospital and Community Psychiatry, 45,* 913–915.

Fisher, D. (1996). Overcoming schizophrenia. *Journal of Psychosocial Nursing & Mental Health Services, 34,* 33–38.

Frese, F. (1993). Twelve aspects of coping for persons with serious and persistent mental illness. *Innovations and Research, 2,* 39–46.

Frese, F., & Davis, W. W. (1997). The consumer-survivor movement, recovery, and consumer professionals. *Professional Psychology, Research and Practice, 28,* 243–245.

Galanter, M. (1988). Zealous self-help groups as adjuncts to psychiatric treatment: A study of Recovery, Inc. *American Journal of Psychiatry, 145,* 1248–1253.

Gartner, A., & Riessman, F. (1984). *The self-help revolution.* New York: Human Sciences Press.

Godley, S. H., Sabin, M. C., McClure, C., Smerken, M., & Manion, L. (1988). Paid friends for frequent recidivists: An evaluation of a multifaceted community aide program. *Psychosocial Rehabilitation Journal, 11,* 29–39.

GROW (1979). *GROW comes of age: A celebration and vision.* Sydney: Author.

GROW in America. (1994). *GROW in America Annual Report: July 1, 1993 to June 30, 1994.* Champaign, IL: Author.

Harding, C. M., Brooks, G. W., Ashikaga, T., Strauss, J. S., & Breier, A. (1987a). The Vermont longitudinal study of persons with severe mental illness, I: Methodology, study sample, and overall current status. *American Journal of Psychiatry, 144,* 718–726.

Harding, C. M., Brooks, G. W., Ashikaga, T., Strauss, J. S., & Breier, A. (1987b). The Vermont longitudinal study, II: Long-term outcome of subjects who once met the criteria for DSM-III schizophrenia. *American Journal of Psychiatry, 144,* 727–735.

Harding, C. M., & Zahniser, J. H. (1994). Empirical correction of seven myths about schizophrenia with implications for treatment. *Acta Psychiatrica Scandanavica, 90,* 140–146.

Humphreys, K. (1992). Twelve-step stories and transformation in personal epistemology. In J. Rappaport (Chair), *Community narratives and personal stories.* Symposium conducted at a meeting of the Midwestern Psychological Association, Chicago.

Humphreys, K. (1997). Individual and social benefits of mutual aid and self-help groups. *Social Policy, 27,* 12–19.

Humphreys, K., & Rappaport, J. (1994). Researching self-help/mutual aid groups and organizations: Many roads, one journey. *Applied and Preventive Psychology, 3,* 217–231.

Jacobs, M. K., & Goodman, G. (1989). Psychology and self-help groups: Predictions on a partnership. *American Psychologist, 44*(3), 536–545.

Jamison, K. R. (1995). *An unquiet mind: A memoir of moods and madness.* New York: Knopf.

Jones, M. (1953). *The therapeutic community.* New York: Basic Books.

Katz, A. H. (1981). Self-help and mutual aid: An emerging social movement? Annual Review of Sociology, 7, 129–155.

Katz, A. H. (1993). *Self-help in America: A social movement perspective.* Princeton, NJ: Twane.

Katz, A. H., & Levin, L. S. (1980). Self-care is not a solipsistic trap: A reply to critics. *International Journal of Health Services, 10,* 329–336.

Kaufmann, C. L. (1995). The self-help employment center: Some outcomes from the first year. *Psychosocial Rehabilitation Journal, 18,* 145–162.

Kaufmann, C. L. (1996). The lion's den: Social identities and self-help groups. *The Community Psychologist, 29,* 11–13.

Kaufmann, C. L., Freund, P. D., & Wilson, J. (1989). Self-help in the mental health system: A model for consumer-provider collaboration. *Psychosocial Rehabilitation Journal, 13,* 520.

Kaufmann, C. L., Schulberg, H. C., & Schooler, N. R. (1994). Self-help group participation among people with severe mental illness. *Prevention in Human Services, 11,* 315–331.

Kaufmann, C. L., Ward-Colasante, C., & Farmer, J. (1993). Development and evaluation of drop-in centers operated by mental health consumers. *Hospital and Community Psychiatry, 44,* 675–678.

Kelly, J. G. (1966). Ecological constraints on mental health services. *American Psychologist, 21,* 535–539.

Kelly, J. G. (1971). Qualities for the community psychologist. *American Psychologist, 26,* 897–903.

Kennedy, M. (1989, June). *Psychiatric hospitalizations of GROWers.* Paper presented at the 2nd biennial conference of Community Research and Action, East Lansing, MI.

Kennedy, M. (1995). *Becoming a GROWer: World view transformation among committed members of a mutual help group.* Unpublished doctoral dissertation, University of Illinois, Urbana-Champaign.

Kennedy, M., & Humphreys, K. (1994). Understanding worldview transformation in mutual help groups. *Prevention in Human Services, 11,* 181–189.

Keogh, C. (1979). *How it started...in a nutshell. In GROW comes of age: A celebration and vision* (pp. 10–11). Sydney: GROW

Kloos, B. (1998). *Meaning-making in the context of residential treatment settings for persons with histories of psychological disorders.* Unpublished doctoral dissertation, University of Illinois, Champaign-Urbana.

Kurtz, L. F. (1988). Mutual aid for affective disorders: The Manic Depressive and Depressive Association. *American Journal of Orthopsychiatry, 58,* 152–155.

Kurtz, L. F. (1990). The self-help movement: Review of the past decade of research. *Social Work with Groups, 13,* 101–115.

Kurtz, L. F., & Chambon, A. (1987). Comparison of self-help groups for mental health. *Health and Social Work,* 275–283.

Kurtz, L. F., & Powell, T. J. (1987). Three approaches to understanding self-help groups. *Social Work with Groups, 10,* 69–80.

Kyrouz, E., & Humphreys, K. (1996). Do psychiatrically disabled people benefit from participation in self-help/mutual aid organizations? A research review. *The Community Psychologist, 29,* 21–25.

Lee, D. T. (1971). Recovery, Inc.: Aid in the transition from hospital to community. *Mental Hygiene, 55,* 194–198.

Leff, H. S., Campbell, J., Cagne, C., & Woocher, L. S. (1997). Evaluating peer providers. In C. T. Mowbray, D. P Moxley, C. A. Jasper, & L. L. Howell (Eds.), *Consumers as providers in psychiatric rehabilitation* (pp. 488–501). Columbia, MD: International Association of Psychosocial Rehabilitation Services.

Levin, L. S., Katz, A. H., & Hoist, E. (1976). *Self-care: Lay initiatives in health.* New York: Prodist.

Levine, M., & Perkins, D. V. (1987). *Principles of community psychology: Perspectives and applications.* New York: Oxford University Press.

Levy, L. H. (1976). Self-help groups: Types and psychological processes. *Journal of Applied Behavioral Science, 12,* 310–322.

Levy, L. H. (2000). Self-help groups. In J. Rappaport & E. Seidman (Eds.), *Handbook of community psychology.* New York: Plenum Press.

Lin, K. M., & Kleinman, A. M. (1988). Psychopathology and clinical course of schizophrenia: A cross-cultural perspective. *Schizophrenia Bulletin, 14,* 555–567.

Llewelyn, S. P, & Haslett, A. V. J. (1986). Factors perceived as helpful by the members of self-help groups: An exploratory study. *British Journal of Guidance and Counselling, 14,* 252–262.

Luke, D. A. (1989). *The measurement of change in a self-help context.* Unpublished doctoral dissertation, University of Illinois, Urbana-Champaign.

Luke, D. A., Rappaport, J., & Seidman, E. (1991). Setting phenotypes in a mutual help organization: Expanding behavior setting theory. *American Journal of Community Psychology, 19,* 147–167.

Luke, D. A., Roberts, L., & Rappaport, J. (1993). Individual, group context, and individual-group fit predictors of self-help group attendance. *Journal of Applied Behavioral Science, 29,* 216–238.

Lyons, J. S., Cook, J. A., Ruth, A. R., Karver, M., & Slagg, N. B. (1996). Service delivery using consumer staff in a mobile crisis assessment program. *Community Mental Health Journal, 32,* 33–40.

Manning, S. S., & Suire, B. (1996). Consumers as employees in mental health: Bridges and roadblocks. *Psychiatric Services, 47,* 939–943.

Markowitz, F. E., DeMasi, M. E., Carpinello, S. E., Knight, E. L., Videlca-Sherman, L., & Sofka, C. (1996). *The role of self-help in the recovery process.* Paper presented at the 6th annual National Conference on State Mental Health Agency Services Research and Program Evaluation, Arlington, VA.

Maton, K. I. (1987). Patterns and psychological correlates of material support within a religious setting: The bidirectional support hypothesis. *American Journal of Community Psychology, 15,* 185–207.

Maton, K. I., & Salem, D. A. (1995). Organizational characteristics of empowering community settings. A multiple case study approach. *American Journal of Community Psychology, 23,* 631–656.

Medvene, L. J. (1985). An organizational theory of self-help groups. *Social Policy, 15,* 35–37.

Moos, R. H. (1973). Conceptualizations of human environments. *American Psychologist, 28,* 652–665.

Mowbray, C. T., Chamberlain, P., Jennings, M., & Reed, C. (1988). Consumer-run mental health services: Results from five demonstration projects. *Community Mental Health Journal, 24,* 151–156.

Mowbray, C. T., & Moxley, D. P. (1997a). A framework for organizing consumer roles as providers of psychiatric rehabilitation. In C. T. Mowbray, D. P. Moxley, C. A. Jasper, & L. L. Howell (Eds.), *Consumers as providers in psychiatric rehabilitation* (pp. 35–44). Columbia, MD: International Association of Psychosocial Rehabilitation Services.

Mowbray, C. T., & Moxley, D. P. (1997b). Consumers as providers: Themes and success. In C. T. Mowbray, D. P. Moxley, C. A. Jasper, & L. L. Howell (Eds.), *Consumers as providers in psychiatric rehabilitation* (pp. 504–517). Columbia, MD: International Association of Psychosocial Rehabilitation Services.

Mowbray, C. T., Moxley, D. P, Jasper, C. A., & Howell, L. L. (Eds.). (1997). *Consumers as providers in psychiatric rehabilitation.* Columbia, MD: International Association of Psychosocial Rehabilitation Services.

Mowbray, C. T., Moxley, D. P., Thrasher, S., Bybee, D., McCrohan, N., Harris, S., & Clover, G. (1996). Consumers as community support providers: Issues created by role innovation. *Community Mental Health Journal, 32,* 47–67.

Mowbray, C. T., & Tan, C. (1993). Consumer-operated drop-in centers: Evaluation of operations and impact. *The Journal of Mental Health Administration, 20,* 8–19.

Moxley, D. P., & Mowbray, C. T. (1997). Consumers as providers: Forces and factors legitimizing role innovation in psychiatric rehabilitation. In C. T. Mowbray, D. P. Moxley, C. A. Jasper, & L. L. Howell (Eds.), *Consumers as providers in psychiatric rehabilitation* (pp. 2–34). Columbia, MD: International Association of Psychosocial Rehabilitation Services.

Nikkel, R. E., Smith, G., & Edwards, D. (1992). A consumer-operated case management project. *Hospital and Community Psychiatry, 43,* 577–579.

Omark, R. C. (1979). The dilemma of membership in Recovery, Inc.: A self-help ex-mental patients' organization. *Psychological Reports, 44,* 1119–1125.

Parrish, J. (1989). The long journey home: Accomplishing the mission of the community support movement. *Psychosocial Rehabilitation Journal, 12,* 107–124.

Paulson, R. I. (1991). Professional training for consumers and family members: One road to empowerment. *Psychosocial Rehabilitation Journal, 14,* 69–80.

Perry, H. S. (1982). *Psychiatrist of America: The life of Harry Stack Sullivan.* Cambridge, MA: Harvard University Press.

R., Joseph & F., Donald. (1973). The history and work of Schizophrenics Anonymous. In D. Hawkins & L. Pauling (Eds.), *Orthomolecular psychiatry* (pp. 675–679). San Francisco: Freeman.

Raiff, N. R. (1982). Self-help participation and quality of life: A study of the staff of Recovery, Inc. *Prevention in the Human Services, 1,* 79–90.

Raiff, N. R. (1984). Some health related outcomes of self-help participation: Recovery, Inc. as a case example of a self-help organization in mental health. In A. Gartner & F. Riessman (Eds.), *The self-help revolution* (pp. 189–193). New York: Human Science Press.

Rappaport, J. (1977). *Community psychology: Values, research, and action.* Chicago: Holt, Rinehart, and Winston.

Rappaport, J. (1993). Narrative studies, personal stories, and identity transformation in the mutual help context. *Journal of Applied Behavioral Science, 29,* 239–256.

Rappaport, J., Seidman, E., Toro, P. A., McFadden, L. S., Reischl, T. M., Roberts, L. J., Salem, D. A., Stein, C. H., & Zimmerman, M. A. (1985). Collaborative research with a mutual help organization. *Social Policy, 15,* 12–24.

Reidy, D. (1992) Shattering illusions of difference. *Resources, 4,* 3.

Reidy, D. (1994). Recovering from treatment: The mental health system as an agent of stigma. *Resources, 6,* 3–10.

Reischl, T., & Rappaport, J. (1988). *Participation in mutual help groups and coping with acute stressors.* Paper presented at the annual meeting of the American Psychological Association, Atlanta.

Ribisl, K., & Luke, D. A. (1993). Social network characteristics of person with dual diagnosis. *Community Psychologist, 27,* 44–45.

Riessman, F. (1965). The "helper-therapy" principle. *Social Work, 10,* 27–32.

Riessman, F. (1990). Restructuring help: A human services paradigm for the 1990s. *American Journal of Community Psychology, 18,* 221–230.

Riger, S. (1984). Ecological and environmental influences on the individual. In K. Heller, R. H. Price, S. Reinharz, S. Riger, & A. Wandersman (Eds.), *Psychology and community change: Challenges for the future* (pp. 117–143). Pacific Grove, CA: Brooks/Cole.

Roberts, B., & Thorsheim, H. I. (1991). Reciprocal ministry: A transforming vision of help and leadership. *Prevention in Human Services, 10,* 51–68.

Roberts, L. J. (1987). *The appeal of mutual help: The participants' perspective.* Paper presented at the 1st biennial conference on Community Research and Action, Columbia, SC.

Roberts, L. J. (1989). *Giving and receiving help: Behavioral predictors of outcomes for members of a mutual help group.* Unpublished doctoral dissertation, University of Illinois, Urbana-Champaign.

Roberts, L. J., Luke, D. A., Rappaport, J., Seidman, E., Toro, P., & Reischl, T. (1991). Charting uncharted terrain: A behavioral observation system for mutual help groups. *American Journal of Community Psychology, 19,* 715–737.

Rootes, L. E., & Aanes, D. L. (1992). A conceptual framework for understanding self-help groups. *Hospital and Community Psychiatry, 43,* 379–381.

Ryback, R. S. (1971). Schizophrenics Anonymous: A treatment adjunct. *Psychiatry in Medicine, 2,* 247–253.

Salem, D. A., Seidman, E., & Rappaport, J. (1988). Community treatment of the mentally ill: The promise of mutual-help organizations. *Social Work,* 403–408.

Salzer, M. S., McFadden, L., & Rappaport, J. (1994). Professional views of self-help groups. *Administration and Policy in Mental Health, 22,* 85–95.

Segal, S., Silverman, C., & Temkin, T. (1995). Characteristics and service use of long-term members of self-help agencies for mental health clients. *Psychiatric Services, 46,* 269–274.

Shannon, P. J., & Morrison, D. L. (1990). Who goes to GROW? Australian and New Zealand Journal of Psychiatry, 24, 96–102.

Shepard, L. (1992). *So you want to hire a consumer? Employing people with psychiatric disabilities as staff members in mental health agencies.* Burlington, VT: Center for Community Change Through Housing and Support.

Sherman, P. S., & Porter, R. (1991). Mental health consumers as case management aides. *Hospital and Community Psychiatry, 42,* 494–498.

Skirboll, B. W., & Pavelsky, P. K. (1984). The Compeer program: Volunteers as friends of the mentally ill. *Hospital and Community Psychiatry, 35,* 938–939.

Snowdon, J. (1980). Self-help groups and schizophrenia. *Australian and New Zealand Journal of Psychiatry, 14,* 265–268.

Solomon, P., & Draine, J. (1993). *The impact of case management and the efficacy of a consumer case management team: One year outcomes of a randomized trial.* Unpublished manuscript. Philadelphia: Hahnemann University Department of Psychiatry and Mental Health Services.

Solomon, P., & Draine, J. (1994a). Family Perceptions of consumers as case managers. *Community Mental Health Journal, 30,* 165–176.

Solomon, P., & Draine, J. (1994b). Satisfaction with mental health treatment in a randomized trial of consumer case management. *The Journal of Nervous and Mental Disease, 182,* 179–184.

Solomon, P., & Draine, J. (1995a). Consumer case management and attitudes concerning family relations among persons with mental illness. *Psychiatric Quarterly, 66,* 249–261.

Solomon, P., & Draine, J. (1995b). One year outcomes of a randomized trial of case management with seriously mentally ill clients leaving jail. *Evaluation Review, 19,* 256–273.

Solomon, P., & Draine, J. (1995c). One year outcomes of a randomized trial of consumer case managers. *Evaluation and Program Planning, 18,* 117–127.

Solomon, P., & Draine, J. (1995d). The efficacy of a consumer case management team: Two year outcomes of a randomized trial. *The Journal of Mental Health Administration, 22,* 135–146.

Solomon, P., & Draine, J. (1996). Perspectives concerning consumers as case managers. *Community Mental Health Journal, 32,* 41–46.

Stein, L. I., & Test, M. A. (1978). *Alternatives to mental hospital treatment.* New York: Plenum Press.

Stephens, C. L., & Belisle, K. C. (1993). The "consumer-as-provider" initiative. *Journal of Mental Health Administration, 20,* 178–182.

Stewart, M. J. (1990). Expanding theoretical conceptualizations of self-help groups. *Social Science and Medicine, 31,* 1057–1066.

Stoneking, B. C., & Greenfield, T. (1991). *Adding trained consumers to case management teams as service coordinators: Program development, research design, accommodations, and early outcomes.* Paper presented at the annual meeting of the American Public Health Association, Atlanta, GA.

Strauss, J. S., & Carpenter, W. T. (1972). The prediction of outcome in schizophrenia, I: Characteristics of outcome. *Archives of General Psychiatry, 27,* 739–746.

Strauss, J. S., & Carpenter, W. T. (1974). The prediction of outcome in schizophrenia, II: Relationships between predictor and outcome variables. *Archives of General Psychiatry, 31,* 37–42.

Strauss, J. S., & Carpenter, W. T. (1977). Prediction of outcome in schizophrenia, III: Five year outcome and its predictors. *Archives of General Psychiatry, 34,* 159–163.

Tebes, J. K., & Kraemer, D. T. (1991). Quantitative and qualitative knowing in mutual support research: Some lessons from the recent history of scientific psychology. *American Journal of Community Psychology, 19,* 739–756.

Toro, P., Rappaport, J., & Seidman, E. (1987). The social climate of mutual help and psychotherapy groups. *Journal of Consulting and Clinical Psychology, 55,* 430–431.

van Tosh, L. (1993). *Working for a change: Employment of consumers/survivors in the design and provision of services for persons who are homeless and mentally disabled.* Rockville, MD: Center for Mental Health Services.

van Uchelen, C. (1989). *Healing and cognitive control in cross-cultural perspective.* Paper presented at the 2nd biennial conference for Community Psychology Research and Action, East Lansing, MI.

Wechsler, H. (1960). The self-help organization in the mental health field: Recovery, Inc., a case study. *Journal of Nervous and Mental Disease, 130,* 297–314.

Weingarten, R. (1994). The on-going processes of recovery. *Psychiatry, 57,* 369–375.

Weingarten, R. (1997). How I've managed chronic mental illness. In L. Spaniol & C. Cagne (Eds.), *Psychological and social aspects of psychiatric disability* (pp. 123–129). Boston: Boston University Center for Psychiatric Rehabilitation.

Young, J. M., & Williams, C. L. (1987). An evaluation of GROW, a mutual help community mental health organization. *Community Health Studies, 11,* 90–95.

Young, J. M., & Williams, C. L. (1988). Whom do mutual-help groups help? A typology of members. *Hospital and Community Psychiatry, 39,* 1178–1182.

Zimmerman, M., Reischl, T. M. Seidman, E., Rappaport, J., Toro, P., & Salem, D. A. (1991). Expansion strategies of a mutual help organization. *American Journal of Community Psychology, 19,* 251–278.

Zinman, S. (1986). Self-help: The wave of the future. *Hospital and Community Psychiatry, 37,* 213.

Zinman, S., Harp, H. T., & Budd, S. (1987). *Reaching across: Mental health clients help each other.* Riverside, CA: California Network of Mental Health Clients.

# If Work Makes People with Mental Illness Sick, What Do Unemployment, Poverty, and Social Isolation Cause?

*Joseph Marrone and Ed Golowka*

At the time of original publication Joseph Marrone was with Columbia River Mental Health Services, Vancouver, WA.

This article originally appeared in *Psychiatric Rehabilitation Journal*, 1999, 23(2), 187–193 and is reprinted with permission.

Helen Keller, an icon of the disability rights movement, said: "People do not like to think. If one thinks one must reach conclusions; conclusions are not always pleasant." Much of the advocacy and professional writing in the psychiatric rehabilitation field over the last decade has been devoted to exploding the myth of hopelessness and irreversible decline attendant to the diagnosis of schizophrenia in people. One particular area of interest and research has been in the capacity of people with serious and persistent mental illness to work successfully. Not much attention, however, has been devoted to an exploration of the topic of this article, that is, if people with psychiatric rehabilitation *can* work, then the obvious companion postulate is that people with mental illness *should* work. Disability advocacy for employment has emphasized the untapped capacity of people with significant disabilities to make a contribution to our society as citizens through working. The argument that people with disabilities can't work is essentially an empty one, as there are many examples that show that people with a wide variety of significant disabilities can work. The authors espouse the view that working is both a right and a responsibility for citizens with disabilities. Adults with disabilities are the only group in this country for whom not working has been considered an acceptable lifestyle.

The importance of high expectations has been well established as a tool in successful goal achievement and life advancement. The challenge for helpers is ensuring that this pressure of high expectation is initially borne more by rehabilitation staff members who are charged with assisting people with psychiatric disabilities to realize success, and not merely transferred through as an added burden to the clients they serve.

One cautionary note and clarification must be made. These arguments are not meant to do either of the following:

1. Negate the real barriers (e. g., medical insurance, lack of meaningful career opportunities, fear of the unknown, history of failed attempts) or financial tradeoffs (loss of food stamps, Section 8 housing subsidies, spe-

cial program supports) people with all disabilities face in leaving Social Security or Public Assistance rolls (SSI, SSDI, TANF);

2.  Imply that an acceptable strategy is for professional helpers to adopt a get tough approach with people with mental illness who are scared or reluctant to attempt employment. In fact, the change from the role of patient or client to a new role as worker in society is fragile at best. The journey to employment requires a more sensitive approach from all involved individuals (the worker, the professionals, family, and friends) to the extent that everyone can successfully leverage the potential and ability of the worker with an appreciation of the limitations that are part of the illness.

The authors feel that finding the solutions to #1 and avoiding the inappropriate tactics of #2 are closely connected. Rehabilitation professionals and other helpers can do a better job in assisting people, advocating in their best interests, and accepting some risks in service to working on behalf of the people with psychiatric disabilities that they are charged with serving. The limited use of the existing SSI and SSDI work incentives that have been in place since 1981 show that the disincentives are an important but not all-encompassing piece of the problem. The most egregious example is the almost nonexistent use of the Title 1619b provision that allows people on SSI in most instances to keep their Medicaid coverage while earning significantly more than what is considered full employment (in Massachusetts, that figure or threshold amount was approximately $24,000 in 1998). This, in the face of the fact that health insurance and health care benefits are at the forefront of barriers to employment that consumers and advocates consistently cite.

The authors propose that ultimately people with disabilities do, in fact, have to accept personal responsibility to choose employment as part of the social contract of citizenship. Nevertheless, the answers do not lie solely within their purview. Rather, staff members must improve their capacity to inspire, aid, challenge constructively, support, and advocate for the people with whom they work. Staff members must also hold themselves more accountable for building their own competencies and achieving meaningful results vis-à-vis employment outcomes—not accept mediocre results as justifiable because of the severity of the disability or the system disincentives.

*People should work because unemployment is much worse for your mental health than the stresses of employment.* No hard data exist showing that helping people move into employment (even nagging them into it) is bad. Van Dongen (1996) has made the case that work, rather than increasing stressors, helps distract people from their symptomatology. People like Gary Bond (1998), Bob Drake (1994), and Russert & Frey (1991) in their work have made a good case for employment as a necessary addition to current programs of psychiatric rehabilitation, notwithstanding the fact that employment has always been given "lip service" since the inception of the Community Support (CSP) movement. Even those efforts haven't been targeted on really encouraging and motivating people to choose work. Issues that unemployment, particularly long-term unemployment, brings to the fore are depression, feelings of worthlessness, self-pity, self-absorption, higher risk of substance abuse, greater chance of isolation, and poverty.

In preparation for writing this piece, one of the authors conducted an extensive literature search specifically for any clinical studies that showed the ill-effects of employment on the mental health of people with serious mental illness. No such clinical research studies were found. There is a rather large body of existing data showing poor outcomes in psychiatric vocational rehabilitation, but no information regarding actual ill effects (in contrast to consumers' fears because of perceived or potential problems).

Clearly, much anecdotal material does persist in the field and cannot be discounted. However, the authors' point is that a widely shared concern about negative consequences attendant to working is not based on "hard" data and is contrary to admittedly limited, but nonetheless encouraging, findings about the benefits of employment. In essence, what staff members do if they don't encourage people to work is advocate that they increase the factors that exacerbate, rather than ameliorate, their problems. When the individual says, "I can't go on this interview. I'm too scared that I won't get the job," the helper must be confident in saying, "What can I say or do to help you feel more comfortable about going on this job interview?" This conversation is risky but necessary. The relevant theme that resonates most strongly throughout the literature is that successful employment and positive mental health are essentially very different domains. If anything, a stronger relationship exists between un- or underemployment and the occurrence or persistence of psychological problems, than with employment itself. Also, the potential for significant improvement in overall quality of life through work is quite real.

*It's a responsibility of citizenship. It's "part of the deal."* It's a right that people should enjoy. People with psychiatric disabilities have become increasingly concerned, as they rightly should, about issues of civil rights and citizenship and empowerment. A major component of the civil rights movements in the U.S.—whether focusing on racial equality, gender, age, sexual orientation issues, the union movement, or the ADA—has been around *freedom to gain access to,* not *freedom from employment.* It is somewhat disingenuous to rightfully demand respect and dignity as a person beyond the label of serious and persistent mental illness, yet expect to be free from the obligations and expectations of full citizenship in our society. Once again, if we accept the premise that people with mental illness *can* work, then it seems we should move naturally to the concomitant proposition that people with mental illness *should* work. People often say that it is up to the person to choose if he or she wants to work. To those who suggest that, three thoughts are offered.

We often restrict people's ability to choose things. For example, discussions abound about people who have "unrealistic" career goals, who expect us to get them high-paying career jobs although they lack the requisite skills. Or, even more dramatically, consider about the person who develops a romantic attachment to a helper and wants to have intimate relations with him or her.

The authors would challenge the readers of this piece to go home tonight and sit down with their spouses, lovers, roommates, or adult children and announce to them that they have chosen not to work anymore. Our assumption is that the spouse, lover, etc. would not treat this declaration neutrally with a response of "Whatever you decide, dear" but rather would have a firm opinion about the feasibility of that option.

Access to employment in U.S. society is both a right and a responsibility. Citizens are expected to be productive and participate in a society integrated by race, gender, age, ethnic origin, and disability. Because the U.S. is a free society, the government cannot mandate that everyone feel this way. But societies are governed by laws and publicly stated values (in the U.S., the Constitution, Declaration of Independence, Civil Rights Act of 1964, Title IX, and ADA are prominent examples). The psychiatric rehabilitation funding agency or provider is part of a broader community context, whose values and actions are guided by public law and regulation. It cannot force its clients, or any other citizens, to embrace employment and integration. However, it can wholeheartedly endorse, in statement and action, policies that support these two principles because as a public and community service entity it must reflect the core social values of the society of which it is a part. It is incumbent upon any funding or community service agency to clarify what activities it wishes to support and encourage—not merely to identify what it will tolerate.

*Work is not enough in a person's life, but it's a better start on the rest of the "American Dream" than unemployment and poverty.* Billie Holiday has stated most succinctly that "you need a little love in your life and some food in your stomach before you can hold still for some damn fool's lecture about how to behave." Clearly, there are many aspects of a person's life that influence quality of life other than employment—for example, physical and mental health, intimate relationships, friendships and social networks, spirituality, children, and the quest for meaning and self-identity. However, one would be hard pressed to argue that staying in the state of unemployment and poverty enhances a person's access to or capacity for these other dimensions of a quality life. Yet this is essentially what we as helpers and advocates do when we recommend against or don't actively promote pursuing employment for people with mental illness in the face of possible stressors inherent in that choice. Successful employment does not guarantee satisfaction or fulfillment in other arenas. This fact should not mitigate our efforts to help people master this aspect—if for no other reason that this is at least a concrete area that helpers can measure and affect positively. Other more ephemeral elements, while no less and sometimes more important to individual quality of life, are much more resistant to the attentions of community rehabilitation professionals.

Jobs should not define the totality of the meaning of "success" for people with disabilities any more than they should be seen as definitive standards for achievement by others. Purely person-referenced outcomes like happiness, enjoyment, and contentment are things that service providers should hope to inspire within the people they serve, but nevertheless are outside the bailiwick of the results for which they can logically be held accountable. The basis for the funding of community rehabilitation providers is to help their clients with disabilities improve their life situations vis-à-vis employment and income. Providing rehabilitation services without using improved vocational performance goals as indicators seems spurious. Providers' contracts from funding sources should contain the outcomes desired, and subsequent fiscal allocations should be subject to modification based on program goal achievement and adherence to some recognized local, national, or international standards of good practice.

*Getting a job quickly is more likely to lead to a career than just planning.* It is crucial for people with psychiatric disabilities to be helped to achieve both rapid employment entry and career development and growth opportunities within the labor force. There is often a presumption that good planning naturally leads to actions in service to those plans. This seemingly logical progression of events is not the norm in planning, whether viewing the lives of people with disabilities or those without. People who have not partaken of early educational and vocational experiences or whose communication skills are impaired often are "novice decision-makers" vis-à-vis life planning. People with disabilities, often under the guise of protection, are held to higher standards of skill development, before choices are accepted, than others in the community (Jenkinson, 1993).

Just as important as assisting people to dream and think about careers is helping them develop an understanding of an essential fact of work life: a person cannot have a career without a job. All the insight, dreaming, visioning, positiveness, and planning in the world will not give anyone, including a person with mental illness, a foundation to a career without a concomitant focus on gaining relevant work experience. The same is true of the opportunity to develop contacts that can only be nurtured in the context of mutual business, as well as personal interconnectedness, self-confidence, and energy that comes from participating in a world much wider than the protected sanctuaries of psychiatric rehabilitation or clinical day services. The continued importance of education and lifelong learning of all sorts, whether in supported education or not, cannot be minimized in terms of ultimate career development. If one has a clear career goal (e. g., lawyer, doctor, researcher) or lacks minimal educational credentials (e. g., GED), then it may be advisable to pursue educational opportunities more than work experience. However, in the absence of such a compelling need, then the person with a psychiatric disability and his or her advocates should strongly consider real world work experience to be a key tool to use in career planning.

*It does not get easier later on.* Delaying entry into the work force does not make job entry easier. While people with serious mental illness certainly need more support than merely job and skill acquisition to make a smooth transition into employment, helping people move rapidly into employment does not appear to be deleterious to the mental or emotional health of people with serious mental illness. The longer people delay their vocational aspirations, the more danger they face of insufficient work experience for career advancement, age discrimination, concerns raised by interviewers of unexplained, or atypical career paths, and lack of exposure to information technology that permeates much of even the entry-level modern work force. Indeed, rapid job entry instead of step-by-step adjustment even holds the potential of greater success and fewer negative consequences.

Perhaps there would be more concern about pushing people too rapidly into employment and too narrowly equating life success with work success if there was any tendency in the community psychiatric rehabilitation world to do so. However, the overwhelming preponderance of evidence over the last few decades is that rather than consumers' moving too hastily into employment options, the opposite is true. The pace of vocational achievement in even the most stellar psychiatric vocational rehabilitation programs seems quite lethargic in comparison to the employment and training program results considered successful with people without disabilities. Historically, these lower standards of achievement have been ascribed to the reasons cited earlier, such as "severity of the disability" or the "system disincentives." Perhaps it is now time for staff members to consider the possibility that, in addition to these well-established stumbling blocks other blocks exist in the nature of minimal expectations for achievement, diminished capacity for hope and positiveness, and lack of systemic accountability for poor performance of staff members and programs.

*Employment is a more dependable and less stressful way of life than SSI, SSDI, or TANF benefits.* It is obvious that employment brings stresses and psychological strains, no matter the weight of the relative contribution or problems that these bring for a person's mental well-being. As noted earlier, there has been a great deal of attention paid to this potential problem, even in the face of little evidence of pernicious effects of employment. Much less, if any, discussion is found about the obvious fact that depending on the public system to equitably treat people with psychiatric disabilities who are also poor, is just as risky, (or, as the authors would submit, is more risky) than a job. Particularly in the current conservative climate dominating the political culture and the nation-wide challenge of "welfare reform" and "benefit roll reduction," the status quo is increasingly tenuous and fraught with uncertainty for people who rely on the provision of public human service delivery. Since political trends ebb and flow, perhaps a more important consideration is the fact that a person's choice to maintain the current situation in his or her life does not ensure that other elements do not fluctuate. Even people who have consciously chosen not to move ahead in a rehabilitative fashion may still face the variety of crises that are prevalent and, for some, inevitable in everyday life for people with few economic resources—for example, human service program staff turnover, poor health, loss of loved ones, eviction, and the aging process and attendant feelings of mortality. The status quo of unemployment and poverty does not make people impervious to changes out of their control; rather, it makes them more susceptible to having these life challenges taking a greater emotional toll.

*It's a way to meet people and expand social networks.* Work acts as a training opportunity for the enhancement and development of social skills. Bellack & Musser (1993), Lieberman (1989), and Mosher and Burti (1992) all have amply looked at social dysfunction and performance and their impact on independent living. Yet the idea of work as a viable training environment for social skills development is as obvious to some outside the field of rehabilitation as it is not understood by many who do work in the field. In a recent interview, an assistant professor of economics at MIT discussed her success in her field by saying, "It's very difficult to be told that you have a lot of potential when you're still in the process of achieving things; I'm still learning how good I am and what I can accomplish." When work makes you feel good about who you are and what you can do, then your desire to connect with others and to be part of larger communities of people is stimulated.

With time, work provides its own safety net for people. But a strong network of services and supports must be developed in order for individual rehabilitation and vocational goals to be reached. The support needed and provided by co-workers can elevate the employment experience from one of familiar isolation to one of relatedness and comfort. Individuals come to work because of the people with whom they work, not just for the job that needs to be done.

The skills learned and developed during times of employment—managing stress and uncertainty, communicating with others, delegating symptoms to a place of less influence and importance—will be helpful during times of unemployment. It is a normal part of a working life to be unemployed at times. But it is unhealthy and counterproductive to become or to be allowed to become demotivated because of this experience. Returning to pre-employment situations (isolation in an apartment or a return to a psychosocial day program) will not aid the recovery process. Any other understanding of how employment aids the recovery process should be carefully negotiated and discussed with the individual and should be seen only as a transitional state between jobs.

It gives people more status than the "consumer" role. The status of "consumer" envisions somebody who takes, gorging on the metaphorical meals served by the "system": supervised housing, financial subsidies such as SSI and SSDI, medication clinics, and other highly structured and dependent relationships with the mental health system. But successful and happy people don't just take; they give, not only to themselves, but to a larger community Or as Winston Churchill said, "We make a living by what we get. We make a life by what we give." Work provides status in our culture. To say, "I'm not working" raises questions and assumptions about who you are, or are not. Work carries value and status.

Overprotectiveness in the name of public safety, or gratuitous concern and caring for those less fortunate, becomes a form of oppression and stigma in and of itself—preventing growth, independence, and opportunity for the individual most in need. As C.S. Lewis said, "Of all the tyrannies, a tyranny sincerely exercised for the good of its victims may be the most oppressive." Until individuals living with psychiatric disabilities are part of a work force, attitudes associated with stigma such as repulsion and pity for the mentally ill will never be replaced with some acceptance or tolerance. A new view and a new paradigm for integration remain elusive. But one connecting and healing thread remains intact: employment is healing and recuperative for anyone. Employment clearly has status in our culture. As noted in by Radin (1997): "Having a job is critical to a feeling of being seen as a contributing member of our society" (p. 17).

As "consumers" become "workers," the need for intensive case management and outpatient services becomes only significant as a service to be accessed when needed and necessary. This abandonment of the traditional locus of care, from a formalized mental health system to an individual empowerment model where work becomes an expectation, often precipitates defensive posturing around issues of setting up the person for failure, or the need to go slowly to make sure that the person will not decompensate.

People have dreams of careers, have struggled through a career, and have skills and abilities. As more individuals are living longer with their mental illness without the institutional experience of decades ago, the connection with work becomes more reasonable, more available as an option, and more of an expectation. The individual is usually ready. He or she has been waiting, and waiting for a long time for that opportunity to be, or again be, successful and to feel good. Even though these feelings of status and worth may not be immediately available, somehow, with support, most individuals know it is the right thing to do.

*It's a way to help people develop possibilities for intimacies, love, and sex.* The development of meaningful and reciprocal relationships is a hallmark of adult adaptation and functioning. As new workers negotiate their complex relationships with employers, coworkers, and the larger community, then the outcomes of intimacy, friendships, and reconnections with family become more satisfying options. Trust is not an instinct with which we are born. It is earned and carefully negotiated. Many individuals living with psychiatric disabilities have developed a lack of trust and a skepticism of most professional interactions based upon years of dealing with a mental health system that often prompts disappointment and discouragement. Establishing rapport that is reliable and affirming is critical for the individual and the job coach.

In an article titled "The Connection Gap," Laura Pappano wrote, "More than ever, our lives are lived with fewer important connections. More of us live alone, eat alone, watch TV alone. We marry later and divorce more often. We work more. We travel solo, eat at the bar alone, and go to the movies by ourselves. We bank and shop by phone. We look for love on the Internet. And we don't visit anymore on Sundays. No wonder one-third of Americans tell pollsters they are lonely" (p.14). She talks about the lack of social interactions that "create social capital and trust among members of a community" (p.20), concluding that "Reconnecting is critical for our survival, both as individuals and as a society" (p.23). The work experience begins to bridge the loneliness of living and the need to develop reciprocal and trusting relationships.

There is more to do in your life. To create a limited vision of what individuals with mental illness can and cannot do because of their disability only wastes the gift that is human potential. The shift away from a formal mental health system to a health system responding to each person's basic needs—work, love, shelter, food—requires a dialogue between competing viewpoints and values that are struggling to be heard and debated. Any person's life is more that just eating and sleeping. But for individuals living with psychiatric disabilities, these two actions are often prominent in a daily repertoire of activities. Add to these such diversions as watching television and smoking cigarettes, and you often have an accurate snapshot of "patienthood". The artificiality of day treatment centers, clubhouses, visits to the medication clinic, or to a therapist does not necessarily assist an individual with integration into a "normal" life. And for many individuals, these experiences are further clouded by the growing use of alcohol illegal drugs, creating the "patient with dual diagnoses" (Fowler, 1998; Minkoff and Drake, 1991).

Psychiatric disability is a disease of losses. The individual can lose his or her family and friends, housing, income, appearance, skills, self respect, and, most importantly, hope. Employment can limit these losses and provide an opportunity to do and enjoy more in life. There is mounting empirical support for the idea that improves skills in one area does not necessarily balance with improvements in others. Thus, getting a job may not automatically translate into good social skills. But certainly the development of employment based interpersonal relationships often involve finding closeness and love, enhancing life, and fostering opportunity.

*To work, helps make daily life more interesting plus leisure time that has more meaning.* Work and working are inherently more interesting and fulfilling than hanging around a drop-in center or reflecting incessantly on one's own life. While the functional limitations of psychiatric disability can interfere with obtaining or retaining a job, the actual pursuit of a job becomes a daily conversation with oneself and with one's support network. As the worker feels more empowered to work, to look for a job, to set up an interview, and to accept a job offer, then achievement is absorbed into a daily routine. Each day takes on a cumulative dignity and provide a sense of belonging.

In tandem with working, leisure then has more meaning. Early on in the disease, the pursuit of purposeful leisure activities is lost and estranged from daily life. As self esteem and awareness are improved through work, the individual can benefit from an increased curiosity about what to do with more money, days off, and new friends. Work serves as a prompt for the new and interesting opportunities to plan vacations, organize breaks with co-workers, and socialize after work with a cup of coffee or a beer. Identity and self expression are developed and fostered, creating a new life that is exciting, scary, depressing, and interesting.

*Working provides a distraction from disability.* The distractions offered by medications, therapy, counseling, and community treatment often serve as diversions from creating a fulfilling life. While important and unavoidable for many, they are inadequate in improving quality of life or in at least affecting some long term and meaningful gain in and of themselves. Employment ("working for a living") is more formative. The processes of talking about going to work, searching for a job, interviewing for a position, and keeping and losing a job, are cumulative in terms of facing a truth about expectations and dreams. Life's depth of field becomes sharper and more focused to the individual worker. The worker's relationship with others becomes more integrated and self-curative. Service providers must appreciate the limiting effects of protecting the individual from stress (and the attendant fear of their own professional failure as a caregiver if the client decompensates). The person's shift in consciousness from illness to work issues enhances and supports the recovery process.

People who work worry about their job. Will I do it right? Will my co-workers like me? Will I lose my job? These are legitimate thoughts when so much is at stake. And these worries distract from the usual symptoms of mental illness. When there is something to look forward to or be afraid to lose, when you have a dream to hold onto, then you are distracted, at least temporarily. Working is an intimate experience; it sustains a sense of being and, within our culture, it identifies a contributing member of society. In balance, these new anxieties might be more manageable than the symptoms and negative behaviors that would need to be managed if work was not part of daily life.

Much literature supports guarded expectations around the ability of individuals with mental illness to handle the stresses of competitive employment and independent living (Blankertz, 1994; Ferdinandi, 1996). Lamb (1986) has said, "We all want chronic schizophrenics to experience the heightened self-esteem and gratification that a life of employment, of feeling needed, and of being productive provide...[T]he clinical reality (is) that most chronic schizophrenics cannot handle the stress of competitive employment, and that, for the minority that can, entry-level, low stress jobs should most often be the goal. Otherwise, we simply give the person another experience of failure and further lower his self-esteem" (p. 355). Much thinking about impairment and handicaps has changed in the intervening years. The person is no longer the disability, so that the chronic schizophrenic is today an individual living with the disease of schizophrenia or with a disability; the supported employment movement encourages choice and entry at a level that is more akin to expressed desires. Stress, as noted in the beginning of this article, does not lead to decompensation or hospitalization, in and of itself. The concept of failure is only relative to the experience of trying something new. Success can be measured secondary to processing a job loss and not projecting an "I told you so" or "He isn't ready to work" attitude. Can self esteem become any lower that it was when the individual began some steps towards employment, even if he or she eventually loses a job? There is more than a dollop of disingenuousness in citing individual and family apprehension as an insurmountable barrier to community employment. It is part of the responsibility of staff members to assist the individual and family in understanding what community employment is and how dismissing the concept out of hand will negatively impact the individual's life.

The actual words of these new workers are filling the ears of vocational rehabilitation staff members. The voices that they are hearing are from the customers that they are waiting on in a department store, not from inside a secret world in their head; the visions they see are not transitory and frightening, but they are their co-workers in the break room talking about getting more money or sharing complaints about a supervisor; the paranoia that others, the unknown, are out to get them, is replaced with being unappreciated by their bosses and why can't they get a raise in pay. Their stories are real, and they are welcomed distractions from a usual collection of negative symptoms and behaviors that had previously supported a lonely and isolated existence.

As employment for individuals living with psychiatric disabilities becomes an acceptable norm and expectation, then the barriers of stigma, class bias, and discrimination diminish. The proof that individuals can work and should work is as *apparent* as the myth that the disease of mental illness precludes vocational growth is *transparent*. It is not acceptable or ethical that the potential value of one individual can be diminished by a disability. We must support the right to work with a knowledge that work is inalienable to the privilege of being a citizen.

### REFERENCES

Bellack, A. S., & Mueser, K. T. (1993). Psychosocial Treatment for Schizophrenia. *Schizophrenia Bulletin, 19*(2), 317–336.

Blankertz, L. (1994). The psychosocial workforce: A preliminary overview. *Psychosocial Rehabilitation Journal, 18*(1), 135–140.

Bond, G. (1998). Principles of the individual placement and support model: Empirical Support. *Psychiatric Rehabilitation Journal, 22*(1), 11–23.

Drake, R. E., Becker, D. R., Biesanz, J. C., Torrey, W. C., McHugo G.H., & Wyzik, P. G. (1994). Rehabiltative day treatment vs. supported employment: Vocational outcomes. *Community Mental Health Journal, 30*(5), 519–532.

Ferdinandi, A. D. (1996). Predicting rehabilitation outcome among patients with schizophrenia. *Psychiatric Services, 49*(7), 907–909.

Fowler, I. L. (1998). Patterns of current and lifetime substance use in schizophrenia. *Schizophrenia Bulletin, 24*(3), 443–455.

Jenkinson, J. (1993). Who shall decide? The relevance of theory and research to decision making by people with an intellectual disability. *Disability, Handicap, and Society, 8*, 361–374.

Lamb, H. R. (1986). Some reflections on treating schizophrenics. *Archives of General Psychiatry, 43*(10), 354–358.

Liberman, R. P. (1989). *Social skills training for psychiatric patients.* New York: Pergamon Press.

Minkoff, K., & Drake, R., Eds. (1991). *New directions for mental health services: Dual diagnosis of major mental illness and substance disorders.* San Francisco: Jossey Bass.

Mosher, L. R., & Burti, L. (1992). Relationships in rehabilitation: When technology fails. *Psychosocial Rehabilitation Journal, 15*(4), 11–17.

Pappano, L. (1995). The connection gap. *Boston Globe Magazine,* 9/24/95, p. 14, 20, 23.

Radin, C. A. (1997). Ready, willing, and disabled. *Boston Globe Magazine,* 2/9/97, p. 17.

Russert, M. G., & Frey, J. L. (1991). The PACT vocational model: a step into the future. *Psychosocial Rehabilitation Journal, 14*(4), 7–18.

Van Dongen, C. (1996). Quality of life and self-esteem in working and non-working people with mental illness. *Community Mental Health Journal, 32*(6), 535–548.

# Correlates of Vocational Recovery for Persons with Schizophrenia

*Zlatka Russinova, Nancy J. Wewiorski, Asya Lyass, E. Sally Rogers and Joseph M. Massaro*

At the time of original publication Zlatka Russinova, Nancy J. Wewiorski, Asya Lyass, E. Sally Rogers and Joseph M. Massaro were all affiliated with the Center for Psychiatric Rehabilitation, Boston University, Boston, MA.

This article originally appeared in the *International Review of Psychiatry*, 2002, 14(4), 303–311 and is reprinted with permission. The *International Review of Psychiatry* is published by Taylor & Francis Ltd (http://www.tandf.co.uk/journals).

**Abstract:** The correlates of vocational recovery and vocational success among persons with schizophrenia were examined to identify prospective attributes that might be malleable and accessible to intervention. A national, non-representative sample of 109 individuals with a self-reported diagnosis of a schizophrenia spectrum disorder that met criteria for vocational recovery completed a survey on sustained employment of people with serious mental illness. Eighty-two participants (75%) had uninterrupted employment during the 2 years prior to entering the study while the rest sustained employment for at least 12 months during the same period of time. Respondents worked from 10 to 64 hours per week in jobs ranging from unskilled to professional and managerial positions. In multivariate analyses, previous work history and current receipt of Supplemental Security Income (SSI)/Social Security Disability Income (SSDI) were correlated with current work hours per week; educational level and employment in consumer self-help/advocacy settings were associated with occupational status; and current receipt of SSI/SSDI was correlated with current salary per hour. This study provides evidence that some individuals with a schizophrenia spectrum disorder have the capacity to achieve and maintain successful employment despite the challenges presented by this serious mental illness.

## INTRODUCTION

The work capacity of people with serious mental illness has been a long-standing concern in the field of psychiatric rehabilitation (Anthony, Cohen, Farkas & Gagne, 2001; Lehman, 1995; Zarate, Liberman, Mintz & Massel, 1998). Estimates of the employment rate for persons with schizophrenia have ranged from less than 15% (Anthony & Jansen, 1984) to as high as 40% (McGlashan, 1988). Drake and colleagues (1998) reported competitive employment rates ranging from 13% to 35% for clients with serious mental illness across 10 different community mental health centers in the state of New Hampshire. The highest rates were observed in mental health centers with more effective vocational rehabilitation programs, suggesting that capacity to work may be influenced by the provision of services designed to facilitate work functioning. In the current era of novel and more effective treatments for schizophrenia and related disorders, it is important to identify those factors associated with employability that are malleable and may be responsive to social policy changes or evidence-based interventions.

The growing interest of researchers, practitioners, and consumers in the concept of recovery from severe mental illness (Anthony, 1993; Spaniol, Gagne & Koehler, 1999) necessitates a more precise operationalization of its components and dimensions. In this article, we introduce the term "vocational recovery" as a specific component of the overall process of recovery from a disabling mental illness. Vocational recovery constitutes a level of vocational functioning above a specified threshold of vocational achievement. Specifically, we define vocational recovery as the outcome of preserving, regaining, or acquiring competitive employment after being affected by a serious mental illness. We propose a model of vocational recovery with two dimensions: a) stability of workforce participation; and b) degree of workforce participation. Stability of workforce participation reflects a person's capacity to sustain employment over time and is operationalized by the number of months of employment per year. We propose 6 months of employment per year as the recovery threshold for stability of workforce participation. The second dimension, degree of workforce participation, relates to the amount of time that is spent working and is operationalized by the number of work hours per week. We propose a recovery threshold of 10 hours per week, a level consistent with the Social Security Administration requirements for a trial work period (Social Security Administration, 1995).

In addition to vocational recovery, we introduce vocational success as another concept relevant to assessing the vocational capacity of individuals with serious mental illness. While vocational recovery relates to a person's overall capacity to work, vocational success relates to a person's status in the society based on job position and level of earnings. A person's job position can range from unskilled labor to professional and managerial work. Hollingshead's nine level hierarchy of occupational status (Hollingshead, 1975) was selected to operationalize this indicator of vocational success. Vocational success also can be measured by the level of earnings, which we operationalize as salary per hour.

Historically, schizophrenia has been viewed as a disorder that is incompatible with a high level of vocational success. For example, the authors of the *DSM-IV* call into question the diagnosis of schizophrenia if a person is functioning at a high level vocationally. While the diagnostic accuracy of individuals who identify themselves as having schizophrenia must be carefully scrutinized, it is important to determine empirically the levels of vocational recovery and vocational success that are possible for this population.

The purpose of the present study is to examine the correlates of vocational recovery and vocational success among persons with schizophrenia. In addition, the study provides a descriptive profile of a select group of individuals with schizophrenia who have sustained employment. While this study is limited by descriptive data, we anticipate its findings will spur future studies that probe more deeply into the heterogeneity of schizophrenia with regard to vocational recovery.

## METHODS

### Overview of the Study

The correlates of vocational recovery and vocational success for individuals with schizophrenia spectrum disorders were examined in the context of a larger, ongoing prospective longitudinal study of sustained employment among persons with serious mental illness. The larger sample of subjects met the study eligibility criteria if they demonstrated a) sustained employment, and b) lifetime presence of serious mental illness. Determination of lifetime serious mental illness was based on meeting one or more of the following criteria: 1) receipt of Supplemental Security Income (SSI) or Social Security Disability Income (SSDI) for psychiatric disability at any time, 2) at least one psychiatric hospitalization, or 3) negative impact and interruptions in work due to mental illness. Presence of sustained employment was determined by meeting all of the following criteria: 1) current competitive employment of at least 10 hours per week, 2) at least 12 months of employment in the past 2 years, and 3) at least 6 months of continuous employment in the past year. Thus, all study participants met the recovery thresholds for the two previously identified dimensions of vocational recovery: stability of workforce participation and degree of worlforce participation. Study participants completed a mail survey at baseline and provide follow-up survey data at 12-month intervals. Only baseline data are presented in this article.

### Sample

We used snowball-sampling techniques to recruit a national non-representative sample through consumer advocacy organizations, mental health and rehabilitation providers, internet and newsletter announcements, and direct solicitation of participants in a prior research study of professionals and managers with mental illness. We screened for eligibility via a brief telephone interview or email correspondence and then mailed each eligible respondent a survey packet containing a description of the study, consent form, reimbursement form, and baseline survey instrument. We mailed up to two follow-up prompts to eligible prospective participants who did not return a completed baseline survey. Participants were paid $10 when their completed survey was returned. During the enrollment period (1999–2000), 696 eligible participants returned baseline surveys. Among these 696 respondents, 109 individuals reported a diagnosis of schizophrenia, schizoaffective disorder or unspecified psychosis. The data collected from these 109 respondents are presented below.

### Measures

A baseline survey instrument, developed in consultation with mental health experts and consumer advocates, and containing both created items and existing psychometric measures, was organized into eight major sections: Current Employment; Satisfaction with Current Employment; Past Employment; Everyday Life; Work and Everyday Life; Challenges at Work; Psychiatric Condition; and Personal Background.The Empowerment Scale (Rogers, Chamberlin, Ellison & Crean, 1997), Ladder Scale (Cantril, 1967), and BASIS-32 (Eisen, Dill & Grob,1994) were among the psychometric measures included in the baseline survey. The Empowerment Scale is a 28-item self-report measure of personal empowerment with possible subscale and overall mean scores between "1" (low) and "4" (high); it has reported internal consistency of 0.85–0.86 for the full scale and 0.55–0.91 for subscales (Rogers et al., 1997). The Ladder Scale measures subjective general well-being using 1–10 ratings of one's life at three points in time: present, 2 years ago, and 2 years in the future (Cantril, 1967). The BASIS-32, a 32-item self-report measure of current level of difficulty in major symptom and functioning domains, has reported full scale internal consistency of 0.89 and subscale test-retest reliability of 0.65–0.8l. Subscale and overall mean scores range from "O" (no difficulty) to "4" (extreme dffficulty) (Eisen et al., 1994).

### Procedures

To categorize respondents' jobs, we created a coding scheme using the job categories defined by the Bureau of Labor Statistics (US Department of Labor, 2000) and Hollingshead's (1975) levels of occupational status ranging from "1" (lowest) to "9" (highest). Thus, each job was assigned a code for occupational category and for occupational status. We also coded jobs into one of four organizational settings relevant in the employment of mental health consumers: 1) consumer self-help and advocacy, 2) mental health service delivery, 3) health or human service delivery, and 4) non-helping settings. The first two authors independently coded each job on occupational category, occupational status, and organizational setting. Any coding discrepancies were resolved by consensus. The social status of each respondent was determined using Hollingshead's Two-Factor Index of Social Position, an index ranging from a low of 11 to a high of 66 that takes into account both the person's educational level and occupation (Hollingshead, 1975). Salary per hour was derived from reported salary and hours per week. Annualized salary for up to two current jobs was computed from reported work hours per week and computed salary per hour and then summed to produce total annualized salary per year.

### Independent and Dependent Variables

The major analyses focused on identifying significant correlates of the following vocational outcome variables: months of employment in the past 2 years, total work hours per week, occupational status, and salary per hour. The variables considered as possible correlates for each of the outcome variables were age, race, gender, educational level, marital status, number of dependents, substance abuse history, age of onset of psychiatric symptoms, proportion of lifetime with diagnosed psychiatric condition, hospitalization history, diagnosis (schizophrenia or schizoaffective), use of medication, BASIS-32 score, Empowerment Scale score, Ladder Scale score, work history, current receipt of SSI or SSDI, and organizational setting of current primary job.

### Statistical Analysis

All analyses were performed using SPSS Version 10.0.5. For continuous variables, we examined the descriptive statistics of sample size, mean, standard deviation, minimum, maximum, and median. For categorical variables, we examined the distribution of participants in each category by number and percent. Because of missing data, the total $n$ does not equal 109 for all variables. Data were missing for no more than six subjects on any given parameter.

The relationship of independent variables to the vocational outcome variables was assessed using simple regression for continuous independent variables and one-way analysis of variance (ANOVA) for categorical variables. Multivariate regression and analysis of covariance (ANCOVA) were also used to find the best set of variables related to each continuous outcome variable. All multivariate analyses were performed using a backward stepwise approach with a cut-off alpha level of 0. 15. Chi-square was used to test the relationship between two categorical variables. In all analyses, $p < 0.05$ was considered statistically significant. The reliability of standardized scales was determined using Cronbach's alpha.

### RESULTS

#### Demographic And Clinical Characteristics

The demographic and clinical characteristics of the sample are listed in Table 1. Overall, the sample included respondents who had long histories of

**Table 1. Demographic and clinical Characteristics of Study Participants** (*n* = 109)

| Variables | *n* | (%) | Mean ± SD | Range |
|---|---|---|---|---|
| Age | | | 43.26 ± 7.40 | (26–61) |
| Gender (female) | 63 | (58%) | | |
| Ethnicity | | | | |
|     Caucasians | 97 | (89%) | | |
| Marital Status | | | | |
|     Never married | 52 | (48%) | | |
|     Divorced, separated or widowed | 30 | (27%) | | |
|     Married or living with a significant other | 27 | (25%) | | |
| Education | | | | |
|     Graduate degree | 29 | (27%) | | |
|     B.A. degree | 39 | (36%) | | |
|     Some college | 28 | (26%) | | |
|     High school diploma | 10 | (9%) | | |
|     Less than high school education | 2 | (2%) | | |
| Annual Household Income | | | | |
|     Less than $10,000 | 18 | (17%) | | |
|     Between $10,000 and $30,000 | 63 | (58%) | | |
|     Between $30,000 and 50,000 | 19 | (18%) | | |
|     Over $50,000 | 7 | (6%) | | |
| Diagnosis | | | | |
|     Schizophrenia | 52 | (48%) | | |
|     Schizoaffective disorder | 48 | (44%) | | |
|     Schizophrenia/schizoaffective disorder | 7 | (6%) | | |
|     Unspecified psychosis | 2 | (2%) | | |
| Age of Diagnosis | | | 23.7 ± 6.87 | (12–40) |
| Duration of Illness | | | 19.60 ± 9.04 | (3–39) |
| Current Medications | | | | |
|     Newer antipsychotics: | | | | |
|         Clozapine | 12 | (11%) | | |
|         Risperidone | 23 | (21%) | | |
|         Olanzepine | 21 | (19%) | | |
|         Quetiapine | 10 | (9%) | | |
|     Conventional antipsychotics | 35 | (32%) | | |
|     No antipsychotics | 5 | (5%) | | |
|     No psychotropic medications | 3 | (3%) | | |
| Mental health treatment in past 6 months | | | | |
|     Individual and/or group psychotherapy | 82 | (75%) | | |
|     Crisis services | 14 | (13%) | | |
|     Inpatient treatment | 8 | (7%) | | |
|     Self-help groups | 32 | (29%) | | |
|     Consumer-run programs | 20 | (18%) | | |
|     Clubhouse programs | 9 | (8%) | | |
| Psychiatric hospitalizations in the past 2 years | | | | |
|     None | 69 | (63%) | | |
|     One | 16 | (15%) | | |
|     Two | 8 | (7%) | | |
|     Three or more | 10 | (9%) | | |
|     Missing/not sure | 6 | (6%) | | |

serious mental illness, with 101 (93%) reporting at least one psychiatric hospitalization. The proportion of their lifetimes that respondents had lived with mental illness ranged from 7% to 75%. One hundred and three (95%) respondents reported receiving some type of mental health treatment in the past 6 months and 35 (32%) had received SSI or SSDI in the past month. Forty (37%) participants admitted having a problem with alcohol or substance abuse at some point and 29 (27%) thought alcohol or substance use had affected their work in the past. Forty-four (41%) respondents reported having a serious medical condition as well, and 18 (17%) rated their general health as fair or poor.

Despite their extensive psychiatric histories, respondents were functioning well at baseline. One hundred and one (93%) respondents lived independently and 96 (88%) had a residence with no connection to the mental health system. Twenty-three (21%) respondents had one or more dependents and seven (6%) lived in a household that included their children. The mean ± SD full-scale score on the BASIS-32 was 0.85 ± 0.58 (Cronbach alpha = 0.9 1), indicating little current difficulty with symptoms and functioning. The mean ± SD score on the Empowerment Scale was 2.94 ± 0.32 (Cronbach alpha = 0.85), indicating a moderately high level of personal empowerment. The mean ± SD rating of current general well-being (Ladder Scale) was 6.6 ± 2.04, median was 7.0, and mode was 8.0. During the past month, 100 respondents (92%) had contact, by phone or in person, with a relative outside their household and 100 (92%) had contact with a friend who was not a roommate. There were 59 (54%) participants who reported having weekly contact with both a friend and a relative outside their household.

There was no difference between diagnostic groups (schizophrenia versus schizoaffective disorder) on any demographic, mental health, psychosocial, or vocational variables other than gender, those with a diagnosis of schizoaffective disorder were more likely to be female ($\chi^2$ = 5.89, $df$ = 1, $p$ = 0.02).

### Vocational Characteristics

Among the 77 (71%) respondents who reported having some employment prior to the onset of their illness, 70 (91 %) had worked for more than 1 year and 60 (78%) had retained a single job for longer than 1 year. Fifty-two respondents (47%) reported experiencing a work interruption longer than 1 year as a result of their psychiatric condition. While 64 participants (59%) reported using vocational services at some point, only 18 (17%) reported using such services to obtain their current position. The mean ± $SD$ number of months employed in the past 24 months was 22.79 ± 2.73 with 82 (75%) respondents reporting continuous employment during the past 24 months. The number of months in their current primary job ranged from 1 to 283 with a mean $SD$ of 58.15 ± 58.27 and median of 39.5.

Respondents' total work-hours per week for up to two jobs ranged from 10 to 64 with a mean ± $SD$ of 33.92 ± 12.76 and median of 37.5. Sixty-five respondents (60%) worked at least 35 hours per week and 92 (84%) worked at least 20 hours per week. Among the 65 respondents working 35 or more hours per week, 54 (83%) had worked continuously for the past 24 months; among the 27 respondents working between 20 and 35 hours per week, 16 (59%) had worked continuously for the past 24 months; and among the 17 respondents working between 10 and 20 hours per week, 12 (71%) had worked continuously for the past 24 months. Hours per week in the primary job ranged from 7 to 60 with a mean ± $SD$ of 32.07 ± 11.91 and median of 37.5. The 19 respondents with a second job worked 1.5 to 24 hours per week in that job (mean ± $SD$ = 10.63 ± 6.06, median = 8.0). For both primary job and total employment, the modal number of work hours per week was 40.

Compared to those working part-time (PT), those working at least 35 hours (FT) had higher social position ratings on the Hollingshead 2-FISP (mean ± $SD$ [FT] = 46.89 ± 11.53, mean $SD$ [PT] = 39.37 ± 13.3 1, $t$ = -3,119, $df$ = 106, $p$ = 0.002), had higher occupational status ratings on the Hollingshead scale (mean ± $SD$ [IT] = 5.86 ± 1.97, mean ± $SD$ [PT] = 4.50 ± 2.3 1, $t$ = -3.304, $df$ = 107, $p$ = 0. 00 1), were less likely to live alone ($\chi^2$ = 4.8 5 1, $df$ = 1, $p$ = 0.027), were more likely to live with a spouse ($\chi^2$ = 6.333, $df$ = 1, $p$ = 0.011), were less likely to live in housing connected with the mental health system ($\chi^2$ = 7.53, $df$ = 1, $p$ = 0.020), were less likely to have used any vocational services ($\chi^2$ = 9.477, $df$ = 1, $p$ = 0.002), and were more likely to have had continuous employment for the past 24 months ($\chi^2$ = 5.33, $df$ = 1, $p$ = 0.021).

Table 2 presents data on the distribution of current primary jobs by occupational category and by organizational setting, and shows the average occupational status rating (Hollingshead occupational level) and average social position rating (Hollingshead 2-Factor Index of Social Position) for respondents in each category.

Salary per hour in the primary job ranged from $1.28 to $40.00 with a mean ± $SD$ of $12.65 ± 7.51 and a median of $10.60. There were five individuals (all were either self-employed or working in food services) who had a computed salary per hour that fell below $5.15 per hour. Annualized salary for respondents' primary job ranged from $1,200 to $77,740 with a mean ± $SD$ of $22,325 ± 16,312 and median of $20,930. Total annualized salary ranged from $1,200 to $77,740 with a mean ± $SD$ of $22,955 ± 16,504 and median of $21,112.

| Job category | n | (%) | Hollingshead Occupational Factor | | Hollingshead Two-Factor Index of Social Position | |
| --- | --- | --- | --- | --- | --- | --- |
| | | | Mean ± SD | Range | Mean ± SD | Range |
| Executive/admin | 14 | (13%) | 7.14 ± 0.66 | 6–9 | 52.43 ± 3.55 | 45–60 |
| Professional/technical | 40 | (37%) | 6.90 ± 1.41 | 4–9 | 53.33 ± 8.53 | 35–66 |
| Marketing/sales | 6 | (5%) | 4.83 ± 0.75 | 4–6 | 41.80 ± 3.03 | 38–46 |
| Admin support/clerical | 21 | (19%) | 5.00 ± 0.77 | 4–6 | 42.43 ± 5.22 | 35–51 |
| Service | 17 | (16%) | 1.88 ± 0.86 | 1–3 | 24.24 ± 5.80 | 11–33 |
| Mechanical/repair | 3 | (3%) | 4.00 ± 0.00 | (4) | 35.00 ± 3.00 | 32–38 |
| Construction | 1 | (1 %) | 4.00 | (4) | 32.00 | (32) |
| Production | 4 | (4%) | 4.2 ± 1.26 | 3–6 | 39.25 ± 7.85 | 35–51 |
| Transport/material moving | 0 | | | | | |
| Handling/cleaning/general labor | 3 | (3%) | 1.33 ± 0.58 | 1–2 | 22.67 ± 5.51 | 17–28 |
| All categories | 109 | (100%) | 5.31 ± 2.21 | 1–9 | 43.90 ±12.76 | 11–66 |
| **Organizational setting** | | | | | | |
| Self-help/advocacy | 14 | (13%) | 6.93 ± 0.92 | 5–9 | 51.14 ± 4.67 | 43–60 |
| Mental health | 19 | (17%) | 5.89 ± 1.15 | 4–8 | 47.16 ± 7.52 | 35–58 |
| Health/human services (except mental health) | 12 | (11%) | 5.33 ± 1.97 | 2–8 | 43.67 ±12.32 | 22–61 |
| Non-helping settings | 64 | (59%) | 4.78 ± 2.48 | 1–9 | 41.35 ±14.53 | 11–66 |
| All settings | 109 | (100%) | 5.31 ± 2.21 | 1–9 | 43.90 ±12.76 | 11–66 |

## Univariate and Multivariate Analyses of Vocational Outcomes

Results of the univariate and multivariate analyses for months of employment, total work hours per week, occupational status, and salary per hour are presented in Table 3.

No statistically significant associations were found at the univariate level between employment stability during the last 2 years and any relevant independent variable except receipt of SSI/SSDI, with individuals receiving SSI/SSDI working fewer months.there were no significant associations found at the multivariate level. The final multivariate model for work hours per week suggests that people who have had at least one job before experiencing symptoms, and who currently are not receiving SSI/SSDI tend to work more hours per week. The final multivariate model for occupational status suggests that people who have more education and who work in selfhelp/advocacy settings tend to have higher occupational status. The final multivariate model for salary per hour suggests that people who currently are not receiving SSI/SSDI tend to have a higher salary per hour.

**Table 3. Univariate and Multivariate Analyses for Months of Employment, Total Work Hours per Week, Occupational Status, and Salary per Hour ($n = 109$)**

| Months of Employment in Past 2 Years | F value | df | p-value |
|---|---|---|---|
| *Univariate analyses:* | | | |
| Independent variable | | | |
| SSI/ SSDI income | 4.569 | 1,104 | 0.035 |
| *Multivariate analysis:* | | | |
| Independent variable | | | |
| None | | | |

| Total Work Hours per Week | F value | df | p-value |
|---|---|---|---|
| *Univariate analyses:* | | | |
| Independent variable | | | |
| Marital status | 4.960 | 2,106 | 0.009 |
| Work history | 4.823 | 1,107 | 0.030 |
| SSI/SSDI income | 63.572 | 1,106 | < 0.001 |
| *Multivariate analysis:* ($R^2 = 0.421$) | | | |
| Independent variable | | | |
| SSI/SSDI income | 68.768 | 1 | < 0.001 |
| Work history | 8.409 | 1 | 0.005 |

| Occupational Status (Hollingshead) | F value | df | p-value |
|---|---|---|---|
| *Univariate analyses:* | | | |
| Independent variable | | | |
| Age | 6.291 | 1,107 | 0.014 |
| Gender | 5.159 | 1,107 | 0.025 |
| Educational level | 5.771 | 5,102 | < 0.001 |
| Marital status | 3.084 | 2,106 | 0.050 |
| SSI/SSDI income | 24.148 | 1,106 | < 0.001 |
| Organizational setting | 4.604 | 3,105 | 0.005 |
| *Multivariate analysis:* ($R^2 = 0.479$) | | | |
| Independent variable | | | |
| Educational level | 6.860 | 5 | < 0.001 |
| Organizational setting | 6.626 | 3 | < 0.001 |
| SSI/SSDI income | 2.655 | 1 | 0.106 |

| Salary per Hour | F value | df | p-value |
|---|---|---|---|
| *Univariate analyses:* | | | |
| Independent variable | | | |
| Age | 6.317 | 1,105 | 0.013 |
| Educational level | 2.919 | 5,100 | 0.017 |
| Marital Status | 4.277 | 2,104 | 0.016 |
| SSI/SSDI income | 37.685 | 1,104 | < 0.001 |
| *Multivariate analysis:* ($R^2 = 0.302$) | | | |
| Independent variable | | | |
| SSI/SSDI income | 38.046 | 1 | < 0.001 |
| Hospitalization history | 3.687 | 1 | 0.058 |

## DISCUSSION

This study presents substantial evidence that vocational recovery and vocational success are feasible for individuals carrying a schizophrenia spectrum diagnosis. Several correlates of successful employment were identified.

Contrary to our initial hypothesis, the study did not identify correlates of stability of workforce participation in multivariate analyses. However, it is important to note that because all study participants met the study criteria for sustained employment, the observed distribution of this variable was very skewed toward the high end of the measurement range since 82 respondents worked continuously for the past 24 months. While the survey inquired only about duration of work in the 2 years prior to the time of the survey, it is very likely that the majority of respondents had been working for much longer than 2 years. This lack of variability in sustained employment undoubtedly reduced the number of significant associations between background variables and work functioning in this sample. As an illustration of this, we would expect the employment status of individuals, with or without mental illness, who have worked for lengthy periods of time to be less and less influenced by prior work history the longer current employment persisted. We anticipate that the longitudinal, 5-year follow-up data from the current study will permit another examination of the relationship between attributes of the subjects and their work outcomes.

As expected from prior research, we did find that respondents working full-time had more stable and sustained employment in the 2 years prior to the survey. Thus, work history did correlate with the work intensity or capacity as it also did with the number of hours worked per week. Also as expected, the disincentive effects of Social Security benefits appeared to reduce the number of hours worked per week—a finding which may relate to the lower work capacity and endurance of individuals receiving disability pensions and/or jeopardizing of Social Security benefits when working hours and income exceed the mandated thresholds.

This study also provides evidence that people with schizophrenia have the capacity to sustain employment at all levels of occupational status, from unskilled to professional positions. One-fifth of the sample was employed in professional or managerial jobs while the majority of study participants had positions that clustered in the middle range of job status, such as technical, clerical, marketing and mid-level human services jobs. As expected, educational level was correlated with occupational status. Employment in a self-help or advocacy setting also was correlated with occupational status. On the whole, respondents with jobs in consumer self-help/advocacy settings had the highest levels of social prestige. A possible explanation of this finding is that self-help/advocacy organizations are more open to hiring persons with schizophrenia into top positions.

Study participants were employed in all four types of organizational settings identified earlier although almost two-thirds of our sample were employed in non-helping settings. Given the prevailing belief that the labor market provides persons with schizophrenia with limited opportunities primarily in low-level jobs (Warner & Polak, 1995) and the recent initiatives to employ people with serious mental illness as consumer/providers of mental health services (Mowbray, Moxley, Jasper et al., 1997), this finding was surprising. The individuals in non-helping settings had jobs covering the entire continuum from unskilled to professional employment, with approximately 25% of them holding professional or managerial jobs. Future studies need to examine more closely the relationships between actual employment of persons with schizophrenia, their job preferences, and employment availability within various sectors of the economy.

The mental health characteristics of our sample shed additional light on the capacity of individuals with schizophrenia to achieve vocational recovery. Although previous studies (Marneros, Deister & Rhode, 1992) have found persons with schizoaffective disorder to have a better prognosis than persons with schizophrenia, we found no significant difference between these groups on any of the clinical, psychosocial, and vocational variables in our study. Gender was the only demographic variable for which a significant difference was found between these two diagnostic groups. Psychiatric symptomatology measured with the BASIS-32 also did not correlate with any of the vocational outcome variables. This finding should be considered in light of the fact that individuals in this sample generally reported mild psychiatric symptomatology, possibly related to their adherence to both drug and psychosocial treatment regimens. For example, data on the types of psychotropic medications used suggests that most respondents take medications to control psychotic symptoms.

The factors that were associated with vocational outcomes—Social Security benefits, education, prior work history, and vocational participation in mental health advocacy and organizations—are all potentially malleable; that is, it is possible to consider designing interventions for persons with schizophrenia that could improve readiness and capacity for employment through such initiatives as supported education, work incentives from Social Security, supported employment, and expanded employment opportunities for peer advocates and counselors within mental health programs. As an example of the latter, the Los Angeles County Department of Mental Health has developed a career ladder for mental health advocates and actively recruits for these positions from among consumer self-help organizations.

We also examined the relationship between successful employment and a more multifaceted definition of recovery, applying the criteria for recovery suggested by Liberman and his colleagues (2002). Because we collected data on variables that did not exactly correspond with those of Liberman, Kopelowicz, Ventura & Gutkind (2002) we approximated their recovery criteria to our sample. For example, we used a value of two or less on Items 16, 17, 22, and 23 on the BASIS-32 as the criterion for psychotic symptom remission and used 20 or more work hours per week as the criterion measure of vocational functioning. The other recovery criteria were applied exactly as specified by Liberman et al. (2002). Our sample included 84 (77%) individuals who met the criterion for symptom remission, 92 (84%) who met the criterion for vocational functioning, 101 (93%) who met the criterion for independent living, 76 (70%) who met the criterion for peer relationships, and 48 (44%) who met all four recovery criteria. It is interesting to note that there were 9 respondents (8%) who met all recovery criteria except the one for symptom remission. Although they are few in number, these individuals with schizophrenia provide evidence that greater than moderate psychiatric symptoms do not necessarily prevent successful vocational functioning.

### Study Limitations

A major limitation of this study is the use of self-report data. Given the stigma associated with this diagnosis, false report of schizophrenia was assumed to be low. However, we took specific steps to validate the accuracy of a self-reported schizophrenia spectrum diagnosis. For example, 101 (93%) respondents reported current use of an antipsychotic medication. We assumed a current diagnosis of a schizophrenia spectrum disorder to be highly likely for these 101 respondents. Four of the remaining eight individuals reported positive symptoms of schizophrenia on the BASIS-32. Thus, we assumed a current schizophrenia type diagnosis to be very likely for these individuals. Among the remaining four respondents, a schizophrenia-spectrum diagnosis was considered probable: two reported negative symptoms on the BASIS-32 and listed paranoid schizophrenia as their only lifetime psychiatric diagnosis; the other two individuals reported no current difficulty with either positive or negative symptoms but reported a schizophrenia spectrum disorder as their only lifetime psychiatric diagnosis (one listed schizoaffective disorder and the other listed undifferentiated schizophrenia). Based on these analyses, we concluded that a schizophrenia-spectrum disorder was highly likely and, therefore, was considered to be a valid diagnosis for the individuals in this sample.

Another limitation of this study is the lack of generalizability of its findings. Because the study is based on a non-representative sample comprised of highly selected cases of vocational recovery and success, the results cannot be generalized to the larger population of individuals suffering from schizophrenia or even to all persons with schizophrenia who have sustained employment. Nonetheless, the findings are heartening in countering the pessimism and stigma associated with schizophrenia providing documentation of the capacity of individuals with this disorder to work for sustained periods of time in the competitive employment sector.

## CONCLUSIONS

The highly selected sample of persons with schizophrenia spectrum disorders who sustained gainful employment for at least 2 years demonstrate the substantial vocational capacity of this unique sample of individuals, suggesting that some individuals within the larger population of persons with schizophrenia have a substantial vocational potential. The individuals in this study were able to work consistently over time at varying degrees of workforce participation in jobs that ranged from the lowest to the highest levels of compensation and occupational status. Although schizophrenia presents major challenges for the individuals affected by this condition, it does not obviate the possibility of successful employment. It is important that additional research be designed to focus on the factors determining vocational recovery. As we use hypothesis testing designs to clarify the differences between individuals who have recovered their capacity to work and those who continue to experience severe work dysfunction, policymakers, planners, mental health providers, and consumers will be able to make more informed decisions in their efforts to promote vocational recovery and success among persons with schizophrenia.

Acknowledgements

This work was supported by a grant (#11133 G80124) from the National Institute on Disability and Rehabilitation Research, USA Department of Education.

## REFERENCES

Anthony, W. A. (1993). Recovery from mental illness: the guiding vision of the mental health service system in the 1990s. *Psychosocial Rehabilitation Journal, 16*(4), 11–23.

Anthony, W. A., Cohen, M., Farkas, M., & Gagne, C. (2001). *Psychiatric rehabilitation, Second Edition.* Boston: Center for Psychiatric Rehabilitation.

Anthony, W. A., & Jansen, M. A. (1984). Predicting the vocational capacity of the chronically mentally ill: Research and policy implications. *American Psychologist, 39,* 537–544.

Cantril, H. (1967). *The pattern of human concerns.* New Brunswick: Rutgers University Press.

Drake, R. E., Fox, L. S., Leather, R. K., Becker, D. R., Musumeci, J. S., Ingram, W. R., & McHugo, G. J. (1998). Regional variation in competitive employment for persons with severe mental illness. *Administration and Policy in Mental Health, 25*, 493–504.

Eisen, S. V ., Dill, D. L., & Grob, M, C. (1994). Reliability and validity of a brief patient-report instrument for psychiatric outcome evaluation. *Hospital and Community Psychiatry, 45*, 242–247.

Hollingshead, A. B. (1975). *Four factor index of social status.* An unpublished manuscript.

Lehman, A. F. (1995). Vocational rehabilitation in schizophrenia. *Schizophrenia Bulletin, 21*, 645–656.

Liberman, R. P., Kopelowicz, A., Ventura, J., & Gutkind, D. (2002). Operational criteria and factors related to recovery from schizophrenia. *International Review of Psychiatry, 14*, 256–272.

Marneros, A., Deister, A., & Rhode, A. (1992). Comparison of long-term outcome of schizophrenic affective and schizoaffective disorders. *British Journal of Psychiatry, 161* (Suppl 18), 44–51.

McGlashan, T. H. (1988). A selective review of recent North American long-term follow-up studies of schizophrenia. *Schizophrenia Bulletin, 14*, 515–542.

Mowbray, C. T., Moxley, D. R, Jasper, C. A., et. al. (Eds) (1997). *Consumers as providers in psychiatric rehabilitation.* Columbia, MD: International Association of Psychosocial Rehabilitation Services.

Rogers, E. S., Chamberlin, J., Ellison, M. L., & Crean, T. (1997). A consumer-constructed scale to measure empowerment among users of mental health services. *Psychiatric Services, 48*, 1042–1047.

Social Security Administration. (1995). *Red book on work incentives.* A summary guide to Social Security and Supplemental Security Income: Work incentives for people with disabilities.

Spaniol, L., Gagne, C., & Koehler, M. (1999). Recovery from serious mental illness: What it is and how to support people in their recovery. In R. P. Marinelli & A. E. Dell Orto (Eds), *The psychological and social aspects of disability* (4th Edition). New York: Springer Publishing Company.

U.S. Department of Labor. (2000). *Occupational outlook handbook.* Indianapolis: JIST Works.

Warner, R. & Polak, P. (1995).The economic advancement of the mentally ill in the community: 11. Economic choices and disincentives. *Community Mental Health Journal, 31*, 477–492.

Zarate, R., Liberman, R. P., Mintz, J., & Massel, H. K. (1998). Validation of a work capacity evaluation for individuals with psychiatric disorders. *Journal of Rehabilitation, 64*.

# From Psychosis and Alienation to Recovery

*Christine Mahoney Holst*

At the time of original publication, the author's affiliations were cited as follows: Christine Mahoney Holst, BA, is a native and current resident of West Chester County, Pennsylvania. She works as a full time sales administrative assistant for a company that designs and sells equipment for the recycling of non-ferrous metals. In her free time she enjoys writing, instructing an aquatic fitness class, at the YMCA, and participating in activities for the mental health community.

This article originally appeared in the *Psychiatric Rehabilitation Journal*, 2000, 23(4), 397–400, and is reprinted with permission.

Two weeks after giving birth I wanted to know why my baby winced and her face turned purple for no apparent reason. I noticed that I could cause the effect when I gently circled her inside ankle knuckle. According to my baby's hospital records, she exhibited the same symptoms shortly after birth. I called the Neo-Natal Intensive Care Unit of El Camino Hospital in Mountain View, California, where my baby spent the first week of her life. A nurse on duty spooked me by telling me how serious my baby's condition could become.

Two days later on May 21, 1994, forces assembled and trapped me into an involuntary psychiatric commitment. The diagnosis was post-partum psychosis. I was 2 weeks and 2 days post-partum with my first and only child, when my husband, mother-in-law, newborn, and I entered the El Camino Hospital Emergency Room. My husband and his mother took turns speaking privately with hospital staff members. I did not have a clue as to why we were there. We were supposed to be going to an appointment at the pediatrician's office in Los Altos, California.

### Recipe for a Breakdown

As I sat in the emergency room waiting area, I grew tired, weak, and exhausted. When I could not remain awake any longer, I succinctly told my husband, "I need sleep." He motioned to a place out of the way on the carpeted floor where I could lie down, using my soft, leather covered credenza to rest my head.

I eagerly slipped down and fell asleep. Seconds later, hospital staff members startled me awake. Next they escorted me to a room, sat me in a chair, and abandoned me, which made me feel insignificant. I said a little prayer to God, "I give up." Then I immediately broke down.

Seated in the chair, my eyes went into Rapid Eye Movement (REM). Then tremors surged through my muscles giving me what felt like a full body massage. My head rolled gently from side to side. My shoulders heaved up and down. My chest dropped forward to my knees and my arms to my fingertips stretched out and released. This convulsing continued for what seemed like half an hour.

### Alienating Accusations

This full-blown breakdown was never mentioned again. Instead, I was locked into a 72-hour hold, classified as gravely disabled, citing that I was over-stimulating my baby with massages. I was told that I was a danger to my baby, a claim based on statistics, so said the psychiatrist. They criticized my judgement and thoughts, telling me I was delusional, out of touch with reality, and in denial. I was blind-sided by these accusations since I was unfamiliar with my surroundings and my situation. Furthermore, my mom was not notified of my crisis prior to hospitalization, and my mother-in-law denied that anything was wrong with me. These two insults breached fiduciary responsibility, and impaired my ability to reason.

Other reasons for impairment to my thinking were the psychiatrist's unwillingness to develop trust as well as her plan to overmedicate me. A nurse refused to administer the prescribed Haldol when I requested it. There was no follow-up therapy or explanation for being secluded, punished, restrained, and forcibly medicated by injection. There were no privileges during confinement to get second opinions from my primary mental health providers. The psychiatrist withdrew the writ of habeas corpus and released me from the hospital when my insurance ran out. I could not help but speculate that I was hospitalized to keep the psychiatric unit functioning, and not because I was sick.

During my hospitalizations I did not want to return home. My husband was suffering from an anxiety disorder. He was put under a doctor's care a couple of days before our baby was born. I felt inappropriately targeted as a source of his anxieties. I could not express the joy I felt about our baby without conflict arising between my husband and me. I felt my husband was jealous over the bond I felt and expressed about our daughter. His criticism of my joy caused me to feel mentally unsafe with him. Returning home was not a desirable option because my husband declared in a letter his intention to file for divorce.

For the following three years, I was in and out of more than 12 different hospitals, in four states, resulting in more than 10 involuntary commitments and a variety of diagnoses. I was running scared from the entrapments of the psychiatric system. Somehow I knew that I needed help, but I wanted it without being locked up, punished, threatened, or mistrusted. I needed the legal intervention of a Superior Court judge to either free me from future psychiatric commitments or commit me to treatment until I was well.

### Distorted Reality

I believed I was doing the right thing by refusing Haldol, an anti-psychotic medication, especially after my assigned nurse refused to administer it to me because she did not see any symptoms requiring it. The incident undermined my thinking and ability to trust. I turned inward, hoping and trusting that God had a plan for me. I prayed hard for God to give me a sign. Reality took on a whole new meaning as I became watchful, awaiting signs from God.

Following my release from El Camino Hospital, I believed that I was the promised Jesus Christ incarnate. Being ever watchful, I heard in a song that my favorite uncle died; I sent condolences to my aunt. I was fearful that if I did not interpret the song as a sign, my uncle would be in grave danger. It seemed to me that my thinking could be as statistically sound as were the accusations that I would harm my daughter.

Fortunately my "information" about my uncle was wrong. And, for my peace of mind, my aunt and uncle have forgiven me for the upheaval caused by my letters. Further, my aunt and uncle have been good and generous to me, following my progress and recovery, and welcoming me back into their home in California when I travel there to visit my daughter.

Letter writing was my primary outlet for relieving frustration. After release from El Camino Hospital I took up writing letters to anyone, including Janet Reno, U.S. Attorney General, who I thought could help me get a writ of habeas corpus court hearing, but nothing came of it. Eventually, once I stopped lactating (about 4 months post-partum), I headed for Pennsylvania where I hoped to get help—for what I was not exactly sure. But my hope was for humane treatment.

### Recovery in Pennsylvania

What finally set me on the road to recovery was getting my equivalent writ of habeas corpus hearings in Pennsylvania. Twice, a judge ordered a 6-month hospital commitment with treatment. I fought the first ruling with every bit of courage I could muster until I felt recognized as an individual, and not as a statistic. The professional staff members at Haverford State Hospital rallied around me without punishment, restraints, injections of medication, or solitary confinement.

Presently, I am in full recovery, living in Downingtown, Pennsylvania, and working full time as a sales administrative assistant, a job I enjoy and need in order to afford my medications. Through a special county subsidy program, called CHIPPs, I live in a Community Rehabilitation Residence (CRR), which is a board and maximum care housing arrangement operated by Kelsch Associates. I adhere to goal-planning, bi-weekly psychotherapy sessions, monthly medication reviews, and weekly intensive case management meetings through Human Services, Inc.

I am grateful to the taxpayers, voters, and representatives of the county and state of Chester County, Pennsylvania, who made my recovery possible. Their support for the needs of mental health consumers both in and out of the hospital is tremendous. Twice, in my escapades between California and Pennsylvania, I had to return to my hometown in Pennsylvania to get better.

### Partial Recovery

The first time back in Pennsylvania I was stabilized through the efforts of my brother, his wife, and my mom, as well as Crisis Residential, and Community Services for Human Growth. My brother and his wife gave me a place to stay. Mom linked me up with Crisis Residential. Crisis Residential offered a staffed house for me to stay in voluntarily for up to 14 days instead of a hospital. I needed Crisis Residential for relief from the side effects from the medications prescribed in Iowa. When I could no longer perform my duties at the butcher shop where I worked part-time through the influence of my brother, I retreated to Crisis Residential.

Upon release from Crisis Residential, I was placed in an outpatient program, called Partial, at Community Services for Human Growth, Inc. in Phoenixville, Pennsylvania. Partial was a place to go to during the week instead of staying at home. It helped restore my confidence and set goals that would help me move forward with my life. I resumed part-time work at the butcher shop. As I got stronger, I became able to work as a temporary administrative assistant. Community Services for Human Growth then placed me on outpatient psychotherapy one day per week and monthly medication reviews. Within 6 months I was able to return to California to be near my daughter.

I was stabilized but not fully recovered during my first stay in Pennsylvania. Full recovery would have meant that I could link symptoms with diagnosis and thereby justify psychotropic medication. With such knowledge, I could make good judgements regarding medications, report unusual behavior about myself, and obtain continuity in treatment while living anywhere in the USA.

### Recipe for a Relapse

The risks of not understanding a diagnosis or symptoms became apparent after changing psychiatrists. In Pennsylvania, I was diagnosed as having bi-polar (manic-depressive) disorder, and in California, a change disorder. Because I was stable, I did not expect my California psychiatrist would change medications. However, after seeing me for several months, he decided on a change. I was forced to decide between him or the medications. I chose to trust my psychiatrist and accepted the medication change. He continued my lithium treatment but switched me from the anti-depressant, Wellbutrin, to Prozac.

I did not want to change medication because I felt I was functioning just fine, working and living in the community, and conforming to my treatment plan. However, because I had many months invested in my psychiatrist at the time, I did not want to terminate the relationship and start over elsewhere. I felt I needed his recommendation to see my daughter more often and without supervision. Not only that, but I saw a note in my legal brief at my divorce attorney's office that another psychiatrist had recommended the same medication change. I could not reasonably turn down the Prozac since two psychiatrists concurred independently.

The Prozac set off mania in me, which led to non-compliance with medications, a relapse of psychosis, periods of memory lapses, and a series of hospitalizations in California and Pennsylvania. I probably should add that I might have complicated matters by taking the herb gingko biloba while on Prozac.

### Journey Toward Recovery

My California landlord intervened for my return to family in Pennsylvania for recovery. After 6 months of crazy behavior in Pennsylvania, splitting my time between acts of good faith and condemnations of others, I ended up being court-committed for up to 6 months of treatment in Haverford State Hospital.

It took me a couple of weeks to settle into my new environment at Haverford. I fought my stay by contacting the FBI, 911, and Patients Rights Advocates. I communicated by phone and by mail. Responses started to pour in. The superintendent of the hospital even got involved. He sat in on one of my treatment team sessions, which he followed up with a note to me, asking me to stop fighting the system and to pour my energies into working with my treatment team. That made a tremendously positive impression on me. First, someone cared enough to write a letter to me; second, the letter was from someone with authority; third, the letter was non-threatening; fourth, the letter contained some insight as to what was going on with my treatment team; and fifth, the letter expressed hope for my recovery.

Another thing that made a difference with me was my dad's involvement. Every week he sat in on my weekly treatment team meetings. Afterwards he would sit with me just to talk. During day-to-day conversation, he shared his favorable impressions of my caretakers. He helped me to come around and see things in a positive light. And one thing he did not do was to force the issue of medication, for which I was grateful.

At Haverford I was treated with the dignity one could expect with any illness; mine just happened to be a mental illness. I felt good about being treated as a whole person and not someone to be feared. The staff members explained the progression of moving from unit to unit until discharge, which provided me with hope. No one in any of my previous hospitalizations had taken the time to do that. Previous hospitalizations were paternalistic in nature and medication clouded any discussions of hope and recovery.

### Privileges

A valuable bit of insight I finally learned at Haverford was that my psychiatrist was my team leader. As such, she approved any privileges, from grounds privileges, to day passes off campus, to work programs, to upgrading to a less structured treatment unit, to any activity that would take place beyond the doors of the locked unit. She seldom belabored the medication issue, except during scheduled treatment meetings. If I had a concern that required her attention in the meantime, such as privileges or medication, she would fit me into her schedule. Her presence on the unit nearly everyday made her approachable and helped me get on Zyprexa, an anti-psychotic medication with few side effects and that I will likely take for life.

My treatment team at Haverford reached out to find on-campus employment suitable to my skills and education. My outlook for the future brightened and soon more good things followed. I taught computer classes, wrote, and published two issues of the campus newsletter, and earned a scholarship to attend the Pennsylvania Mental Health Consumers' Association conference in Erie, Pennsylvania. It was very rewarding to see and meet consumers prospering in the community and contributing to progress in the mental health field at all levels.

One other service that contributed to my recovery is the Consumer Satisfaction Team (CST) of Chester County, Pennsylvania. CST checks in periodically with county mental health consumers to ensure all of their needs are being serviced appropriately and advocated as necessary. They visited me while I was hospitalized at Haverford and now while I am housed at a CRR. They advocate both good points and areas for improvement to my service providers. Little things have come up and have been promptly dealt with.

Gradually I am attaining my goals, of which I have many, including traveling to see my daughter in San Jose. I hope to see more of my daughter, without supervision, for overnight visits, and with privileges to transport her to outings when I am in town.

**THE CENTER FOR PSYCHIATRIC REHABILITATION AT BOSTON UNIVERSITY** is a research, training, and service organization dedicated to improving the lives of persons who have psychiatric disabilities by improving the effectiveness of people, programs, and service systems.

Our work is guided by the most basic of rehabilitation values: that first and foremost, persons with psychiatric disabilities have the same goals and dreams as any other person. They want a decent place to live, suitable work, and the company and support of friends and family. The mission of the Center is to increase knowledge in the field of psychiatric rehabilitation and to apply this body of knowledge to train personnel, to develop effective rehabilitation programs, and to assist in organizing both personnel and programs into efficient and coordinated service delivery systems.

The Center for Psychiatric Rehabilitation publishes textbooks, curricula for training and practice, a journal, and other resources related to psychiatric rehabilitation and recovery developed for use by practitioners, students, researchers, and people with psychiatric disabilities and their family members.

A complete listing of products and ordering information, as well as other Center information, is available online at www.bu.edu/cpr/ or at the address below.

Center for Psychiatric Rehabilitation
Sargent College of Health and Rehabilitation Sciences
Boston University
940 Commonwealth Avenue West
Boston, MA 02215
http://www.bu.edu/cpr/
Phone 617/353-3549
Fax 617/353-7700

The Center for Psychiatric Rehabilitation is partially funded by the National Institute on Disability and Rehabilitation Research and the Center for Mental Health Services, Substance Abuse and Mental Health Services Administration.

To order Center publications, visit our website at www.bu.edu/cpr/